SENSOR
AND
ANALYZER
HANDBOOK

HARRY N. NORTON

Prentice Hall, Inc., Englewood Cliffs, NJ   07632

Library of Congress Cataloging in Publication Data

Norton, Harry N.
    Sensor and analyzer handbook.

    Includes bibliographies and index.
    1. Measuring instruments.   2. Transducers.   I. Title.
TA165.N6   621.3815'48   81-15844
ISBN 0-13-806760-0   AACR2

Editorial/production supervision and interior design by *Mary Carnis*
Cover design by Edsal Enterprises
Manufacturing buyer: *Gordon Osbourne*

Printed in the United States of America

10 9 8 7 6 5 4 3 2 1

ISBN   0-13-806760-0

Prentice-Hall International, Inc., *London*
Prentice-Hall of Australia Pty. Limited, *Sydney*
Prentice-Hall of Canada, Ltd., *Toronto*
Prentice-Hall of India Private Limited, *New Delhi*
Prentice-Hall of Japan, Inc., *Tokyo*
Prentice-Hall of Southeast Asia Pte. Ltd., *Singapore*
Whitehall Books Limited, *Wellington, New Zealand*

Contents

Contents

Preface

More than a decade has passed since the publication of my *Handbook of Transducers for Electronic Measuring Systems* by Prentice-Hall (1969). The 1960s saw a constantly increasing use of transducers and other sensing devices, most of which had been developed to fill the needs of the aerospace field. This trend continued through the 1970s, but on a significantly expanded scale. The availability of new transducers engendered additional applications and new sensing techniques, new data acquisition methodologies, and the development of new transducer designs. The widening market stimulated the application of recent technology to sensing devices and the proliferation of digital data handling and processing systems encouraged users to use electronic systems, instead of pneumatic or mechanical systems, for data acquisition, data processing, and display, for measurement as well as control purposes. A further impetus to the development of electronic sensing and analyzing devices came from recent government regulations based on a new awareness of our environment and its deterioration. New sensors and analyzers were needed to measure and control the many types of pollution in its physical (e.g., noise, vibration) and chemical forms, and such sensors were needed in increasing quantities. Again, the growth of these applications stimulated creativity and innovation among the designers of sensing and analyzing devices.

The many developments of new sensor and analyzer designs and of designs modified for use in new disciplines, as well as the entry of many new engineers, scientists, teachers, managers, and technologists into the fields where such devices are used increasingly, posed the need for a new handbook that covers such devices. Such a book should be comprehensive, applications-oriented, readily understandable by workers having little more than a high-school degree (with a science major); it should also be encyclopedic in nature, covering essentially all existing and close-to-existing electronic sensing and analyzing devices, with the more commonly used designs explained in more detail. The book should also provide a brief explanation of the basic concepts underlying the physical quantities and chemical properties that are sensed or analyzed, and it should explain the units in which the measured quantities are expressed, bearing in mind that all technologically developed countries except the United States are using the SI (International System of Units) or, at least, some form of the "metric system," and that the United States will, sooner or later, switch to such a system of units. Additionally, the book should explain sensor fundamentals, in general, and design and performance characteristics that are of particular importance for each category of sensors.

This handbook is intended to meet all these requirements to the best extent possible within the constraints of encompassing all this information in a single, compact book. Some instrument descriptions are noticeably condensed; however, a bibliography, at the end of each chapter, points to sources of additional, more detailed information. The book should be useful as a reference book by trade schools, colleges, and universities, especially at the undergraduate level, as well as by everyone working with instrumentation in all industries and sciences in areas ranging from sensor design, through sensor application and marketing, to the interpretation and use of data generated by sensors, and including those working on larger systems which contain one or more instrumentation systems whose operation they need to understand.

Harry N. Norton

Acknowledgments

In the preparation of this book I was greatly encouraged and inspired by my colleagues at the Jet Propulsion Laboratory, by former members of standards committees of the Instrument Society of America, by the officers of the International Measurements Confederation (IMEKO), by the many dedicated workers in the instrumentation field with whom I had the pleasure of exchanging information, and by many personal friends and members of my family. Encouragement also came from many users of my *Handbook of Transducers for Electronic Measuring Systems* (Prentice-Hall, 1969), and inspiration came from reading about the significant technological advancements achieved by numerous brilliant researchers in the many fields covered in this book.

I would like to express my particular gratitude to the following, who contributed to the preparation of the book by reviewing the chapters indicated and giving me the benefit of their comments: Chapter 1, Bob Jonasen; Chapter 2, Frank Ziol; Chapter 3, Eigil Borresen; Chapter 4, Bill Clayton; Chapter 5, Leonard Snyder; Chapter 6, Albert Metzger, also John Haynes; Chapter 7, Bob Ferber; Chapter 8, Herbert Segall, also Heinz Boettger, Mahadeva P. Sinha, Blair Lewis, and Paul Swanson.

Harry N. Norton

Introduction I: Instrumentation Systems

I.1 INTRODUCTION

Instrumentation systems are broadly categorized as either *measurement* systems or *control* systems. In measurement systems a quantity or property is measured and the measured value is displayed. In control systems the information about a quantity or property that is being measured is used to control the quantity or property so that its measured value equals a desired value. The measured value may or may not be displayed. *Analysis* systems are measuring systems whose purpose is to display the nature and proportion of the constituents of a substance or quantity. Measuring devices as well as analyzing devices are used in control systems, the latter primarily when the proportions of a specific constituent of a substance are to be controlled.

I.2 MEASUREMENT SYSTEMS

The simplest measuring system is a measuring device which also displays the measured value (e.g., a mercury-in-glass thermometer or a pressure gage). If the measured value needs to be recorded at certain times, either an operator with a clipboard and wristwatch can be employed for this purpose, or an automatic camera can be used to take a series of photographs of the measuring/indicating device together with a clock.

To indicate the measured value at a point some distance away from the measuring point a means of transmitting information from the measuring device to the display (or recording) device must be added to the system. Mechanical systems employ a cable (e.g., automobile speedometer cable) or other mechanical link to accomplish this; pneumatic systems use tubing carrying air whose pressure is varied by the measuring device. The most popular remote-indicating measuring systems, however, are electronic measuring systems.

I.2.1 Basic Electronic Measuring Systems

A basic electronic measuring system is shown in Figure I-1. It consists of:

1. The *transducer* (or *sensor*), which converts the *measurand* (measured quantity, property, or condition) into a usable electrical output.
2. The *signal conditioner,* which converts the transducer output into an electrical quantity suitable for proper operation of the display device.
3. The *power supply,* which feeds the required electrical power to the signal conditioner, provides excitation for all except "self-generating" types of transducers, and may also furnish electric power to certain types of display devices.
4. The *display device* (or readout device), which displays the required information about the measurand.

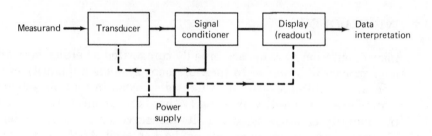

Figure I-1. Basic electronic measuring system.

Transducers, because of their immense variety, constitute the key portion of each of the measuring systems in which they are used. Signal conditioners may vary in complexity from a simple resistance network or impedance-matching device to multistage amplifiers with or without demodulators, analog-to-digital converters, and other elaborate circuitry. Among commonly used display (readout) devices are circular-chart and strip-chart recorders, analog or digital meters, character printers, oscilloscopes (which may be equipped with a camera so that permanent records can be obtained), and discrete-level indicator lights.

A few types of measuring systems (e.g., synchro systems) operate without any signal conditioning. Most systems, however, employ signal conditioning either packaged as a separate unit, or included in the transducer or the readout equipment. Similarly, the power supply function may be included in the readout equipment or provided as a separate unit.

I.2.2 Multiple-Data Measuring Systems

Most measurement systems are designed to handle and display the outputs of two or more transducers. The transducers feeding into such a multiple-data measuring system can be of the same type (e.g., several thermocouples) or of different types (e.g., temperature, pressure, and vibration transducers). Signal conditioning in the system can be minimized by "standardizing" the transducer output, that is, having each transducer provide the same full-scale output to the system, regardless of type or measuring range.

Typical multiple-data measuring systems are illustrated in Figure I-2. Each system provides for at least some amount of signal conditioning in addition to whatever conditioning is incorporated within the transducer. Transducer excitation power, if any, is either connected to all transducers simultaneously or switched to each transducer (in selectable systems) as it is being

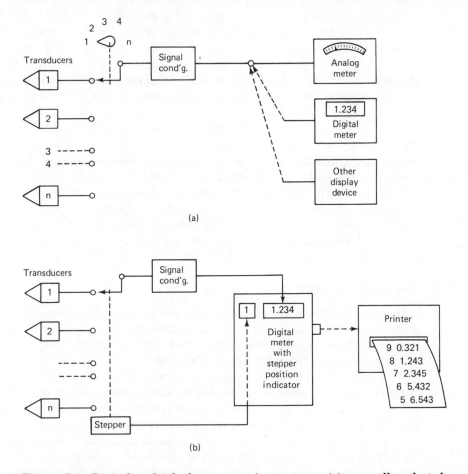

(a)

(b)

Figure I-2. Typical multiple-data measuring systems: (a) manually selected measurements; (b) automatically selected measurements; (c) simultaneously displayed measurements.

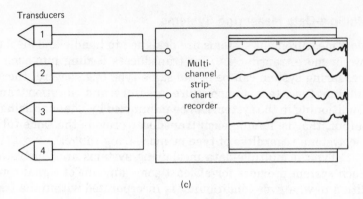

Transducers

Multi-channel strip-chart recorder

(c)

Figure I-2 (continued)

read out, usually by a second set of contacts in the stepper or selector switch. The latter method reduces transducer power consumption substantially.

The simplest system, as shown in Figure I-2a, is one in which the transducer to be read out is selected manually, such as by means of a rotary selector switch. When a number of different measurements must be monitored repeatedly at relatively short intervals, a system such as the one shown in Figure I-2b can be used where an automatically operating stepper or sequencer scans the transducer outputs and the readout device also displays an identifying number for the measurement being displayed. The temporary ("volatile") display on a digital meter can be augmented or replaced by a permanent record such as one obtainable from a printer. A simultaneous display of several measurements on a multichannel strip-chart recorder, as in the example of Figure I-2c, is most frequently used when several related measurements are expected to fluctuate rapidly. Numerous variations of the systems illustrated exist, including those in which the transducer outputs, together with a timing signal *(clock)* and a means of identifying each measurement, are stored on magnetic tape which can be played back later into one or more display devices.

I.2.3 Telemetry Systems

Although all remote-display electronic measuring systems could be termed *telemetry* systems, this term is usually reserved for multiple-data systems using a modulated high-frequency carrier to transmit the information about the measurements from one point to another.

A generalized basic telemetry system is illustrated in Figure I-3. The outputs from the transducers or other sensing devices, which may or may not require signal conditioning, are fed to a commutator *(multiplexer),* which combines them into a single *composite* signal. This signal is applied to the high-frequency transmitter, where it modulates the output of an oscillator. The modulated *carrier* is amplified and then fed to an antenna. The transmitting antenna, which is usually highly directional, radiates the modulated carrier toward a receiving antenna. The received signal is amplified and applied to a *demodulator,* which separates the modulating information from the high-

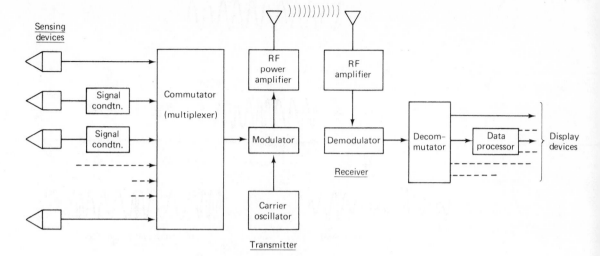

Figure I-3. Basic telemetry system.

frequency carrier. This process reconstitutes the composite signal at the receiving end of the system. A *decommutator* is then employed to extract signals corresponding to the respective sensing-device outputs, so that each measurement can be displayed and evaluated individually. A *data processor* may or may not be required for the desired form of display.

In some types of telemetry systems the radio link is replaced by a conducting link. An example of this is the *carrier-current system* used by utility companies, in which the modulated carrier is coupled directly on a power transmission line, then decoupled from this line at the receiving end. Another example is *landline* (or "hardline") telemetry, where either a modulated high-frequency carrier is transmitted to a remote receiving station through a coaxial cable, or multiconductor shielded cables are used to feed a number of individual transducer outputs to a remote display center.

I.2.3.1 Carrier modulation. The manner in which the transmitter's carrier signal is modulated—the type of *modulation*— deserves a more detailed description since it normally determines the nomenclature of the telemetry system (see Figure I-4). The frequency of an *amplitude-modulated* (AM) carrier remains constant while its amplitude changes with the modulating signal. The frequency and amplitude of a *phase-modulated* (PM) carrier remain constant while its phase changes with the modulating signal. The amplitude of a *frequency-modulated* (FM) carrier remains constant while its frequency changes with the modulating signal.

I.2.3.2 Multiplexing. Two different methods are used to combine individual measurements into a composite signal for transmission over a single data link.

Frequency-division multiplexing (see Figure I-5) allows the continuous display of several measurements. Each sensing-device output is fed to a different *subcarrier oscillator* (SCO). Each SCO is tuned to a different frequency

(a)

Phase modulation (PM)

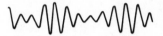

Amplitude modulation (AM)　　　　　　　Frequency modulation (FM)

(b)

Figure I-4. Principal types of carrier modulation: (a) unmodulated carrier; (b) modulated carrier.

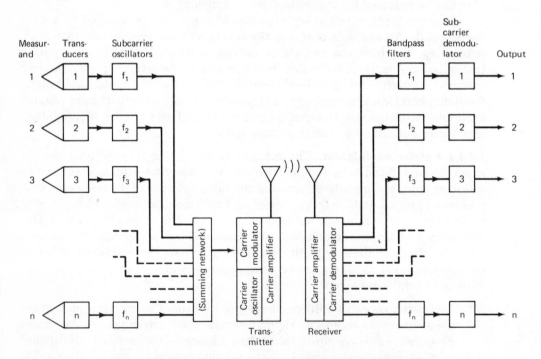

Figure I-5. Frequency-division multiplex telemetry system.

in the general range 0.4 to 70 kHz. The SCO outputs are then linearly summed to form the composite signal. At the receiving station the composite signal is fed through band-pass filters, one filter for each SCO used in the transmitter, and tuned to the respective SCO frequency. The demodulated output of each band-pass filter then represents the corresponding measurement.

Time-division multiplexing involves the time sharing of a number of individual measurements. This method does not permit a continuous display of each measurement. However, the measurement can be reconstituted from samples of the sensing-device output if the sampling occurs frequently enough. The sampling rate for any given measurement depends on its expected rate of fluctuation with time. The measurements are sampled by *commutating* them, that is, by switching them sequentially into a common output circuit.

Figure I-6 shows a simple commutation scheme as well as a method for *subcommutation* which permits a number of relatively slowly varying *measurement* signals to be switched sequentially into one segment of a commutator to whose other segments the relatively rapidly varying measurement signals

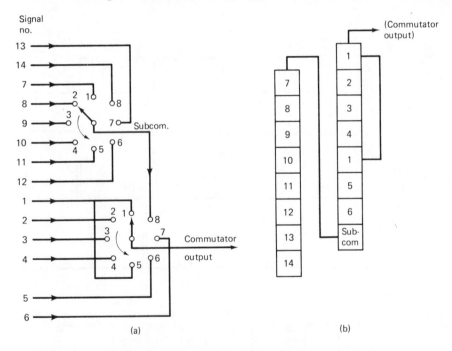

Figure I-6. Commutation and subcommutation: (a) electromechanical representation; (b) solid-state representation.

are connected. In the example illustrated, the commutator output contains signal 1 sixteen times as often as signals 8 through 15, and it contains signals 2, 3, 4, 5, and 6 eight times as often as signals 7 through 14. This is becuse the subcommutator advances by only one segment for each fulx rotation of the commutator, and because signal 1 is *cross-strapped* from commutator segment

1 to segment 5. The example shows a representation typical for electrome-chanical commutators as well as an equivalent layout for a solid-state com-mutator that uses solid-state switching logic instead of a motor-driven rotary switch.

The reverse process, *decommutation,* is used at the receiving end of the data transmission system to separate the time-sharing measurement signals from the commutated composite data stream. To synchronize the decommutator

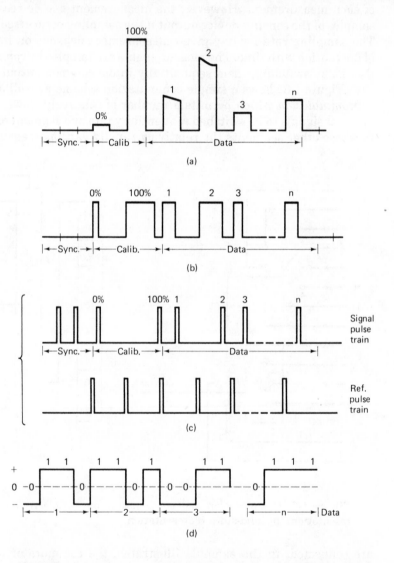

Figure I-7. Time-division multiplex methods: (a) pulse-amplitude modulation (PAM); (b) pulse-duration modulation (PDM); (c) pulse-position modulation (PPM); (d) pulse-code modulation (PCM) (NRZ waveform, 4-bit binary code).

with the commutator, the transmitted data contain appropriate synchronization signals. They can also contain calibration reference signals, such as the zero- and full-scale levels of a measurement-circuit reference voltage, useful in evaluating the received data accurately.

One of the following four basic methods (see Figure I-7) is generally used to modulate the telemetry subcarrier or carrier with time-division-multiplexed composite signals. In each method the sequential sampling of measurement signals results in a series of pulses *(pulse train)*. The simplest of these methods is *pulse-amplitude modulation* (PAM), in which the amplitude (height) of each pulse is an analog of the measurement-signal value at the time it is being sampled by the commutator. The other three methods require a converter to modify the analog measurement signals into the appropriate pulse-type signals.

In *pulse-duration modulation* (PDM) the duration of each pulse *(pulse width)* represents the value of the measurement-signal sample. In *pulse-position modulation* (PPM) this value is represented by the position, in time, of a pulse. A reference pulse train can be transmitted together with the signal pulse train to serve as a repetitive time reference for the positions of the signal pulse. Both PDM and PPM are forms of *pulse-time modulation.*

Pulse-code modulation (PCM) is the most efficient of the four modulation methods because the transmitter power needed to send a given amount of information is less than for the other three methods. The analog signals are converted into a pulse code, usually a series of binary digits, by an analog-to-digital converter (ADC). The value of the sampled measurement signal is thus represented as a discrete amplitude increment, by a digital word. The number of bits used to form each word dictates the resolution obtainable for the data; for example, 127 discrete increments are available when 7-bit words are used (2^7 - 1), whereas 511 discrete increments are available when 9-bit words are used in a PCM system (see Table I-1).

Alternative methods of digital encoding are *frequency-shift keying* (FSK), used in PCM/FM systems, and *phase-shift keying* (PSK), where the transducer output is converted into fixed-step changes of the phase of the modulating signal.

In some time-division multiplex systems a "zero" reference pulse, of the same type as the signal pulse but of a fixed low level, is inserted between consecutive signal pulses. The resulting *return-to-zero* (RZ) waveform affords only a 50% duty cycle but facilitates signal separation after decommutation. The PAM illustration (Figure I-7a) shows such a waveform. When no such signal separation is required, the 100% duty cycle *non-return-to-zero* (NRZ) waveform is used.

Combined multiplexing (time division as well as frequency division) is often used in FM systems in which groups of measurements are commutated into subcarrier oscillators.

The nomenclature of a telemetry system is given by the type of modulation used; for example, in a PAM/FM system a PAM pulse train frequency-modulates the radio-frequency (RF) carrier.

Table I-1 Resolution of Digitized Analog Measurement as Function of Length of Digital Word

Number of Discrete Increments	Word Length (bits)
1	1
3	2
7	3
15	4
31	5
63	6
127	7
255	8
511	9
1,023	10
2,047	11
4,095	12
8,191	13
16,383	14
32,767	15
65,535	16
131,071	17
263,143	18
524,287	19
1,048,575	20
2,097,151	21
4,194,303	22
8,388,607	23
16,777,215	24
33,554,431	25

I.3   ANALYZING SYSTEMS

Analyzing systems are special types of measurement systems generally intended to obtain information about the component parts (ingredients, constituents) of a substance, a process, a parameter, or a phenomenon.

Examples of *chemical analysis* systems are those used to determine the relative abundance of constituents of a mixture, to identify the presence or absence of a specific constituent in a mixture, or to examine properties of a mixture or one or more of its ingredients. The mixture can be solid, liquid, or gaseous.

Examples of *physical analysis* systems are those used to determine the relative energy within a number of narrow frequency bands of a complex waveshape, to show the statistical distribution of the height of current pulses observed over a given time interval, or to identify the amplitude distribution of emitted or incident energy in various directions.

This book describes only those analyzing devices that are electronic in nature. Hence, the chemical analysis systems considered can generally be described as those providing a display of the output of a sensing device which responds to a physical or chemical characteristic of the substance being analyzed such that the desired information can be either obtained directly or inferred by reference to other information. Physical analysis systems are measuring systems in which either a number of interrelated measurements are displayed on a single display unit (e.g., a structural analysis system) or in which specific components of the output of one transducer are displayed separately (e.g., a vibration analysis system).

I.4 DATA CONDITIONING, PROCESSING, AND DISPLAY

I.4.1 Analog Data

The "raw" data provided by a measuring or analyzing system often require a number of different operations to be performed on them to facilitate the determination of the required information (the *data reduction*).

Amplifiers can be used to make the full-scale amplitude of the system output data compatible with the capabilities of a given display unit. Filters can be used to remove noise from data signals or to eliminate high-frequency components *(low-pass filter)*, low-frequency components *(high-pass filter)*, or frequency components above and below a given frequency band *(band-pass filter)*. *Amplitude discriminators* can be employed to create an "on– off" signal as a function of the difference in amplitude between the data signal and a reference signal. *Frequency discriminators* (frequency-to-dc converters) convert

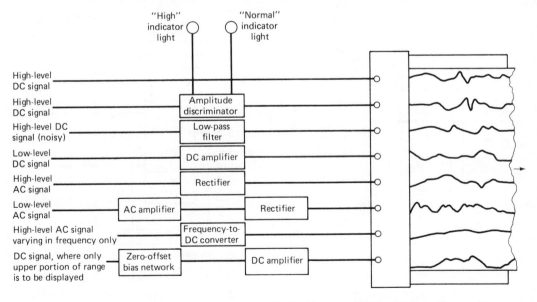

Figure I-8. Analog data conditioning (with display on multichannel oscillograph).

frequency variations into amplitude variations. *Rectifiers* convert ac amplitude variations into dc amplitude variations. Bias networks can be used to display only that portion of a data signal that is above or below a preset level. A composite system containing such devices is shown in Figure I-8.

Data can be recorded on magnetic tape or stored in a computer memory for later playback or readout *(data storage)*. Analog data can be digitized *(analog-to-digital converter)*. Digital data can be converted into analog form *(digital-to-analog converter)*.

I.4.2 Digital Data

The processing of digital data, such as PCM telemetry data or digitized analog data, is usually handled by computer systems. The availability of digital computer systems, varying widely in cost, capability, and complexity, has facilitated data reduction to such an extent that they have become attractive to designers and users of even relatively small measuring or analysis systems.

A typical system for digital data processing and display is illustrated in Figure I-9. The incoming composite data stream (from which any RF carrier has been removed) usually consists of a number of sequential data frames. Each data frame starts with a frame synchronization word (typically between 7 and 31 bits in length) and one or more additional identifier words (often including a word indicating at what time the data were acquired); these are followed by the data words. Each word is a group of bits representing either one digitized analog measurement, one event count, or one group of state or mode indications. It is desirable to keep the length of all data words (the number of bits in each word) the same.

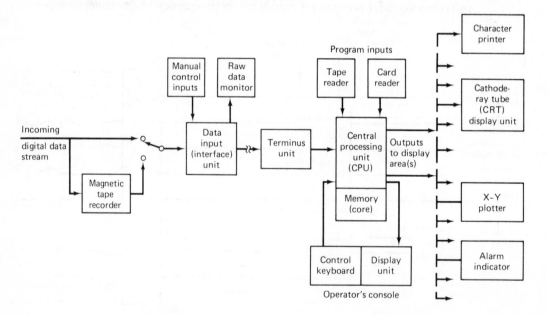

Figure I-9. Digital data processing and display system.

The data stream is usually stored on magnetic tape. In some systems it is necessary to delay any further processing at that time, such as when the computer is at a different location or when the computer is not available to the user at the time data are being received. The tape is then played back through the computer at a later time *(recorded data processing)*. In the system illustrated, the data stream is simultaneously fed directly to the computer *(real-time data processing)*. If any errors occur during processing, or if the data must be processed again for other reasons, the recorded data are then still available on a reel of magnetic tape.

The data are interfaced to the computer at the data input unit, at which point manual controls can be applied and the raw data can be monitored on a display device such as an oscilloscope. If the cabling between data input unit and computer is relatively long, a terminus unit is used to condition the data stream for acceptance by the computer.

The essential portions of the data computer are the central processing unit (CPU) and the memory (typically a magnetic core). Programs required to process the data and to display them in the desired form on various display devices are stored on magnetic tape, punched paper tape, or on decks of punched cards. Reader units then apply the appropriate programs to the CPU and its memory. At least one operator's console is a part of the computer system. A keyboard control unit allows the operator to modify or override stored data-processing programs, to alter data display, and to perform diagnostic operations when computer functions are improper.

Among the variety of display units available for computer systems, the most popular are printers and cathode-ray-tube (CRT) units, both of which can display data in alphanumeric form (numbers and characters of the alphabet). Printers provide a permanent record of data on paper tape, strip, or sheet. Tape printers provide a single-line printout on a narrow paper tape (as in "ticker-tape" machines). Strip printers print one or two relatively short groups of characters per line of an approximately 2-inch-wide paper tape (similar to cash-register receipt strips). Line printers (page printers) print a relatively large number of characters on one line of a wide prefolded paper sheet, then reset to the next line so that sequential pages of data printouts can be obtained. CRT units can similarly show page-type displays of data in alphanumeric form, but do not provide a permanent record. They can also be programmed for display in graphical form. When permanent data records are required in graphical form, X-Y plotters are employed to provide plots of the variation of a given measurand with time or another reference or measurand.

Computer systems allow many different types of special data processing in addition to a sequential display of decommutated data. A few examples are:

1. Conversion of the decimal equivalent of a digital data word into a decimal number representative of the measured value, expressed in engineering units on the basis of a calibration record *(engineering-unit conversion)*.

2. Limiting the display of each measurement to those times when the

change of the measured value, compared to its previous value, is significant (i.e., exceeds a specified tolerance). Such *data suppression* facilitates the evaluation of data from a multimeasurement system by a single observer and results in shorter data records.

3. Comparing each data value to predetermined upper and/or lower limits and providing an alarm when the limit is exceeded *(alarm limit test)*. The alarm can be in the form of a special character (e.g., an asterisk) next to the display of the data word. It can also be in the form of a warning light or audible tone.

4. Accumulating successive values of the same measurement over a specified period of time, averaging those values, and then displaying the average value *(data averaging)*.

5. Accumulation of successive values of the same measurement over a specified period of time (or a specified number of data words), determining the largest of these values, and displaying the largest value *(peak search)*.

6. Performing mathematical operations on data for one or more measurements and displaying the results *(computer-derived data)*, such as multiplying a current measurement with a voltage measurement to display electrical power.

7. Comparing variations of a measurement, over a specified interval, with computer-stored data representative of a "model" of such variations, and displaying data resulting from such a comparison.

I.5 CONTROL SYSTEMS

Although this book is intended to treat electronic sensing and analyzing devices primarily as elements of measuring and analyzing systems, it is recognized that many of the devices described in this book are also used in control systems. The purpose of measuring and analyzing systems is to provide the user with information (data). In control systems employing a human operator as part of the control loop, this information can then be used by the operator to effect a control function manually (e.g., increase a temperature, reduce a pressure, stop a flow, fill a tank, or change a speed). In automatic control systems the output of the sensing or analyzing device is used to effect a control function without the use of a human operator. The former are known as *open-loop* control systems, the latter as *closed-loop* control systems.

The most commonly used automatic control systems are closed-loop systems employing feedback. A feedback loop includes a forward signal path, a feedback signal path, and a signal summing point, which together form a closed circuit. A typical basic closed-loop control system is illustrated in Figure I-10. It operates in the following manner (equivalent terms commonly used in process control are shown in brackets):

A specific quantity within a *controlled system* [*process*] is to be maintained

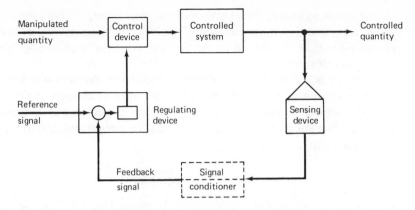

Figure I-10. Basic control system.

at a specified magnitude. This *controlled quantity* [*controlled variable*] is measured by a sensing device, usually a transducer [*transmitter*]. The output of the sensing device, which may or may not have to be conditioned in some manner, is fed to a *comparing element, or summing point* [*set point*] in a *regulating device* [*controller*]. At this point, the signal fed back from the *sensing device* [*feedback signal*] is compared with a *reference signal* [*set-point signal*]. If the two signals are of the same magnitude, or within a relatively narrow tolerance from each other [*dead band*], no further action occurs. If the two signals differ from each other by an amount larger than that tolerance, a regulating signal is sent to a *control device* [*final controlling element*]. This signal causes the control device to change a quantity or condition *(manipulated quantity)* [*manipulated variable*] in the controlled system. The control action remains in effect until the controlled magnitude is at its proper level, as indicated by the feedback signal equaling the set-point signal.

One example of a simple feedback control system is speed control of an internal combustion engine. If the angular speed (rate of rotation) of the engine's output shaft is to be the controlled quantity, a tachometer can be connected to the shaft. The output of the tachometer is compared with a preset reference signal. Differences between the two signals then cause a valve to operate so as to admit more or less fuel to the engine and, hence, to maintain the angular speed of the output shaft at the desired value.

There are many types of control action. The simplest is *on– off control,* as exemplified by the thermostatic furnace control used in most homes. When the room temperature drops below the set point, the furnace is turned on. When the temperature rises and reaches the set point again, the furnace is turned off. This control action usually results in a noticeable temperature change, particularly if the dead band of the controller is too wide. When the temperature of a heating device must be kept at a more constant level, such as in many industrial applications, *proportional control* can be applied. This control action provides a continuous linear relation between the output and the input of the controller. A small deviation in the temperature from the desired value, as sensed by a temperature transducer, causes a small regulating action to restore the temperature to that level. A large deviation causes a large regulating action. In this manner the temperature is controlled more closely than by on-off control.

Among additional types of control action is *derivative control,* in which the controller output is proportional to the rate of change of the output, and *integral control,* in which the rate of change of the output is proportional to the input. The set point may be set manually, automatically, or in accordance with a program.

Bibliography

1. **Borden, P. A., and Mayo-Wells, W. J.,** *Telemetering Systems.* New York: Reinhold Publishing Corp., 1960.

2. **Stiltz, H. L.** (Ed.), *Aerospace Telemetry.* Englewood Cliffs, NJ: Prentice-Hall, Inc., 1961.

3. **Tyson, F. C.,** *Industrial Instrumentation.* Englewood Cliffs, NJ: Prentice-Hall, Inc., 1961.

4. **Bair, E. J.,** *Introduction to Chemical Instrumentation.* New York: McGraw-Hill Book Company, 1962.

5. **Cerni, R. H., and Foster, L. E.,** *Instrumentation for Engineering Measurement.* New York: John Wiley & Sons, Inc., 1962.

6. **Holzbock, W. G.,** *Instruments for Measurement and Control.* New York: Reinhold Publishing Corp., 1962.

7. **Cook, N. H., and Rabinowicz, E.,** *Physical Measurement and Analysis.* Reading, MA: Addison-Wesley Publishing Co., Inc., 1963.

8. **Stein, P. K.,** *Measurement Engineering.* Phoenix, AZ: Stein Engineering Services, 1964.

9. **Doebelin, E. A.,** *Measurement Systems: Application and Design.* New York: McGraw-Hill Book Company, 1966.

10. **Shinskey, F. G.,** *Process Control Systems.* New York: McGraw-Hill Book Company, 1967.

11. **Roots, W. K.,** *Fundamentals of Temperature Control.* New York: Academic Press, Inc., 1969.

12. **Peatman, J. B.,** *The Design of Digital Systems.* New York: McGraw-Hill Book Company, 1972.

13. **Considine, D. M.** (Ed.), *Process Instruments and Controls Handbook* (2nd ed.). New York: McGraw-Hill Book Company, 1973.

14. **Fink, D. G.** (Ed.), *Electronic Engineers' Handbook.* New York: McGraw-Hill Book Company, 1975.

15. **Kuo, B. C.,** *Automatic Control Systems* (3rd ed.). Englewood Cliffs, NJ: Prentice-Hall, Inc., 1975.

16. **Krauss, M., and Woschni, E.-G.,** *Messinformationssysteme* (Measurement Information Systems). Berlin, GDR: VEB Verlag Technik, 1975.

17. **Jones, B. E.,** *Instrumentation, Measurement and Feedback.* Maidenhead, England: McGraw-Hill Book Company (UK) Ltd., 1977.

18. **Morrison, R.,** *Grounding and Shielding Techniques in Instrumentation* (2nd ed.). New York: John Wiley & Sons, Inc., 1977.

19. *Standards and Practices for Instrumentation* (5th ed.). Research Triangle Park, NC: Instrument Society of America, 1977.

Introduction II:
Transducer Fundamentals

II.1   NOMENCLATURE AND TERMINOLOGY

Most sensing devices, and many elements of analyzing devices, are really *transducers*. A transducer is simply a device that provides a usable output in response to a specific *measurand:* the physical quantity, property, or condition that is to be measured. But transducers have been, are being, and will probably always be called by different names in different technical disciplines. In the process industries they are usually called *transmitters* (e.g., pressure transmitter, temperature transmitter). In some facilities they are called *sensors* (e.g., pressure sensors, force sensors, temperature sensors). In some fields, notably in the area of electro-optical devices, they are called *detectors,* and it would be very difficult to convince workers in this area to call an "IR detector" an "infrared light-intensity transducer." At one time, the word "cell" was popular for certain transducers. The term "load cell," meaning force transducer, is still very popular. Most of us think of a "gage" as a dial-type indicator;, however, at various times transducers have been referred to as "gages." Some transducers, particularly when they are small in size, are still occasionally called "pickup" (e.g., "vibration pickup"). Transducers that have configurations enabling them to be immersed into a fluid are often called "probes" (e.g., probe-type temperature transducers are often called "temperature probes"). Many contractions ending in "-meter" are still used: for example, "accelerometer" for acceleration transducer, "flowmeter" for flow-rate transducer, "tachometer" for angular-speed transducer. Although efforts at standardizing on the use of the term "transducer," as described below, have been reasonably successful, many of the alternative terms have remained so popular that the author felt no serious compunctions about using them in this handbook.

During the aerospace boom of the 1960s a great many new types of transducers were specified, designed, manufactured, and used. The chaotic nomenclature situation became a nuisance, especially to users. An effort to produce a usable standard for transducer nomenclature and terminology was undertaken by the Instrument Society of America, initially to benefit primarily the aerospace industry, later to facilitate communications with regard to transducers in all industries and sciences. Under the chairmanship, later the directorship, of the author, a standard was drafted, concurrently with the author's preparation of the *Handbook of Transducers for Electronic Measuring Systems* (Prentice-Hall, Inc., 1969, now out of print). ISA S37.1, "Electrical Transducer Nomenclature and Terminology," was published in 1969 and was adopted as American National Standard, ANSI MC6.1-1975 in 1975. The adherence to such standards, particularly in the United States is, of course, voluntary. Many users and a number of manufacturers have been using the nomenclature and the terminology of this standard to varying degrees. Its perusal is recommended to readers of this handbook and the author has attempted to adhere to practices set forth in the standard to the extent deemed practical.

The description of a transducer is generally based on most or all of the following considerations:

1. What is intended to be measured *(measurand)*?
2. What is the operating principle of the electrical portion of the transducer in which the output originates *(transduction element, transduction principle)*?
3. What element in the transducer responds directly to the measurand *(sensing element)*?
4. What noteworthy special features or povisions are incorporated within the transducer?
5. What are the upper and lower limits of the measurand values the transducer is intended to measure *(range)*?

The following example should serve to demonstrate the foregoing outline. The device being described is a temperature transducer for a specific range and with specific characteristics; it is of the immersion-probe type; it incorporates circuitry to convert the resistance changes of a platinum-wire element into a dc voltage; its measuring range, for full-scale output, is 50 to 150°C. This transducer can, therefore, be described as a "50–150°C, dc output, probe-type, platinum-wire, resistive temperature transducer" (here the *sensing element* is the platinum wire and the *transduction principle* is "resistive"). This description is probably more complete than would usually be necessary. In listings, drawing titles, and similar uses the order of the descriptors is reversed: for example, "Transducer, acceleration, piezoelectric, triaxial, ±30*g*." In general, it is better to describe too much than too little.

II.2 TRANSDUCTION PRINCIPLES

The design and operation, including the transduction principles, of typical transducers is covered in the main body of this book, organized by measurands. The most commonly used transduction principles are described below. It should be noted that some of the basic transduction elements described and illustrated are of types not requiring external excitation (electromagnetic, piezoelectric, photovoltaic, and thermoelectric transduction). Such transduction elements are known as *self-generating*.

Capacitive transduction elements convert a change in measurand into a change of capacitance (Figure II-1). Since a capacitor consists, basically, of two electrodes separated by a dielectric, the capacitance change can be caused either by motion of one of the electrodes to and from the other electrode, or by changes in the dielectric between two fixed electrodes.

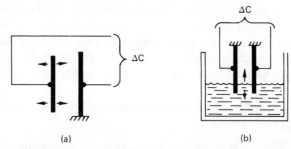

(a)   (b)

Figure II-1. Capacitive transduction: (a) moving plate, constant dielectric; (b) fixed plates, changing dielectric.

Inductive transduction elements convert a change in measurand into a change of the self-inductance of a single coil (Figure II-2). The inductance changes can be effected by the motion of a ferromagnetic core within a coil or by externally introduced flux changes in a coil having a fixed core.

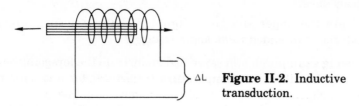

ΔL   **Figure II-2.** Inductive transduction.

Reluctive transduction elements (Figure II-3) convert a change in measurand into an ac voltage change due to a change in the reluctance path between two or more coils (or separated portions of one or more coils), with ac excitation applied to the coil system. This category includes "variable-reluctance," "differential-transformer," and "inductance-bridge" elements, as described in more detail in Section 1.4.2. The change in reluctance path is usually effected by the motion of a magnetic core within the coil system.

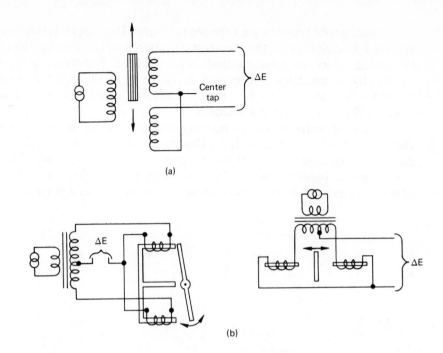

(a)

(b)

Figure II-3. Reluctive transduction: (a) differential transformer; (b) inductance bridges (variable-reluctance).

Electromagnetic transduction elements convert a change in measurand into an electromotive force (output voltage) induced in a conductor by a change in magnetic flux, in the absence of excitation (Figure II-4). The change in flux is usually effected by relative motion between an electromagnet and a magnet or portion of magnetic material.

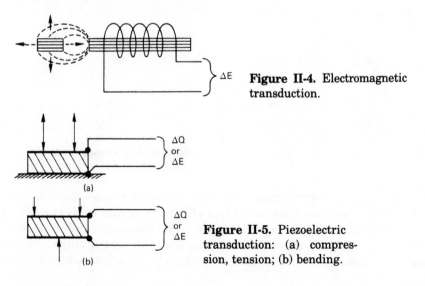

Figure II-4. Electromagnetic transduction.

(a)

(b)

Figure II-5. Piezoelectric transduction: (a) compression, tension; (b) bending.

Piezoelectric transduction elements (Figure II-5) convert a change in measurand into a change in the electrostatic charge (Q) or voltage (E) generated by certain materials when mechanically stressed. The stress is typically developed by compression or tensions forces, or by bending forces exerted upon the material (the *crystal*) directly by a sensing element or by a mechanical member linked to a sensing element.

Resistive transduction elements convert a change in measurand into a change of resistance (Figure II-6). Resistance changes can be effected in conductors as well as semiconductors by such means as heating or cooling, applying mechanical stresses (so as to utilize the *piezoresistive effect*), wetting or drying of certain electrolytic salts, or moving the wiper arm of a rheostat.

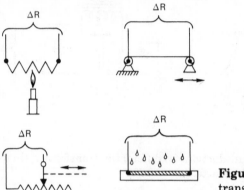

Figure II-6. Resistive transduction.

Potentiometric transduction elements convert a change in measurand into a *voltage-ratio* change by a change in the position of a movable contact *(wiper)* on a resistance element across which excitation is applied (Figure II-7). The ratio given by the wiper position is basically a *resistance ratio*.

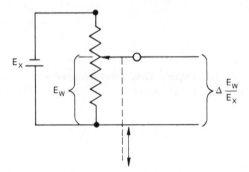

Figure II-7. Potentiometric transduction.

Strain-gage transduction elements convert a change in measurand into a change of resistance due to strain, in either two or four arms of a Wheatstone bridge. This transduction principle is a special version of resistive transduction; however, it involves either two or four resistive strain transducers *(strain gages)* connected into a Wheatstone-bridge circuit across which excitation is

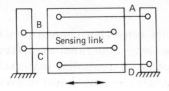

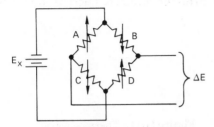

Figure II-8. Strain-gage
transduction.

applied, so that the output is a voltage change (Figure II-8). Upward arrows, in the illustration, indicate increasing resistances, and downward arrows indicate decreasing resistances, in the arms of the bridge, that are simultaneously effected (in a *four-active-element bridge*) by a measurand change due to the placement and connection of the individual resistive elements; in the example illustrated (an unbonded-strain-gage element) the indicated directions of resistance changes would occur as the sensing link moves toward the left.

Photoconductive transduction elements convert a change in measurand into a change of the resistance (or conductance) of a semiconductor material due to a change in the amount of illumination incident upon the material (Figure II-9).

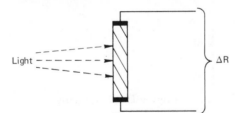

Figure II-9. Photoconductive
transduction.

Photovoltaic transduction elements convert a change in measurand into a change in the voltage generated when the illumination incident upon a junction between certain dissimilar materials changes (Figure II-10).

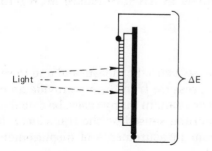

Figure II-10. Photovoltaic
transduction.

Thermoelectric transduction elements convert a change in measurand into a change in the electromotive force *(emf)* generated by a temperature difference between the junctions of two selected dissimilar materials (due to the *Seebeck effect*). In the basic thermoelectric element shown in Figure II-11, a junction between the output terminals (at which temperature T_2 prevails) would be formed, for example, by a voltmeter connected across the terminals.

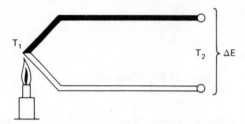

Figure II-11. Thermoelectric transduction.

Ionizing transduction elements convert a change in measurand into a change in ionization current, such as through a gas between two electrodes (Figure II-12).

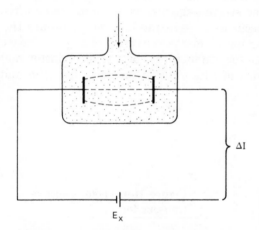

Figure II-12. Ionizing transduction.

II.3 GENERAL CHARACTERISTICS

Characteristics generally applicable to transducers are explained below. The preferred term (usually the term defined in ANSI Standard MC6.1-1975) is printed in *italic*.

II.3.1 Measurand Characteristics

A transducer is usually designed to sense a specific measurand and to respond only to this measurand: for example, pressure transducers provide an output indicative of pressure. Other measurands can, in many cases, be calculated by their known relationship to the measurand sensed by the transducer: for example, velocity can be calculated from measurements of displacement and time. A variety of determinations can be inferred from one or more transducer output signals: for example, bearing wear can be inferred from acceleration transducer outputs, smoke density from light sensor outputs, and electrical power from the outputs of a current sensor and a voltage sensor. Each transducer, however, is specified by its basic measurand and its measuring range.

The *range* of a transducer is specified by the upper and lower limits of measurand values. Range can be *unidirectional* (e.g., "0 to 2.5 cm") or *bidirectional,* symmetrically (e.g., "±45°") or asymmetrically (e.g., "−2 to +10g"), or *expanded (zero-suppressed)* (e.g., "70 to 120 psig," "500 to 800 rad/s"). The algebraic difference between the two range limits is the *span.* The span of a ±30° angular-displacement transducer is 60°; the span of a 70- to 120-psig pressure transducer is 50 psig.

The *overrange* (sometimes called overload, or maximum measurand) is the maximum magnitude of measurand that can be applied to a transducer without causing a change in performance beyond specified tolerances. A specified amount of *recovery time,* after removal of overrange, may have to be allowed to elapse before the transducer again performs within specified tolerances.

II.3.2 Electrical Design Characteristics

The basic electrical design characteristics of a transducer, excitation (preferred to "input" since the measurand is also an "input"), output, grounds, and output, input, source, and load impedances are explained below and illustrated in Figure II-13, in which the transducer is viewed as a "black box," that is, without regard to its internal workings and just as a device with which other equipment must electrically interface.

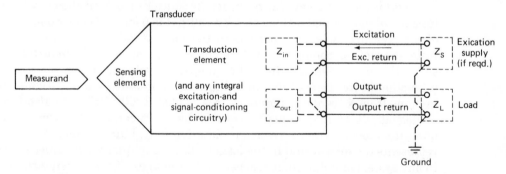

Figure II-13. Basic "black-box" electrical characteristics of a transducer.

With the exception of self-generating types, transducers require *excitation,* an external electrical voltage (or current) applied to them for their proper operation. The impedance of the excitation supply, presented to the transducer is the *source impedance* (Z_S). The impedance of the transducer, presented to the excitation supply, is the *input impedance* (Z_{in}). The impedance of the excitation cabling is considered part of the source impedance. The impedance across the output terminals of the transducer is the *output impedance* (Z_out). The impedance presented to the output terminals of the transducer by the associated external circuitry (e.g., output-conditioning circuitry, display device), referred to as the *load,* and by the impedance of the cabling between transducer (output terminals) and load, is the *load impedance* (Z_L).

The excitation return and output return may be isolated from each other (e.g., when strain-gage transduction is employed), or they can constitute a single return (e.g., when potentiometric transduction is used), as indicated by the dashed jumper between transducer terminals; one of the return wires is then omitted. The return lines are usually electrically isolated from the case of the transducer, which itself may or may not be grounded by mounting. The return lines may both be connected to a ground near the excitation supply and load, or they may remain ungrounded *(floating ground)*. The excitation and output cabling (or only the output cabling) may have to be *shielded* when it is subject to electromagnetically or electrostatically induced transients along its path, when cabling is relatively long, and when output signal levels are relatively low. The shield is usually grounded near the load, sometimes also at the transducer end, depending on the system grounding philosophy used.

When two or more portions of a transducer (one of them may be the case) are electrically insulated from each other, the resistance between them, as measured while a specified dc voltage is applied, is the *insulation resistance*. The degree of insulation can also be expressed in terms of the *breakdown voltage rating,* the magnitude of ac or dc voltage that can be applied across specified insulated portions without causing arcing and without causing conduction between the portions, above a specified value of current. The *breakdown voltage,* which is established by a test generally considered destructive, is the magnitude of voltage at which arcing or excessive conduction occurs.

Output is the electrical quantity, produced by a transducer, which is a function of the applied measurand. The output is usually a continuous function of the measurand *(analog output)* in the form of voltage amplitude, voltage ratio, current, or sometimes just as changes in capacitance, inductance, and so on. *Frequency output,* where the number of cycles or pulses per second are a function of the measurand, and *frequency-modulated output,* frequency deviations from a "center" frequency (e.g., "3000 ± 200 Hz"), are also forms of analog output. *Digital output* represents the measurand in the form of discrete quantities coded in some system of notation (e.g., binary code). When output represents the measurand in the form of discrete or quantized values not coded in any system of notation, it has been referred to as *discrete-increment output;* such an output is exemplified by that of a switch-type transducer.

End points are the output values at the lower and upper limits of the range of a transducer. They can be the mean of end-point readings determined over two or more consecutive calibration cycles. When end points are specified, a tolerance is usually applied to them (e.g., "0.00 ± 0.02 and 10.00 ± 0.01 V dc"). No such tolerances are allowed for *theoretical end points,* the points between which the theoretical curve is established (see Section II.3.4.1). Theoretical end points are not necessarily established at 0% measurand, 0% output (lower end point) and 100% measurand, 100% output (upper end point); however, when they are set at these values they are referred to as *terminal end points*.

As for any other electronic device, it is important for transducers to be appropriately matched to, and interfaced with, the associated measurement system. One of the areas that tends to be overlooked is matching output impedance to load impedance. A mismatch in these impedances can cause *loading error*, which increases with the ratio of output impedance to load impedance. Careful attention must also be paid to manufacturer-recommended excitation supply characteristics.

Certain electrical characteristics need to be watched (and probably need tolerances assigned to them in a transducer specification) when excitation-conditioning or output-conditioning circuitry is incorporated within a transducer. The output of an ac-to-dc converter (demodulator) in a transducer, for example, may contain a measurable ac component *(ripple)*. The output from an integrally packaged amplifier may contain random disturbances *(noise)* and may be subject to changes in the characteristics of amplifier components that result in *gain instability*. When the output of a transducer is sinusoidal ac, it may contain distortions due to the presence of harmonics (frequencies other than the fundamental frequency); this *harmonic content* is usually expressed as a percentage of the rms output of the transducer.

II.3.3 Mechanical Design Characteristics

Mechanical design characteristics are specified for transducers primarily for three purposes: to facilitate handling and installation, to prevent malfunction or performance degradation that could be caused by the measured fluid or the environment, and to interface the transducer properly with the system as part of which it is expected to operate.

The configuration, dimensions, mounting provisions and their dimensions, and the type, size, and location of all external electrical, mechanical, and fluid connections are always specified, as are any provisions for external zero and gain adjustments. Case material and case sealing must be known whenever the application requires it, and it is often necessary to state what materials can reasonably be expected to come in contact with a measured fluid (or what measured fluids may and may not come in contact with the portions of a transducer exposed to them). Standards developed by governmental or other organizations often apply to transducers when, for example, they must operate as part of a sealed system, or when they must be explosion-proof, waterproof, or operate in a high-temperature or nuclear-radiation environment.

One characteristic that can be classified as "mechanical" and often needs more attention than it has been given is nameplate information, inscribed either on a separate nameplate that is attached to the transducer case, or directly into the transducer case. Except for those rare cases when such information is limited because the transducer is extremely small, it is usually possible to inscribe fairly complete information about the transducer on a nameplate or nameplate area on the case. As a minimum, the information should include properly worded nomenclature (if a "brand-name" term must be used it can always be added to the nomenclature) and the most pertinent characteristics, such as range, excitation, output, part number and serial number, manufacturer's name and address, identification of external electrical connections (pin or lead labeling), and, of course, any additional information that may be required by applicable specifications, standards, industrial codes, or special needs of the user.

II.3.4 Performance Characteristics

Transducer performance characteristics can be categorized as follows:

1. *Static characteristics* which describe performance at room conditions, with very slow changes in measurand, and in the absence of any shock, vibration, or acceleration (unless one of these is the measurand); although there is some disagreement as to what conditions constitute *room conditions,* they have generally been established as the following (unless specifically stated otherwise): a temperature of $25 \pm 10°C$, a relative humidity of 90% or less, and a barometric pressure of 880 to 1080 mbar (88 to 108 kPa).

2. *Dynamic characteristics,* which relate to the response of a transducer to variations of the measurand with time.

3. *Environmental characteristics,* which relate to the performance of a transducer after exposure (*nonoperating* environmental characteristics) or during exposure (*operating* environmental characteristics) to specified external conditions (such as temperatures, shock, vibration).

4. *Reliability characteristics* which relate to the life expectancy of a transducer and to any hazards that may be presented by its malfunction to the system in which it is intended to operate.

II.3.4.1 Static characteristics. An ideal or theoretical output/measurand relationship exists for every transducer. If the transducer were ideally designed by ideal designers and if it were made from ideal materials by using ideal methods and workmanship, the output of this ideal transducer would always indicate the true value of the measurand. The output would follow exactly the prescribed or known *theoretical curve* which specifies the relationship of the output to the applied measurand over the transducer's range. Such a relationship can be stated in the form of a table of values, a graph, or a mathematical equation. Figure II-14 illustrates a theoretical curve, in general terms (percent of full-scale output, % *FSO*, vs. measurand expressed in percent of range) as well as for the example of a pressure transducer whose range is 0 to 1000 psia (0 to 6895 kPa) and whose output is 0 to 5 V dc, for the case of a *linear* output/measurand relationship, which causes the curve to be a straight line.

The output of an actual transducer, however, is affected by the nonideal

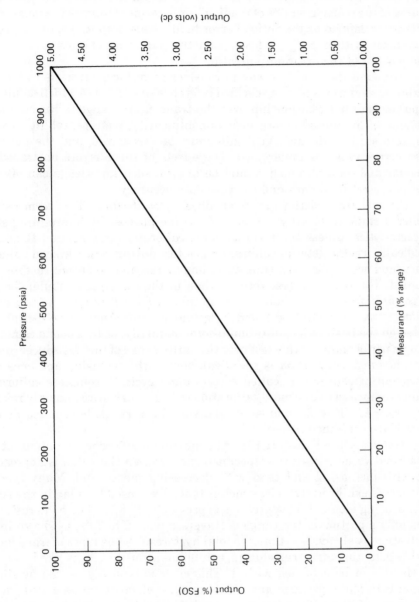

Figure II-14. Output/measurand relationship of ideal linear-output transducer (including application of general example to a typical dc output pressure transducer).

behavior of the transducer, which causes the indicated measurand value to deviate from the true value. The algebraic difference between the indicated value and the true (or theoretical) value of the measurand is the transducer's *error*. Error is usually expressed in % FSO, sometimes in percent of the output reading of the transducer ("% of reading") or in terms of units of the measurand. *Accuracy* is defined as the ratio of error to full-scale output, usually expressed in the form "within ±____% FSO," sometimes in terms of units of measurand or in percent of the error/output ratio.

Although the simplest way to consider transducer errors is in terms of maximum deviations from a specified reference line or curve which defines the output/measurand relationship over the transducer's range *(error band),* the existence of individual errors such as nonlinearity, nonrepeatability, hysteresis, zero shift, and sensitivity shift must be recognized, and the nature of these errors must be understood. The effects of these errors on transducer behavior and data obtained should be known; such knowledge can often be used to correct final data and increase data accuracy.

Error characteristics are determined by *calibration*. This term usually implies a *static calibration,* performed for the purpose of determining static characteristics, unless the term *dynamic calibration* (see Section II.3.5.2) is specifically used. A (static) calibration is a test during which known values of measurand are applied to a transducer and corresponding output readings are recorded. The resulting test record, when in the customary tabular form, is the *calibration record*. When it is in graphical form it is referred to as *calibration curve*. It should be noted here that a calibration curve can also be plotted on the basis of a calibration record, manually, or by use of a computer. A single performance of this test over the entire range of the transducer (unless a *partial-range calibration* is specified), once with increasing and once with decreasing measurand, is called a *calibration cycle*. A complete calibration usually comprises two or more calibration cycles, which are commonly referred to as "Run 1," "Run 2," and so on. Individual errors, as determined by calibration, are explained below.

Hysteresis (see Figure II-15) is the maximum difference in output, at any measurand value within the (specified) range, when the value is approached first with increasing and then with decreasing measurand. Many types of transducers exhibt hysteresis, which is typically caused by a lag in the action of the sensing element. Hysteresis is expressed in % FSO. The hysteresis seen when only a portion of the range is traversed (e.g., 0 to 30%, as shown in the illustration) is always less than the total hysteresis. Some types of transducers, notably potentiometric transducers, exhibit an error that looks like hysteresis but should not be confused with it. This error is typically caused by sliding friction between wiper arm and potentiometric element and is called *friction error*. Such friction effects can be minimized by *dithering* the transducer, applying intermittent or oscillatory acceleration forces to it (this process is sometimes called "tapping"). When such a transducer is dithered during a calibration, its true hysteresis can be established. However, unless dithering is specified, friction error is included with hysteresis. *Friction error* is often de-

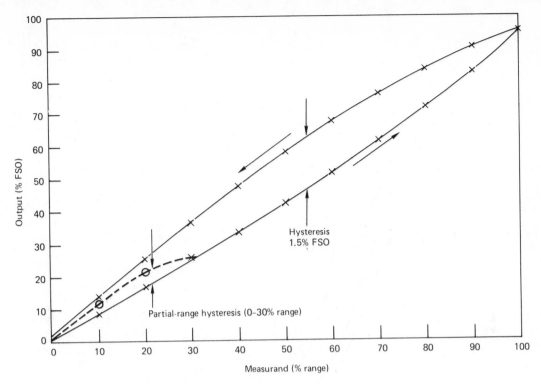

Figure II-15. Hysteresis (scale of errors 10:1).

termined, as such, as the maximum change in output, at any measurand value within the range, before and after minimizing friction within the transducer. A calibration during which dithering is employed (e.g., by mounting a small buzzer against the transducer) is called a *friction-free calibration*. Such a calibration should really be used only when the intended application of the transducer can reasonably be expected to minimize friction error equally.

Repeatability (sometimes called "reproducibility") is the ability of a transducer to reproduce output readings when the same measurand value is applied to it consecutively, under the same conditions, and in the same direction. It is expressed as the maximum difference between output readings, as determined by two calibration cycles (see Figure II-16), unless otherwise specified, and expressed as "within____% FSO." If the sampling is increased by increasing the number of calibration cycles, a better statistical measure of repeatability can be obtained.

Linearity is the closeness of a transducer's calibration curve to a specified straight line. It is expressed as "within ±____% FSO" (in a specification) or as "within +____, −/____% FSO" (as a result of a calibration), as the maximum deviation of any calibration point from the corresponding point on the specified straight line during any one calibration cycle. When more than one calibration run is made, the worst linearity seen during any one calibration cycle is stated. "Linearity," when not accompanied by a statement explaining

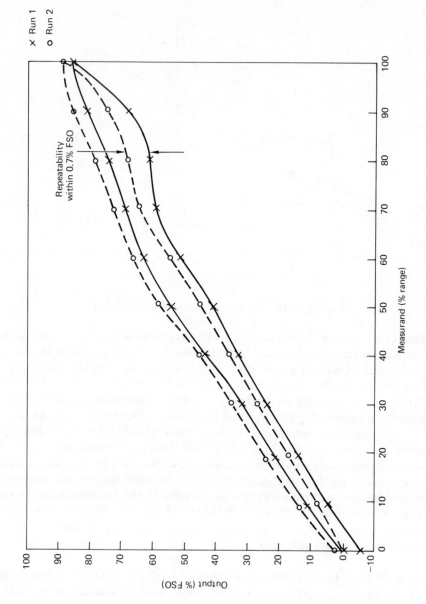

Figure II-16. Repeatability (scale of errors 10:1).

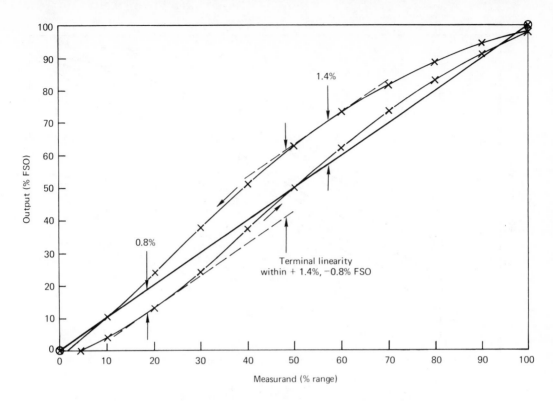

Figure II-17. Terminal linearity (scale of errors 10:1).

what sort of straight line it is referring to, is meaningless. A transducer may have an independent linearity within ±0.5% FSO while its terminal linearity is within ±3.5% FSO. The specific type of reference line is stated either by adding a modifier to the word "linearity" (e.g., "terminal linearity") or by adding a statement such as "referred to the best straight line." The various types of linearity are explained below.

Theoretical-slope linearity is referenced to the *theoretical slope,* the straight line between the *theoretical end points.* These are usually close to 0% FSO (for 0% range) and close to 100% FSO (for 100% range) but can be purposely offset (e.g., 5% FSO at 0% range, and 95% FSO at 100% range). Since no tolerances apply to theoretical end points, this straight line can always be drawn without referring to any measured values.

Terminal linearity is referenced to the *terminal line* (see Figure II-17), a special form of theoretical slope for which the theoretical end points are exactly 0% and 100% of both range and full-scale output.

End-point linearity is referenced to the *end-point line,* the straight line between the *end points,* the outputs at the upper and lower range limits obtained and averaged (unless otherwise specified) during any one calibration. End-point tolerances should be specified.

Independent linearity is referenced to the *"best straight line"* (see Figure

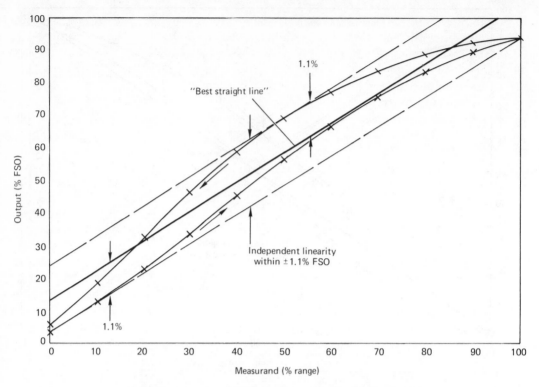

Figure II-18. Independent linearity (scale of errors 10:1).

II-18), a line midway between the two parallel straight lines closest together and enveloping all output values on a calibration curve. The best straight line can only be drawn after a calibration has been completed.

Least-squares linearity is referenced to the *least-squares line,* that straight line for which the sum of the squares of the residuals is minimized. The term "residual" refers to the deviations of output readings from their corresponding values on the straight line calculated. The calculation is usually performed with the aid of a computer.

Some additional types of linearity have been used at times, such as "independent linearity with forced zero" or "with fixed *Y*-intercept," which require that the best straight line also passes through a specified point *(point-based linearity).* It has been argued that specifications (and calibration results) for linearity actually include hysteresis, since linearity is determined by means of a bidirectional calibration cycle; some commercial literature, therefore, refers to "combined linearity and hysteresis," referred to a specific straight line, typically the "best straight line."

Conformance (or "conformity") is a term that has sometimes been applied to the closeness of a calibration curve to a specified curve for an inherently nonlinear transducer. It is typically referred to a theoretical curve, although least-squares and other fits have also been used.

Resolution and *threshold* are both descriptive of "smallest increment" but are quite different characteristics. When the measurand is continuously varied over the range, the output of certain transducers will not be perfectly smooth. Instead, the output will change in small (but measurable) steps. This is typical for potentiometric transducer with wirewound elements; small step changes in the output occur as a result of the wiper sliding from wire turn to wire turn. The magnitude of output step changes, as the measurand is continuously varied over the range, is the *resolution* of the transducer. It is expressed in % FSO. The magnitude of such step changes is not equal for potentiometric transducers with wirewound elements. Some steps will be larger, some smaller, varying with minute variations in turn spacing and wire thickness. The term *average resolution*, then, is applied to the reciprocal of the total number of output steps over the range, multiplied by 100 and expressed in % FSO (or percent of voltage ratio, % *VR*). The magnitude of the largest of all observed output steps, also expressed in % FSO or % VR, is the *maximum resolution*. The resolution of digital-output transducers (for which step changes are inherent and equal) is given by the number of bits in the data words or, in the case of incremental digital-output transducers, by the number of "on" indications obtained per unit length or angle or revolution. When there are no measurable step changes in the output of a transducer, it is said to have "continuous resolution" (sometimes erroneously referred to as "infinite resolution," erroneous since "infinitesimal" would be more appropriate).

A measurand change of finite magnitude is required to cause a change in the output of any transducer or, generally, any sensing or analyzing device (in the context of this handbook). In some transducer types those minimal measurand changes are not measurable. In others they may be measurable but are negligible for a given application, or they may be significant only at the lower limit of the range. The smallest change in measurand that will result in a measurable change in output is the *threshold* of the transducer. It is usually stated in terms of measurand and may have different values in different portions of the range.

Sensitivity (which has, at times, been confused with threshold) is simply the ratio of the change in output to the change in the value of the measurand. It establishes the slope of the calibration curve.

There are three characteristics which are sufficiently time-dependent to be more properly categorized as "reliability characteristics"; however, they can be determined either by a variant of a static calibration or by static calibrations repeated after a period of time. They comprise creep, zero shift, and sensitivity shift. *Creep* is a change in output occurring over a specific time period while the measurand is held constant (at a value other than zero) and while all environmental conditions are held constant. *Zero shift* is a change in the *zero-measurand output* over a specific period of time, at room conditions (in a specification it is the maximum allowable of such a change over a specified period of time). The *zero-measurand output* (sometimes colloquially called "the zero") is the output of a transducer, under room conditions unless otherwise specified, with nominal excitation and zero measurand applied. Zero shift is characterized by a parallel displacement of the entire calibration curve. *Sensitivity shift* is a change in the slope of the calibration curve due to a change in sensitivity. This characteristic can also be specified as the maximum allowed such shift over a specified period of time, at room conditions, or at other specified conditions.

The *error-band concept* was originally developed by the author, assisted and inspired by his colleagues at a large aerospace facility, to simplify the specification and determination of transducer errors. An *error band* is the band of maximum deviations of output values from a specified reference line or curve due to causes attributable to the transducer. Since such deviations may be due to nonlinearity, nonrepeatability, hysteresis, zero shift, sensitivity shift, and so on, it can be seen that transducer characteristics are easier to specify and determine when individual characteristics need no longer be specified and determined. An error band is specified in terms of "±____% FSO," and is determined on the basis of maximum deviations observed over at least two consecutive calibration cycles (so as to include repeatability) and then expressed as "+____%, −____% FSO." A specific reference line or curve must be stated for an error band, and the term "error band" is modified by a term denoting applicable environmental conditions and, when required, other special conditions. The types of straight lines an error band can be referred to are the same as those used for linearity (see above).

The *static error band* is the error band applicable at room conditions and in the absence of any shock, vibration, or acceleration (unless one of these is the measurand). Figure II-19 illustrates a static error band, referred to the terminal line, as it may have been specified (as "±2.0% FSO") and as it may have been determined over two consecutive calibration cycles. It can be seen that the actual error band, "+1.5%, −1.1% FSO," indicates that the transducer is well within specifications. Further scrutiny of the calibration curves (which, however, is not needed for making an accept/reject decision) shows enough information for determination of individual characteristics when such knowledge is required. When a number of transducers of the same design, range, and output ("of the same part number and dash number") are used in a given measurement system, and if errors within the error band specified for this transducer are acceptable to the system, the calibrations for each of these transducers (as long as each unit was accepted) can be considered *interchangeable* (within the error-band tolerances). This means that it would not be necessary to use individual calibration records for data reduction; the individual calibrations then serve merely as "acceptance records."

Static error bands can be referred to any of the lines explained for *linearity*. They can also be referred to any curve that can be specified by means of a graph, a table of values, or a mathematical equation. Figure II-20 shows a static error band referred to a theoretical curve (i.e., one that can be drawn before any measured values are obtained); the shape of the curve was selected arbitrarily, for the purpose of illustration. Narrower static error bands can be obtained when linearity, or conformance to a prescribed curve, is not required. Such requirements can be waived when it is intended to reduce final data on

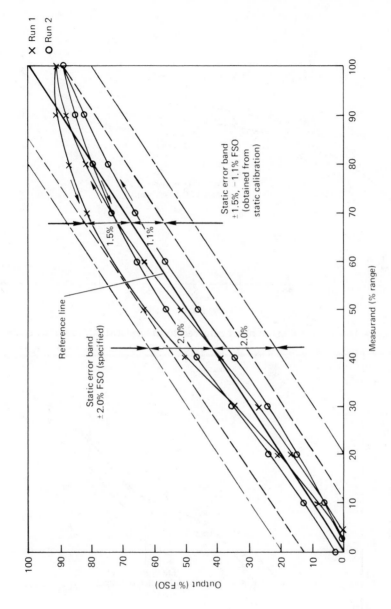

Figure II-19. Static error band referred to terminal line (error scale 10:1).

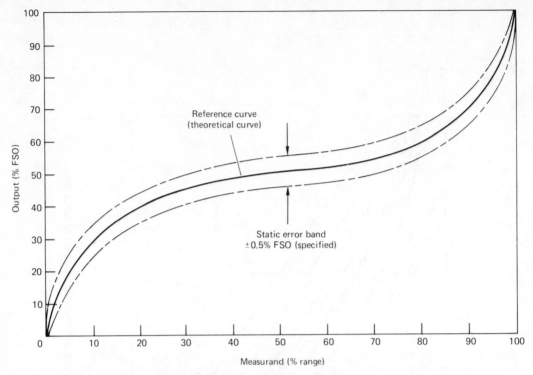

Figure II-20. Static error band referred to theoretical curve (error scale 10:1).

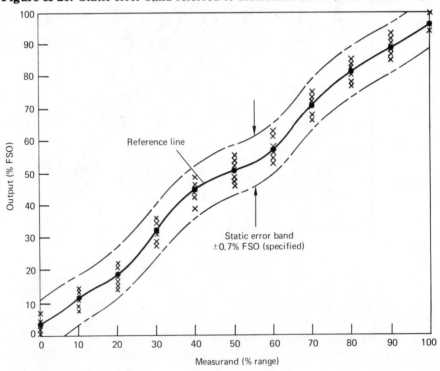

Figure II-21. Static error band referred to mean-output curve (error scale 10:1).

the basis of a complex curve, different for each transducer. This type of data reduction virtually mandates the use of a computer; however, programs that will plot a curve on the basis of multiorder polynomials are fairly common. An example of such an error band is shown in Figure II-21. This static error band is referred to a *mean-output curve,* the curve through the mean of output readings obtained during a specified number (three, in the example shown) of consecutive calibration cycles; it can be seen that the deviations of output readings are due to nonrepeatability and hysteresis. In some applications transducer accuracy is of prime importance in only a limited portion of the range; accuracy in the other portions can be sacrificed. For such cases a "stepped" static error band can be used (see Figure II-22 for an example; the theoretical end points were arbitrarily offset).

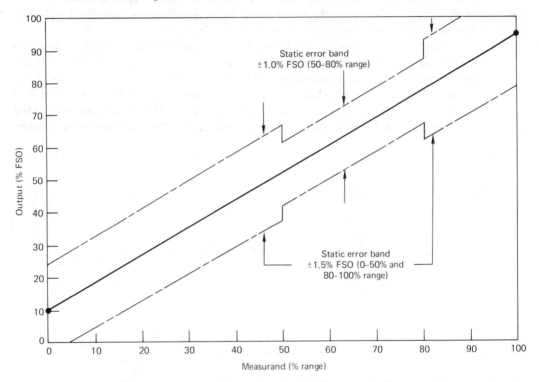

Figure II-22. "Stepped" static error band referred to straight line between theoretical end points 10% FSO at 0% range, 95% at 100% range (error scale 10:1).

The selection of a reference line for a static error band of a bidirectional-range transducer frequently involves the consideration of the intercept of the line with the zero-measurand level. If a theoretical slope or curve, or a terminal line is used, such a consideration is generally unnecessary. When an end-point line is used, and end-point tolerances are established, additional tolerances may have to be applied to the zero-measurand output. A stepped static error band, narrower near the zero measurand than near the end points, has been found useful for some of the more specialized measurement requirements.

II.3.4.2 Dynamic characteristics. When a transducer is used for a measurement where rapid measurand variations occur, or where step changes in measurand have to be monitored with good fidelity, the transducer's dynamic characteristics must be established. These can be stated and determined in terms of frequency response, or response time, or damping and natural frequency, depending on transducer type and application. It should be noted that some of the determinations require test methods and equipment of fairly high complexity as well as considerable expertise in test personnel. Tests have been standardized for many types of transducers by professional societies and by government laboratories such as, in the United States, the National Bureau of Standards. Unless otherwise stated in a specification, specified dynamic characteristics are applicable at room conditions.

Frequency response is the change with frequency of the output/measurand amplitude ratio within a stated range of frequencies of a sinusoidally varying measurand applied to a transducer. It is also the change with frequency of the phase difference between this measurand and the output. It is usually specified as "within ±____% (or ±____dB) from____to____Hz"; it should be referred to a frequency within the specified frequency range and to a specific measurand

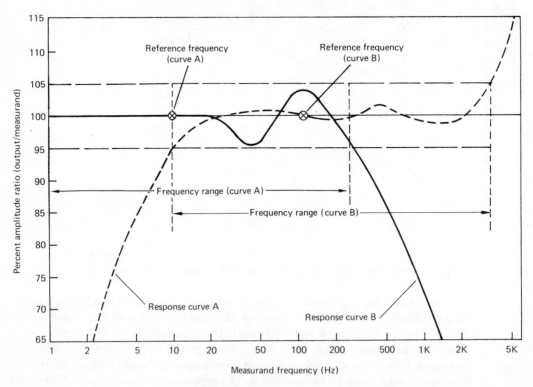

Figure II-23. Frequency response.

value. Figure II-23 shows two typical response curves, considering only amplitude ratio, not phase difference (the output will lag behind the measurand). Curve A shows the response of a transducer that can be used for static as well as dynamic measurements; in this example the frequency response is within ±5% from 0 to 300 Hz, referred to 10 Hz. Curve B shows the response of a transducer usable only for dynamic measurements; the response is within ±5% from 10 to 3500 Hz, referred to 100 Hz. Reference amplitude was not stated for these generalized examples. A commonly found colloquial expression for the response of curve A is that the response is "from *dc* to 300 Hz (within ±5%)." Similarly, the response of curve B could be called "*flat* (within ±5%) between 10 and 3500 Hz."

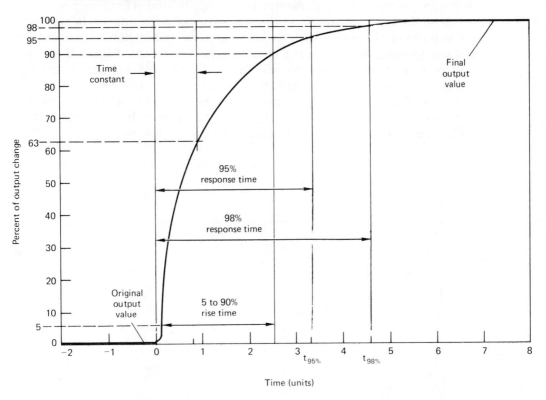

Figure II-24. Response time, rise time, and time constant.

Response time, rise time, and time constant characterize the response of a transducer (that is not underdamped) to a step change in measurand (see Figure II-24). When such a step change is applied, the output will change toward the final value (100% output change) over a period of time and nonlinearly. The length of time required for the output to rise to a specified percentage of its final value (as a result of a step change in measurand) is the *response time*. The percentage is typically stated in the form of a prefix to "response time," e.g., "95% response time" or "98% response time." A special term and symbol have been assigned to 63% (actually 63.2%) response time: *time constant* (τ). Another term, *rise time,* is used to state the length of time for the output to rise from a small specified percentage to a large specified percentage of its final value. Unless otherwise specified (e.g., "5 to 90% rise time" in Figure II-24) the percentages should be assumed to be 10% and 90% of the final value. The general term for a transducer's response to a step change in measurand is *transient response.* In some cases it is possible to calculate frequency response from a transducer's transient response, its mechanical properties, or its geometry; if so, it should be referred to as *calculated frequency response* and the basis for calculation should be identified.

Damping is the energy-dissipating characteristic which, together with natural frequency (see below), determines the upper limit of frequency response as well as the transient-response characteristics of a transducer. In response to a step change in measurand, an *underdamped* system oscillates about its final steady value before coming to rest at that value (see Figure II-25); an *overdamped* system comes to rest without overshoot; and a *critically damped* system is at the point of change between the underdamped and overdamped conditions. When a transducer's sensing element is set into free oscillation, the frequency of this oscillation is the *natural frequency.* It is important that this oscillation is free, not forced. Natural frequency has also been defined as

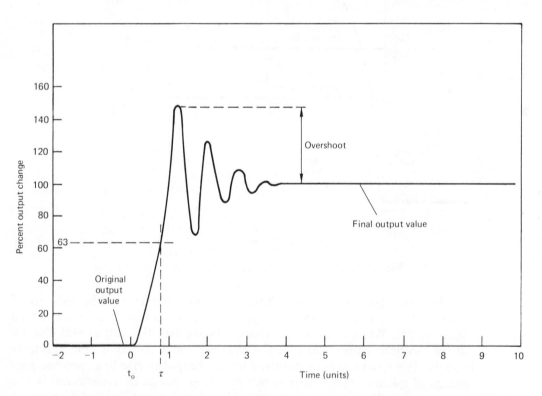

Figure II-25. Response of underdamped transducer to step change in measurand.

that frequency of a sinusoidally applied measurand at which the output lags the measurand by 90°. Figure II-25 shows that time constant is still a valid characteristic of an underdamped transducer but that such characteristics as 95% response time could not be stated due to the *overshoot* and oscillations about the final value; the frequency of this oscillatory transient is the *ringing frequency* of the transducer.

The ratio of the actual damping to the degree of damping required for critical damping is the *damping ratio*. A damping ratio of 1.0 indicates critical damping, damping ratios larger than 1.0 signify overdamping, and damping ratios less than 1.0 mean underdamping. Among the means used to effect damping in a transducer are those relying upon the viscosity of a fluid *(viscous damping)* and those relying upon the current induced in electrical conductors by changes in magnetic flux *(magnetic damping)*.

II.3.4.3 Environmental characteristics. The static performance characteristics as well as the dynamic performance characteristics of transducers are specified, and verified, as those which the transducer exhibits at room conditions and in the absence of any external conditions *(environmental conditions)* that may affect the transducer performance. When a transducer can reasonably be expected to operate under conditions other than those under which it was calibrated *(operating environmental conditions)*, the *environmental effects* must be known and the resulting deviations from static performance *(environmental errors)* must be limited by tolerances (in a specification) and determined by tests. Such additional environmental tests (temperature tests, vibration tests, ambient-pressure tests, etc.) may have to be performed on each transducer used; more commonly they are performed on a *sampling* basis (test one of every *n* transducers of each model and range), sometimes only on a *qualification* basis (test one representative transducer). Environmental testing of sensing and analyzing devices requires considerable skill and expertise from test personnel as well as appropriate test equipment and test setups whose behavior in the course of a test is well understood.

Besides operating environmental conditions, there are other environmental conditions to which a transducer may be exposed, but the transducer is not expected to operate within specified tolerances (or operate at all) while exposed to them. However, the transducer is expected to perform within specified tolerances *after exposure* to such *nonoperating environmental conditions*. When nonoperating environmental conditions, including those encountered during storage (e.g., in a warehouse, or installed in its application awaiting activation of the system in which it is to operate), shipping, and handling, are known or suspected to alter the behavior of a transducer, they should be included in a specification and the absence of out-of-tolerance nonoperating environmental effects should be verified by testing.

Temperature effects must be known, and accounted for, for essentially all types of transducers. The *operating temperature range* is the range of ambient temperatures, given by their lower and upper extremes (e.g., "−50 to +250 °C") within which the transducer is intended to operate and within which all specifications related to temperature effects (unless they specifically relate to nonoperating temperatures) apply. Some manufacturers of transducers incorporating elements intended to compensate for temperature effects call this the "compensated temperature range." When the temperature of a *measured fluid* can cause significant temperature effects in the transducer, the *fluid temperature range* is specified, sometimes instead of the operating temperature range, and then governs temperature-related specifications.

For some transducers, temperature effects (thermal effects) are stated only in terms of the zero shift *(thermal zero shift)* and sensitivity shift *(thermal sensitivity shift),* which cause a parallel displacement and a slope change, respectively, of the calibration curve. Knowledge of these individual errors is useful when the temperature prevailing while a measurement is made is known and appropriate corrections to final data are intended to be made. However, thermal effects on hysteresis and repeatability are not included in such specifications.

A more general and inclusive way of specifying thermal effects on performance characteristics is given by use of the term *temperature error,* the maximum change in output (at any measurand value within the transducer's

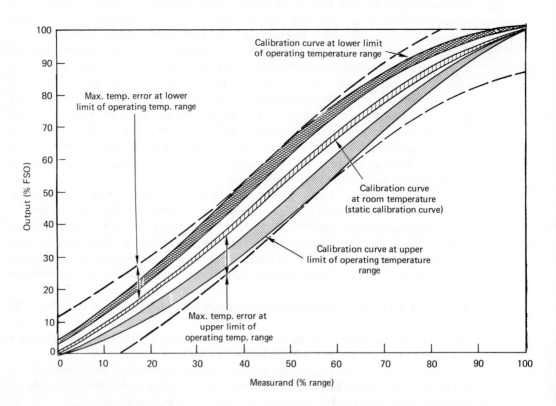

Figure II-26. Temperature error (at operating temperature range limits) (scale of curve shifts exaggerated).

Introduction II: Transducer Fundamentals

range) when the (operating or fluid, as applicable) temperature is changed from room temperature to specified temperature extremes (see Figure II-26). The simplest way of specifying tolerances on thermal effects is provided by the error-band concept; its use also facilitates verification. The *temperature error band* is simply the error band (see Section II.3.5.1) that is applicable over the operating (or fluid) temperature range. This form of specification is particularly useful when the error band is referenced to a theoretical slope, such as the terminal line (see Figure II-27).

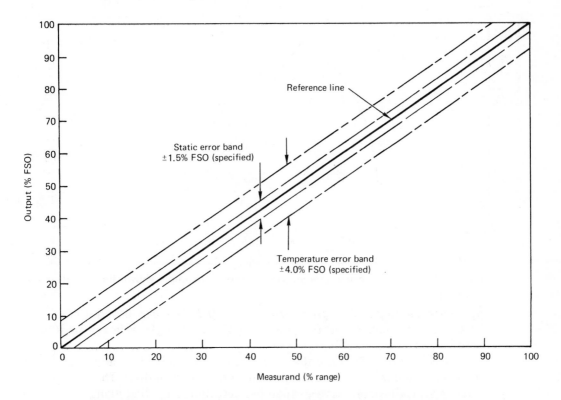

Figure II-27. Temperature error band referred to terminal line (error scale 2:1).

It is also important to specify the *maximum (ambient or fluid) temperature,* the highest (or lowest) temperature that a transducer can be exposed to without being damaged or subsequently showing a performance degradation beyond specified tolerances.

When a transducer is exposed to a step change in (ambient or fluid) temperature, a transient output deviation *(temperature gradient error)* can appear in its output (see Figure II-28). Tolerances on this error should be specified for a stated rate of change of temperature, for the two temperatures between which the step change occurs, and for a specific measurand value.

Temperatures will also affect dynamic characteristics, particularly when they employ viscous damping. Specifications should then cover thermal effects

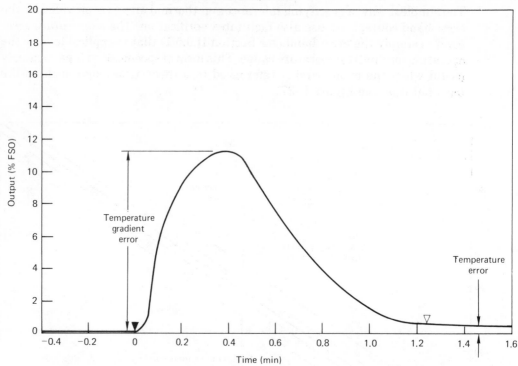

Figure II-28. Temperature gradient error (typical example shown for output at zero measurand).

appropriately (e.g., "Damping ratio: 0.7 ± 0.2, between 0 and 100°C," and "Frequency response: within ±5% from 30 to 5000 Hz, referred to 100 Hz, between −20 and +120°C").

Acceleration effects are the effects of quasi-steady-state accelerations on internal elements of a transducer, causing errors in its output. The acceleration error is typically more severe when acceleration is applied along one axis of a transducer than when it is applied along other axes. Error-causing acceleration may act directly on a mechanical sensing element or its linkage and cause spurious deflections; it can act upon structural supports, causing distortion which may even result in failure; it can act upon bearing-supported rotating members, causing eccentric loading and increased friction; and it can cause mass shifts, deformations, and distortions in other ways.

When a transducer is intended to be used in an application where it will be subjected to such accelerations (e.g., on moving vehicles or on moving structural or mechanical members), the possibility of acceleration errors must be considered and tolerances on such errors must be prescribed. In order to reach an understanding about these with the transducer's manufacturer, it is important to agree on a labeling of the axes (see Figure II-29). It can then be established that the transducer is more sensitive to accelerations along the, say, *X*-axis. It may then be possible for the user, knowing his application, to install the transducer so that accelerations along that transducer axis are minimized.

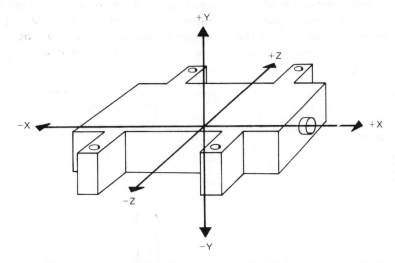

Figure II-29. Typical labelling of acceleration axes for a transducer.

Acceleration error is the maximum difference (at any measurand value within the transducer's range) between output readings taken without and with the application of specified constant acceleration along specified axes. In a specification the maximum expected acceleration in each axis and, if necessary, in each of the two directions, are specified in conjunction with the maximum allowable acceleration error [e.g., "Acceleration error: ±2.5% FSO for: 10 *g* (+*X*), 2 *g* (−*X*), 5*g* (±*Y*), 3 *g* (±*Z*)." This error can also be specified or determined in terms of *acceleration sensitivity* within a stated range of acceleration values acting along specified axes (e.g., "0.2%/*g*, over 0 to 10 *g*, *X*-axis, and 0.15%/*g*, over 0 to 10 *g*, *Y*- and *Z*-axes"). For acceleration transducers, sensitivity to accelerations acting along other than the measured axis is known as *transverse sensitivity*.

When the error-band concept is used, the *acceleration error band* will include acceleration errors as well as static errors, the latter to the extent that they may not be reduced by accelerations, which occurs in some designs.

Some types of transducers are so sensitive to acceleration forces that even the acceleration due to earth gravity can cause undesirable effects. The error due to the orientation of a transducer relative to the direction in which gravity acts upon it is called *attitude error*. When this error, in the different transducer axes, is known, it is then often possible to install the transducer in such a position that attitude errors are minimized.

Vibration effects, the effects of vibratory acceleration, can affect transducers in the same manner as steady-state acceleration. More severe effects, however, are connected with the frequencies of vibration. As the vibration frequency is varied over a stated range, and along a specific axis, amplified vibrations *(resonances)* of internal elements can occur at one or more frequencies. Figure II-30 illustrates typical vibration effects; a potentiometric transducer was chosen for this example which includes evidence of a reduction in friction error due to vibration; it also shows vibration error at several resonances as well as the equivalent *vibration error band,* at the largest resonance, identified as one-half the vibration error band since error bands always have bipolar tolerances.

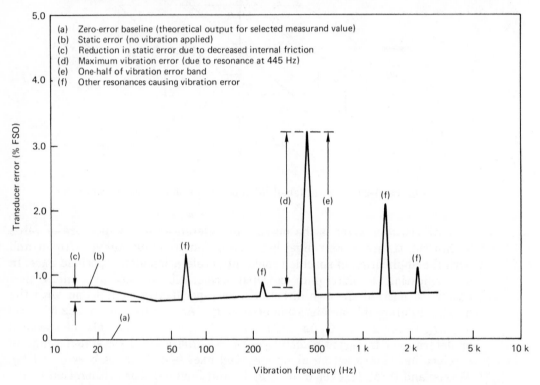

Figure II-30. Typical results of vibration test on potentiometric transducer at a given program of vibration amplitudes, from 10 to 3000 Hz, at one measurand value, along one transducer axis.

Vibration error is the maximum change in output (at any measurand value within the tranducer's range) when vibration levels of specified amplitudes and range of frequencies are applied to the transducer along specified axes (at room conditions). It should be noted that different resonances and, hence, different vibration errors may be observed for different measurand values, particularly when the transducer incorporates a mechanical sensing element. It may be necessary, therefore, to predict the measurand value most likely seen by the transducer while it is exposed to the most severe vibration environment and then to specify and verify vibration errors at that value.

Ambient-pressure effects can be observed in some transducer designs when

Introduction II: Transducer Fundamentals

they are calibrated at room barometric pressure and then used either at very high altitudes, or on aircraft or spacecraft, where ambient pressures approach a vacuum, or when they are used far underground (e.g., in deep mines or wells) or at deep submersions underwater, where pressures are very high. Transducer performance can be affected by resulting case deformations and changes to the internal geometry of a transducer. It can also be degraded, to the point of failure, when a poorly sealed transducer is exposed to a vacuum environment and internal materials outgas, wires self-heat in the absence of air as a heat-transfer medium, internal sealed cavities start to bulge or leak, or corona-arcing occurs across high-voltage terminals.

Ambient-pressure error is the maximum change in output (at any measurand value within the transducer's range) when the ambient pressure is changed between specified values, usually between room pressure and a lower or higher ambient pressure. Such errors can also be stated in terms of an *ambient-pressure error band*. Ambient-pressure error has been referred to as "altitude error," at times, with ranges of (low) pressures stated in terms of altitude above sea level.

Mounting effects can occur during the installation of a transducer, and result in subsequent performance changes, when, for example, the mounting surface of the transducer is not evenly machined so that the case gets deformed when all mounting hardware is tightened, or when the torque applied to the coupling nut on a pressure fitting causes sensing-element deformations. *Mounting error* is the error resulting from mechanical deformation of the transducer caused by mounting the transducer and making all electrical and measurand connections. Mounting error is not commonly included in specifications; however, it may be necessary to verify its absence (e.g., by performing an in-situ calibration check).

Other operating environmental effects on the behavior of a transducer during its normal operation, and which should be known and included in specifications, include: humidity, or immersion in liquid (affects poorly sealed transducers, starting with a reduction of insulation resistance); corrosive (and insulation-reducing) effects of high salt concentrations (or concentrations of other corrosive substances) in the ambient atmosphere; various effects of measured fluids on sensing elements of transducers; the influence of ambient electromagnetic fields on transduction elements and integral circuitry; and the effects of radiation (nuclear, ionizing) on various internal transducer elements.

Nonoperating environmental effects on the performance of a transducer subsequent to its exposure to such environmental conditions should be understood and, if necessary, limited by inclusion in a specification. These environmental conditions do not only include temperatures, vibration, shock, moisture, etc., encountered during storage, shipping, and handling; they may also include environmental conditions, in excess of limits of operating conditions specified for a transducer, that can be encountered while the transducer is installed in its intended application. All overrange, or overload, characteristics can be classified as nonoperating conditions. Some examples of nonoperating environmental conditions that tend to be overlooked are: room temperature, for a light sensor or radiation sensor which normally operates while cooled to low temperatures; any significant vibration, for any transducer used on a satellite, where it need not operate until after separation of the satellite from its booster stages; and low temperature, together with a liquid state, of a fluid that is intended to be measured only when it is gaseous and at a significantly higher temperature.

Type-limited environmental effects are significant to certain transducer types, or transducers for certain measurands, in addition to the generally applicable (to varying degrees) environmental effects described above. These include:

1. *Conduction error,* the error in a temperature transducer due to heat conduction between the sensing element and the mounting of the transducer.

2. *Strain error,* the error resulting from a strain imposed on a surface to which a transducer is mounted; this error is significant primarily for surface-temperature transducers and is not intended to relate to strain gages.

3. *Reference-pressure error,* the error resulting from changes of the reference pressure, the pressure relative to which a *differential-pressure transducer* measures pressure, within a specified reference-pressure range.

4. *Transverse sensitivity,* the response of acceleration transducers to acceleration forces in axes transverse to the sensing axis.

II.3.4.4 Reliability characteristics. Although some operating and most non-operating environmental characteristics relate to a transducer's reliability, the characteristics considered here are only those relating to the useful life of a transducer as well as to any characteristics that may have adverse effects on the system in which the transducer is installed when a transducer fails in a particular mode.

The operating life of a transducer can be expressed in one of two ways: *operating life,* when stated as such, is the (specified) minimum length of time over which the transducer will operate, either continuously or over a number of on/off cycles whose duration is specified, without changing its performance characteristics beyond specified tolerances; or *cycling life,* the (specified) minimum number of full-range excursions (or specified partial-range excursions) over which a transducer will operate (as specified) without changing its performance beyond specified tolerances.

In some cases it may also be necessary to specify or be concerned about a transducer's *storage life,* the length of time over which it can be exposed to specified storage conditions without changing its performance beyond specified tolerances.

Reliability characteristics relating to adverse effects on the system in which a transducer is installed are generally application-dependent. They include any characteristics controlled by applicable health and safety codes. They further include any characteristics deemed important after a determination of effects of failure modes has been made. An example may be results of internal short-circuiting (protection may be included in the associated electrical system or may have to be included within the transducer). Another example is the *burst-pressure rating* of a transducer, the pressure that may be applied to the sensing element or the case, as specified, of a transducer without rupture of sensing element or case, respectively. When a sensing element ruptures, the measured fluid may come in contact with materials it is not compatible with and the results may range from measured-fluid contamination to an explosion. When a case ruptures, portions of it may hit surrounding personnel or equipment and cause damage.

II.4 GENERAL CRITERIA FOR SELECTION

The selection of a transducer will usually involve most or all of the following basic considerations:

Measurement

1. What is the real purpose of the measurement?
2. What is the measurand?
3. Will the measurand only increase, or only decrease, or both?
4. What range of measurand values will be displayed in final data?
5. What overrange conditions may occur before or during the time data are required?
6. With what accuracy must the measurement be presented in final data?
7. What are the dynamic characteristics of the measurand (fluctuation frequency range, step changes)?
8. What frequency response or response time must be visible in final data?
9. What is the physical and chemical nature of the fluid to be measured?
10. Where and how will the transducer be installed?
11. How and to what extent may a transducer modify the measurand while it is being measured?
12. What ambient environmental conditions will the transducer be exposed to?

Data System

1. What is the general nature of the data system (e.g., radio telemetry, ground telemetry, individual direct display)?

2. What is the nature of the major elements of the data system:

   a. Signal conditioning, multiplexing, pretransmission buffering?

   b. Data transmission link?

   c. Data processing?

   d. Data storage?

   e. Data display?

3. What are the accuracy and frequency response characteristics of the end-to-end data system immediately downstream of the transducer?

4. What form of transducer output will the data system accept with minimum additional signal conditioning?

5. What load impedance will be seen by the transducer?

6. Is frequency filtering or amplitude limiting of transducer output required, and can the data system handle these?

7. To what extent does the data system provide for detection of, or provide corrections for, errors in the transducer output?

8. What transducer excitation voltage is most readily available?

9. How much current may the transducer draw from the excitation supply?

Transducer Design

1. What constraints are imposed on the transducer's mass, excitation, power drain, and configuration?

2. What are the transducer output requirements?

3. Which transduction principle should be utilized in the transducer?

4. What static accuracy characteristics, dynamic characteristics, environmental (operating and nonoperating) characteristics must the transducer provide?

5. What are the effects of the measured fluid(s) on the transducer?

6. Will the transducer affect the measurand so that erroneous data are obtained?

7. What operating or cycling life is required?

8. What constraints are imposed on the design by any applicable governmental standards or industrial codes?

9. What are the failure modes of the transducer? What hazards would a failure present to the system in which it is installed, to adjacent components or systems, to the area in which it operates, to personnel working in that area, or to the data system?

10. What is the lowest level of technical competence of any and all personnel expected to handle, install, and use the transducer? What

human-engineering requirements should affect the transducer design?

11. What test methods will be used to verify performance? What tests will be performed by the manufacturer and what tests will be run by the user? Are those tests adequate? Are test methods correct? Are test methods simple and well established?

Availability

1. Is a transducer that fulfills all requirements available "off the shelf"?

2. If the answer to question 1 is "no," consider the following:
   a. Will minor redesign of an existing transducer be sufficient or will a major development effort be required?
   b. What manufacturer has demonstrated his ability to produce a transducer similar to the required item?
   c. What past experience exists in dealing with a proposed manufacturer?
   d. Can the transducer be delivered in time to meet installation schedules?

Cost Effectiveness

1. Is the cost of the transducer compatible with the measurement function it will provide?

2. What costs will be incurred by required transducer testing, periodic recalibration, handling, and installation?

3. Which requirement levied on the transducer is the major cost driver?

4. What minor compromises in requirements could lead to substantial savings?

5. What modifications to the data system may lead to reduced costs of a number of different transducers used in that system, and what cost trade-offs would be involved?

Bibliography

1. "International Electrotechnical Vocabulary (2nd ed.): Group 37, Automatic Controlling and Regulating Systems," *Publication 50 (37)*. Geneva: Central Office of the IEC, 1966.

2. **Rohrbach, C.**, *Handbuch für elektrisches Messen mechanischer Grössen* (Handbook for electrical measurements of mechanical quantities). Düsseldorf, FRG: VDI-Verlag GmbH, 1967.

3. **Ostrovskij, L. A.**, *Elektrische Messtechnik* (Electrical Measurement Technology;

German translation by D. Hofmann from original published in USSR, 1965). Berlin, GDR: VEB Verlag Technik, 1969.

4. **Liptak, B.G.,** *Instrument Engineers Handbook,* Vol. 2. Radnor, PA: Chilton Book Co., 1970.

5. **Norton, H. N.,** *Trilingual Dictionary of Measurement Terms* (English–German–French). Lausanne: Scriptar Ltd., 1970.

6. **Stein, P. K.,** "Measurement System Performance Capabilities as Governed by the Input Conditioning Design," *Laboratory for Measurement Systems Engineering Publication No. 30.* Tempe, AZ: Arizona State University, 1970.

7. **Herceg, E. E.,** *Handbook of Measurement and Control.* Pennsauken, NJ: Schaevitz Engineering, 1972.

8. "Process Measurement and Control Terminology," *SAMA Standard PMC 20.1-1973.* New York: Scientific Apparatus Makers Association, 1973.

9. "Measurement and Instrumentation," *ACTA IMEKO 1973* (Proceedings of the International Measurement Congress). Amsterdam: North-Holland Publishing Co., 1974. (*Note:* ACTA IMEKO are published for each of the triennial congresses, including 1976, 1979, etc., sponsored by: IMEKO, POB 457, H-1371 Budapest 5, Hungary.)

10. **Klein, H. A.,** *The World of Measurements.* New York: Simon and Schuster, 1974.

11. "Electrical Transducer Nomenclature and Terminology," *ANSI Standard MC6.1-1975 (ISA S37.1).* Research Triangle Park, NC: Instrument Society of America, 1975.

12. "Process Instrumentation Terminology," *ISA Standard S51.1.* Research Triangle Park, NC: Instrument Society of America, 1976.

chapter one

Solid-Mechanical Quantities

1.1 BASIC CONCEPTS

1.1.1 Length, Angle, and Motion

Length is a fundamental unit in mechanics. The length of a straight line is the number of times that a specified measuring rod must be applied successively until the line has been covered completely. The length of a curve is defined in the same manner except that the measuring rod must be flexible so that it always conforms exactly with the portion of the curve to which it is applied. The length of a straight line between two points is the *distance* between two points, the spatial separation between two points or objects. *Proximity* is the spatial closeness between two points or objects.

An *angle* is the figure obtained by drawing two straight lines from one point or by the figure formed by two surfaces diverging from the same line. The angle represents the amount of rotation of one line about a fixed point on the other line or the amount of rotation of one surface from the other surface if both diverge from the same line. If the line on which the fixed point is located is considered the *initial* line and the line rotating about the point is the *terminal* line, the angle is positive if the terminal line rotates counterclockwise and negative if the terminal line rotates clockwise.

The concepts of position, motion, and displacement are so closely inter-related in the measurement field that the terms "position transducer" or "motion transducer" have been used instead of the more correct term "displacement transducer" for the identical sensing device. *Position* is the spatial location of a body or point with respect to a reference point. *Motion* is the change in position of a body or point with respect to a reference system. *Displacement* is the vector representing a change in position of a body or point with respect to a reference point. *Linear displacement* is a displacement whose instantaneous direction remains fixed. *Angular displacement* is the angle between the two coplanar vectors determining a displacement. The number of *degrees of freedom* of a mechanical system is the minimum number of independent coordinates required to define completely the position of all parts of the system at any instant of time.

The concepts of velocity and acceleration involve the use of another fundamental unit in mechanics: time. *Velocity* is the time rate of change of displacement with respect to a reference system; it is a vector quantity. *Speed* is the magnitude of the time rate of change of displacement; it is a scalar quantity. *Acceleration* is the time rate of change of velocity with respect to a reference system; it is a vector quantity. The instantaneous values of velocity and acceleration are the first derivative and the second derivative, respectively, of displacement. The displacement, velocity, and acceleration can be linear (translational, rectilinear) or angular (rotational). Their interrelationship can be stated in the following manner:

<table>
<tr><td>*Linear*</td><td>*Angular*</td></tr>
<tr><td>$$v = \frac{dx}{dt}$$</td><td>$$\omega = \frac{d\theta}{dt}$$</td></tr>
<tr><td>$$a = \frac{d^2x}{dt^2}$$</td><td>$$\alpha = \frac{d^2\theta}{dt^2}$$</td></tr>
</table>

where x = linear displacement
  θ = angular displacement
  v = linear velocity
  ω = angular velocity
  a = linear acceleration
  α = angular acceleration
  t = time

Average velocity is the total displacement divided by the total time taken by this displacement. *Average speed* is the magnitude of the average velocity vector. The *translational velocity* (v) of a rotating member is the product of the radius of the member (r) and its angular velocity (ω), or $v = \omega r$.

The concepts of attitude, bearing, and elevation are related to angular position. *Attitude* is the relative orientation of a vehicle or an object represented by its angles of inclination to three orthogonal reference axes. *Attitude rate* is the time rate of change of attitude; it is often referred to as "rate of rotation" or just "rate." A *bearing* is a direction at a reference point given by the angle in the horizontal plane between a reference line and the line between the reference point and the point whose bearing is specified; bearing is usually measured clockwise from the reference line. An alternative term for bearing, applied primarily to celestial navigation, is *azimuth*. *Elevation* is similarly defined as the direction at a reference point given by the angle in the vertical plane between a reference line and the line between the reference point and the point whose elevation is specified.

1.1.2 Vibration

Vibration (mechanical vibration) is an oscillation wherein the quantity is mechanical in nature (e.g., force, stress, displacement, velocity, acceleration). *Oscillation* is the variation, usually with time, of the magnitude of a quantity with respect to a reference system when this variation is characterized by a number of reversals of direction. *Harmonic motion* is a vibration whose instantaneous amplitude varies sinusoidally with time. *Mechanical impedance* is the complex ratio of force to velocity during simple harmonic motion. It is a quantitative measure of the ability of a structure to resist a vibratory force.

Periodic vibration is vibration having a waveform that repeats itself in all its particulars at certain equal time increments. A *period* is the smallest increment of time for which the waveform of a periodic vibration repeats itself in all its particulars. A *cycle* is the complete sequence of magnitudes of a periodic vibration that occur during one period. The *frequency* of a periodic vibration is the reciprocal of its period. The *phase* of a periodic vibration is the fractional part of a period through which the vibration has advanced, as measured from an arbitrary reference.

Random vibration is nonperiodic vibration whose magnitude at any given time can be described only in statistical terms. [*Note:* It is usually taken to mean Gaussian random vibration, whose instantaneous amplitude distribution follows a Gaussian ("normal error curve") distribution.]

The *frequency spectrum* of a vibratory quantity is a description of its instantaneous content of components, each of different frequency and usually of different amplitude and phase. The mean and rms magnitudes of a vibratory quantity are defined by

$$\overline{A} = \frac{1}{t} \int_0^t A(t) \, dt \qquad \text{and} \qquad A_{\text{rms}} = \sqrt{\frac{1}{t} \int_0^t [A(t)]^2 \, dt}$$

where $\overline{A}$ = mean magnitude
$A(t)$ = vibratory quantity
t = time (over which the averaging is done)
A_{rms} = rms magnitude

Power density of random vibration is the mean square magnitude per unit bandwidth of the output of an ideal filter having unity gain, responding to this vibration. It is defined as

$$W(f)^2 = \frac{A(f)^2_{\text{rms}}}{\Delta f}$$

where $W(f)$ = power density

$A(f)^2_{\text{rms}}$ = mean-square magnitude

Δf = bandwidth (usually chosen as 1 Hz)

A *power-density spectrum* is a graphical representation of values of power density displayed as a function of frequency so as to represent the distribution of vibration energy with frequency.

Shock (mechanical shock) is a sudden nonperiodic or transient excitation of a mechanical system. *Jerk* is the time rate of change of acceleration with respect to a reference system.

1.1.3   Mass, Force, and Torque

Mass is the inertial property of a body. It is a measure of the quantity of matter in a body and of the resistance to change in motion of a body. *Weight* is the gravitational force of attraction. On earth, it is the force with which a body is attracted toward the earth (mass times local acceleration due to gravity).

Force is the vector quantity necessary to cause a change in momentum. When an unbalanced force acts on a body, the body accelerates in the direction of that force. The acceleration is directly proportional to the unbalanced force and inversely proportional to the mass of the body. Force is related to mass and acceleration by Newton's second law: $F = ma$. This law is expressed in the *absolute system* of units as

$$F = kma$$

where F = force (acting on mass m)

m = mass

a = acceleration

k = proportionality constant depending on units used

whereas, in the *gravitational system* of units, it is expressed as

$$F = \frac{Wa}{g}$$

where F = force (producing acceleration a)

W = weight (in same units as force)

a = acceleration (acting on body of weight W)

g = acceleration due to gravity (in same units as a)

Torque is the moment of force. It is the product of the force and the perpendicular distance from the axis of rotation to the line of action of the force. (*Note:* This distance is referred to as *lever arm.*) Torque is defined as

$$T = Fl = I\alpha$$

where T = torque

F = force

l = length of lever arm

I = moment of inertia

α = angular acceleration

The *moment of inertia* of a body is the resistance to angular acceleration. It is defined as

$$I = \sum mr^2 = \frac{T}{\alpha}$$

where I = moment of inertia

m = mass (of one particle of the body)

r = crank length (between particle and axis of rotation)

The moment of inertia of a solid cylindrical shaft, of mass M and radius r, about its own axis is $I = \frac{1}{2} Mr^2$.

1.1.4 Elasticity, Strain, and Torsion

Strain is the deformation of a solid resulting from stress. It is measured as the ratio of dimensional change to the total value of the dimension in which the change occurs. *Poisson's ratio* is the ratio of transverse to longitudinal unit strain. *Stress* is the force acting on a unit area in a solid.

The *modulus of elasticity* is the ratio of stress to the corresponding strain (below the proportional limits). It is defined, by Hooke's law, as

$$E = (\text{constant}) = \frac{s}{\varepsilon}$$

where E = modulus of elasticity

s = stress

ε = strain

The tensile and compressive moduli of elasticity are defined as

$$E_t = Y \left(= \frac{s}{\varepsilon} \right) = \frac{F_t/a}{\Delta L/L} \quad \text{and} \quad E_c \left(= \frac{s}{\varepsilon} \right) = \frac{F_c/a}{\Delta L/L}$$

where F_t = force (tension)

F_c = force (compression)

a = cross-sectional area (normal to direction of force application)

ΔL = elongation or contraction (of solid along the direction of force application)

L = original length of solid

Y = Young's modulus ("stretch modulus of elasticity")

E_t = tensile modulus of elasticity

E_c = compressive modulus of elasticity

The *elastic limit* is the maximum unit stress not causing permanent deformation of a solid.

Torsion is the twisting of an object, such as a rod, bar, or tube, about its axis of symmetry. The *torsional deflection* of a solid cylindrical shaft is

$$\theta = \frac{32TL}{\pi d^4 E_s}$$

where θ = helical angle of deflection

T = torque, lb-in

d = shaft diameter, in

L = length of shaft under torsion, in

E_s = shear modulus of elasticity, lb_f/in^2

The *shear stress*, due to torsion, in a solid cylindrical shaft is

$$S_s = \frac{16T}{\pi d^3}$$

where S_s = maximum shear stress, lb_f/in^2

T = torque, lb-in

d = shaft diameter, in

1.1.5   Units of Measurement

1.1.5.1 The International System of Units (SI). The SI (Système International d'Unités), which was derived from the *metric absolute system,* has been adopted as a standard by virtually all countries. It is based on seven fundamental units and two supplementary units.

The fundamental units are: the *meter (m)** as unit of length, defined as

---

*Unless specific government-sanctioned rules apply, the spelling "meter" should be considered interchangeable with "metre."

exactly 1 650 763.73 wavelengths in vacuum of the radiation corresponding to the transition between the energy levels $2p_{10}$ and $5p_5$ of the krypton-86 atom; the *kilogram (kg)* as unit of mass, defined as the mass of the international prototype kilogram kept in the custody of the Bureau International des Poids et Mesures (BIPM), Sèvres, France; the *second (s)* as unit of time interval, defined as the interval occupied by exactly 9 192 631 770 cycles of the radiation corresponding to the $(F = 4, M_F = 0)$ to $(F = 3, M_F = 0)$ transition of the cesium-133 atom when unperturbed by exterior fields; also the *ampere (A)* as unit of electric current, the *kelvin (K)* as unit of temperature, the *candela (cd)* as unit of luminance, and the *mole (mol)* as unit for the amount of substance. The latter four units are discussed in more detail in their appropriate chapters.

The two supplementary units are the *radian (rad)* as unit of plane angle and the *steradian (sr)* as unit of solid angle.

All other units of measurement, in the SI, are derived from these fundamental units and, to a limited extent, the supplementary units. Solid-mechanical quantities are expressed in the following SI units (and some of their most commonly used decimal multiples and submultiples):

Linear displacement: *meter (m), centimeter (cm), millimeter (mm)*

Angular displacement: *radian (rad), milliradian (mrad)*

Linear velocity: *meter per second (m/s), centimeter per second (cm/s)*

Angular velocity: *radian per second (rad/s)*

Linear acceleration: *meter per second squared (m/s²)*

Angular acceleration: *radian per second squared (rad/s²)*

Attitude and attitude rate: same as for angular displacement and angular velocity, respectively

Mass: *kilogram (kg), gram (g)*

Force: *newton (N);* the interrelation of the newton with the basic SI units is: N = kg·m/s²

Torque: *newton-meter (N·m)*

Mass moment of inertia: *kilogram-meter squared (kg·m²)*

Strain: (dimensionless ratio; e.g., *mm/m)*

Stress: newton per square meter *(N/m²)*

Modulus of elasticity: newton per square meter *(N/m²)*

1.1.5.2 Other units compatible with use of the SI. Certain solid mechanical quantities have been commonly expressed in units that are not part of the SI but can be expected to remain in use simultaneously with SI units.

Angular displacement and attitude: the *degree* (°), the *minute* of arc (') or "arc-minute," and the *second* of arc (") or "arcsecond" will probably coexist with the radian for quite some time. One radian equals 57.296

(roughly 57.3) degrees. One degree equals 0.01745 radian. $1° = 60' = 3600''$. Note that the symbol "deg" for degree of arc should no longer be used.

Angular speed: angular speed, particularly when applied to shaft speed or rate of rotation, is more commonly expressed in *revolutions per minute (r/min)* than in rad/s. One revolution $= 2\pi$ rad $= 360°$. The symbol "rpm" is obsolete.

Linear acceleration: acceleration (and shock and vibration amplitude) is often still expressed in g. The g can be converted to units of the SI as well as the American Customary system. Note that its symbol conflicts with that of the gram (g). The quantity g is the acceleration produced by the force of earth gravity. Gravity varies with the latitude and elevation of the point of observation. The value of g has been standardized by international agreement as follows:

$$1 \text{ standard } g = 9.806\ 65 \text{ m/s}^2 = 980.665 \text{ cm/s}^2 =$$
$$386.087 \text{ in/s}^2 = 32.1739 \text{ ft/s}^2$$

The above can be simplified, where allowable, to

$$1\ g = 9.81 \text{ m/s}^2 = 981 \text{ cm/s}^2 = 386 \text{ in/s}^2 = 32.2 \text{ ft/s}^2$$

Strain: since strain is a dimensionless ratio of two lengths (both expressed in the same system of units) it is best expressed in *microstrain* ($\mu\varepsilon$) for medium and small deformations and in *percent* (%) for large deformations. One $\mu\varepsilon$ is the ratio of 10^{-6} of a length unit to this length unit (e.g., μm/m, μin/in).

1.1.5.3 Other metric systems. The *metric absolute systems* of units are still in use but are intended to be superseded by the SI. These are the "mks" system (based on the *meter* as unit of length, the *kilogram* as unit of mass, and the *second* as unit of time) and the "cgs" system (based on the *centimeter* as unit of length, the *gram* as unit of mass, and the *second* as unit of time). The unit of *force* in the cgs system is the *dyne*. Its interrelation with the fundamental units is: 1 dyne $= $ g·cm/s^2. Its relation to the SI unit of force is 1 dyne $= 10^{-5}$ N.

The *metric gravitational system* has been used widely in engineering work. Gravitational systems introduce the concept of *weight,* the force due to gravity exerted by the earth on a mass. The units are the same as those used in the cgs or mks systems; however, the kilogram (or gram) is a unit of *force* rather than of mass. The "metric slug" is the unit for a 9.806 65 - kg mass.

1.1.5.4 The American Customary system of units. This system was referred to as the "British system" until Great Britain switched to the SI. It is still in common use in the United States and in a few small non-European countries. It exists in the form of an absolute as well as a gravitational system. The *absolute ("fps")* system is based on the *foot (ft)* as unit of length, the *pound*

Solid-Mechanical Quantities

(lb) as unit of mass, and the *second* as unit of time. The unit of force in the fps system is the *poundal* (1 poundal = lb·ft/s²). The *gravitational* system is based on the *foot* as unit of length, the *pound* as unit of force, and the *second* as unit of time. The unit of mass exists only as the gravitational unit of a 32.1740-lb mass, a unit called the *slug*. The following American Customary units are used for solid mechanical quantities:

Linear displacement: *foot (ft), inch (in), milli-inch (mil)*

Angular displacement: (use SI or SI-compatible units, as explained above)

Linear velocity: *feet per second (ft/s), inches per second (in/s)*

Angular velocity, angular speed: (use SI or SI-compatible units, as explained above)

Linear acceleration: *feet per second squared (ft/s²)*, or *g* (see SI-compatible units)

Table 1-1   Conversion Factors for Solid-Mechanical Quantities

To Convert from:	to	Multiply by:
acre	m²	4.047×10^3
astronomical unit	m	$1.495\ 98 \times 10^{11}$
circular mil	m²	5.067×10^{-10}
degree (angle)	rad	1.745×10^{-2}
dyne	N	1.000×10^{-5}
fathom	m	1.829
foot	m	0.3048
galileo	m/s²	1.000×10^{-2}
inch	m	2.540×10^{-2}
kilogram—force	N	9.807
kilopond—force	N	9.807
light year	m	$9.460\ 55 \times 10^{15}$
mil	m	2.540×10^{-5}
mile (nautical, U.S. and international)	m	1.852×10^3
mile (U.S. statute)	m	1.609×10^3
minute (angle)	rad	2.909×10^{-4}
ounce—force	N	0.2780
ounce—mass	kg	2.835×10^{-2}
parsec	m	$3.083\ 74 \times 10^{16}$
poundal	N	0.138 255
pound—force	N	4.448
pound—mass	kg	0.4536
pound-foot square (moment of inertia)	kg·m²	4.214×10^{-2}
pound-inch square (moment of inertia)	kg·m²	2.9264×10^{-5}
second (angle)	rad	4.848×10^{-6}
slug-foot square	kg·m²	1.3558
slug	kg	14.594
ton (long, 2240 lb$_m$)	kg	1.016×10^3
ton (short, 2000 lb$_m$)	kg	9.0718×10^2
ton (metric, "tonne")	kg	1.000×10^3
yard	m	0.9144

Angular acceleration: (use SI unit)

Mass: *pound mass (lb$_m$)*

Force: *pound force (lb$_f$)*

Weight: expressed in lb$_f$ (usually shown just in "lb"); a statement of weight should be accompanied by a statement of the gravitational acceleration (in *g*, ft/s², or m/s²) at the location where the object was weighed or is assumed to be located. Unless otherwise stated, the value of the weight is assumed to apply at a gravitational acceleration of 1 standard *g* (9.806 65 m/s²)

Torque: *pound (force)-inches (lb$_f$-in), also lb$_f$-ft, ounce (force)-inches (oz-in)*

Mass moment of inertia: *slug-ft²*

Stress: *lb$_f$/in²* or other units of force per unit area

Modulus of elasticity: *lb$_f$/in²* (typical)

1.1.5.5 Conversion factors. Conversion factors used to convert non-SI units of measurement of solid-mechanical quantities to SI units are shown in Table 1.1. Conversion factors are shown, or rounded off, to four significant figures except when the factors are very large or when the last digit is very close to a "5."

1.2 ACCELERATION AND VIBRATION

1.2.1 Sensing Method

All acceleration transducers *(accelerometers)* use a sensing method in which the acceleration acts upon a *seismic mass* (proof mass), restrained by a spring, and whose motion is usually damped in a spring–mass system (Figure 1-1).

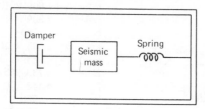

Figure 1-1. Basic spring-mass system of an acceleration transducer.

When acceleration is applied to the accelerometer case, the mass moves relative to the case. When the acceleration stops, the spring returns the mass to its original position (Figure 1-2). The small black and white circular symbol is commonly used to denote the location of the gravitational center of seismic mass. If acceleration were applied to the transducer case in the opposite direction, the spring would be compressed rather than extended.

Under steady-state acceleration conditions the displacement *y* (in cm) of the seismic mass is given by the acceleration *a* (in cm/s²) multiplied by the

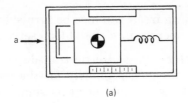 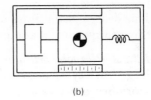

(a)   (b)

Figure 1-2. Displacement of seismic mass: (a) acceleration applied; (b) acceleration removed.

ratio of the mass M (in grams) to the spring constant k (in dynes/cm, where 1 dyne $= 10^{-5}$ N), or $y = aM/k$. Under dynamic (varying) acceleration conditions the damping constant becomes a factor in a modified version of this relationship. The spring extension (and mass displacement) is proportional to acceleration only below the natural frequency of the spring–mass system. The response characteristics of such systems are adequately described in available textbooks dealing with mechanical vibrations.

The seismic mass must be restrained from motion in any but the sensing axis. The (linear) displacement of the mass or spring (or the force exerted by the mass on an elastic member) is the quantity that is sensed by the transduction element of linear accelerometers. The seismic mass of an angular accelerometer, such as a disk pivoted at its center and restrained by a spiral spring, responds to angular acceleration with an angular displacement.

1.2.2 Design and Operation

1.2.2.1 Capacitive accelerometers. The capacitive transduction principle is employed in some accelerometer designs, which typically use a diaphragm-supported seismic mass or a flexure-supported disk-shaped seismic mass as the moving electrode and either one or two fixed electrodes (stator plates). As accleration is applied, the proximity between moving and fixed electrodes changes. This results in a change of capacitance, a simple capacitance variation if one stator plate is used, and a differential change in two capacitances if the moving electrode is located between two stator plates. Various signal-conditioning schemes have been applied to such transduction elements. The element can be connected into an ac bridge and a change in transducer ac output voltage (or dc output, if the signal is rectified) occurs. The element can be connected as the capacitor in the LC or RC portion of an oscillator circuit so that a change in transducer output frequency results in response to changes in applied acceleration. The capacitance changes in a two-stator transduction element have also been used in a switching circuit so that a pulse train is generated in which pulse width and distance between pulses are the result of the changes in the two capacitances. Single-stator elements have been used in some servo accelerometers. An experimental triaxial accelerometer design uses a freely moving spherical metallic mass and three stator elements arranged in three mutually orthogonal axes, in a spherical evacuated cavity containing the mass, to provide outputs in the form of capacitance changes for acceleration along any axis.

This design, sometimes called "drag free," can also be furnished with a set of three torquer coils and can then operate in a closed-loop servo mode.

1.2.2.2 Piezoelectric accelerometers.

Piezoelectric transduction is used in a large variety of accelerometers intended primarily for the measurement of vibratory acceleration and shock. A typical design is shown in Figure 1-3.

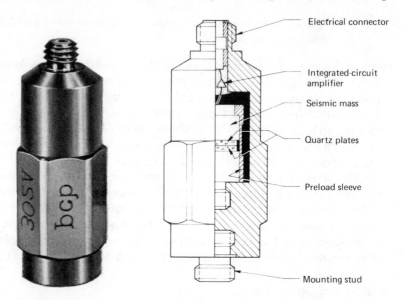

Figure 1-3. Piezoelectric accelerometer (general-purpose, with built-in integrated-circuit amplifier). (Courtesy of PCB Piezotronics, Inc.)

Acceleration is sensed along the longitudinal axis of the unit. It acts on the seismic mass which exerts a force on the piezoelectric crystals (quartz, in this unit), which then produces an electrical charge. The quartz plates are preloaded so that either an increase or a decrease in the force acting on the crystals (due to acceleration in either direction) causes changes in the charge produced by them. Two or more crystals are connected for output multiplication when quartz, which has relatively low sensitivity, is used as the piezoelectric element. Ceramic crystals are also used in many piezoelectric accelerometers. Typical ceramic materials used for this purpose are barium titanate, a lead zirconate–lead titanate mixture, lead metaniobate, and more often, mixtures whose composition is considered proprietary by their manufacturers and which are designated by registered trade names such as Piezite (Endevco) or Glennite (Gulton).

Piezoelectric crystal materials differ in their essential characteristics, sensitivity, frequency response, bulk resistivity, and thermal response. Some ceramic elements (but not quartz) have been reported to exhibit a zero shift when exposed to an environment that includes high stress and high noise. The upper limit of the operating temperature range is given by the *Curie point,* or Curie temperature of the material (the piezoelectric effect was discovered by

Pierre and Jacques Curie in 1880). At this temperature, ceramic elements, which are polarized by exposure to an orienting electric field during cooling after firing, lose their polarization. Curie points vary from 120 °C for barium titanate to about 570 °C for lead metaniobate; however, some proprietary ceramics with Curie points above 950 °C have also been developed.

Of the various possible internal mechanical designs (seismic mass and crystal and their support), the center-mounted and inverted center-mounted compression-type designs and the shear design (in which the piezoelectric crystal is stressed in a shear mode instead of a compression mode) provide minimized *case sensitivity,* that is, sensitivity to acoustic noise, temperature transients, and strains in the mounting surface, all acting on the case of the accelerometer. Another important factor in mechanical design is minimization of sensitivity to transverse acceleration (acceleration along axes other than the sensing axis).

The frequency range (over which the frequency response is flat within ±5%) of most piezoelectric accelerometers usually has a lower limit between 1 and 3 Hz and an upper limit between 2 and 10 kHz (in a few designs 25 kHz or higher). Special design features are incorporated in accelerometers used for seismographic applications, such as the unit shown in Figure 1-4, which has a frequency range of 0.04 to 150 Hz. The same accelerometer is also shown in Figure 1-5a.

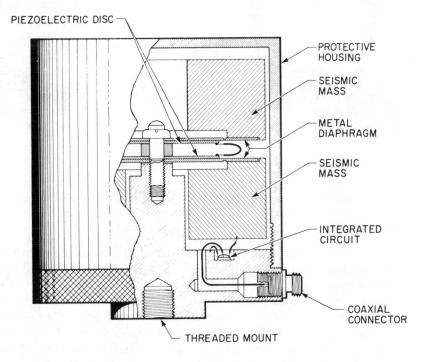

Figure 1-4. Piezoelectric accelerometer for seismographic applications. (Courtesy of BBN Instruments Co.)

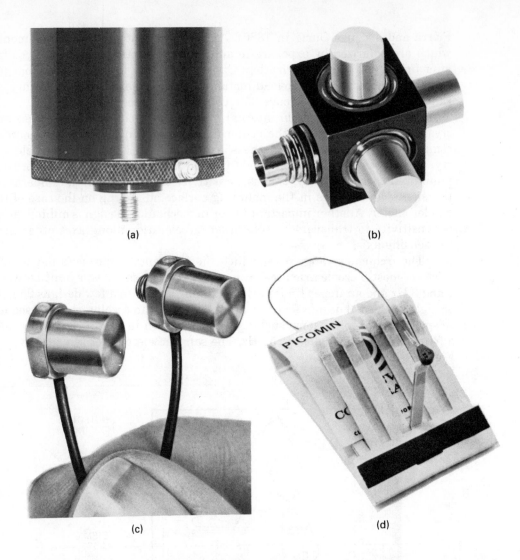

(a)

(b)

(c)

(d)

Figure 1-5. Special piezoelectric accelerometer designs: (a) seismographic; (b) triaxial; (c) miniature; (d) subminiature. [(a), (b) and (c) courtesy of BBN Instruments Co.; (d) courtesy of Endevco Dynamic Instrument Division.]

Other special piezoelectric accelerometer designs include the triaxial unit (Figure 1-5b), essentially an assembly of three precisely aligned accelerometers on a single block with mounting provisions, and with a single electrical connector. Some applications require very small, low-mass accelerometers and units such as the two accelerometers shown in Figure 1-5c, each of which has a mass of 1.8 g, and the subminiature accelerometer shown in Figure 1-5d, which has a mass of only 140 mg, were created for such applications.

Virtually all piezoelectric accelerometers are characterized by a relatively low output signal and a very high output impedance. This poses a requirement

Solid-Mechanical Quantities

for associated amplifiers which also act as impedance converters. The amplifier is connected to the transducer by a cable and provides a low output impedance and a sufficiently high signal amplitude to the display device or telemetry system. The cable is a critical component of such an accelerometer system. It must be thin, flexible, coaxial, shielded, impervious to moisture, and of very low capacitance. It must also be free from *triboelectric noise* (noise caused by friction between conductor and insulator). It should also be kept as short as possible so that capacitance and noise are minimized. The electrical connectors, on both ends, should also be moisture-proofed, after mating, for most applications to avoid lowering the insulation resistance in this high-impedance portion of an accelerometer system.

Voltage amplifiers employ several cascaded stages to reduce the system impedance and amplify the transducer signal. However, changes in capacitance at their input side, such as by a change in coaxial-cable length, can change the calibration of the accelerometer system. This problem is minimized in *charge amplifiers*, operational amplifiers with capacitive feedback. Advances in semiconductor integrated-circuit technology have made it possible to incorporate impedance-converting amplifiers into the transducer case, and an increasing number of accelerometer designs now include this feature. The diagram shown in Figure 1-6 illustrates an accelerometer system of this type.

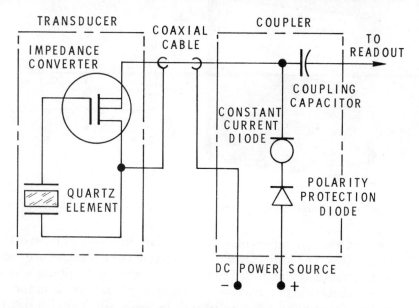

Figure 1-6. System diagram for accelerometer with integral signal conditioning (Piezotron system). (Courtesy of Sundstrand Data Control, Inc.)

A single-conductor coaxial cable provides for amplifier excitation as well as for carrying the transducer output signal. Accelerometers with integral signal conditioning are limited in their operating-temperature range to temperatures over which the semiconductor device can operate. Appropriate grounding techniques must be employed (particularly when separate signal conditioners are used) to avoid ground loops.

1.2.2.3 Potentiometric accelerometers. Potentiometric accelerometers are characterized by a high output signal and a relatively narrow frequency range, extending typically from zero to 20 Hz, for lower ranges of acceleration, to around 60 Hz for higher ranges (the higher the range, the stiffer the spring and the higher the natural frequency). They can also be produced at relatively low cost and are used in applications where slowly varying acceleration is to be measured with moderate accuracy and where cost is a significant factor.

The displacement of the spring–mass system, in these transducer designs, is mechanically linked to a wiper arm which moves along a potentiometric resistance element. The linkage can provide amplification of displacement if needed. The design shown in Figure 1-7 employs a conductive-plastic resistance

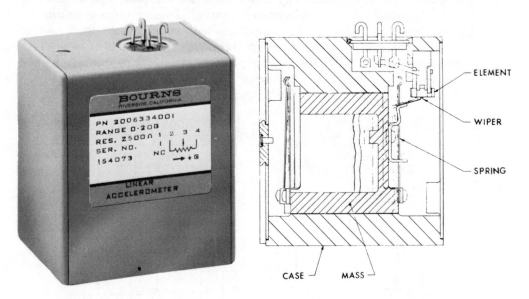

Figure 1-7. Potentiometric accelerometer. (Courtesy of Bourns, Inc., Instrument Div.)

element which is sufficiently short to allow direct attachment of the wiper arm to the mass. The unit shown is gas-damped. Other designs are viscous-damped or magnetically damped. Damping is needed to minimize any noise in the output that could be introduced by whipping of the wiper arm and large changes in instantaneous contact resistance between wiper and resistance element. Gas damping is often preferred because it does not require the additional mass of magnetic-damping provisions and because it is not as much subject to temperature effects as viscous damping (e.g., damping attained by using silicone oil).

It is fairly easy to design potentiometric accelerometers so that the effects of transverse acceleration are minimized. In some designs the mass is con-

70

Solid-Mechanical Quantities

strained from motion in any but the specified axis by having it move along a coaxial shaft. The design illustrated employs flexural ("E"-shaped) springs as well as having the mass slide within a precision-molded plastic block that is part of the transducer case. Mechanical stops are usually provided to limit mass displacement when overrange accelerations are seen by the unit. Placing the wiper arm at the center of the resistance element, when no acceleration is applied, allows bidirectional measurements.

1.2.2.4 Reluctive accelerometers. This category of accelerometers comprises units of the linear variable differential transformer *(LVDT)* type as well as those of the impedance bridge (inductance bridge) type. The former (LVDT type) is illustrated in Figure 1-8. The differential transformer windings are

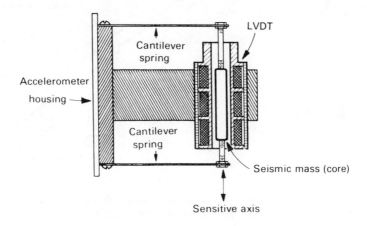

Figure 1-8. Reluctive (LVDT) accelerometer. (Courtesy of Schaevitz Engineering.)

the primary winding between the two secondary windings. The spring–mass system is constituted by the transformer core, which is the seismic mass, suspended inside the windings by parallel cantilever springs. The displacement of the ferromagnetic core, due to applied acceleration, results in output-voltage changes in the two secondary windings when an ac voltage is applied to the primary winding.

In many inductance-bridge accelerometer designs the displacement of the seismic mass causes the inductances of two suitably mounted coils to vary in the opposite direction; that is, the inductance of one coil increases while the inductance of the other coil decreases due to their relative proximity to a moving ferromagnetic armature. The two coils are connected as two arms of an inductance bridge, the other two arms of which are usually resistive. An ac output voltage variation is produced at the bridge output terminals when ac excitation is applied to its input terminals, with variations in applied acceleration.

Inductance-bridge (impedance-bridge) accelerometers can also be so designed that one of the two inductances is not affected by seismic-mass dis-

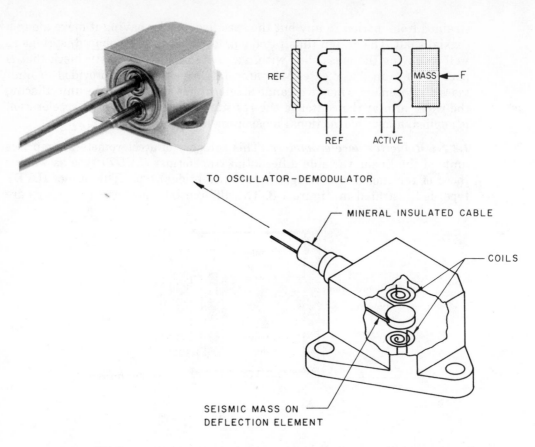

REF   MASS ◄—F

REF   ACTIVE

TO OSCILLATOR–DEMODULATOR

MINERAL INSULATED CABLE

COILS

SEISMIC MASS ON
DEFLECTION ELEMENT

Figure 1-9. Reluctive (impedance-bridge, eddy-current type) accelerometer. (Courtesy of Kaman Sciences Corp.)

placement and acts as a reference inductance while the effective inductance of the second coil (active coil) changes with variations in proximity to the seismic mass. This principle is employed in the accelerometer shown in Figure 1-9. This design (covered by Patent 3,238,479, March 1, 1966) also differs in another significant aspect. The electrical characteristics of the active coil change as eddy currents increase in the conductive plate (seismic mass) as it moves closer to the coil. Since no ferromagnetic materials need to be employed, the problem of temperature limitations due to the Curie point of such materials is avoided. This feature, together with use of high-temperature materials and construction, permits this accelerometer to operate at temperatures up to 650 °C. It is also suitable for operation in high-nuclear-radiation environments, not only by choice of materials, but also because the reference and active coils are equally affected by such radiation, so that radiation effects (as well as temperature effects) tend to be canceled. Each coil is connected in parallel with a capacitor, and the impedance bridge (whose other two arms are resistive) is excited by a high-frequency ac voltage.

Solid-Mechanical Quantities

The ac output of reluctive accelerometers varies in phase as well as amplitude. It can be converted to dc by means of a phase-sensitive demodulator. An oscillator can be employed to provide the ac excitation when operation of the accelerometer from a dc supply is required. The frequency of the excitation voltage must be substantially higher than the upper limit of the accelerometer's frequency range. The frequency range of inductance-bridge designs is usually higher than that of LVDT types because of the relatively smaller displacement of their seismic mass.

1.2.2.5 Servo accelerometers. Servo accelerometers use closed-loop servo systems of the force-balance, torque-balance, or null-balance type to provide very close accuracy as well as a high-level output signal, but at a relatively higher cost than most other designs. Figure 1-10 illustrates the operating principle of a typical servo accelerometer. Acceleration causes the pendulous seismic mass to move. As soon as motion is detected by the position sensing device,

(a)

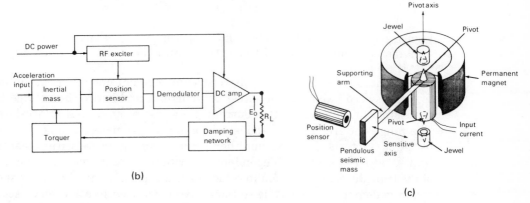

(b)

(c)

Figure 1-10. Servo accelerometer with pendulous mass and reluctive displacement sensor: (a) accelerometer; (b) block diagram (R_L, load resistor); (c) simplified mechanism. (Courtesy of Schaevitz Engineering.)

a signal is produced which acts as the error signal in the servo loop. The position sensor in this design is of the RF-excited eddy-current type (similar to the active element of the transducer shown in Figure 1-9). After demodulation and amplification, the signal passes through a passive damping network and is then applied to a torquing coil located at the axis of rotation of the mass. The torquer shown for this design is similar to the D'Arsonval movement used in electric indicating meters; the jewel bearings are also typical for such meter movements. The torque developed is proportional to the current applied to the coil, and it balances, in magnitude as well as direction, the torque acting on the seismic mass due to acceleration, preventing further motion of the mass. The current through the torquing coil is, therefore, proportional to acceleration. This current then passes through the stable load resistor. The voltage across this resistor, E_o, is the output voltage of the transducer.

In angular accelerometers of the same design the seismic mass is balanced; in linear accelerometers (as illustrated) it is unbalanced. However, pendulous-mass linear accelerometers tend to be affected by angular acceleration. Such pendulosity errors are eliminated in the design shown in Figure 1-11, which is of the force-balance type. A rectilinear displacement of the axial

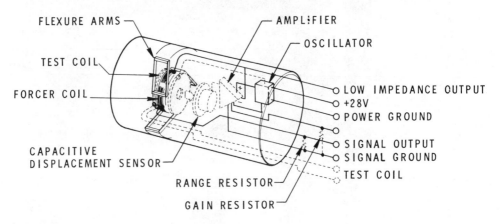

Figure 1-11. Servo accelerometer with nonpendulous mass and capacitive displacement sensor. (Courtesy of Sundstrand Data Control, Inc.)

seismic mass is sensed by a capcitive sensing element and a forcing coil is used to attain servo balance. The forcer coil current, and hence the voltage across a resistor through which this current passes, is proportional to acceleration. The range and frequency response of servo accelerometers can be established by the characteristics of the amplifier and damping network, within reasonable limits, rather than being dependent on primarily mechanical characteristics of the transducer. In addition to reluctive and capacitive displacement sensors, strain-gage and photoelectric sensors have been used in some servo-accelerometer designs. A frequency-modulated or digital output can also be provided, and some designs are available with a discrete output (acceleration switch) at one or more set points.

1.2.2.6 Strain-gage accelerometers. In strain-gage accelerometers the displacement of the spring–mass system is converted into a change in resistance, due to strain, in two or four arms of a Wheatstone bridge (strain-gage bridge). The strain gages can be of the unbonded metal wire, bonded metal wire or foil, or bonded semiconductor types. The term "piezoresistive" is often applied to transducers incorporating semiconductor strain gages. The gages are mounted either to the spring, to a separate stress member additional to the spring, or between the seismic mass and a stationary frame.

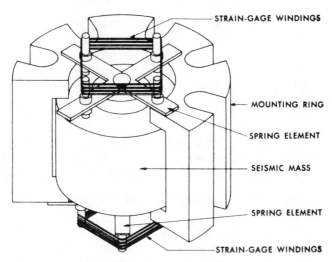

Figure 1-12. Unbonded-strain-gage-accelerometer. (Courtesy of CEC Div., Bell & Howell Co.)

The unit shown in Figure 1-12 contains a cylindrical seismic mass and has two strain windings wound between four insulated posts attached to each of two cross-shaped springs, one above and one below the mass. The windings contribute to the spring action. As the mass displaces (vertically, in the illustration), the tension in one pair of strain gages increases and the tension in the opposite pair of windings is reduced. The windings are electrically connected as a four-active-arm bridge, whose output, when dc excitation is applied to the bridge, is proportional to acceleration and whose polarity indicates direction of acceleration. This design employs viscous damping, using silicone oil, to provide a damping ratio of about 0.7, at room temperature.

A similar principle (two gages acting in tension, two in compression) is used in the accelerometer shown in Figure 1-13. This unit, however, has two semiconductor gages bonded to both sides of a cantilever spring to which the seismic mass is attached. Since semiconductor strain gages are significantly more sensitive than metal foil or metal wire gages, the spring–mass system of such devices can be made stiffer and the mass displacement can be kept smaller, so that the frequency response as well as the output signal amplitude can be considerably higher. Temperature compensation resistors are provided

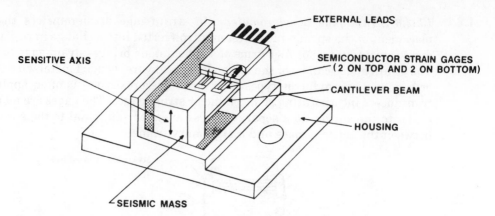

Figure 1-13. Bonded-semiconductor-strain-gage accelerometer. (Courtesy of Entran Devices, Inc.)

within the transducer case. Angular strain-gage accelerometers typically employ a centrally pivoted, elastically restrained mass with strain gages bonded to the elastic members. Triaxial accelerometers have also been designed.

1.2.2.7 Vibrating-wire accelerometers. In these transducer designs acceleration cuases a change in the resonant frequency of a wire kept in tension within a permanent magnetic field with the wire is caused to vibrate by passing a current through it. In one linear accelerometer the wire tension is varied by a minute displacement of the seismic mass to which one end of the wire is attached. In an angular accelerometer design the wire frequency varies with Coriolis forces acting on the vibrating wire due to applied angular acceleration (rate of turn). The inherent frequency-modulated output (deviation from the frequency at zero g or at zero rad/s^2) can be demodulated to provide a dc output. Choice of frame and wire material and wire attachment is critical in such accelerometers to avoid temperature errors that could be caused by differential thermal expansion within the mechanical assembly. With proper design, construction, and burn-in, such transducers can provide very close repeatability.

1.2.2.8 Gyroscopic accelerometers. The usability of pendulous gyroscopes as accelerometers is given by their precession characteristics. The rate of precession depends on the force exerted by the pendulous mass. Acceleration acting on that mass causes a pendulosity torque which can be opposed by a spring to provide acceleration sensitivity and an output proportional to acceleration.

1.2.2.9 Acceleration switches. Acceleration switches provide a discrete output at one or more set points. Normally open or normally closed switching is available. Various methods are used, including magnetic switches actuated by seismic-mass displacement, replacing a potentiometric element by a contact strip, and providing an electronic gate for an otherwise analog output. In some simple acceleration switches, with a single set point, a pair of contacts gets closed with a predetermined displacement of the seismic mass.

1.2.3 Performance Criteria

The most critical characteristics of accelerometers are range and frequency response. Piezoelectric transducers offer the highest ranges (to over 100,000 *g* for some shock accelerometers) as well as the highest frequency response (up to tens of kHz). However, their sensitivity is relatively low and most designs require an amplifier for each transducer. Their frequency response also drops off rapidly below 2 to 5 Hz (except for some seismographic transducers) and are generally not usable for measuring steady-state or even slowly varying acceleration. Semiconductor-strain-gage ("piezoresistive") transducers have a somewhat lower frequency response (usually up to several kHz) but do respond to steady-state acceleration. In many applications some amplification of their

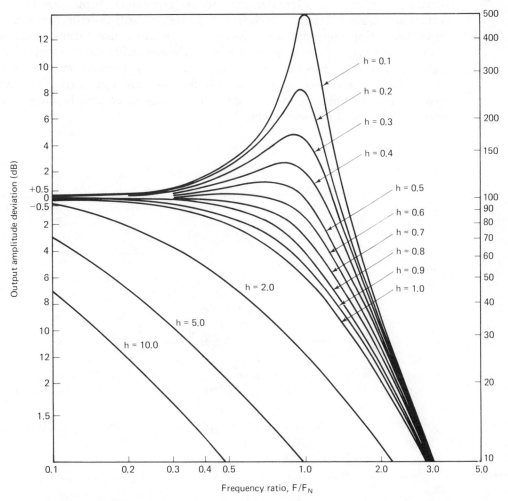

Figure 1-14. Response of a spring-mass system to a sinusoidally varying acceleration (*h*, damping factor; F_N, natural frequency.)

output is required. Potentiometric transducers have the lowest frequency response (from dc to 15 to 25 Hz). Other types are somewhere in between as far as frequency response is concerned. Servo accelerometers can be used for very low ranges (well below 1 *g* for full-scale output).

Transducers employing fluid or magnetic damping are usually designed with a damping ratio of 0.7 and their usable frequency response depends on the damping ratio used (and its variation with temperature). Figure 1-14 shows relative response curves for various damping ratios as a function of the ratio of frequency (*F*) to natural frequency. Electronic filters can be connected into high-frequency-response accelerometer systems when the data transmission equipment requires such limitation.

Other important performance characteristics are full-scale output (or sensitivity), transverse acceleration sensitivity (erroneous output due to acceleration acting along other than the sensing axis), mounting error, temperature errors (including temperature transients which can cause output errors due to the pyroelectric effect in some piezoelectric accelerometers), sensitivity to high sound-pressure levels, and overrange capability. Transducer mass can be an important characteristic, particularly for dynamic acceleration measurements; the mass must be low enough not to cause structural loading at and around the point of measurement.

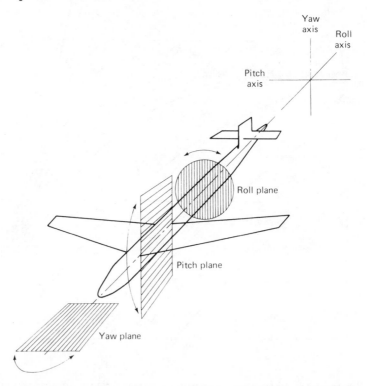

Figure 1-15. Identification of vehicle planes and axes for attitude reference.

1.3 ATTITUDE AND ATTITUDE RATE

1.3.1 Sensing Methods

The methods of sensing attitude can be categorized on the basis of the reference system with respect to which the orientation of a vehicle or body is determined. The vehicle's own reference system is given by design. A design drawing shows the exact location of the pitch, yaw, and roll axes (see Figure 1-15). These axes are alternatively identified as X-, Y-, and Z-axes, respectively. The designation for ships and aircraft usually follows the convention shown in Figure 1-15. For some types of vehicles, such as for certain spacecraft, the letter designation of their axes may be used without reference to pitch, yaw, and roll.

1.3.1.1. Inertial-reference sensing. The motion of a rotating body obeys Newton's first law of motion in an inertial frame of reference in which no forces are exerted on the body and the body is not accelerated. Unless acted upon by some unbalanced torque, a rotating body will continue turning about a fixed axis. This law is applied in the *gyroscope (gyro),* basically a wheel rotating within a frame. If the frame is affixed to a fixed portion of a vehicle and the vehicle changes its attitude, this attitude change can be sensed as the change in angle between the frame and the axis of rotation of the wheel.

1.3.1.2 Gravity-reference sensing. The force of gravity acting on a mass can be used to establish a vertical reference axis; the common plumb bob uses this principle. If the mass is suspended within a frame and the frame is affixed to a fixed portion of a vehicle or body, changes in attitude can be sensed as changes in the angle between the frame and the axis of suspension of the mass.

1.3.1.3 Magnetic-reference sensing. If a magnetic field remains fixed in position, its poles can establish a reference axis. A bar magnet aligns itself to the poles of a magnetic field, such as that of the earth, as exemplified by the action of a compass needle. When the bar magnet can freely rotate within a frame, changes in attitude can be determined as the angle between the pole-to-pole axis of the magnet and the frame, which is affixed to a fixed portion of a vehicle.

1.3.1.4 Flow-stream-reference sensing. The direction along which a fluid flows past a vehicle moving in the fluid can be used as reference for the attitude of the vehicle, provided that the vehicle itself does not alter the direction of the flow stream. This condition can be satisfied by placing a sensing element, so designed as to align itself with the flow stream, well ahead of the forward end of the vehicle. The attitude sensed in this manner is usually referred to as *angle of attack;* its measurement is limited to use on high-speed aircraft and rockets and to rapidly descending atmospheric-entry vehicles.

1.3.1.5 Optical-reference sensing. One or more reference axes for the orientation of a vehicle can be established by aiming an electro-optical device on the vehicle at a light-radiating celestial body whose position is known at the time of measurement, or by aiming such a device at a point of known position where a step change in light reflection or refraction occurs as seen from the vehicle. The electro-optical device produces an output indicative of the angle of incidence or change in the perceived position of the light source or point of a perceived light-intensity change.

1.3.1.6 Radio-reference sensing. The interaction between a beam of electro-magnetic radiation (at radio frequencies) emanating from a point of known position at a known direction and with known characteristics on the one hand, and a receiving device on the vehicle, capable of detecting changes in the angle of incidence of the beam, on the other hand, can be used to sense vehicle attitude. Two or more transmitter/receiver combinations can be used by a vehicle for improved measurement accuracy.

1.3.2   Design and Operation

1.3.2.1 Attitude gyros. In a simple gyro (see Figure 1-16) a rapidly spinning rotor, on an axle, is supported within a rotatable frame *(gimbal)* which is supported by bearings attached within a case. The axis about which the gimbal is free to rotate *(gimbal axis)* is perpendicular to the axis about which the rotor spins *(spin axis)*. Since the spatial position of the spin axis remains fixed while the rotor is spinning, an attitude change of the case (angular displacement about the gimbal axis) results in an angular displacement between gimbal shaft and case. This displacement can be transduced by any angular-displacement transduction element (e.g., an annular potentiometric element with a wiper arm attached to the gimbal shaft).

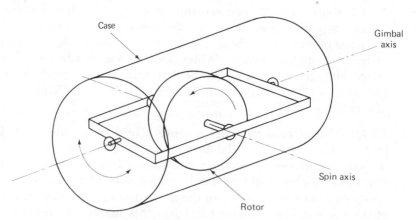

Figure 1-16. Basic gyro.

The angular momentum of the gyro rotor is the essential stability char-acteristic of a gyro. The greater the angular momentum, the greater is the force required to deflect the spin axis from its position. Angular momentum

(H) is the product of rotor angular velocity (ω) and the moment of inertia of the rotor (I_r), or

$$H = \omega I_r$$

These quantities are vector quantities; that is, they have magnitude as well as direction. The relationship poses basic design criteria for gyros. Since a large angular momentum is desirable, the rotor spin rate should be high and the moment of inertia of the rotor should be large. These characteristics must then be traded off against gyro mass, size, and spin-motor power requirements. The moment of inertia of a hollow cylinder is roughly double that of a solid cylinder of the same mass and diameter. Hence, most gyro designs employ a rotor in the shape of a wheel with a thick rim and thin web so that the shape of a hollow cylinder is approached.

When a torque is applied about any axis other than the spin axis, the spin axis will rotate about an axis which is perpendicular to the axis about which the torque is applied and which is also perpendicular to the spin axis. If, for example, a torque were applied in the plane of the gimbal frame of the gyro shown in Figure 1-16, the rotor would tend to balance this torque by deflecting angularly about the gimbal axis. The rotation of the spin axis produced by a torque is known as *precession*. The precession rate is constant when the torque is held constant. The mechanism will rotate about the axis of the applied torque only when it is not free to precess.

When precession of the spin axis from its intended position is caused by unwanted torques, it is called *drift*. Such torques can be caused by a number of drift sources inherent in the design and construction of the gyro, such as friction in gimbal bearings, rotor radial mass unbalance, unbalance within the gimbal assembly, forces exerted by electrical leads, and friction within the transduction element. They can also be caused by magnetic interaction and by external environmental conditions.

The mechanism illustrated in Figure 1-16 represents a *single-degree-of-freedom* gyro: the number of orthogonal axes about which the spin axis is free to rotate is one. In most practical applications a two-degree-of-freedom gyro *(free gyro)* is used; in free gyros the spin axis is free to attain any attitude. This is accomplished by adding a second gimbal which supports the bearings of the inner gimbal (which, in turn, supports the rotor). The inner and outer gimbal axes are orthogonal to each other. A transduction element is then located at both the inner and outer gimbal bearings. The outputs of the two transduction elements ("pick-offs") can represent attitude in any two of the three vehicle planes (pitch, yaw, roll). Potentiometric and reluctive transduction elements are used in many of the simpler gyro designs. Capacitive and photoelectric transduction are used in more advanced designs to detect spin-axis deflections.

Most gyros are equipped with a device that enables the gimbal(s) to be preset (locked) in a specified reference position. This process is known as *caging* and the device is called a caging mechanism. After spin-up of the rotor in the desired axis, the gyro is *uncaged,* such as by means of an electrical solenoid. Caging/uncaging is not be confused with *gimbal lock,* a condition that can occur when the inner gimbal aligns itself parallel to the outer gimbal, causing a loss of inertial reference. The reference can be reestablished by caging the gyro, repositioning the spin axis in the desired reference axis, then uncaging the gyro.

DC as well as ac motors are used to drive the gyro rotor. The rotor of the drive motor can also act as the gyro rotor. In some designs characterized by a short operating life (e.g., in rockets) hot gas, from a pyrotechnic charge, has been used, in conjunction with a small turbine, to provide the spin function. AC induction or synchronous motors tend to produce lower drift in gyros.

A variety of other means have been devised to reduce drift. The spin assembly, within a sealed enclosure, floats in a viscous liquid to give the assembly neutral buoyancy *(floated gyro).* This technique eliminates purely mechanical suspension and reduces bearing friction. In the *gas-bearing* gyro pressurized gas is used as flotation fluid. When the gyro rotor is freely suspended (bearingless) any retarding forces are minimized and the (nonpowered) rundown time of the gyro is very long. In the *electrostatic gyro* this is accomplished by suspending the spherical rotor in an electrostatic suspension system. In the *cryogenic* gyro a spherical rotor, made of a material that becomessuperconductive at the temperature of liquid helium, is maintained at that temperature. It is freely suspended within a magnetic-field coil system by interaction between this field and the magnetic field due to current flow in the superconductor. The *tuned-rotor gyro* consists of three concentric annular structures, concentric with the spin axis. The outer structure is the rotor. It is attached to the two inner structures, the gimbals, by flexures. The unit is so designed that the resonant frequency of the flexures is tuned to the rotational frequency of the rotor. Under these conditions the torques imposed by the flexures (which take the place of bearings) become negligible, and drift is minimized. This type of unit is relatively simple to construct. The (synchronous ac) motor can be external to the spin assembly. The latter is usually backfilled with argon to minimize friction in the assembly.

Many gyros are equipped with *torquers,* devices such as rotary solenoids, which exert controlled amounts of torque on a gimbal. Torquers are used to correct for drift rates due to known sources. Closed-loop torquer control can be attained by feeding an error signal, due to drift rate, into a servo amplifier that powers the torquer.

Specialized versions of the two-degree-of-freedom gyro have been designed for specific vehicle applications. The *vertical gyro* is a pitch/roll attitude sensor. A two-axis erection system maintains the spin axis in a vertical (gravity-referenced) position so that both gimbal axes are in a plane parallel to the ground surface. The *directional gyro* is a yaw-attitude transducer. The rotor spin axis is maintained in the horizontal position (parallel to the ground surface). The gyro is installed on the vehicle so that the outer gimbal is parallel to the yaw axis. The direction of the spin axis (in the horizontal plane) is established upon uncaging. The direction of the spin axis can also be referenced to the coordinates of the earth's magnetic field, such as by slaving the gyro to a compass synchro-transmitter. The directional gyro then operates as a *gyro compass*.

1.3.2.2 Rate gyros. The time rate of change of attitude is measured by the attitude-rate gyro (*rate gyro,* "rate sensor") directly in terms of angular velocity. A rate gyro (see Figure 1-17) is essentially a single-degree-of-freedom gyro whose gimbal is elastically restrained and whose motion is damped. When the rate gyro senses changes in attitude rate about its measurand axis *(input axis),* it produces an output signal due to gimbal deflection about the *output axis* by precession. Attitude rate is a vectorial quantity; hence, the output signal represents both magnitude and direction of attitude rate.

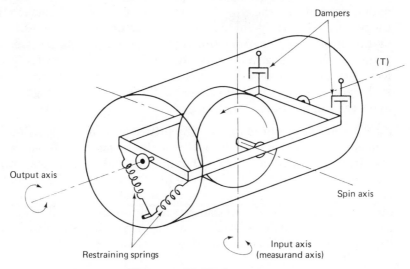

Figure 1-17. Basic rate gyro.

When a constant level of attitude rate is sensed, a relatively simple relationship defines the static response of a rate gyro, since restraining torques due to damping and to gimbal inertia can be neglected. This relationship is

$$\theta = \frac{H\Omega}{K}$$

where θ = gimbal deflection angle (output angle)

H = gyro angular momentum

Ω = attitude rate

K = restraining-device spring constant

The gimbal deflection, or an equivalent displacement about the axis defined as the gimbal axis, can be transduced by various means, ranging from simple potentiometric or reluctive elements to a vibrating wire responding to Coriolis forces. The "restraining springs" can take the form of leaf springs, torsion bar, torsional springs, flexures, magnetic springs, or other, nonmechanical means. Among damping devices are dashpot, paddle-in-liquid, viscous-shear, hydraulic-bleed, and eddy-current types; the damping function can also be controlled electronically. Servo operation, using a torquer in the control loop, can be attained in torque-balance rate gyros in a manner similar to that described for servo accelerometers.

One of the more successful nonelectromechanical rate gyro designs is the *laser gyro*. Its essential elements are two gas lasers, a closed (e.g., triangular) optical path, and an interferometer. The lasers are so arranged that the two beams generated travel along the optical path in opposite directions. As attitude rate changes, the apparent path lengths of the two beams change (one path gets "shorter," the other "longer"). The apparent change in phase between the two beams, at the point where the interferometer is located, is then detected by the interferometer, from which the gyro output signal is obtained. Laser gyros usually incorporate optical or mechanical dithering to prevent "phase lock" (no output change) that can occur at low attitude rates. Resolution in such gyros improves with increased path length; hence, high-resolution laser gyros tend to get fairly large in size.

1.3.2.3 Rate-integrating gyros. The (attitude-) rate-integrating gyro is a design derivative of the rate gyro. It is a single-degree-of-freedom gyro without the elastic restraint of the gyro, having, instead, viscous restraint of the spin axis about the output axis (Figure 1-18). Precession of the gimbal produces an output signal that is proportional to the integral of the attitude rate sensed about the input axis. The viscous shear in the damping liquid, which fills the case, including, particularly, the gap between spin-assembly case and external case, provides the integration effect. Various modes of operation can be ob-

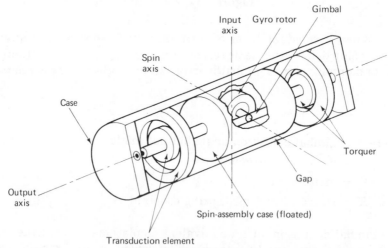

Figure 1-18. Rate-integrating gyro.

tained, depending on the type of command signal applied to the torquer on the output shaft. The term "hermetic integrating gyro (HIG)" has been applied to this design because the case must be hermetically sealed to contain the liquid used for floatation as well as damping.

The related *double-integrating gyro* has no elastic or viscous restraint of the gimbal about the output axis. The dynamic behavior is established primarily by the inertial properties of the gimbal. The output signal is proportional to the double integral of the attitude rate of the case about the input axis.

1.3.2.4 Gravity-referenced attitude transducers. The force of gravity can be used to establish a very useful vertical reference, as anyone who has used a plumb bob or bubble level knows. Transducers used to measure angular displacement from vertical are relatively simple designs employing a solid or liquid mass upon which gravity acts and which is either linked to a transduction element or is an active part of it. Since angular deviation from vertical is often called "inclination," such transducers have also been referred to as *inclinometers*.

The simplest of these design is the *pendulum*-type transducer. It consists of a weight, in the shape of a flat segment of a circle, which is mounted so that it can rotate by means of a ball bearing to which it is attached at its tip. The ball bearing is at the center of a nonconductive disk. A curved potentiometric element is mounted to this disk, and a wiper arm is attached to the weight. A slip ring forms the connecting contact for the wiper arm. The weight remains vertical. As the case, to which the nonconductive disk is attached, is rotated, the wiper arm slides over the potentiometric resistance element.

The *electrolytic-potentiometer* type of transducer resembles the liquid-filled glass tube in a carpenter's level. The small, curved tube is partially filled with a liquid electrolyte. The "common" or "wiper" contact extends completely through the tube. The "end terminals" protrude partially into the tube, one at each end. As the tube is angularly deflected from a true horizontal position (orthogonal to true vertical), the resistance to the common electrode increases from one electrode and decreases from the other. This device needs to be ac-excited to avoid polarization of the electrolyte. Designs of this type can have a full-scale range around $\pm 1°$.

Small variations from true horizontal have also been measured by a *capacitive* transducer. Two metallic half-disks are suspended closely above the surface of a pool of mercury contained in a cylindrical cavity (the internal configuration needs to be circular). As the device is tilted, the capacitance between the mercury, which acts as the common "rotor" electrode, and one of the "stator" electrodes increases while it decreases to the other "stator" electrode. This device can be connected into an ac bridge circuit so that changes in capacitance are converted into ac output changes.

A *torque-balance, reluctive inclinometer* produces an output proportional to the sine of the angle of deviation from vertical. It employs a pendulous mass and operates in a manner similar to that of a torque-balance servo accelero-

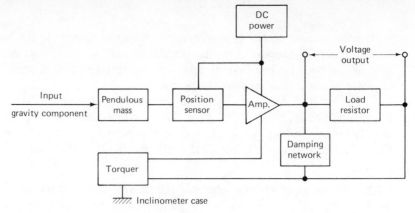

Figure 1-19. Torque-balance inclinometer: block diagram. (Courtesy of Schaevitz Engineering.)

meter (which, essentially, the inclinometer is). As illustrated in the block diagram, Figure 1-19, motion of the mass is detected by a (reluctive) position sensor whose output is amplified and fed to a torquer, a coil, in a magnetic field, which counteracts the torque applied to the pendulous mass due to de-

Figure 1-20. Typical torque-balance inclinometers. (Courtesy of Schaevitz Engineering.)

viations from vertical. The current supplied to the coil is, thus, proportional to changes in the gravitational force. When the current is passed through a load resistor a voltage output is produced. Typical inclinometer designs of this type are shown in Figure 1-20.

1.3.2.5 Magnetic-referenced attitude sensors. The *compass* is a well-known example of such sensors. Sensing devices related to the compass are used on most seaborne and airborne vehicles to indicate *bearing,* the vehicle's attitude in the terrestrial horizontal plane with reference to the earth's magnetic field. The reference is a line between the vehicle and magnetic north. "True north" can be established from this indication together with knowledge of the global variations in the magnetic field. A simple version of such a "north seeker" uses a bar-magnet assembly to move a wiper arm across a potentiometric element. Other designs use reluctive, notably synchro, transduction and may operate in a closed-loop servo mode. A pendulous suspension is commonly used to stabilize the sensing mechanism in a true horizontal plane. In the *gyrocompass* the combined use of friction and a gravitational restoring torque causes the equilibrium position of the rotor's spin axis to align itself with the north-south reference line. The *flux-gate compass* employs three cores, having an excitation as well as an output winding, which are so arranged that they are balanced in the absence of an external magnetic field. The magnitude and direction of the earth's magnetic field then causes unbalance voltages proportional in magnitude to the field's magnitude, and proportional in phase to the direction of the field. A phase-sensitive detection circuit or indicator is used to provide an output indicative of direction, or indicate direction, respectively. The *induction compass* uses a rotating coil as sensing element. The voltage induced in the coil is at its maximum when the rotational axis of the coil is perpendicular to the magnetic field.

1.3.2.6 Flow-stream-referenced attitude sensors. The *angle-of-attack* transducers which are used on high-speed airborne vehicles sense attitude with reference to the direction of the fluid stream ambient to the vehicle. Some designs use a single, rotatable, wedge-shaped vane for this purpose. The unit is so installed that the sharp edge of the vane points forward and then, while in flight, aligns itself to the direction of the ambient air stream. The transduction element responds to vane rotation. The *ogive* angle-of-attack transducer uses a freely swiveled projectile-shaped body with four fins, one every 90° around the body. As the finned body aligns itself with the airstream its relative motions about the pitch and yaw axes are detected by two transduction elements, one for each axis. The ogive transducer is usually installed at the tip of a boom extending well forward of the nose of the vehicle. Such an installation is also typical for *pressure-differential* angle-of-attack transducers, which use a pair of pressure ports, tubulated to a differential-pressure transducer, to sense the direction of air flow relative to a given vehicle axis. It should be noted that only the angle about the pitch axis is properly referred to as angle of attack. The angle about the yaw axis is more correctly termed *angle of sideslip.* Some versions of angle-of-attack transducers have also been designed to operate in water rather than in air.

1.3.2.7 Optical-referenced attitude sensors. Electro-optical sensors are commonly used for attitude determinations on spacecraft, sometimes also in research-balloon payloads and on special-applications aircraft. They sense attitude with reference to a line between the vehicle and a light-emitting or light-reflecting target whose position is known. Typical targets are the sun, certain stars, and the light-to-dark boundary *(limb)* of the earth or another planet. The choice of the target determines the name of the sensor: for example, *sun sensor, star sensor* (or "star tracker" or, on spin-stabilized spacecraft, "star pipper") and *limb sensor* or *horizon sensor.* The sensors employ mostly photoconductive, sometimes photoemissive elements with response in the visible or infrared portion of the spectrum. They produce a known (often the maximum) output signal when they are "looking" directly at the specified target and known (by calibration) variations in the output signal with deviations from a straight vehicle-to-target line. The most common use of such sensors is in closed-loop attitude-control systems.

1.3.2.8 Radio-referenced attitude sensors. The most widely used sensor in this category is the *radio compass,* essentially a radio receiver with a highly directional rotatable antenna ("loop antenna"). When the antenna is rotated so that the received signal is at a maximum, the position (and yaw attitude) of the vehicle relative to the line between the vehicle and the radio transmitter can be determined as a function of the angular position of the receiving antenna. When the expected deviations of the vehicle's attitude from a received radio beam are relatively small, the receiving antenna can be fixed and the variations in the output signal from the receiver can be used to indicate attitude deviations. This principle is used in an aircraft's *glide path* receiver, which receives a radio beam of known direction from a transmitter located at an airport and indicates deviations (in pitch) from this beam during the aircraft's final approach. The same principle is used on some spacecraft to either keep a movable *(articulable)* antenna, which is used for receiving as well as transmitting, pointed at the source of the beam or to keep the spacecraft in an attitude referenced to the direction of one or more radio beams. The latter is effected by using received-signal deviations as error signals in a closed loop ("beam rider") attitude-control system.

1.3.3 Performance Criteria

General performance characteristics to be considered for attitude and attitude-rate transducers comprise primarily range and full-scale output, zero-measurand output (or output at a reference level of measurand), linearity, hysteresis and repeatability, threshold, resolution, and stability. Drift rate is probably the most essential performance characteristic of gyros. Depending on design and construction, gyro drift rates can be between less than 0.5 to over 100° per hour. Other performance characteristics to be considered for gyros are run-up and run-down time of the rotor, overall warm-up time, caging and uncaging time, and erection rate. Damping ratio and natural frequency, and sometimes time constant ("characteristic time"), are specified for rate gyros, as are variations of damping ratio with operating temperature. Among environmental performance characteristics, the effects of acceleration, shock, and vibration are the most critical for gyros and other electromechanical attitude and attitude-rate transducers. Acceleration and vibration can cause errors in gyros due to *mass unbalance* (lack of coincidence of the center of supporting forces and the center of mass) and *anisoelasticity* (inequality of compliance of the rotor and gimbal assembly in different directions). Operating temperatures are critical to electro-optical sensors.

1.4 DISPLACEMENT, POSITION, AND MOTION

1.4.1 Sensing Methods

Most displacement transducers sense displacement, detect motion, or sense position by means of their *sensing shaft,* which is mechanically connected to, or in other mechanical contact with the point or object whose displacement is to be measured. Exceptions to this are the *noncontacting* displacement sensing devices in which optical, inductive, and so on, coupling is used between the measured object and the sensing element.

To understand the importance of sensing shafts, and their coupling

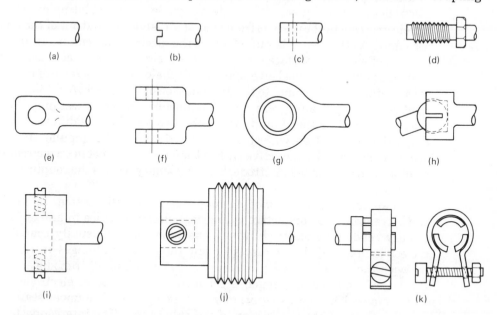

Figure 1-21. Displacement-transducer shaft ends and couplings: (a) plain; (b) slotted; (c) through-hole; (d) threaded; (e) lug; (f) clevis; (g) bearing; (h) ball joint; (i) coupler; (j) bellows-coupler; (k) collet-and-clamp.

means, one must simply realize that the output of the transducer indicates the position of the sensing shaft, not of the driving point. To make the two equal requires a shaft of the proper shape and strength as well as a suitable coupling device. The latter must be designed so that it will be free of unwanted play and backlash and so that there is no slippage in it after it is fastened. Some displacement transducer designs incorporate provisions, with known tolerances, to allow for minor misalignments between the point of measurement and the sensing shaft. Typical shaft ends and couplings for linear and angular displacement transducers are shown in Figure 1-21. Spring-loaded shafts (Figure 1-22) are required for certain applications, such as those in which only a relatively small portion of the measured object's total displacement is to be measured (the portion closest to the transducer). Spring-type sensing shafts are also used widely on switch-type position-sensing devices.

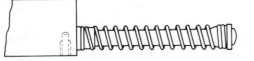

Figure 1-22. Spring-loaded shaft.

1.4.2   Design and Operation

1.4.2.1 Capacitive displacement transducers. Figure 1-23 illustrates the basic design versions of transducers in which a change in capacitance is proportional to a change in displacement. In the *moving-dielectric* design both capacitor electrodes are fixed in position. A sleeve, made of an insulating material with a dielectric constant different from that of air, slides in and out of the electrode assembly. As the sleeve is pulled out of the electrode assembly, an increasing amount of electrode surface sees air as the dielectric and a decreasing amount of surface area sees the sleeve material as dielectric. This results in a change of capacitance proportional to the axial motion of the sleeve. A similar principle has been used in transducers used to determine the thickness of a film of one liquid on top of another liquid, where the two liquids have different dielectric properties (e.g., oil on water). In a related design the angular motion of a semicircular shield (conductive rather than dielectric) between a circular electrode and an arc-shaped electrode, both stationary, varies the coupling between the two electrodes.

Two versions of the *moving-rotor* design are illustrated. In the *single-stator* transducer a conductive cylindrical electrode slides in and out of a stationary conductive electrode whose inside surface is usually coated with a dielectric material. Rotor displacement thus causes changes in capacitance between the two electrodes. In the *split-stator* (balanced) transducer the rotor consists of a number of ganged, electrically interconnected electrodes, each of which moves between two stationary (stator) plates. The upper stator plates, interconnected, form one section of the split stator. The interconnected lower plates form the other section. As the rotor plates move, their capacitance to one section increases while their capacitance to the other section decreases. The electrodes can be connected as two active arms of an ac bridge circuit.

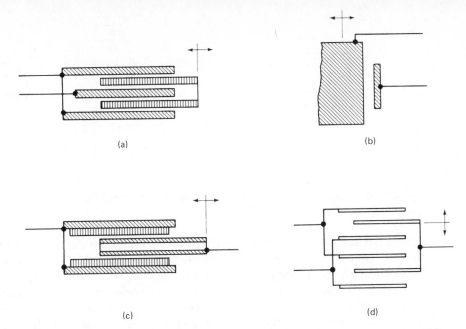

Figure 1-23. Capacitive displacement transduction elements: (a) moving dielectric; (b) moving rotor, noncontacting; (c) moving rotor, single stator, coupled; (d) moving rotor, split stator, coupled.

In the *noncontacting* capacitive displacement transducer the measured object (which must be partly or wholly electrically conductive) acts as the rotor which moves relative to the transducer, which is simply a stator, insulated from its mounting. This mounting, as well as the measured object, should be grounded.

A number of known sources of error should be avoided in the design and use of capacitive transducers. The capacitance of the interconnecting cable between transducer and electronics must be very low and must remain fixed in its value. It is usually advantageous to keep this cable very short and package the electronics close to, or integral with the transduction element. The transducer must be so constructed that no unwanted motion such as end play can occur. The electrode design should be free from the effects of fringing. It should be protected from stray fields. Compensation for temperature effects should be included in the design, or the transducer and associated circuitry should be so designed that no significant temperature errors occur. Linearization of transducer output can be provided either electrically or by shaping the electrodes appropriately.

1.4.2.2 Inductive displacement transducers. Transducers converting displacement, usually linear displacement, into a change of the self-inductance of a single coil can be grouped into coupled and noncontacting versions (see Figure 1-24). The coupled designs employ a sliding, magnetically permeable core, which moves within a coil (bobbin). The sensing shaft is attached to the moving core. As the core moves, the coil changes its self-inductance. The coil can be

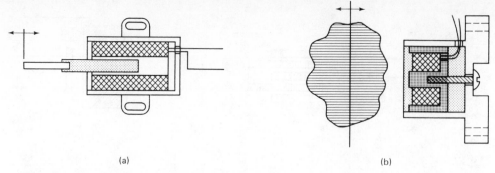

(a)   (b)

Figure 1-24. Basic types of inductive displacement transducers: (a) coupled; (b) non-contacting.

connected into an *LC* oscillator circuit so that inductance changes result in output frequency changes. More frequently, the coil acts as one arm of an impedance bridge whose ac output (when the bridge is excited with ac current) reflects the inductance changes. A second coil (reference or balancing coil) is usually connected into the adjacent arm of the impedance bridge. This coil, whose inductance is not influenced by displacement changes, is often packaged integrally with the sensing coil. This reduces undesirable effects due to long connecting leads, causes both coils to see the same thermal environment, and in some cases, provides adjustments to the reference coil at the point of measurement.

Noncontacting designs are used more commonly than coupled designs. Relative proximity of the sensing coil to the measured object causes changes

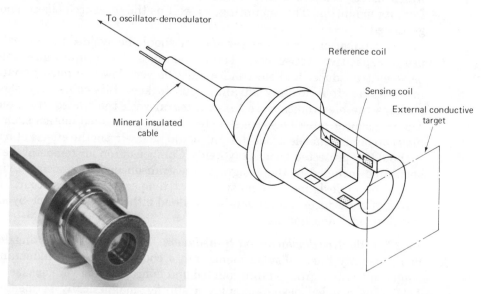

Figure 1-25. Inductive (eddy-current type) displacement transducer. (Courtesy of Kaman Sciences Corp.)

in the coil's inductance. Although measurements are feasible when the object is made of a highly conductive diamagnetic or paramagnetic material, they are more successful when the object is made of a ferromagnetic material and has a high permeability. The full-scale measuring ranges of such transducers are typically below 1.5 cm.

A design variation of a noncontacting inductive displacement transducer is illustrated in Figure 1-25. Displacements of the measured object, which must be conductive but need not be ferromagnetic, cause changes in *eddy currents*, which, in turn, cause changes in the impedance of the sensing coil. A reference coil is integrally packaged into the transducer. Transducers of this type have been designed to operate continuously at temperatures as high as 600°C. An associated electronics unit provides bridge excitation at RF frequencies as well as bridge balance adjustments and ac to dc conversion.

A related design is the *electromagnetic proximity transducer,* which contains a coil with a fixed core. Such transducers respond to changes in proximity to a metallic object (change in magnetic flux). They are often used as sensing coils in certain tachometer and flowmeter designs.

1.4.2.3 Reluctive displacement transducers.

1.4.2.3 Reluctive displacement transducers. This category includes all transducers that convert displacement into an ac voltage change by a variation in the reluctance path between two or more coils (windings) in the presence of ac excitation to the coils. Several of the types illustrated in Figure 1-26 are very widely used, including use as transduction elements for transducers measuring other than displacement. Most popular is the *differential transformer* type, which is used for linear as well as angular displacement measurements *(LVDT = linear variable differential transformer* and *RVDT = rotary variable differential transformer).* The same holds true for the less widely used *inductance bridge* type. The *induction potentiometer, synchro* ("selsyn"), *resolver, microsyn,* and *shorted-turn signal generator* are used to sense angular displacements only.

The operation of an LVDT is illustrated in Figure 1-27. Of the three coaxial windings, the center winding is the primary and the windings to each side of it are the secondaries, which, in their most elementary connection scheme, are connected together at one of their two terminals (as shown in Figure 1-29). When ac excitation is applied to the primary winding and the ferromagnetic core *(armature)* moves within the coil assembly the coupling between the primary and each of the two secondaries changes. As a result, the output voltage magnitude and phase at the secondary (output) terminals changes from the *null,* which occurs when the core is centered between the two secondaries. Note that output changes tend to become nonlinear near the ends of core travel. The operation of an RVDT, such as the one illustrated schematically in Figure 1-26b, is similar (see Figure 1-28). In addition to the basic winding configuration shown, there are a considerable number of other configurations, including split or center-tapped primaries and multiple secondaries with different types of interconnections (e.g., those intended to reduce phase angle changes).

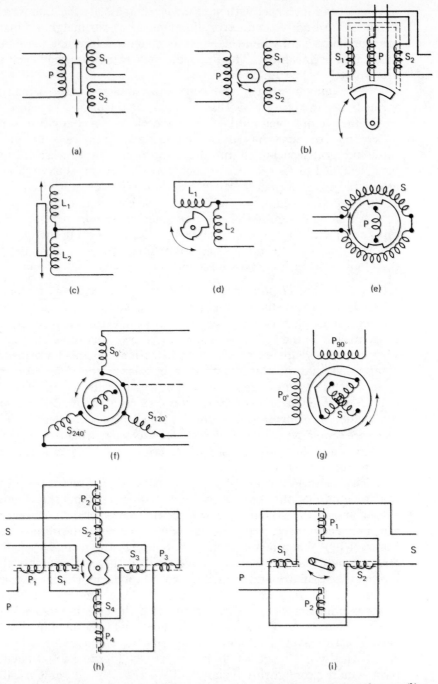

Figure 1-26. Reluctive displacement transducers: (a) differential transformer (linear); (b) differential transformers (angular); (c) inductance bridge (linear); (d) inductance bridge (angular; (e) induction potentiometer; (f) synchro; (g) resolver; (h) microsyn; (i) shorted-turn signal generator.

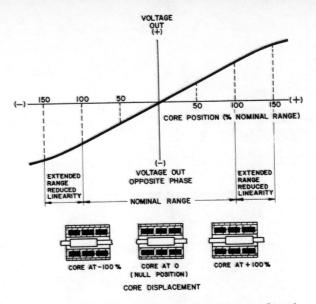

Figure 1-27. Output voltage and phase as a function of core position for a linear variable differential transformer. (Courtesy of Schaevitz Engineering.)

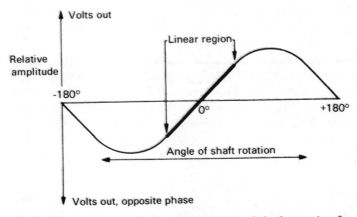

Figure 1-28. Output voltage as a function of shaft rotation for a rotary variable differential transformer. (Courtesy of Schaevitz Engineering.)

The construction of a typical LVDT displacement transducer is illustrated in Figure 1-29. The primary winding and the two secondary windings are wound over a hollow coil form, made of a nonmagnetic and insulating material. The ferromagnetic core is threaded to accept one of a variety of sensing shafts. The winding assembly is potted within a cylindrical case and the connecting leads are brought out of the potted assembly. The case is usually made of a ferromagnetic metal so that it acts as a magnetic shield. A transducer of similar design but incorporating integrally packaged dc–dc conversion circuitry is

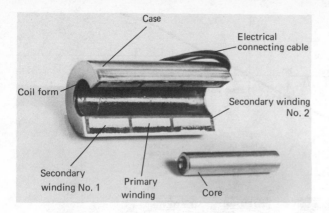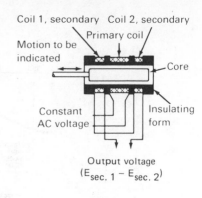

Figure 1-29. Reluctive (LVDT) linear displacement transducer. (Courtesy of Schaevitz Engineering.)

shown in Figure 1-30. This design uses a separate magnetic shield as well as a bore liner within which the armature (core) moves. The conversion circuitry, which also provides for internal and external connections, is mounted in the end of the case. The design illustrated operates from a ±15-V dc power supply and provides an output voltage of ±10 V dc. A variety of other excitation voltages can be accommodated by similar transducers, such as 12 V dc (automotive) and 28 V dc (aircraft and aerospace). Other output voltages can also be provided, such as the popular 0 to 5 V dc. As shown in the block diagram of Figure 1-30, an oscillator is used to convert the dc into the ac excitation required by the LVDT, whose output is then demodulated into dc and amplified. Circuitry to protect the electronics from the application of reverse polarity is included in this design. The output can be applied directly to a readout device. It could also be fed to a telemetry set or to a computer.

Displacement transducers with spring-loaded shafts, such as the LVDT

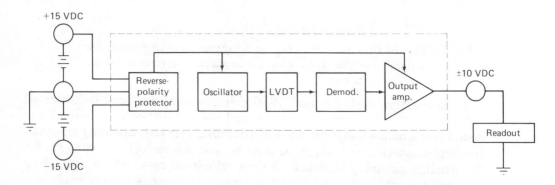

Figure 1-30. Reluctive (LVDT) linear displacement transducer with dc excitation and dc output ("DC-DC LVDT"). (Courtesy of Schaevitz Engineering.)

type shown in Figure 1-31, are sometimes referred to as "gage heads," because they are commonly used in machine tool inspection and gaging equipment. The sensing shaft is guided in a sleeve bearing. The type and fit of the bearing used govern transducer repeatability errors to a large extent. Various sensing-shaft tip configurations are available, as shown in Figure 1-32.

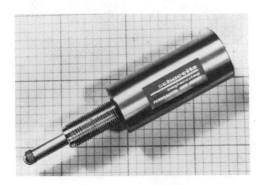

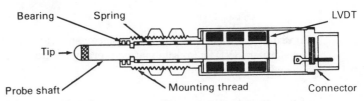

Figure 1-31. Reluctive linear displacement transducer with spring-loaded shaft ("LVDT gage head"). (Courtesy of Schaevitz Engineering.)

Figure 1-32. Typical tips for gage heads. (Courtesy of Schaevitz Engineering.)

Angular-displacement transducers of the differential-transformer type are limited in range to about ±40°, since, for larger angles, the output becomes increasingly nonlinear (see Figure 1-28). In a typical design (see Figure 1-33) the primary and secondary windings are wound on a coil form (stator) and a cardioid-shaped ferromagnetic rotor changes the coupling from the (split) primary to each of the secondary windings. Appropriate shaping of the rotor aids output linearization. Integrally packaged dc–dc conversion circuitry is available for this type of transducer.

Inductance-bridge-type transducers are used for linear (Figure 1-26c) as well as angular (Figure 1-26d) displacement measurements. Two coils and the core are so arranged that the inductance of one coil increases while the inductance of the other coil decreases with motion of the core. The matched set

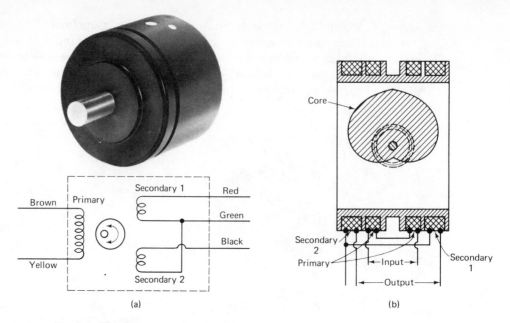

Figure 1-33. Reluctive angular displacement transducer (rotary variable differential transformer, RVDT): (a) schematic diagram; (b) cross section (simplified). (Courtesy of Schaevitz Engineering.)

of two coils forms two arms of a four-arm ac bridge. The other two arms are usually resistive. Dc–dc conversion circuitry can also be integrally packaged with such transducer designs.

The *induction potentiometer* (see Figure 1-26e) has been used in control systems. The coupling between the primary winding, on the rotor which sees the angular displacement, and the single secondary winding (or two windings in series), on the stator, changes with rotor rotation, providing an output which is reasonably linear up to a range of about ±35°.

In the *synchro* (see Figure 1-26f) the single primary winding on the rotor, which moves with the angular displacement to be sensed, interacts inductively with a three-phase stator whose windings are physically spaced 120° apart. In most applications the synchro used for sensing *(synchro transmitter)* provides an electrical output which is used to control the mechanical position of the rotor in a second synchro *(synchro receiver)*, which can then be used as a display device (see Figure 1-34) or to do other mechanical work. When used to drive a synchro receiver the synchro transmitter operates as *torque synchro*. When its rotor moves to a given angular position, the stator of the synchro receiver causes a torque to act on its rotor. This torque is reduced to zero only when the receiver's rotor assumes the same angular position. When the electrical output of a synchro is used for purposes other than driving a synchro receiver, the synchro transmitter can be referred to as *control synchro*.

The *resolver* (Figure 1-26g) differs from the synchro mainly in the number and spacing of its windings. Both the two-phase rotor and the two-phase stator

Solid-Mechanical Quantities

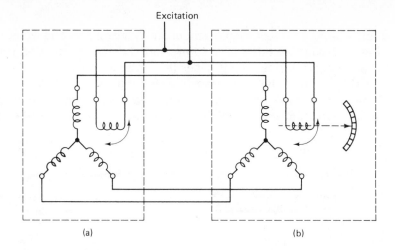

Excitation

(a)   (b)

Figure 1-34. Synchro transmitter-receiver system: (a) transducer synchro (transmitter); (b) read-out synchro (receiver).

have windings spaced 90° apart. When used as a measuring transducer, the resolver has one of its two rotor windings shorted.

The *microsyn* (Figure 1-26h) and the related *shorted-turn signal generator* (Figure 1-26i) are more suitable as measuring transducers than the synchro and resolver, although all four of these rotary transformer devices are mostly used in control systems. This is because the microsyn and shorted-turn signal generator operate off single-phase ac excitation and provide a single-phase output proportional to rotor displacement. Both devices have a four-pole stator, usually made of laminated iron plates. Each of the microsyn poles is wound with two coils, a primary and a secondary winding. The primaries are all connected in series. The secondaries are also in series but are so connected that the voltage induced in coils S_1 and S_3 opposes the voltage induced in coils S_2 and S_4. The ferromagnetic rotor has a unique "butterfly" configuration. Angular displacement of the rotor, from its null position, causes a change in the reluctance path to coils S_1 and S_3 which is opposite to that to coils S_2 and S_4. The resulting unbalance creates a net output voltage in the secondary.

The four poles of the shorted-turn signal generator are each wound with only one coil. Opposing pairs constitute the primary and secondary winding set, respectively, at right angles to each other. The ring-shaped rotor is a single-turn shorted coil. Flux is induced in the rotor by the ac excited primaries. An output is produced in the secondaries when the rotor moves from its null position and produces flux linkages to them. The shorted turn can be machined integrally with the sensing shaft.

1.4.2.4 Potentiometric displacement transducers. These are relatively simple devices in which a sliding contact *(wiper),* attached to, or otherwise mechanically linked with the sensing shaft, moves over a resistance element. The wiper is electrically insulated from the sensing shaft. Potentiometric transducers exist for linear- as well as angular-displacement measurements (see

Figure 1-35). In linear-displacement transducers a second wiper and wiper bus (Figure 1-35b) are often used to prevent those problems that could be caused by a flexing, relatively long wiper lead. The output is a displacement-proportional fraction of the excitation voltage (applied across the "+" and "−" terminals). The resistance element *(potentiometric element)* can be provided with one or more additional electrical connections *(taps)* at specified positions.

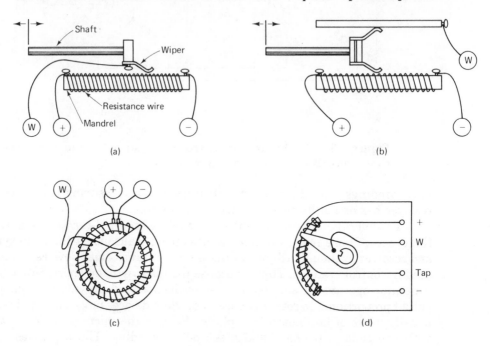

Figure 1-35. Basic types of potentiometric displacement transducers: (a) linear (basic); (b) linear (with wiper bus); (c) angular (single-turn); (d) angular (sector, tapped).

When the potentiometric element is wirewound (typically platinum or nickel alloy wire) the resolution steps are given by the number of wire turns per unit length. To obtain small steps, the total element resistance can be made large (5000 to 10,000 Ω) and thin wire (approximately 0.01 mm in diameter) would then be used. This, however, results in a variable, relatively high output impedance that may cause loading errors. Continuous-resolution ("infinite resolution") potentiometric elements have been made of conductive plastic, a carbon film, a metal film, or a ceramic-metal mix ("cermet"). The mandrel, around which the winding is wound, is made of an insulating material or of an insulation-coated metal. To allow for overtravel beyond a specified displacement range, the mandrel can be extended and provided with conductive strips (or wire turns soldered together) that are electrically connected to (or part of) the respective excitation terminal.

Wipers exist in a number of different designs (see Figure 1-36). They are typically made from precious-metal alloys or spring-tempered copper alloys.

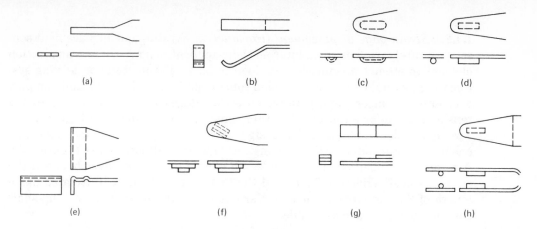

Figure 1-36. Typical wiper configurations; (a) plain; (b) plain, hook type; (c) dimpled; (d) rod type; (e) knife edge; (f) knife edge, offset; (g) leaf spring; (h) dual.

Leaf-spring and dual wipers are used in transducers expected to see severe shock or vibration environments. Wiper contact force is typically adjusted to between 4 and 15 g. The contact as well as the resistance element are sensitive to externally introduced contamination; hence, a good sliding seal for the sensing shaft and a good seal for the electrical connections are important.

Displacements sensed by angular-displacement transducers of the potentiometric type range between less than 10° and over 3500°. For small ranges some internal mechanical amplification is often employed. Helical resistance elements are used in multiturn potentiometers for ranges in excess of 360°. Single-rotation transducers can be designed with mechanical end stops or for continuous rotation; in either case, the presence of excitation terminals at the ends of the potentiometric element limits their active range to about 357°. Linear-displacement transducers with very large measuring ranges (up to about 8 m) use a spring-loaded cable-and-pulley arrangement, with the pulley rotation either geared down to drive a single-turn rotary potentiometer or that rotation used to drive a multiturn potentiometer.

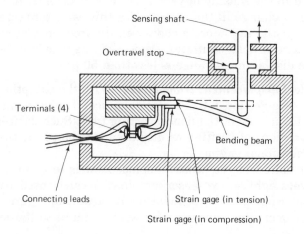

Figure 1-37. Basic design of strain-gage displacement transducer.

1.4.2.5 Strain-gage displacement transducers. Strain-gage displacement sensors are rarely used as such, but find their applications mostly as transduction element in other transducers (e.g., load cells, accelerometers) or sensing systems (e.g., for bulk weighing, tension control, profiling). They typically employ a bending beam or flexure to which strain gages are attached, one in the tension-sensing orientation, the other sensing compression (see Figure 1-37). Two-active-element half-bridge designs are most common. An example, this one using semiconductor ("piezoresistive") gages, is illustrated in Figure 1-38. A ceramic encapsulant also provides an elastic insulation layer between the stainless-steel deflecting beam and the two gages. The unit illustrated has a length of 38 mm (without leads). Various mounting bases and sensing-shaft tip configurations are available.

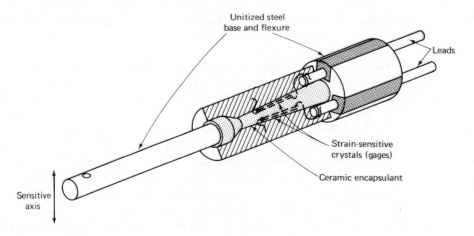

Figure 1-38. Semiconductor-strain-gage displacement sensor. (Courtesy of DSC Inc.)

1.4.2.6 Vibrating-wire displacement transducers. The vibrating-wire principle has been applied to the sensing of very small displacements. A change of displacement causes a change in the tension of a thin wire connected into a feedback oscillator circuit, and hence a change in the frequency at which the wire, placed in a magnetic field, oscillates. Devices of this type have been used where the full-scale displacement range is less than 50 μm.

1.4.2.7 Electro-optical displacement transducers. With the exception of electro-optical encoders (see Section 1.4.2.8), electro-optical displacement sensing devices are almost invariably of the noncontacting type. Such devices can be used for the measurement of position or displacement; however, their main use has been in dimensional gaging.

When a surface of an object, whose displacement is to be measured, is sufficiently reflective, a light source/sensor combination can be used to measure relatively small displacements. This principle is illustrated in Figure 1-39; the output of the sensor decreases exponentially with distance to the measured

Solid-Mechanical Quantities

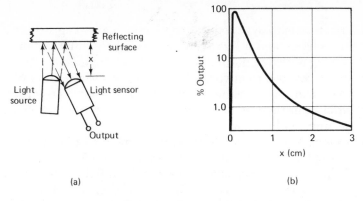

(a)   (b)

Figure 1-39. Displacement sensing by reflection method (basic): (a) optical arrangement; (b) typical response.

object. Related designs use fiber optics to transmit and to receive the light reflected by the measured surface; they can be used to measure very small displacements with fine resolution. When the measured surface is not inherently reflective, a reflector can be attached to it. Light beams can be of constant intensity (dc) or modulated (ac) at low or high frequencies (depending on the response time of the light sensor and the application); they can also be chopped or pulsed. Infrared light-emitting diodes (LEDs) are often used as a light source.

One of the methods employed in electro-optical dimensional gaging is illustrated in Figure 1-40. In this edge view of a typical basic setup, the height and/or width of an object can be measured in terms of the amount of occultation of the beam between source and sensor. When the light sensor is a multiline array of light-sensitive elements, or another type of imager such as a vidicon camera, the shape of the measured object, and its variations in height and in width, can be determined very accurately by processing the sensor output data and either displaying the resulting image or comparing it with a model of the "standard" image. Such systems are very useful for quality control of machined or otherwise fabricated parts.

The well-collimated, coherent, monochromatic light beams from lasers have made these devices an important element in electro-optical dimensional measuring systems. One of the methods employing a laser for the measurement of product thickness or, generally, distance between the sensing head (laser light source and two light sensors) and a surface, is the *triangulation* method. The spot of laser light on the surface is viewed by two light sensors at the same angle but from opposite directions. Surface position relative to a reference position can be determined from the two light sensor outputs. A variation of

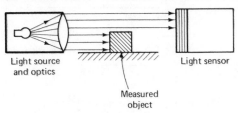

Figure 1-40. Dimensional gaging by occultation method.

this method employs two laser beams at equal but opposite angles to the normal to the surface and a light sensor viewing the intersection of the beams with a viewing direction normal to the surface. The imaging-type sensor detects the distance between the two laser spots of the surface, from which distance to the surface (and, e.g., thickness of the material whose bottom surface is at a known position) can then be determined. Laser scanning, which can be obtained by deflecting the beam with an oscillating mirror, is also used for dimensional gaging as well as flaw detection in the product of rolling mills.

Applying interferometric techniques to reflected-laser-light displacement and dimensional measuring systems resulted in developments of the *laser interferometer* (Figure 1-41). The optical principle of this instrument is based on that of the Michelson interferometer, a principle used also in many other applications, such as infrared spectroscopy. The laser beam is split into two orthogonal beams by a beam splitter. One beam is directed at a fixed flat mirror which reflects it back to the beam splitter. The other beam is either directed at a mirror which displaces along the direction of the beam, and whose displacement is to be measured, or, as shown in the illustration, at a reflector, from which it reflects toward another fixed mirror. In the latter case, it is the displacement of the reflector (or the object to which it is attached) which is being measured. The second mirror returns the beam along the same path, back to the beam splitter. Here the beam recombines and (optically) interferes with the reference beam. The interference is constructive when the difference between the two beam paths is an integral number of wavelengths; it is destructive when the path difference is an odd integral of half-wavelengths. As the reflector moves and changes the path length of the "measuring" beam, one

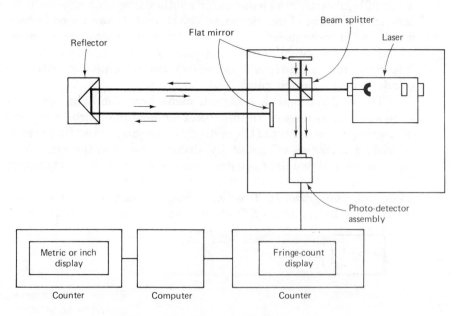

Figure 1-41. Laser interferometer system.

Solid-Mechanical Quantities

complete interference fringe is detected by the photodetector (light sensor) for every wavelength change in the path length. The displacement is then determined from a fringe count; this provides a digital output characterized by extremely high precision.

Advances in developments of the laser interferometer, such as the two-frequency laser and the holographic interferometer, have extended its measurement capabilities, which now also include measurements of angles (with resolution of a fraction of an arc-second), alignment, straightness, and flatness.

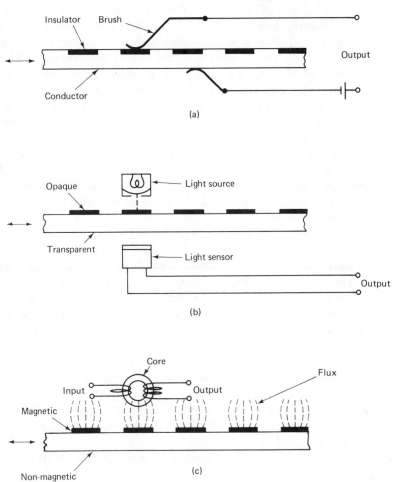

Figure 1-42. Encoder transduction methods: (a) brush type; (b) photoelectric type; (c) magnetic type.

1.4.2.8 Linear and angular encoders. Linear as well as angular displacement can be sensed and converted into a digital output more simply than most other measurands and without using an analog-to-digital converter. The devices providing such a digital output in response to displacement changes are known as *linear encoders* and *angular encoders,* respectively. Three different trans-duction methods are employed in encoders (see Figure 1-42). In the *brush-type* encoder the moving disk or strip contains conducting and insulating segments on its surface. The conducting segments are all connected to a common terminal. When the pick-off brush is in contact with a conducting segment, a contact closure occurs. When the brush is in contact with a insulating segment, an open contact results. When a source of excitation voltage is connected between the common contact and the associated signal processing circuitry, an output voltage (a "1") is seen during contact closure, and no output (a "0") is seen when the brush contact is open. In the *photoelectric* or *optical encoder* a transparent disk or strip is provided with a pattern of opaque segments on its upper surface. These interrupt a light beam and prevent it from illuminating a light sensor. Hence, an output "1" is produced when the light sensor is below a transparent segment, and a "0" results from the light sensor being below an opaque segment. In the *magnetic encoder* the disk or strip is provided, on its surface, with a pattern consisting of magnetized and nonmagnetized segments. A ferromagnetic core, provided with an input winding and an output winding, is placed above this surface. An input ("interrogate") signal is applied to the input winding. When the core is above a nonmagnetic segment the core remains unsaturated and an output signal (a "1") is produced. When the core is above a magnetic segment, the flux from the segment causes the core to be saturated and no output signal (a "0") is produced.

Practical, reliable designs exist in all three types, although the contactless optical and magnetic encoders are more widely manufactured and used. Brush-type units contain contact patterns made of precious-metal foils on an insulating substrate, with the common contact part of the pattern, and brushes in brush holders both designed to increase operating life. Optical encoders use light-emitting diodes (LEDs) increasingly, and the opaque/transparent pattern is applied by sophisticated methods such as by vacuum bombardment through a precisely cut mask on a glass substrate. Generally, techniques used to manufacture miniature printed circuits are often applied to both of these encoder types. Magnetic encoders tend to use a ferrite disk on which the magnetic pattern is inscribed very precisely. Techniques employed in the design and manufacture of high-capacity, modern, digital tape recorders have been used to improve magnetic encoders. Sinusoidal ac as well as pulse signals are used in their input and output sides.

Digital displacement transducers (encoders) exist in two forms:

1. The *incremental encoder* (see Figure 1-43) produces equally spaced pulses from one or more tracks; the pulses are fed to and accumulated in an up/down counter and the count is indicative of displacement; the starting point can be arbitrarily selected and the associated readout equipment can be zeroed for the new setting. Alternatively, an index-ing pulse can be provided by an additional "1"-producing segment in the code pattern.

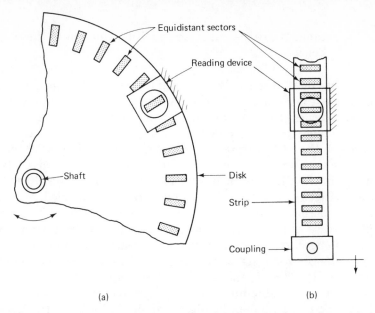

(a)   (b)

Figure 1-43. Operating principle of incremental encoders: (a) angular; (b) linear.

2. The *absolute encoder* (see Figure 1-44) produces a digitally encoded number, indicative of position, by an array of reading heads and a multitrack pattern on the code disk or strip. A variety of codes are used in addition to the binary code represented by the pattern shown in the illustration; linear codes include the "V-scan," "Gray," and BCD (binary-coded decimal) codes; nonlinear codes such as sine, cosine, and

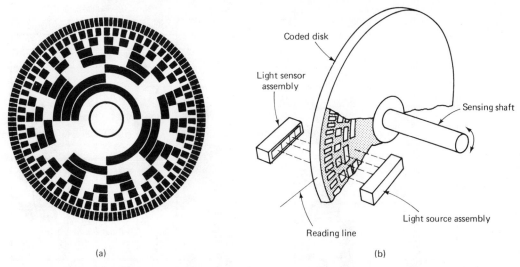

(a)   (b)

Figure 1-44. Basic absolute (photoelectric, angular) encoder: (a) typical code disk; (b) encoder elements.

tangent are also used. A brief introduction to these codes is included below.

The most frequently used digital codes used in absolute encoders are illustrated in Figure 1-45. The natural binary, or just *binary code* is the simplest code for use with arithmetic or comparison-computing circuitry. It is easily understood by personnel working with digital electronics systems. It is based on the relative position of bits having a value of "0" (or "no") and those having a value of "1" (or "yes") in a data word of a given length. The data words in the illustration have a length of 4 bits. The shaded portions of the code patterns indicate a "1." In practice, these shaded portions would correspond to a contact in the case of brush-type encoders, a nonmagnetized segment in the case of magnetic encoders, and a transparent segment in the case of optical encoders. The binary code is based on powers of 2; hence, a "1" in the last bit—the *least significant bit,* or *LSB*—the 2^0 bit, indicates the arabic number "1" ($2^0 = 1$, and a "1" or "yes" indication in that bit position means "one"). Other arabic numbers are indicated by a "1" or "0" in the other bit positions. For example, the digital number "1001," in the binary code, is read as follows: bit position 2^3 (which is 8): yes; bit positions 2^2 and 2^1 (which are 4 and 2, respectively): no; bit position 2^0 (which is 1): yes. The resulting arabic number, then, is $8 + 1$, or 9. The number of discrete increments obtainable from an encoder are given by $2^n - 1$, the "-1" because "zero" always exists as one of the numbers. If, for example, we want to know how many bits (and how many tracks on an encoder) are needed to indicate angular displacements

Arabic number	(Natural) Binary		Gray (Binary)		Binary Coded Decimal (BCD)			
	Digital number	Code pattern	Digital number	Code pattern	Digital number		Code pattern	
					Tens	Units	Tens	Units
	8 4 2 1	$2^3\ 2^2\ 2^1\ 2^0$		$G_3\ G_2\ G_1\ G_0$	8 4 2 1	8 4 2 1	2^0	$2^3\ 2^2\ 2^1\ 2^0$
0	0 0 0 0		0 0 0 0		0 0 0 0	0 0 0 0		
1	0 0 0 1		0 0 0 1			0 0 0 1		
2	0 0 1 0		0 0 1 1			0 0 1 0		
3	0 0 1 1		0 0 1 0			0 0 1 1		
4	0 1 0 0		0 1 1 0			0 1 0 0		
5	0 1 0 1		0 1 1 1			0 1 0 1		
6	0 1 1 0		0 1 0 1			0 1 1 0		
7	0 1 1 1		0 1 0 0			0 1 1 1		
8	1 0 0 0		1 1 0 0			1 0 0 0		
9	1 0 0 1		1 1 0 1		0 0 0 0	1 0 0 1		
10	1 0 1 0		1 1 1 1		0 0 0 1	0 0 0 0		

Figure 1-45. Digital code structures for absolute encoders.

of a full circle to better than 1 second of arc, we first convert seconds to numbers of increments for a full circle ($60 \times 60 \times 360 = 1\ 296\ 000$), then look up a table of powers of 2 and find that the nearest power of 2 giving a resolution better than 1 in 1 296 000 is 21; $2^{20} - 1$ is only 1 048 575, but $2^{21} - 1 = 2\ 097\ 151$. In angular encoders the LSB is normally the outermost track. Table I-1 shows number of increments versus number of bits.

For error detection by associated computing circuitry an additional track for a *parity bit* can be added to binary-coded disks and strips. This track is so coded that, for every position of the encoder, either an odd number of "1's" is always obtained *(odd parity)* or an even number of "1's" is always obtained *(even parity)*.

The *binary-coded-decimal (BCD)* code is a combination of the binary system and the Arabic decimal system. Four-bit binary data words are so arranged that the last word indicates "units," in binary code, the next-to-last data word indicates "tens," and so on. The difference between the BCD and natural binary codes can be seen if we examine the digital representations (and the code pattern) for the Arabic number "10" in Figure 1-45. A number such as "835" would be represented by "1000 0011 0101."

A disadvantage of binary code disks is that two or more bits can change simultaneously during a single position change within the resolution of the encoder as, for example, when going from 7 (0111) to 8 (1000). Certain other codes were developed to get around any problems that may be caused by this. One of these is the *Gray code* (also shown in Figure 1-45), named after Frank Gray of Bell Laboratories. In this code pattern the state of the LSB is changed only every two counts, rather than every count as in the binary code. This reduces possible reading ambiguities and permits tracks to be closer together, hence reducing the overall size of an encoder. If fed into computer circuitry, this code must first be converted into binary form.

The *V-scan* method has been used in absolute encoders to minimize reading ambiguities. It uses either a pair of brushes, one behind the other, on each except the LSB tracks, and external logic, or has each of the tracks (except the LSB track) of the code pattern split in half and each half slightly displaced from each other so that one half is "leading," the other "lagging" (as is the case for the two brushes per track); the V-disk arrangement also requires external logic circuitry to prevent ambiguous readings.

Various methods have been used to improve the reading capability of incremental encoders, which, in their basic version, produce a simple train of equidistant pulses, with the pulse indicating a "1" and the baseline a "0." One method is to add a track and form a code pattern equivalent to a series of 2-bit data words. Other methods involve the use of *interfering patterns* (see Figure 1-46), usually obtained by placing a stationary reticle or other mask over the moving pattern. When the "$N + 1$" pattern is used the rotating disk has n segments and a stationary disk placed between the rotating disk and the reading devices has $n + 1$ segments. The reading devices (light sensors) are placed 180° apart. As the disk rotates, the output of each sensor is modulated quasi-sinusoidally, with the total number of periods equal to n. The

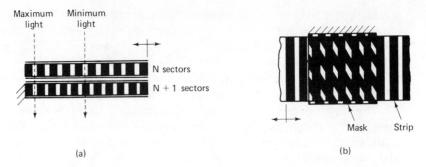

Maximum light   Minimum light

N sectors
N + 1 sectors

Mask   Strip

(a)   (b)

Figure 1-46. Interfering patterns used in encoders: (a) $N + 1$ pattern; (b) moiré pattern.

outputs of the two light sensors can be used for multiplication as well as for direction sensing. The *moiré pattern* is formed by a stationary mask with a light bar pattern similar to that of the moving element but tilted at a small angle with respect to it. As the element (typically a strip in a linear encoder) moves, the light bands, which have the appearance of a series of parallelograms, move up or down, depending on direction of motion. A light sensor (with collimating optics) is placed in front of each of the light bands (arranged vertically). This system provides substantial improvements in resolution. Multiplication has also been obtained mechanically, in angular encoders, by using two disks and a gear train between them so that the "fast disk" rotates many times for each rotation of the "slow disk" in such a *multispeed encoder*. In addition to incremental and absolute encoders there are also "hybrid" encoders, which employ two different techniques, such as absolute encoding or moiré interference patterns for the less significant digits and incremental encoding for the more significant digits. Figure 1-47 shows a linear encoder that is

Figure 1-47. Linear encoder. (Courtesy of Whitwell Electronic Developments Ltd.)

designed to provide this sort of hybrid operation. The design, with its sensing shaft, reading head, and coded strip is also typical for linear encoders in general.

Angular encoders, incremental or absolute, are provided with either an axial sensing shaft, or, when their size is relatively large, with a through hole, an annular rotor, and an annular code disk. The latter type is illustrated in Figures 1-48 and 1-49. This design has a separate electronics unit; others have integrally packaged electronics. The absolute encoder version of this design uses V-scan as well as multiple reading heads of the LSB track, with averaging circuitry, to provide encoding up to 2^{22} bits. The multiple reading and averaging technique is also used in incremental encoders. Semirigid or flexible couplings are often used in conjunction with angular encoders to allow for misalignments and eccentricities in the measured object.

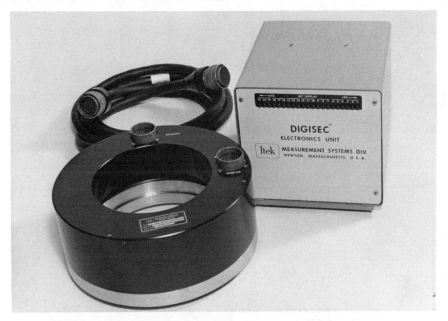

Figure 1-48. Angular encoder (through-hole type). (Courtesy of Itek Corp., Measurement Systems Div.)

1.4.2.9 Position-sensing switches. Directly actuated as well as noncontacting position-sensing switches are very widely used devices. Some of them employ operating principles described in Sections 1.4.2.2 (inductive) and 1.4.2.7 (electro-optical, covered additionally in Chapter 5, especially Section 5.4). The most popular device is the *electromechanical switch,* an example of which is illustrated in Figure 1-50. It is, essentially, a momentary-contact, single-pole double-throw, pushbutton switch. When the plunger is depressed it acts upon a spring linkage and causes the normally closed contact to open and the normally open contact to close. The switch is so installed that the measured object will actuate it when it attains a position that is intended to be known. Switches

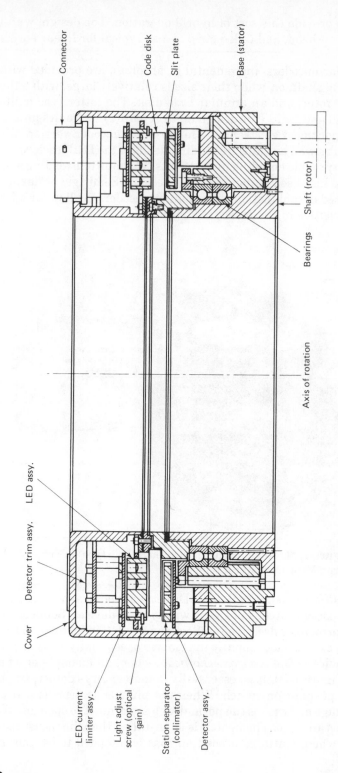

Figure 1-49. Sectional view of through-hole type angular encoder. (Courtesy of Itek Corp., Measurement Systems Div.)

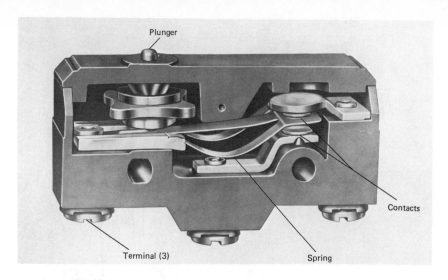

Figure 1-50. Cutaway of electromechanical basic switch. (Courtesy of MICRO SWITCH, A Division of Honeywell.)

of this type can be equipped with various kinds of actuators to facilitate this operation. These include a roller actuator, a leaf-spring actuator, a lever-type actuator, and plunger extensions of various heights, some allowing for large amounts of overtravel, some in a waterproof boot, some with a roller at their tip. These are either an integral part of a switch or can be added to it. Hermetically sealed versions and completely waterproof switches are among the available design variations. Most such electromechanical position-sensing switches are designed for rugged use and for large numbers of actuations. The spring is typically made of beryllium copper and the contacts of silver or gold. Terminals can be of the screw, quick-connect, or solder type.

There are also a number of switch designs that do not rely on electromechanical means to open or close a contact. One of these is the *Hall-effect* switch (see Figure 1-51). This effect was discovered, in 1879, by Edward H. Hall, at the Johns Hopkins University. He found that a difference in potential would appear at opposite edges of a thin rectangle of gold, through which current was flowing, when a magnet is placed so that its field is perpendicular to one face of the gold foil. When this effect was, much later, applied to semiconductors rather than gold and much higher Hall voltages were obtained, a number of useful devices using this effect were developed. Since the voltage is proportional to the current flowing through the semiconductor, the effect lends itself to current measurement. Because the voltage is also proportional to the magnetic flux density, the device can be used where either the flux density itself is to be measured (or changes in it are to cause voltage changes for purposes other than flux measurement); it can also be used in devices where the relative proximity of magnet to semiconductor is to give an indication by a voltage change.

In the switch illustrated, actuation of the plunger causes the vertical

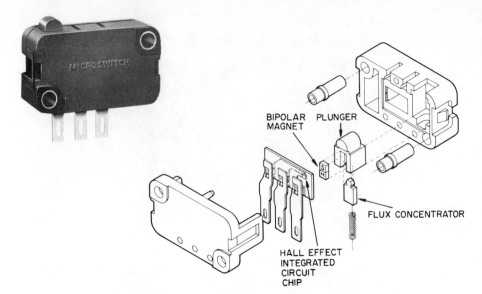

Figure 1-51. Hall-effect-type position-sensing switch (plunger-operated). (Courtesy of MICRO SWITCH, A Division of Honeywell.)

displacement of a magnet, changing its proximity to the Hall generator. A flux concentrator is used to concentrate more of the available flux into the sensor. An integrated-circuit chip associated with the Hall generator provides signal conditioning, including a step-function generator with hysteresis to establish a "dead band" and prevent erroneous actuations due to noise or vibration, and output logic suitable for interfacing. Besides the plunger-actuated switch there are noncontacting versions of this design for which the measured object must be magnetic (or equipped with a magnet).

For the Hall-effect switch as well as the eddy-current type described below, the typical motions of the measured object are either "head-on" (motion to and from the sensor along its longitudinal axis), "slide-by" (lateral or vertical motion past the sensing surface of the switch), or "rotary" (motion of magnetic "teeth" or poles along the rim of a rotating member past the sensing surface). Neither of these types, however, is sensitive to the rate of change of flux coupling which is a drawback of the *electromagnetic* proximity sensor. The *eddy-current*-type proximity switch (see Figure 1-52) is similar to eddy-current-type inductive displacement transducers. It is the (integrally packaged) circuitry that makes it into a switch rather than an analog-output sensor. The measured object must be metallic but need not be ferrous. The measured object (the "target") tends to absorb the electromagnetic field generated in the sensing coil due to the generation of eddy currents, which present a reflected load to the oscillator, reducing its signal level. This change in level is amplified by the integrator circuitry, which drives a Schmitt trigger coupled to an output transistor, thus providing the switching action. An (optional) LED, located in the wall of the rear portion of the housing, furnishes a visible output indication.

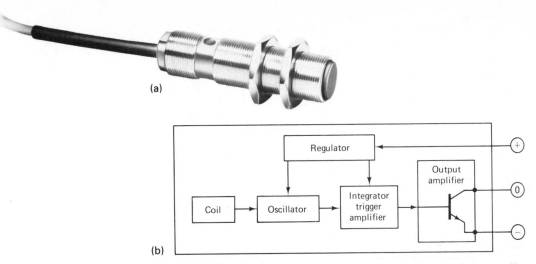

(a)

Regulator

Output
amplifier

Coil → Oscillator → Integrator
trigger
amplifier →

(+)

0

(−)

(b)

Figure 1-52. Eddy-current-type proximity switch: (a) sensor assembly (with integrally packaged electronics); (b) block diagram. (Courtesy of MICRO SWITCH, A Division of Honeywell.)

The unit illustrated is fully shielded; unshielded versions are also available.

Photoelectric position-sensing switches employ a light source and a light sensor to detect the presence or absence of objects that block (or unblock) the light path or cause reflection of the light beam or light-scattering products to be incident on the light sensor. The two primary methods used are direct scan and retroreflective scan. In *direct scan* (Figure 1-53a) a light source and a light sensor ("photoreceiver") are positioned opposite each other and the object to be detected passes between them. The object must be opaque enough as well as large enough to block the light beam sufficiently to cause switching operation. Collimating can be used for source and sensor to aid in the detection of relatively small objects. In *reflective scan* the light source and sensor are placed on the same side of the object to be detected and the light beam is reflected toward the light sensor from an inherently reflective object or from a reflective target installed for scanning purposes. There are three types of reflective scan: retroreflective, specular, and diffuse. With *retroreflective scan* (Figure 1-53b) the light source and sensor are usually mounted in a common housing. The light beam is directed at a retroreflective target, which returns the light along the same path. Acrylic disks or tape, even chalk, are used as retroreflectors; the bicycle-type reflector is a good example. The larger the reflector, the longer the light path can be. Alignment is not very critical and retroreflective position-sensing systems are useful in the presence of vibration. They are also generally useful when the measured objects are relatively translucent, since the light beam is attenuated during both portions of its round trip.

In the *specular scan* technique the measured object must be highly reflective (e.g., polished metal, shiny plastic, mirrors or mirrorlike surfaces; the Latin word *speculum* means "mirror"). As illustrated in Figure 1-53c, the angle of incidence equals the angle of reflectance; hence, positioning of light source

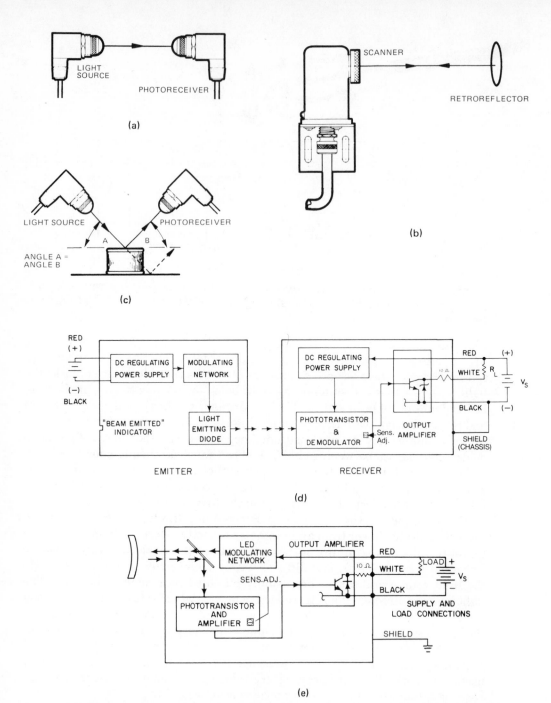

Figure 1-53. Photoelectric switch systems: (a) direct scan; (b) retroreflective scan; (c) specular scan; (d) functional block diagram of separate emitter/receiver system; (e) functional block diagram of self-contained system. (Courtesy of MICRO SWITCH, A Division of Honeywell.)

Solid-Mechanical Quantities

and sensor as well as their distance from the measured object must all be accurately controlled. In *diffuse scan* the measured objects are matte rather than shiny and the light sensor detects scattering products in a manner similar to nephelometry (see Section 5.4).

Light-emitting diodes (LEDs) are commonly used as light sources in photoelectric position-sensing switch systems. The use of infrared light, especially modulated infrared light, with light sensor circuitry tuned to the modulating frequency, has been found to be very effective in minimizing any undesirable effects due to ambient light. The light beam modulation is usually in a pulse mode; high-intensity infrared pulses emanating from an LED improve system efficiency. Figure 1-53d and e show block diagrams for transmittive and reflective position sensing systems, using modulated light.

1.4.2.10 Radar and sonar distance-sensing devices. This category covers sensors, only briefly mentioned here, which emit a pulse of electromagnetic energy at a target and then determine the distance to that target by measuring the time it takes a corresponding reflected signal *(echo)* to be received by the same sensor. This requires the sensor to operate in the transmit mode as well as the receive mode and to be able to provide outputs proportional to the time that elapses between pulse transmission and reception. The number of pulses emitted per second is known as the *repetition rate*. Electromagnetic radiation at ultrasonic (low-frequency RF) wavelengths is used to measure distances underwater and for in situ measurements of relatively large (0.3 to 5 m) displacements. Very short wavelengths characterize sensors such as radar trackers and radar altimeters; they extend downward into the microwave region. Still shorter wavelengths are used in laser altimeters and related distance-measuring sensors. Distance can also be determined from observations of target velocity, using the Doppler effect, by appropriate calculations.

1.4.3   Design and Performance Characteristics

Certain mechanical design characteristics are important to consider for displacement transducers. Some types of angular displacement sensors have standardized case outlines and, particularly, mounting dimensions. This applies specifically to the "servo-mount" or "synchro-mount" configurations, usually a cylindrical case, mounted by clamping it around a circumferential groove near the sensing shaft. The servo-mount "size" gives the outside case diameter (multiplied by 10 and rounded off to the nearest one-tenth of an inch, for models manufactured in the United States) as well as essential mounting dimensions. The case of a "size 11 synchro mount," for example, has a diameter of 1.062 in and a mounting-groove diameter of 1.000 in. Mounting torque or force needs to be specified for some applications.

Overtravel of the sensing shaft beyond the measuring range is often a requirement for linear and angular transducers. It is specified as the difference between each of the range limits and the points to which overtravel (which does not produce any further output changes) is required and, in many cases, mechanical stops are set [e.g., "Overtravel: − 1.5, + 3.0 cm" (where "−" means shaft retraction and "+" means shaft extension)]. Similar overtravel requirements can be specified for angular-displacement transducers, expressed in degrees or radians. The maximum force or torque *(overload)* that may be applied to the sensing shaft, when it reaches a mechanical overtravel stop, without damaging or degrading the transducer, may also have to be specified.

Sensing shaft *concentricity, alignment* (with respect to the case and its mountings), and *radial* as well as *axial play* should be considered for inclusion in a specification, and *backlash* should be specified (or known) for transducers containing gears. The force (or torque, for angular transducers) required to initiate shaft motion, as indicated by a measurable change in output (even after prolonged storage of the transducer), the *starting force* or *starting torque,* must be considered as well as the subsequently applicable *running force* or *running torque* (which is always lower than the starting force or torque). For spring-loaded shafts the *holding force* (at any point after initial motion) should also be specified or known. Requirements for *shaft sealing* should be considered. For angular-displacement transducers, particularly angular encoders, the maximum allowable radial and axial, static as well as operating, *shaft loading* is often specified, as is the *moment of inertia* of the entire rotating mass.

Electrical design characteristics, in addition to those generally applicable, include such encoder-peculiar output characteristics as waveform, phase relationships, pulse shape (including rise and fall times), voltage levels for "0" and for "1," and excitation and load characteristics stated in terms appropriate for digital electronics interfaces.

Among performance characteristics, the definition of *range* is somewhat more complex for displacement transducers than for most other transducer types, because it really needs the definition of some sort of reference point it can be based on. Range, for displacement transducers, has been variously stated as "electrical travel," "electrical stroke," "full-scale deflection," "linear range," "useful range," "useful stroke," or "total stroke." Since the specification of an either unidirectional or bidirectional range is essential to all other performance specifications it is important to specify a reference point for the range of essentially all linear and angular displacement transducers except for such devices as incremental angular encoders. This reference position can be stated in one of two ways: (1) by a precise dimension between a point on the sensing shaft (for contacting transducers) or a point in space near a noncontacting transducer, and a point on the case of the transducer; or (2) by a specific transducer output (frequently the zero-measurand output, or "null") at the reference point. Range polarity must also be defined; usually, it is increasingly positive with displacements away from the transducer or, for angular displacements, in a clockwise direction (clockwise motion of the sensing shaft, looking at the shaft end).

Output is frequently stated in terms of sensitivity rather than full-scale output or end points, leaving it to the user to set the end points; this makes other specifications, such as those for static performance characteristics, more difficult unless the "sensitivity" specification is appropriately supplemented.

For transducers whose output is also a function of excitation, the nominal (or reference) excitation values (e.g., voltage and frequency) must be stated or added to "sensitivity" (e.g., "_____mV/cm/V at 400 Hz), with tolerances assigned to sensitivity. For some types of transducers, output is stated in terms of phase angle (as such, or in addition to voltage amplitude); for some others it is stated in terms of the output or indication of associated signal-conditioning or display equipment in conjunction with which the transducer has been calibrated and must be used.

Encoder output is stated in total counts per turn (revolution) for angular incremental encoders, and in total counts per total length or per unit length for linear incremental encoders. When multiplication of counts is obtained by multiple reading heads and logic circuitry, such multiplication is usually stated. For absolute encoders, output is stated primarily in terms of resolution (number of bits in the data word generated) and type of code used (binary, BCD, Gray, etc.), any antiambiguity logic used (or required externally), and output polarity and notation (linear counts, degrees–minutes–seconds, altitude, etc.). When two or more outputs are provided by a transducer, the interrelationship of these outputs (output correlation) may have to be stated.

Among static characteristics, hysteresis is typically very low for most types of displacement transducers. Resolution is specified primarily for wire-wound-element potentiometric transducers (as is friction error, for all potentiometric transducers) and, of course, for encoders. Repeatability and linearity should always be considered. The near-zero output at the reference position for bidirectional-range transducers is specified as tolerances for null voltage or "zero balance." The specification of phase shift is important for most types of reluctive transducers, in combination with statements of applicable load and excitation characteristics. Mounting error and, for a few types of transducers, attitude error should be accounted for.

The only essential dynamic characteristic is *maximum shaft speed* (above which damage or degradation of performance can occur). This is shown for sustained speed *(operating speed)* as well as speed changes, during run-up or during operation *(slewing* or *slew speed)*, for both angular- and linear-displacement transducers (in revolutions per minute, or units of length per second, respectively).

Criteria for selection of a displacement transducer for a given application are, primarily, the characteristics of the measuring system (low- or high-level signals, dc, ac, frequency-modulated, digital) and measuring range; other essential criteria involve the physical requirements for appropriate installation, the material or surface characteristics of measured objects for noncontacting transducers, resolution requirements (particularly for encoders), stability and life expectancy, and such general characteristics as mass, size, and power requirements. The environment in which the transducer must operate, is, of course, always an important consideration; generally applicable environmental characteristics (temperature, vibration, etc., effects) should always be stated for displacement transducers.

1.5 FORCE, MASS, AND WEIGHT

This section covers force transducers, which are also used for "weighing" (mass determinations). Force transducers are often referred to as "load cells."

1.5.1 Sensing Methods

Most force transducers employ a sensing element that converts an applied force into a mechanical displacement, typically a deformation of an elastic element, which is then converted into an output signal by a transduction element. Two characteristics of elastic deformation are used to sense force: local strain and gross deflection. A maximum level of each occurs at some location in the sensing element, but not necessarily at the same location, and is then detected by the transduction element (which responds either to strain or to deflection). Force-sensing elements are made of homogeneity-controlled materials, usually some type of steel, and manufactured to very close tolerances. Basic design parameters of force-sensing elements include size and shape, material density, modulus of elasticity, sensitivity in terms of local strain and gross deflection, dynamic response, and effects of loading by the transducer on the measured system. Deflection characteristics and measured-system loading are always more or less modified by an attached mass such as a coupling or a portion of the transduction element.

Sensing elements are almost invariably one of the following types: beams, proving rings, columns, or diaphragms.

Typical configurations of *bending beams* are shown in Figure 1-54. The maximum deflection (δ) of a beam occurs at the point of force application, except for the cantilever beam, where it occurs at its free end. The point of maximum strain in a cantilever beam (of constant section in both planes) is at the fixed end. Cantilever beams can also have a "constant-strength" configuration, that is, a triangularly or parabolically tapered shape, narrowest at the point of force application, in one plane and a constant section in the other plane; the strain is then constant along the top or bottom of the beam. In a simply supported beam the point of maximum local strain is at the point of force application. In a restrained (fixed-end) beam maximum strain occurs at both of the fixed ends as well as (in the opposite direction) at the point of force application.

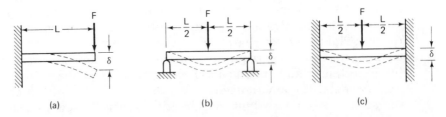

(a)   (b)   (c)

Figure 1-54. Beam force-sensing elements: (a) cantilever; (b) simply supported; (c) restrained.

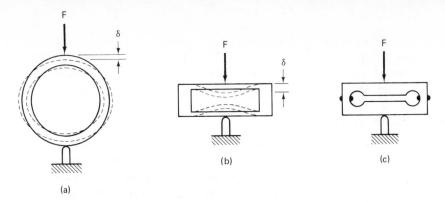

Figure 1-55. Proving-ring force-sensing elements. (a) standard; (b) flat (proving frame); (c) flat with stress concentration holes (dumbell-cut proving frame).

In *proving rings* (sometimes called "proving frames" when of the flat configuration), as illustrated in Figure 1-55, maximum deflection occurs at the point of force application. Maximum strain also occurs at the point of force application, but strain of almost equal magnitude also occurs at points 90° of arc in either direction from the point of force application, and strain sensing is more convenient at these points. Deflection is emphasized in the standard and flat proving rings. Local strain (indicated by black dots) is emphasized in the stress-concentration configuration. The standard proving ring is usually of square or rectangular cross section.

Column force-sensing elements (see Figure 1-56) normally have their point of maximum deflection at their vertical center and their maximum strain at their lateral center. Their characteristics are given primarily by their height-to-width *(L/h)* ratio and, for the hollow cylinder, by wall thickness. Compression *(c)* and tension *(t)* forces are usually sensed as strain (hoop strain in the hollow cylinder), sometimes as changes in magnetic characteristics or natural frequency.

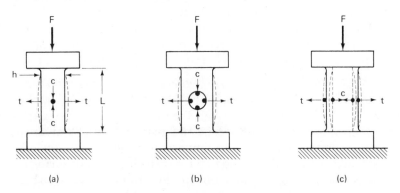

Figure 1-56. Column force-sensing elements: (a) solid cylinder; (b) rectangular with stress-concentration hole; (c) hollow cylinder (strain tube).

Diaphragms (clamped circular plates, see Section 2.6.1) are sometimes used as force-sensing elements. The diaphragm elements have good deflection characteristics and inherently good lateral stability. Maximum deflection and strain occur at the center, where force is always applied.

1.5.2 Design and Operation

1.5.2.1 Capacitive force transducers. A few force transducer designs employ the capacitive transduction principle and deflecting sensing elements. The electrodes are typically connected as the frequency-controlling element in an oscillator so that the transducer provides a frequency-modulated output, which can be sinusoidal or square-wave. At least one design, however, uses the force-balance method and demodulation to provide a dc output.

1.5.2.2 Reluctive force transducers. Reluctive transduction elements, usually LVDT types, sometimes of the inductance-bridge type, are used in force transducers to convert the deflection of sensing elements into an electrical output. LVDT elements respond to the application of bidirectional axial force loads (tension and compression) with changes in output voltage amplitude as well as with a phase reversal when the force changes direction. The sensing and transduction elements are matched so that the linear range of the LVDT corresponds to the deflection of the sensing element for a specified range.

Figure 1-57 shows typical examples of LVDTs used for force transduction. Only the extension spring (Figure 1-57b) is limited to unidirectional (tension) force measurements. The proving ring (Figure 1-57c) and multiple-beam configurations, such as the one shown in Figure 1-57d, are used in commercially available force transducers. Proving rings, however, cause the size of the transducer to be relatively large. Proving rings also exhibit poor lateral stability, and that imposes a requirement for accurate alignment of the applied force vector with their vertical centerline.

Reluctive force transducers have also been designed to use magnetoelasticity, in the stress-concentration section of a rectangular column sensing element, to change the coupling between two windings with variations of permeability, within the column material, due to variations of stress at that location. Essentially all reluctive force transducer designs can be equipped with optional dc-to-ac excitation conversion and ac-to-dc output conversion circuitry.

1.5.2.3 Strain-gage force transducers. Strain-gage force transducers are the most commonly used type, to the extent that, to many workers, the term "load cell" usually implies this type of transducer. Many designs exist for the measurement of compression or tension forces or of both ("universal"). Bonded metal-foil, sometimes metal-wire, gages are most frequently used; semiconductor strain gages are also found in force transducers. Measuring ranges extend from 10 N (1 kp, 2.2 lb$_f$) to 5 MN (500 kp, 1 000 000 lb$_f$). Various beam configurations, flat proving rings (proving frames), and columns are used as sensing elements, the latter typically for high ranges. Many models incorporate overload stops. Threaded male or female end fittings are used; for compression sensing, a load

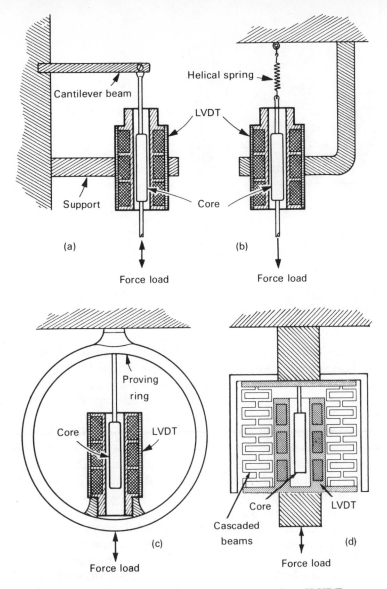

Figure 1-57. Reluctive force transduction: examples of LVDT combined with an elastic member. (Courtesy of Schaevitz Engineering.)

button that has a spherical surface can be threaded on or into an end fitting so that forces need not be applied only axially; other optional end fittings (sometimes furnished integrally machined or permanently assembled) include rod end bearings and clevis fittings.

Typical designs are illustrated in Figure 1-58. The unit shown in Figure 1-58a uses a dual-guided cantilever beam sensing element and a four-active-element strain-gage bridge (most strain-gage force transducers use the latter); it incorporates overload stops and is intended primarily for use in weighing

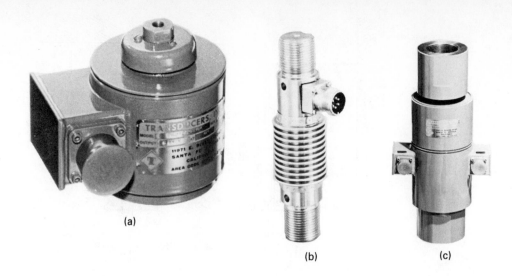

(a)

(b)   (c)

Figure 1-58. Typical strain-gage force transducers: (a) general-purpose, universal, intended for electronic weighing; (b) for tension forces; (c) universal, dual-bridge, for forces up to 5 MN. (Courtesy of Transducers, Inc.)

systems, including those where impact and transient forces must be measured (e.g., conveyor scales and in-motion scales). The tension-force transducer (Figure 1-58b) is meant for installations that are self-aligning (e.g., static monitoring of guy-wire tension, cable overload indicators). The design shown in Figure 1-58c is characterized by high natural frequency, such as is necessary for rocket engine test stands, and is designed for full-scale tension and compression ranges between 2 kN and 5MN (500 to 1×10^6 lb$_f$). The entire sensing element is machined from a single piece of aircraft-grade tool steel. The unit shown is equipped with two independent transduction elements ("dual bridge"), as indicated by the two separate electrical receptacles. Some strain-gage force transducers include three or four such separate strain-gage-bridge elements.

A transducer of somewhat different design is shown in Figure 1-59. The sensing element combines shear stress with a cantilever beam of special design. In this design the maximum bending moment, normally largest at the fixed end of a cantilever beam, is reduced to one-half, without affecting the shear force, by having an extra beam rigidly attached to the free end of the cantilever beam (see Figure 1-59a). The strain gages are attached to a portion of the beam that has been milled out in an "I" shape. The distribution of normal and shear stresses, in response to an applied force, is as shown in Figure 1-59b. A cut-section view (Figure 1-59c) shows two of the four herringbone-pattern strain gages (the other two are on the underside of the beam). The force is recommended to be applied at a point directly over the gages (rather than at the free end of the usual type of cantilever beam); the case is marked with a fine line for showing this point; however, transducer performance will not be affected significantly when the point of force application is displaced. This design has an inherently good linearity. The transducer is normally installed by clamping it at its fixed end (the left end, not shown in Figure 1-59c), which

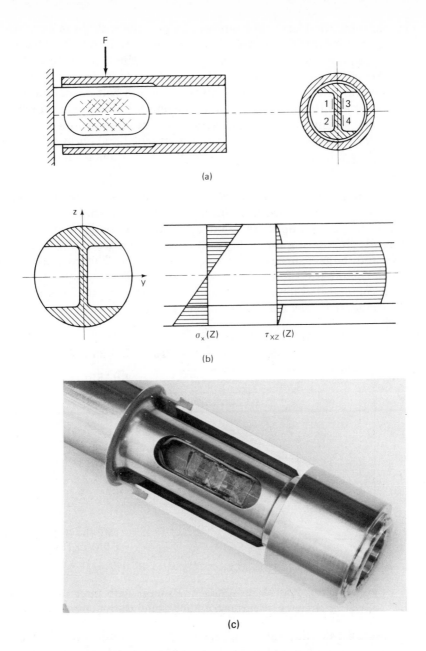

Figure 1-59. Strain-gage force transducer with shear-force sensing element: (a) basic design, showing cylindrical extra beam around cantilever beam and placement of the four strain gages on I-shaped beam; (b) distribution of normal stress (σ) and shear stress (τ) in I-shaped cantilever beam; (c) cut-section view of transducer, with one pair of gages exposed. (Courtesy of AB Bofors, Electronics Div.)

also contains the electrical connector or permits a cable to exit. An arrow is marked on the transducer case so that the case can be rotated, before clamping, to the optimum position for force application (the measuring direction).

Among other versions of strain-gage force transducers are *force washers,* annular transducers suitable for placing under a bolt head, or a nut, typically employing a hollow-column sensing element often just one (¼ bridge) or two (½ bridge) strain gages. A *load beam* is a suitably machined (bending) beam to which strain gages (usually four) are attached and encapsulated, often surrounded by a housing. The load beam has provisions for mounting at both of its ends.

1.5.2.4 *Piezoelectric force transducers.*

Although some measure of near-static response can be obtained from piezoelectric force transducers, when they are used with charge amplifiers, their application is really in the measurement of rapidly fluctuating forces (dynamic force measurement), including impact forces and the measured objects' response to them. These transducers respond only to compression forces; however, they can be mechanically preloaded so that a compression force is continuously exerted on the crystal, constituting a "static level." They can then respond to bidirectionally varying forces.

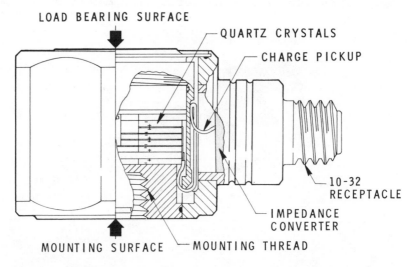

Figure 1-60. Piezoelectric force transducer with integral impedance-converter circuitry. (Courtesy of Sundstrand Data Control, Inc.)

Figure 1-60 illustrates a piezoelectric force transducer. The applied force is exerted, through a preloading member (as indicated by threads), on a stack of quartz crystals, separated by thin electrodes. This design includes circuitry which converts the charge, generated by the crystals across a high impedance, into a voltage at low output impedance. Preloading results in some models having a higher range in compression than in tension. This is also true for most designs of piezoelectric *force links* (see Figure 1-61) which sandwich a quartz force washer (load washer) between two end nuts. A beryllium–copper

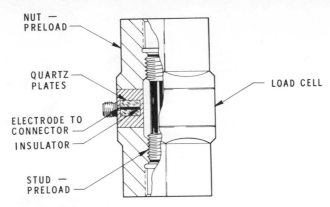

NUT —
PRELOAD

QUARTZ
PLATES

ELECTRODE TO
CONNECTOR

INSULATOR

STUD —
PRELOAD

LOAD CELL

Figure 1-61. Piezoelectric force link. (Courtesy of Sundstrand Data Control, Inc.)

stud fastens the end nuts and preloads the force washer for tension measurements. The end nuts are threaded (female thread) to accept external fittings as required by their installation. Ranges extend from 4.5 kN (1000 lb$_f$) to 120 kN (25 000 lb$_f$) in tension, with compression ranges typically 1.5 of those values.

Piezoelectric *force washers* are force transducers of annular shape which contain one or more annular piezoelectric crystals sandwiched between metallic annuli. In piezoelectric force transducers the combination of metal rings or disks and the crystals, themselves, form the elastic member which responds to applied forces. Most force washers (load washers, load rings) respond only to compression forces. They can be preloaded, to also measure tension, in their installation.

Quartz, in the crystalline form used for piezoelectric elements, is anisotropic (i.e., its properties are different along different directions). Depending on the axis of the crystal along which the slices are cut, disks are obtained which are sensitive only to compression forces (longitudinal piezoelectric effect) or to shear forces in one specific direction (shear piezoelectric effect). These characteristics enable such crystals to be used in *multicomponent force transducers* (see Figures 1-62 and 1-63). With reference to the coordinate system shown in Figure 1-62a, two rings containing disk-shaped crystals can be combined to measure compression *(F$_z$)* and torque *(M$_z$)* simultaneously (Figure 1-62b and c). One ring holds crystals so cut as to utilize the longitudinal effect (compression measurement). The other ring (bottom) holds shear-effect disks which are so oriented that they respond to torque. Compression-sensitive elements can also be combined with shear-sensitive elements in which the disks are so oriented that they respond to F_x or to F_y (Figure 1-63a). Such disks–ring configurations, in which the disks in the rings are paralleled mechanically as well as electrically to multiply sensitivity, can be combined in various two-component transducers. Instead of the disks–ring configuration, whole quartz rings can be used in multicomponent force transducers. The sensitivity of such a ring is not as high as for the paralleled disks. However, somewhat greater sensitivity can be obtained by using them in pairs. Three pairs of whole-quartz

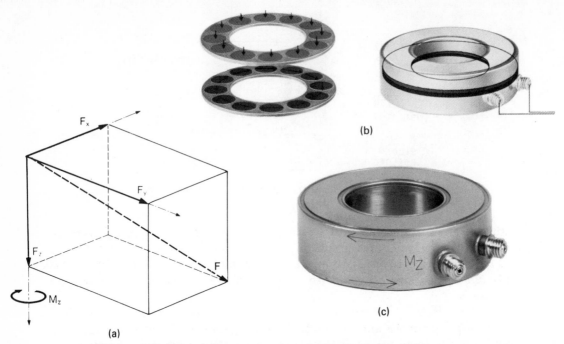

Figure 1-62. Multicomponent force transduction with example of two-component transducer: (a) positive Cartesian coordinate system as used for referencing piezoelectric multicomponent transducers; (b) compression-sensitive (top) and shear-sensitive (bottom) quartz elements in concentric rings arranged for simultaneous measurements of F_z and M_z; (c) two-component (F_z and M_z) force transducer. (Courtesy of Kistler Instrumente A.G.)

rings are employed in the three-component transducer shown in Figure 1-63b and c.

Unless piezoelectric force transducers incorporate integral impedance-conversion (charge-to-voltage conversion) circuitry, they are usually connected to a charge amplifier, an amplifier whose input stage is a dc amplifier, with high input impedance and capacitive negative feedback, which converts the changes in charge (transducer output) into voltage changes. The input stage is then usually followed by an operational amplifier, often one having adjustable negative feedback that permits adjustment of the amplification to the transducer's sensitivity. Voltage amplifiers, with relatively low input impedance, can be used to further amplify the output of transducers with integral impedance converters. Such amplifiers can either be rack-mounted, or otherwise installed in the data-gathering area, or remotely mounted, near the transducer, for unattended operation. In the latter case they must often be packaged to withstand the same environment as the transducer, including impact shocks.

1.5.2.5 Vibrating-element force transducers. Some force transducers have been designed using a wire between two points of a deflecting sensing element. The wire is always in some degree of tension, is located in a permanent mag-

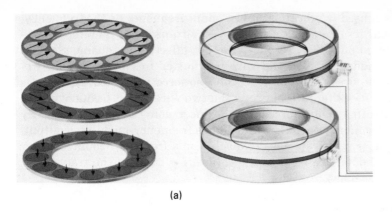

(a)

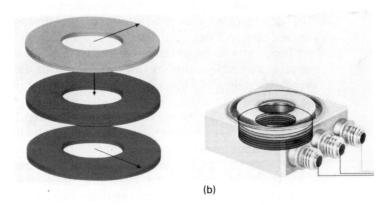

(b)

(c)

Figure 1-63. Multicomponent force transduction with example of three-component transducer: (a) shear-sensitive (F_x and F_y) and pressure (compression)-sensitive quartz-element rings as arranged in two-component (F_x and F_y) and a single-component (F_z) transducer; (b) whole quartz rings for F_x (top), F_z (middle), and F_y (bottom) can be arranged in pairs for a three-component transducer; (c) Three-component transducer provides simultaneous X, Y, and Z outputs. (Courtesy of Kistler Instrumente A.G.)

netic field, and is caused to vibrate at its resonant frequency as the frequency-controlling element in a feedback oscillator. The transducer, therefore, has a frequency-modulated output. A second wire, not affected by sensing-element deflection, can be added. The second wire is adjusted to vibrate at that frequency at which the first wire vibrates when no force is applied. As force is applied, the frequency difference between the two wires (beat frequency) will then increase with increasing force. A transducer using the beat-frequency design provides a frequency output, rather than a frequency-modulated output. A frequency output is relatively easy to display on a frequency counter either as such, or converted, on the basis of the calibration curve of the transducer, into units of force or mass.

1.5.3 Performance Characteristics

The first characteristic to determine for force transducers is whether compression, or tension, or both are to be measured, together with the range (measuring range) and required overload capability (overrange). The range of force transducers (load cells) is sometimes referred to as "capacity."

Force connections and mountings should be defined, in detail, as to dimensions, threads, and for many applications, material of the force connection. When compression buttons (load buttons) are used, their curvature and hardness should be known. The maximum allowable angular misalignment of axial force, applied to the transducer, and, preferably, also the effects on performance of varying amounts of off-axis force application, should be specified.

Overload ratings for force transducers are specified for two conditions: the *safe overload rating* is the overrange force that can be applied to the transducer without causing subsequent performance degradation; the *ultimate overload rating* is the (maximum) force that can be applied without causing structural failure of the transducer (or portions of it). Side loads can be specified in the same manner.

Besides the usually specified electrical characteristics (which depend largely on the type of transduction used as well as on use of any additional conditioning circuitry within the transducer) and performance characteristics, *creep* and *creep recovery* are sometimes required to be known. *Creep at load* is the change in output occurring with time under rated load, with all other conditions remaining constant. *Creep recovery* is the change in no-load (zero-measurand) output occurring with time after removal of rated load at which creep at load was determined.

The normally specified dynamic characteristics are influenced by the amount of maximum sensing element deflection, at the upper range limit (*deflection factor*). The deflection factor is sometimes specified to facilitate determining relative dynamic characteristics (a low deflection factor is typical for fast response).

Among environmental characteristics, one that must be considered for force transducers in some applications (besides the usually specified environmental characteristics) is *ambient-pressure error*. Any case deformations due to changes in ambient pressure can cause sensing element deflections not indicative of force. Ambient-pressure error can become quite apparent particularly in hermetically sealed transducers, when they are exposed to pressures approaching a vacuum or when they are exposed to high ambient pressures (e.g., in underwater applications).

1.6 TORQUE

1.6.1 Sensing Methods

In-line torque-sensing elements for use with rotating shafts are special sensing shafts *(torsion bars, torque bars)* inserted between power source and load (power sink). When torque, the product of force *(F)* and moment arm *(l)*, is applied to a cylindrical shaft (see Figure 1-64) at one end while the other end is held

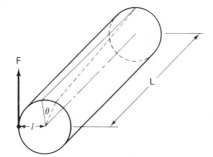

Figure 1-64. Shaft twisting due to torque.

fixed, the shaft will undergo torsional twisting. If a line were scribed on the surface of the shaft, parallel to the axis of rotation, this line would become a portion of a helix. The deflection angle at the input side of the shaft (θ) is proportional to torque and shaft length *(L)* and inversely proportional to (theoretically) the fourth power of the diameter *(D,* or *2l)* and to the modulus of shaft rigidity. The shaft is also subjected to shear stress. Hence, in-line torsion-sensing elements exhibit angular displacement as well as strain, both of which can be converted into output signals by appropriate transduction methods.

Torsion bars typically incorporate a necked-down section, either round or square in cross section (see Figure 1-65). The square configuration is favored in strain-gage torque transducers. It makes the gages easier to mount, enables

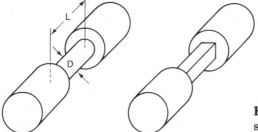

Figure 1-65. Round and square torsion bars.

solder joints between gage and lead wires to be located at the corners of the shaft (where torsion strains are zero), provides a relatively higher resonant frequency, and is less affected by side loads.

Reaction torque is the torque required to prevent the stator of a rotary device from turning with the rotor (e.g., the housing of a generator from rotating with the driven rotor). It can be measured by mounting the housing on bearings, so that it is free to rotate, then attaching a lever arm *(reaction arm)* to the housing and connecting a force transducer between the end of that arm and mechanical "ground," the surface to which the outer portion of the bearing is attached (see Figure 1-66). One or more force sensors can be used in such *reaction-torque dynamometers.* Reaction-torque sensors can also have the sensing and transduction elements incorporated within their case, so that they measure torque between a "driven" and a "fixed" mounting flange.

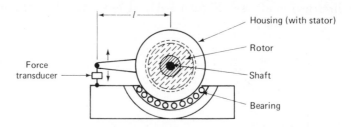

Figure 1-66. Reaction-torque sensing.

1.6.2 Design and Operation

Although various transduction methods have been employed in torque sensors, including the potentiometric method, most practical torque transducers use either reluctive or strain-gage transduction (the latter is most widely used) or methods utilizing the difference in angular displacement between the two ends of a torsion bar to obtain a phase-difference measurement (photoelectrically, electromagnetically, or inductively) or a variable-illumination measurement.

1.6.2.1 Reluctive torque transducers. Torque measurements can be made using the angular deflection of a torsion bar to actuate a linear variable differential transformer (LVDT) through a stiff arm attached radially to the torsion bar, or through a cantilever beam attached similarly. Another method uses a rotary variable differential transformer (RVDT) to sense the angular displacement of the torsion bar or of two facing disks mutually spring-loaded in the plane of rotation. However, better results have been obtained with designs using changes in coupling introduced in either a torsion bar or in a member linked to it, mainly because this obviates the need for slip rings since the primary and secondary windings can then be located on the stationary rather than the rotating member of the device.

One such design is the *torsional variable differential transformer (TVDT)* illustrated in Figure 1-67. The torsion bar (or shaft) is made of nonmagnetic material but has attached to it three tubular sections of a ferromagnetic ma-

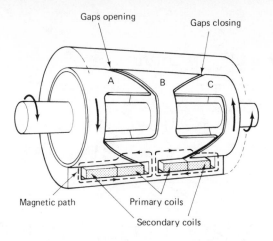

Figure 1-67. Torsional variable differential transformers. (Courtesy Lebow Associates, Inc.)

terial (A, B, C), with gaps, between the center section (B) and the two end sections (A and C), at 45° to the shaft axis. When torque is applied to the shaft ends, one gap will tend to widen and the other gap will tend to close. The reluctance in the gaps will increase and decrease correspondingly and change the coupling between the primary and secondary windings so that one secondary will show a voltage increase, whereas the other secondary will show a voltage decrease. Associated signal conditioning circuitry then uses these outputs to produce a signal whose magnitude is proportional to torque and whose polarity is indicative of the direction of the torque.

Several torque transducer designs use the variations in permeability, due to stress, in a ferromagnetic shaft. The principle underlying this form of operation is illustrated in Figure 1-68. An applied torque creates internal stresses which alter the permeability of the material, as shown, and thus change the coupling between a primary winding (P) and two secondary windings (S_1 and S_2) in an X-shaped coil assembly or an assembly of three multipole-coil rings. The production of output signals from the secondaries, and the conversion of the signals into a signal indicative of torque magnitude as well as direction, is similar to that described previously for the TVDT.

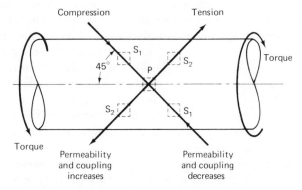

Figure 1-68. Operating principle of variable-permeability reluctive torque transducer.

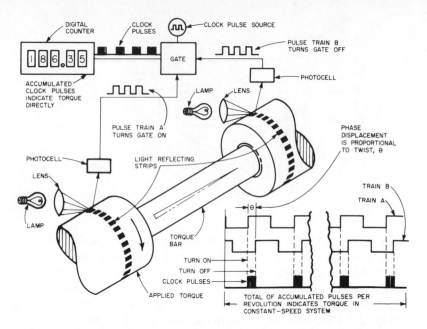

Figure 1-69. Photoelectric torque transducer using phase-displacement method. (Courtesy of Vibrac Corp.)

1.6.2.2 Photoelectric torque transducers. In these types of transducers, light beams, code patterns, and light sensors are used to convert the differential angular displacement between the two ends of a torsion bar, due to applied torque, into an output signal.

A design using the phase-displacement method is illustrated in Figure 1-69. Each end of the torsion bar (torque bar) carries a code pattern made of light-reflecting strips. The patterns are illuminated by collimated light beams and the reflected light is sensed by a light sensor (photocell). The output of each light sensor, then, is a pulse train. With differential angular deflection between the two coded ends of the torsion bar, due to applied torque, the two pulse trains show a difference of phase (synchronism) relative to each other; this phase difference is proportional to torque. The phase difference can be converted into an analog output. However, the nature of the signals lends itself to providing a digital output, as illustrated. Leading edges of one train of pulses gate oscillator clock signals into a digital counter, while the leading edges of the other pulse train gate the clock pulses off. The counter's accumulated total in a given sampling interval, assuming constant shaft speed, is then proportional to phase (time) displacement between the two pulse trains, hence proportional to torque. More complex provisions are required when the shaft speed is not constant.

Photoelectric torque transducers using the variable-illumination method (see Figure 1-70) provide an analog output proportional to torque without use of conditioning or digital circuitry. Two identical code disks, of the same type as used in incremental angular encoders, are attached to the two ends of a

Solid-Mechanical Quantities

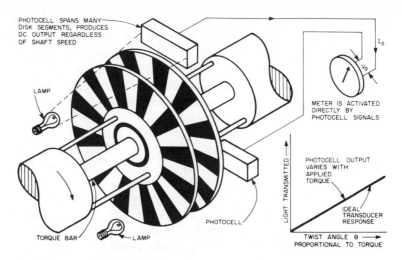

Figure 1-70. Photoelectric torque transducer using variable-illumination method. (Courtesy of Vibrac Corp.)

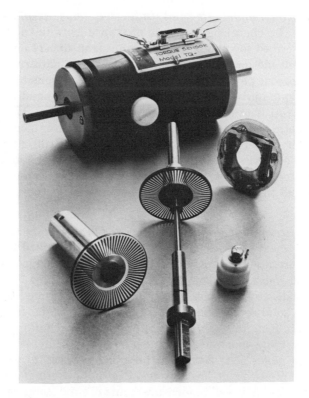

Figure 1-71. Variable-illumination torque transducer and its major internal elements. (Courtesy of Vibrac Corp.)

torsion bar. A light beam passes through both disks and to a light sensor. Relative angular displacement between the two disks, due to torque, changes the amount of "window area," the total area provided by transparent segments of both disks, and hence the amount of light incident upon the light sensor. Two light-source and sensor combinations are used to double the effect.

The output of the two parallel-connected light sensors is adequate for direct display on commercially available microammeters. Figure 1-71 shows a torque transducer, using this principle, and its major elements. The two disks are initially positioned so that they provide a 50% overlap between transparent segments at zero applied torque. Clockwise torque will then increase the window area and resulting output current, whereas counterclockwise torque reduces window area and output current. This enables the output signal to be also indicative of torque direction. The light sensors span several disk segments; this minimizes flicker and assures a very low harmonic content in the output current regardless of shaft speed. A bias source with an adjustable resistor can be used to neutralize the zero-torque output current and then provide a bipolar output current that can be displayed (e.g., on a center-zero meter).

1.6.2.3 Electromagnetic and inductive phase-displacement torque transducers.
The operating principle of transducers in this category is similar to that described for photoelectric torque transducers employing the phase-displacement method. However, the optical code pattern is replaced by either a magnetic code pattern or by gearlike "teeth." A sensing coil assembly is placed in close proximity to each of the two torsion-bar shaft ends so equipped. If the sensing coil is of the electromagnetic type, the "teeth" must be made of ferromagnetic materials and the transducer requires some finite minimum shaft speed for proper operation. When the sensing coil assemblies are of the inductive, eddy-current type, the "teeth" can be of any metallic material. As for the photoelectric transducer described, each coil assembly produces a pulse train, and the phase difference between the two pulse trains is proportional to torque.

1.6.2.4 Strain-gage torque transducers.
Transducers using strain gages to respond to shear stresses in torsion bars, due to applied torque, are widely used to measure a wide range of torques in numerous applications. Round torsion bars and, more frequently, square torsion bars, or their design derivatives have strain gages, typically metal-foil gages, bonded to them (see Figure 1-72). The solid round shaft is still used, at times, for measuring ranges above about 56 N·m (500 lb$_f$·in). Hollow circular shafts provide more bending strength. Flats, machined into the hollow shafts, facilitate the proper mounting of strain gages. The cruciform torsion bar tends to produce relatively high amounts of strain at low torques. The hollow cruciform configuration lends itself particularly well to measurements of small torques. Each of the four bars in such a *torsion frame* is subjected to torsion as well as bending in response to an applied torque, providing a relatively high torsional sensitivity together with good bending strength. The solid square torsion bar is used in high-range

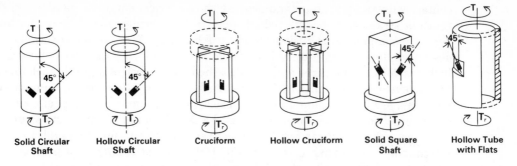

Figure 1-72. Torsion bar configurations for strain-gage torque transducers. (Courtesy of Lebow Associates, Inc.)

torque sensors; it offers ease of gage attachment and increased bending strength compared to round shafts.

Semiconductor strain gages are used in some torque transducer designs. Regardless of the type of gage used, the four strain gages are always connected as a four-active-arm bridge. The four terminals of this bridge circuit can be connected to slip rings. Brushes, typically made of silver graphite, are in

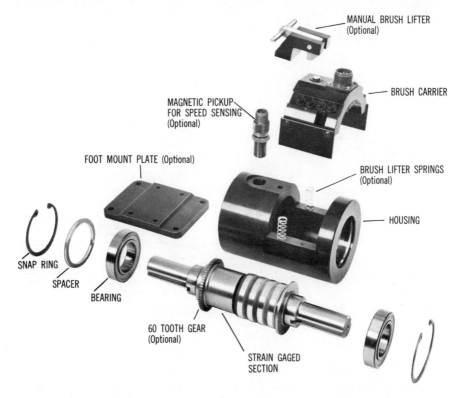

Figure 1-73. Strain-gage torque transducer with slip rings. (Courtesy of Lebow Associates, Inc.)

contact with the slip rings and provide the electrical connections between the rotating strain-gage bridge (which may include bridge-adjustment and temperature-compensation resistors) and the housing of the torque transducer. A design employing slip rings is illustrated in Figure 1-73. This particular design includes optional features such as a toothed-rotor electromagnetic tachometer and a device that permits lifting the brushes off the slip rings when no measurements are being made, to extend the operating life of both sets of contacts. The contact force of the brushes must be large enough to avoid noise due to brush bounce and variations in contact resistance, but small enough to avoid introducing measuring errors in the torque measurement. Slip rings and brushes require periodic cleaning as well as brush replacement.

The need for brushes and slip rings is obviated when a rotary transformer is used for noncontacting coupling of excitation and output to and from the rotating strain-gage bridge (see Figure 1-74). The carrier system electronics

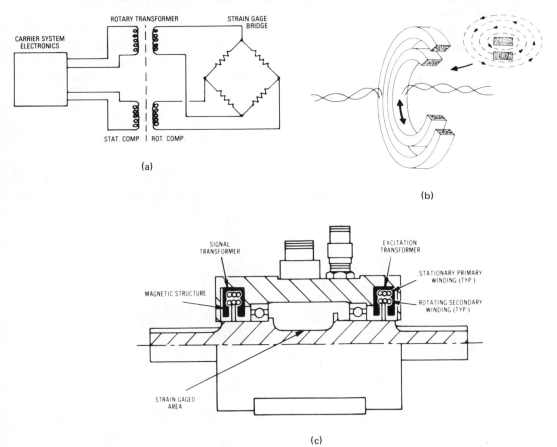

(a)

(b)

(c)

Figure 1-74. Use of rotary transformers in strain-gage torque transducers: (a) functional schematic diagram; (b) coupling between a stationary and a rotating coil; (c) internal construction of transducer. (Courtesy of Lebow Associates, Inc.)

Solid-Mechanical Quantities

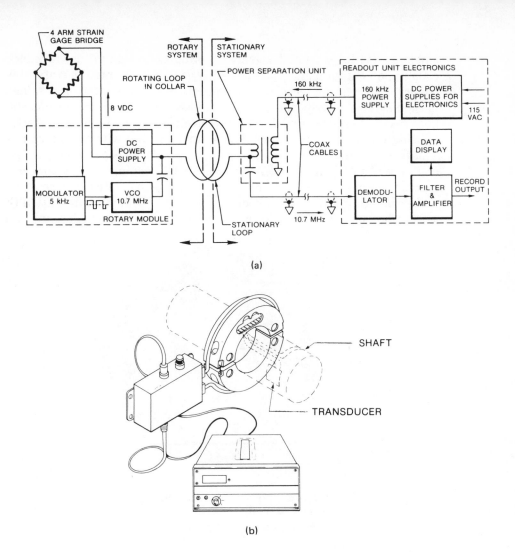

Figure 1-75. Inductive RF coupling between rotating and stationary portions of a torque measuring system: (a) functional block diagram; (b) system installation: rotating loop is contained, together with rotating electronics, in a collar of insulating material, clamped to strain-gaged shaft (torsion bar). (Courtesy of ACUREX Autodata.)

contain an oscillator which provides ac excitation, at 3 kHz or higher, to the excitation primary in the stationary component, from which it is coupled to the excitation winding of the rotary component (Figure 1-74a). The output of the strain-gage bridge is similarly coupled to an amplifier–demodulator in the electronics module. The transformers are a pair of concentrically wound coils, with one coil rotating within (or beside) the stationary coil (Figure 1-74b). High-permeability cores aid flux concentration and improve the coupling between coils. Figure 1-74c shows the layout of the major components in a rotary-transformer type of strain-gage torque sensor.

An alternative method of noncontacting coupling (Figure 1-75) uses a single pair of loops for inductively coupling excitation to the transducer and coupling an output-signal-modulated RF signal back into the stationary electronics. The rotating electronics module is in the form of a split collar which is clamped to the shaft and to which the strain-gage bridge is connected.

Reaction-torque transducers measure the torque required to restrain the housing (or stator) of a rotary device from turning with its rotary member. This torque is detected by a force sensor attached between mechanical "ground" (e.g., top of test bench) and a "moment arm" leading to that portion of the reaction-torque sensor mounted to the device being tested. The sensor can be provided with a coupling shaft or it can have a hollow configuration (Figure 1-76). The housing of the latter is mounted to mechanical "ground" and the

Figure 1-76. Reaction-torque sensor (with hollow configuration). (Courtesy of Lebow Associates, Inc.)

annular sensing flange is bolted to the housing of the device under test whose drive shaft extends through the torque sensor. Te moment arm–force sensor combination is typically achieved by torque-sensitive flexures whose strain is transduced by strain gages. The angular displacement of the coupling shaft or sensing flange of a reaction-torque transducer is in order of 0.2 to 1.0° for full-range reaction torque.

1.6.3 Performance Criteria

Among mechanical design characteristics essential to torque transducers is the type of coupling between sensor and measured object, typically the coupling between two shafts. Various types of rigid couplings are used, including those employing keyways machined into both shafts and a key connecting them, with the key retained by a housing. Some applications (Figure 1-77), mainly those where the sensor is driven or loaded by a power transfer system based

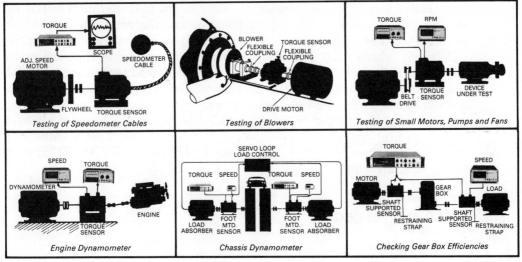

(a)

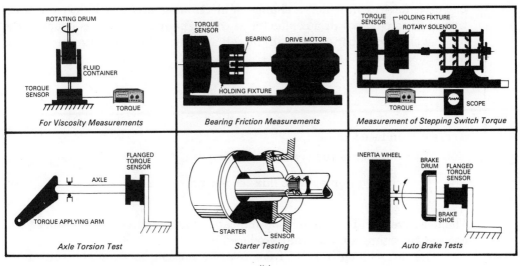

(b)

Figure 1-77. Selected typical applications of torque sensors: (a) some uses of in-line rotating-shaft torque sensors: (b) examples of uses of reaction-torque sensors. (Courtesy of Lebow Associates, Inc.)

on use of pulleys, belts, or gear trains, which can induce high bending loads, require flexible couplings. For torque transducers incorporating bearings, bearing life, bearing loading, and bearing lubrication require attention, as do brushes and slip rings in sensors so equipped. Moment of inertia, torsional stiffness, shaft runout and axial end float are often required to be known or specified.

Torque **141**

Other characteristics, besides those applicable to transducers in general and comprising mechanical and electrical design characteristics as well as performance characteristics (which are also dependent on transduction principle used), which need attention when considering torque transducers for given applications, are the *critical speed* of the shaft of the sensor (at which the shaft becomes dynamically unstable and irreversible damage can result) and the sensor's response to *torsional vibration*, the oscillatory or fluctuating components of the torque being measured. The *maximum speed* of a torque transducer is always given as well below the critical speed. Torque measuring ranges extend from below 0.1 N·m (about 10 oz$_f$ -in) to over 340 kN·m (3 × 10^6 lb$_f$ -in), full scale.

1.7 SPEED AND VELOCITY

1.7.1 Sensing Methods

Linear velocity, when measured in situ, is most commonly sensed by electromagnetic devices in which a change of electromagnetic flux induces an electromotive force (*emf*) in a conductor (a coil). The induced emf is equal to the product of the number of turns in the coil and the change in magnetic flux per unit time, or

$$e = -N \frac{d\phi}{dt}$$

where e = induced emf

   N = number of turns in the winding

   $\dfrac{d\phi}{dt}$ = change in magnetic flux (ϕ) per unit time (t)

The negative sign in the equation indicates that the direction of induced emf opposes the change of flux that produced it.

The flux change results from relative motion between the coil and a permanent magnet. The coil can be fixed, with the magnet moving axially within it, or the coil can be the moving element and the magnet the stationary element. This sensing method is usually applied to the measurement of bidirectionally fluctuating or oscillatory motion.

Linear speed is also measured by sensing speed of rotation and then calculating the translational linear speed, based on knowledge of the radius of the rotating sensing device. Linear speed (c) is the product of speed in rotation (n) and the radius (r) of the rotating member, or $c = nr$, where n is typically expressed in revolutions per second (r/s). This method is used, for example, in "measuring whels," which can be attached to a spring-loaded arm, on a vehicle such as a car, so that they are pressed against the road and rotate with vehicle motion, or they can be pressed against a continuously moving material in a production facility, such as wire, paper, textiles, or steel sheet in a rolling mill, and then provide an output indicative of the speed at which the material moves.

Since acceleration is the time rate of change of velocity, velocity can also be determined by integrating the output of an accelerometer. In many accelerometer applications, integrating circuitry is added to the signal-conditioning circuitry so that outputs are provided in terms of both acceleration and velocity.

Remote sensing of linear velocity is usually performed by devices utilizing the *Doppler effect,* the effect upon the apparent frequency of a wave train produced by relative motion between the source of the wave train and an observer. This effect is the cause for the apparent change in pitch of the sound made by a vehicle moving first toward, then away from an observer. Doppler shifts, as shifts in the spectrum lines in the light emitted from a star ("red shift," "blue shift") are used to determine the relative velocity between the star and earth (where the light is observed). Shifts in the frequency of radio waves transmitted (or transponded coherently with earth-sent radio waves) from a spacecraft are used to determine the velocity of the spacecraft (and its position, by integration). In most Doppler-based remote velocity sensing, however, it is the shift in the frequency transmitted toward, and reflected by a moving object, with the observer at the location of the transmitting and receiving apparatus.

In the reflected-wave method, the frequency of the wave returned from an object traveling at a velocity v is equal to $(f \pm f_D)$, where f is the frequency of the transmitted wave (and of the reflected wave if the object were standing still) and f_D is the frequency shift due to the Doppler effect, with the polarity given by the direction of motion of the object. The Doppler shift, f_D, is given by the velocity component of the object in the direction of propagation of the electromagnetic wave, v', and the wavelength, λ, of this radiation, by $f_D = 2v'/\lambda$. When the reflected wave is compared with the transmitted wave, the velocity of the object can be calculated. When the reflected wave is superimposed upon a portion of the transmitted wave, the Doppler shift can be recorded directly. Interferometric methods have been employed for such direct Doppler-shift determinations. Wavelengths in various portions of the electromagnetic spectrum have been used. Examples are radio frequencies used by continuous wave (*CW*) or pulsed *Doppler radars* (such radar systems are used to police speeding vehicles) and optical frequencies used by CW or pulsed lasers ("laser Doppler velocimeters"). Frequencies in the sonic or ultrasonic range are used not only for determinations of the velocity of underwater vehicles but also for measuring the velocity of sound through liquids as such.

Vertical speed sensing, on aircraft, is performed by differentiating the output of a pressure–altitude transducer (or radar altimeter) so as to indicate vertical speed as the time rate of change of altitude.

Angular-speed sensing (*tachometry*) is used in a very large number of applications. Contacting as well as noncontacting methods are used to measure the speed of rotation of either a shaft or of another portion of a rotating system. These methods are described in Section 1.7.2.

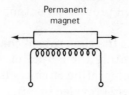

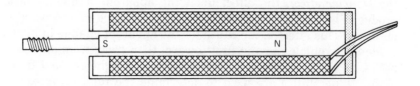

Figure 1-78. Single-coil, shaft-coupled electromagnetic linear-velocity transducer.

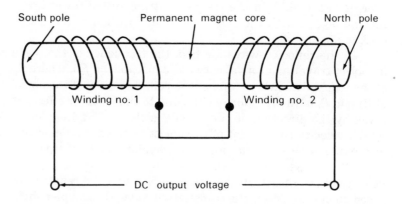

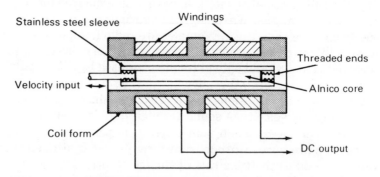

Figure 1-79. Dual-coil electromagnetic linear-velocity transducer. (Courtesy of Schaevitz Engineering.)

Solid-Mechanical Quantities

1.7.2 Design and Operation

1.7.2.1 Electromagnetic linear-velocity transducers. In its simplest form, this type of transducer consists of a coil in a stainless-steel housing and a coaxial cylindrical permanent magnet (core) attached to a shaft with a threaded end (Figure 1-78). The core moves, within the coil, with the motion of the object to which the shaft end is mounted and produces an output, in the coil, proportional to velocity. Another linear velocity transducer design is shown in Figure 1-79; it differs from the basic version in that it contains two coils. The windings are connected out of phase in a series-opposing arrangement. The opposite voltages are summed so that the total induced voltage is proportional to core velocity.

A slightly different principle is used in the fixed-coil design shown in Figure 1-80. A permanent magnet is supported between two springs. Gold–palladium alloy bearing rings are pressed onto the ends of the cylindrical magnet to minimize friction as it moves within a chrome-plated stainless-steel sleeve. Threaded retainers seal the ends of the mechanical assembly. The entire transducer is intended to be mounted to an object whose oscillatory velocity is to be measured. When the frequency of this motion exceeds the natural frequency of the suspended system (about 15 Hz) the magnet remains in an essentially undisturbed position. The coil, fixed within the transducer case, moves, relative to the now stationary magnet, with the motion of the

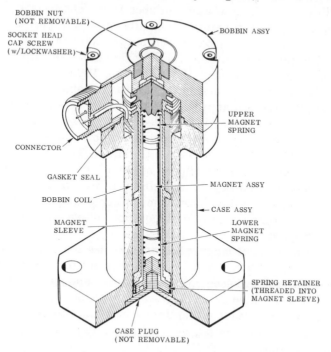

Figure 1-80. Electromagnetic linear-velocity transducer. (Courtesy of CEC Division/Bell & Howell Co.)

measured object. The resulting flux rate of change produces an output from the coil. The output is proportional to velocity. Other designs have the coil as part of a moving structure pivoted at bearings within the transducer assembly. The coil moves within a magnetic field established by the pole pieces of a fixed permanent magnet, and the resulting flux changes produce an output, proportional to velocity, in the moving coil.

1.7.2.2 Other linear-velocity sensing devices.

1.7.2.2 Other linear-velocity sensing devices. Translational devices such as "measuring wheels" use wheels or disks, whose radii are known, attached to tachometers of various designs. Tachometer designs are described below. Devices that sense linear velocity remotely, notably the Doppler-effect devices whose sensing method was briefly described in Section 1.7.1, and which include Doppler sonars, Doppler radars, and laser Doppler velocimeters, will not be described further here. Detailed descriptions of such instrument systems can be found in current technical literature.

1.7.2.3 Electromagnetic tachometer generators. Three types of electric generators are used as tachometers. They provide an output voltage and, in the case of the permanent-magnet ac tachometer, an output frequency proportional to angular speed.

Dc tachometer generators use either a permanent magnet (*dc magneto*) or a separately excited winding as its stator and a conventional generator winding on the commutator-equipped rotor. The brushes associated with the commutator require maintenance after a certain period of use. However, an advantage of these devices is that output polarity is indicative of direction of shaft rotation. The output of a dc magneto is typically 3 to 7 V, that of the stator-winding type about 10 to 20 V, per 1000 r/min.

Ac induction tachometers operate as variable-coupling transformers, with the coupling coefficient proportional to rotary speed. When the primary (input) winding, on the stator, is provided with ac excitation, an ac voltage, at the excitation frequency, appears across the output terminals of the secondary winding, which is also located on the stator. The rotor is usually either of the squirrel-cage type or cup-shaped and made of a high-conductance metal such as copper, copper alloy, or aluminum (*drag-cup tachometer*). Shaft rotation produces a shift of flux distribution which changes the coupling between primary and secondary so that the output voltage amplitude is proportional to angular speed.

Ac permanent-magnet tachometers use the flux changes between a permanent-magnet rotor and a stator winding to provide an ac output which varies with rotary speed both in amplitude and frequency. This type of device has also been called an *ac magneto*. Signal-conditioning circuitry can be used to convert the output either into a non-amplitude-dependent frequency (or pulse-rate) output signal, or into a non-frequency-dependent dc amplitude-varying signal.

1.7.2.4 Toothed-rotor electromagnetic tachometers. Tachometers using a ferromagnetic rotor having the configuration of a gear, or with symmetrically spaced toothlike protrusions, in conjunction with an electromagnetic transduction coil (proximity sensor) are quite commonly used. Transduction-coil assemblies can be of the Hall-effect type, or they can be of the inductive, eddy-current type, in which case the rotor material need not be ferromagnetic but only metallic (and the sensor output amplitude is not significantly affected by rotary speed). Most sensing-transduction coil assemblies, however, are of the electromagnetic type illustrated in Figure 1-81. The coil, which is made of thin magnet wire, is wound around an insulating bobbin form which is slipped over a pole piece attached to the permanent magnet. The assembly is potted within a shell, usually hermetically sealed. The front portion of the shell is often threaded, for ease of sensor installation and the adjustment of the gap between pole piece and rotor teeth. The rotor or, at least, the rotor teeth are made of a ferromagnetic material, typically a magnetic steel. The pole piece conducts a magnetic-flux path from the magnet, creating a magnetic field in front of

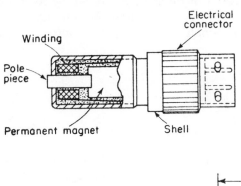

Figure 1-81. Electromagnetic transduction coil assembly.

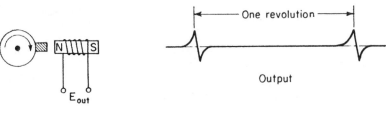

Figure 1-82. Operating principle of electromagnetic, frequency-output tachometer: (a) single-tooth; (b) continuous teeth.

the sensor. When a ferromagnetic tooth passes through this field, the resulting flux change induces an emf in the coil. When the rotating object, whose angular speed is to be measured, is equipped with a single tooth, an output pulse is created once per revolution (see Figure 1-82a). With increasing angular speed the number of pulses per unit time increases proportionally. The pulse rate can then be displayed [e.g., directly on an EPUT (events-per-unit-time) meter]. The increasing rate of change of magnetic flux also produces increasing pulse amplitudes and the amplitude of the output signal is also indicative of angular speed, at least over a portion of the speed range, with varying amounts of linearity.

A greater number of teeth on the rotor produces more pulses per unit time (more pulses per revolution), as illustrated in Figure 1-82b. Continuous teeth are used most frequently. Other rotor shapes include the "Maltese cross" and specially configured cam. Typical configurations, and the waveshapes produced by them, are illustrated in Figure 1-83. It can be seen that gear teeth can be so machined ("fine tooth gear") that the output signal is very close to sinusoidal. This is desirable when a pure frequency output is required by the data system.

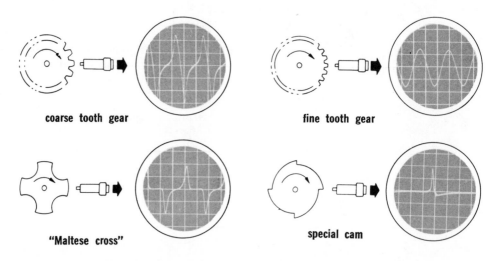

coarse tooth gear

fine tooth gear

"Maltese cross"

special cam

Figure 1-83. Waveshapes produced by various rotor configurations: (a) coarse tooth gear; (b) fine tooth gear; (c) "Maltese cross"; (d) special cam. (Courtesy of Electro Corp.)

The electromagnetic coil assembly must be so installed that there is no magnetic barrier between the pole piece and the rotor. It is best to install them so that there is no barrier of any sort between the two. If the rotor assembly must be sealed from the ambient environment, the coil assembly itself and its mounting provisions can usually provide this seal. If a barrier is still required, the magnetic path from the pole piece can be extended by mounting a soft-steel pin through the barrier (which must still be nonmagnetic) and pressing the pole piece against the outside end of this pin. The sensor must also be so

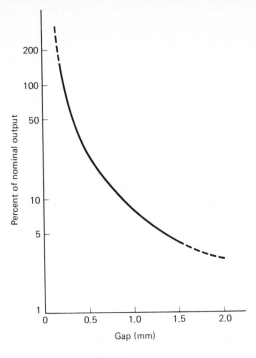

Figure 1-84. Variation of output amplitude with gap between pole piece and rotor teeth.

positioned that the pole piece is as close as possible to the rotor teeth, without, however, causing potential physical contact, including binding due to thermal expansion or unevenness of tooth surfaces. The output pulse amplitude drops sharply with increasing gap (see Figure 1-84), since output is inversely proportional to the square of the gap distance.

The standard pole-piece configuration is cylindrical. However, depending on the application and on the tooth configuration, other shapes may be more suitable. Other available shapes are the conical and the chisel configuration (see Figure 1-85). The chisel point aids in providing a higher output and better resolution in conjunction with fine gear teeth. The conical tip does the same, but to a lesser extent; however, it poses no requirements for orientation that apply to the chisel tip; orientation also makes the gap adjustment more difficult.

Some angular-speed measuring systems require two sensing-coil assemblies, either to provide signals to two different portions of the system or (when the two coils are mounted 90° apart) to obtain a phase difference that can be converted into an indication of direction of rotation by means of digital logic circuitry. Coil assemblies have also been designed with integral signal-con-

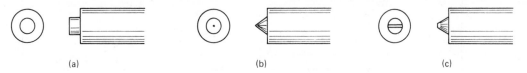

(a)   (b)   (c)

Figure 1-85. Pole-piece configurations: (a) cylindrical pole piece: (b) conical pole piece; (c) chisel pole piece. (Courtesy of Electro Corp.)

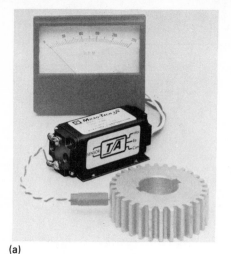

(a)

Figure 1-86. Electromagnetic tachometer with frequency-to-dc conversion: (a) measuring system with toothed rotor, sensing coil assembly connected to frequency-to-dc converter, and dc meter; (b) typical block diagram illustrating frequency-to-voltage conversion; (c) typical waveform diagrams. (Courtesy of Electro Corp.)

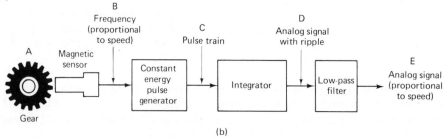

(b)

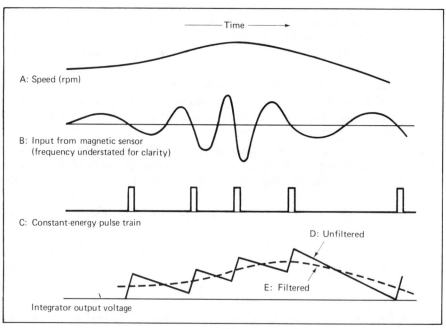

(c)

ditioning circuitry which converts the coil-output pulses, of various shapes, into square-shaped pulses suitable as inputs to digital data systems. Coil assemblies so equipped typically have three interface connections, an excitation "+" terminal (somewhere between 5 and 15 V dc), a common terminal for excitation and output, and an output terminal which provides the square-wave pulses (with between 0 and 0.2 V indicating a "0" and between 3 and 14 V indicating a "1") referred to the common terminal.

When a dc signal is needed by the data system (which can be a simple system with direct analog display on a dc meter), a *frequency-to-dc converter* can be inserted between the sensing coil and the display device or data system. As illustrated in Figure 1-86, such a converter converts the coil-output pulses into constant-energy pulses at the same rate. The pulse train is then electronically integrated to provide a dc voltage proportional to angular speed. The resulting signal may also be fed to a comparator to determine if the angular speed is above or below a certain set point or narrow range of speeds.

1.7.2.5 Electro-optical tachometers. Angular velocity is often measured by photoelectric sensing devices using either the transmittance or reflectance method (see Section 1.4.2.9). The former is used primarily in tachometers that are essentially identical to *incremental angular encoders* with a continuous (360°) coding pattern (see Section 1.4.2.7). Solid-shaft as well as hollow-shaft designs are available. Depending on the geometry of the coding pattern, the output can be either square-wave (TTL-compatible digital) or sinusoidal. Two reading heads are used when quadrature output is required to indicate direction of rotation in addition to angular velocity.

The *reflectance method* is used in a variety of angular-speed sensing systems. The sensing head, which can be hand-held or mounted, contains a light source that emits a collimated beam toward a reflective portion or spot on the rotating object and a light sensor that detects a light pulse whenever the beam is reflected back. Some rotating members have inherently reflective, symmetrically spaced members (e.g., spokes of a wheel). Most rotating objects will require a piece of reflecting tape to be affixed to them (or several symmetrically spaced pieces of tape if count multiplication is required). The output of the light sensor is then a count of revolutions, of the measured object, which can easily be converted into r/s or r/min either by integration to produce an analog signal or by using digital logic for comparison with clock-generated pulses to produce a digital output signal.

Figure 1-87 shows a photoelectric tachometer with direct analog display on the portable, battery-operated indicator. The sensing head, which is connected to the signal-conditioning and display unit by a cable, is shown held by a clip at the top of the unit. Other designs, which frequently are also portable, provide a digital display, usually in r/min, mostly without the need for manual range selection. Fiber optics are also used to carry emitted and reflected light to and from the point of measurement, an advantage when this point is not readily accessible.

A different, but widely used, method of measuring angular speed is offered

Figure 1-87. Portable photoelectric tachometry system. (Courtesy of Power Instruments, Inc.)

by the use of a stroboscope. This method includes the observer in the measuring loop. A stroboscope employs a cold-cathode gas-filled lamp as a source for high-intensity light flashes. The flashes are used to illuminate the rotating object. The number of flashes per minute is subject to continuous manual adjustment. They are then adjusted until the rotating member appears stationary. This occurs when one flash is emitted for each cycle of motion, that is, each full revolution of a rotating object (the stroboscope can also be used to detect nonrotational motion). The number of flashes per minute (corresponding to revolutions per minute) is either read out on a dial attached to the flash-rate adjusting knob or it can be displayed in digital form, as on the stroboscope shown in Figure 1-88, which also shows the typical use of this sensing device.

1.7.2.6 Other angular-speed sensing devices. A number of other types of tachometers have been designed and used at various times, but are not used very commonly. They will be described briefly below.

Capacitive tachometers use rotor plates attached to or machined integrally with the shaft. One, two, or four stator plates are shaped to comply with the rotor electrode configuration. Capacitance changes occur periodically with shaft rotation. When the electrodes are connected into an ac bridge, the bridge output voltage will undergo corresponding changes.

Strain-gage-type tachometers employ a cantilever beam, to which strain gages are bonded, and an eccentric disk or cam attached to the rotating shaft. The beam is in continuous contact with the perimeter of the disk or cam and deflects once per revolution. By appropriate design of the disk or cam a sinusoidal output can be obtained from the strain-gage bridge.

Switch-type tachometers involve the making and breaking of contacts. Magnetic reed switches can be used, actuated by a magnet attached to the

Solid-Mechanical Quantities

(a)

(b)

Figure 1-88. Stroboscope tachometer: (a) stroboscope (with digital readout); (b) "freeze-motion" method of measuring angular velocity. (Courtesy of Power Instruments, Inc.)

rotating shaft or other member. One design uses a pair of rotating contacts between which a capacitor is connected so that it is alternatingly charged with voltages of opposite polarity; the stationary contacts are connected across a dc source in series with a resistor, across which current pulses are then produced. Cam-actuated and yoke-actuated reed switches have been used in such circuits, or in other circuits where a temporary switch contact closure produces an output pulse.

1.7.3 Design and Performance Characteristics

Design and performance characteristics, besides those generally shown and specified for transducers, should include, for electromagnetic linear-velocity transducers, the frequency response (which always has a finite lower limit), the maximum displacement of the internal moving member (core or coil), the maximum acceleration, linearity (which can be specified as applicable at a reference frequency and over a range of linear velocities), and the type of damping employed. These transducers are self-generating and their output voltage is proportional to instantaneous (vibratory) velocity. Sensitivity is usually specified as peak voltage per peak velocity (e.g., "50 mV (peak)/cm/s (peak)" at a selected reference frequency (e.g., 100 Hz), with a tolerance expressed either in mV or percent, and with the minimum value of the load impedance specified. The upper limit of the (velocity) range is always shown; it may be higher than the upper limit of range for which linearity is specified; in this case, it is useful to know the degradation of linearity up to the maximum velocity value. Mounting orientation must be specified (or the amount of attitude error for affected axes should be shown). Besides the output impedance of the coil(s), the (ohmic, dc) output resistance should be given to facilitate continuity checks. The latter applies also to electromagnetic sensing coil assemblies (proximity sensors) used in conjunction with toothed-rotor tachometers.

For remote sensing systems for the measurement of linear velocity a number of characteristics peculiar to such systems (and different from those generally specified for transducers) are stated. One essential performance characteristic for such system is threshold (minimum detectable velocity) at a given distance, as well as resolution at that distance (and preferably also the variation of these two characteristics with distance).

Essential characteristics for angular-speed transducers include the speed range, in r/min (the abbreviation "rpm" is intended to be phased out), the starting and running torque, linearity and the speed range over which it is applicable, and sometimes the moment of inertia. Sensitivity is shown in mV/r/min or V/1000 r/min for dc tachometers. The amount of noise in the output should also be shown. Sensitivity, phase characteristics, and harmonic content are called out for ac tachometers. Toothed-rotor tachometers with electromagnetic sensing-coil assemblies need specifications for variations in output voltage amplitude over a given speed range as well as for one revolution (because of possible nonuniformity in characteristics of teeth), also output frequency in cycles or pulses per revolution, pulse characteristics for nonsinusoidal output, and harmonic content for sinusoidal output. Esential characteristics for encoder-type tachometers are similar to those cited for angular encoders (see Section 1.4.3.1). Frequency response should be shown for all types of tachometers. Maximum sensing distance should be shown, together with target size, for reflectance-type optical tachometers. Maximum total error ("accuracy") should be stated for tachometer systems, including a digital or analog indicator and signal conditioning.

1.8 STRESS AND STRAIN

1.8.1 Sensing and Transduction Methods

Although strain has been measured by reluctive, capacitive, and vibrating-wire sensors and is still often determined by photo-optical (*photostress*) methods, the most commonly used device for such measurements is the resistive strain sensor or *strain gage*. It consists essentially of a conductor or semiconductor of small cross section, which is mounted to the measured surface so that it undergoes the small elongations or contractions due to tension or compression stresses, respectively, in that surface. As a result, the strain gage undergoes a corresponding change in resistance due to stress (*piezoresistive effect*).

The resistance change of a strain gage is usually converted into a voltage by connecting one, two, or four similar gages as arms of a Wheatstone bridge (*strain-gage bridge*) and applying excitation to the bridge. The bridge output voltage is then a measure of the strain sensed by each strain-sensing gage (*active gage, active arm*). Gages are sometimes connected into the bridge but are so mounted that they do not change their resistance with strain (*dummy gage*); they are used for bridge balance or compensation. Strain transduction, therefore, is performed by the active arms of a strain-gage bridge.

Stress is related to strain by *Hooke's law:* the modulus of elasticity is the ratio of stress to strain. Hence, if the modulus of elasticity of the surface (material) is known, and the strain is measured, the stress can be determined. This holds true, at least theoretically, when a single gage is used. When two or more gages are used, the stresses in the sensing directions of each of the gages can be determined by calculations; however, the equations are of varying degrees of complexity, depending on combination and orientation of the gages.

The sensitivity of a strain gage is called the *gage factor,* the ratio of the unit change in resistance to the unit change in length, or

$$\text{GF} = \frac{\Delta R/R}{\Delta L/L} = \frac{\Delta R/R}{\varepsilon}$$

where GF = gage factor

$\Delta R/R$ = unit change of resistance

$\Delta L/L$ = unit change in length

ε = strain

Strain is expressed as the (dimensionless) ratio of multiples of the same length unit, for example, microinches per inch or, generally, in percent (for large deformations) or, most commonly, in microstrain ($\mu\varepsilon$), the ratio of 10^{-6} of a length unit to this length unit.

1.8.2 Design and Operation

1.8.2.1 Metal-wire strain gages. Wire gages, which exist in bondable, surface-transferable, and weldable configurations, are the earliest type of strain gage developed. The wire used in such gages is usually less than 0.025 mm in diameter. Bondable ("bonded") gages are cemented to a dimensionally stable base (*carrier*). Weldable gages are usually sandwiched between two thin metal plates and surrounded by insulating material; the encapsulation is then completed by fastening the two plates together around their edge. Surface-transferable ("free-filament") gages are intended to be removed carefully from their carrier and then cemented to the measured surface. Wire gages present a small surface area to the measured surface; this tends to reduce the possibility of leakage currents from wire to surface.

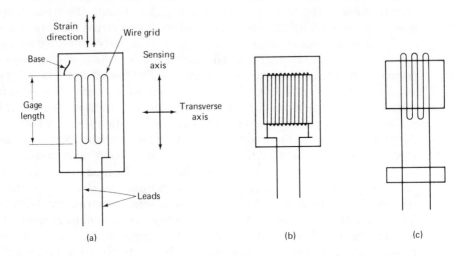

Figure 1-89. Metal-wire strain gages: (a) basic configuration (bondable gage); (b) wraparound gage design; (c) surface-transferable gage design.

Figure 1-89a shows a basic bondable wire gage. The wire (*filament*) is arranged in a zigzag pattern and cemented to the base (carrier). Lead wires are soldered or welded to the ends of the filament, to facilitate external electrical connections. The length of the filament pattern is the active length (*gage length*). A thin cover plate is sometimes affixed over the filament. The wraparound wire gage has been used in some applications (Figure 1-89b). Figure 1-89c shows a surface-transferable gage.

The main criteria for the material of the filament are the following: (1) a high gage factor, (2) a low temperature coefficient of resistance, (3) high resistivity, (4) high mechanical strength, and (5) minimum thermoelectric potential at the junction with the leads. Among materials used are copper–nickel alloys such as Constantan (annealed Constantan is used for post-yield or large-elongation gages), nickel–chromium alloys and iron–chromium–aluminum alloys (used for applications at very high or very low temperatures). Selection of wire material by temperature coefficient allows two materials to be used for one gage, each material having a temperature coefficient of the same magnitude but of opposite polarity. Such temperature-compensated gages can be made by using two half-grids, connected in series, made of the two materials. Lead materials can be copper (often nickel-clad or stainless-steel clad), silver (which can be nickel-clad), and nickel–chromium alloys. Other materials, such as beryllium–copper, are also used.

Carriers are of two basic types, the permanent carriers used for bondable gages and the temporary carriers used for surface-transferable gages. Strippable plastic (e.g., vinyl) carriers, often made in the form of an open frame for wire gages, are most commonly used for surface-transferable gages. Permanent carriers are typically very thin, 0.03 mm or less in thickness. A nitrocellulose paper has been used for general-purpose gages where temperature constraints are moderate. Use of phenolic-impregnated paper increases the operating temperature range, and use of glass-fiber reinforcement (often as lamination) increases it still further. Polyimide resins provide carriers suitable for very low and reasonably high temperatures; with glass-fiber reinforcement the upper temperature limit is increased further, to about 400 °C. Gages can be encapsulated by applying an additional carrier over the exposed surface of the grid. Metallic carriers are used for weldable gages, which may or may not be encapsulated by an additional metallic carrier.

When strain must be measured simultaneously in more than one direction, multielement (*rosette*) gages can be used (see example shown in Figure 1-90). Rosette wire gages are almost invariably of the *stacked* type, with the grids superimposed over each other, with bonding as well as insulation provided by a cement or other appropriate material.

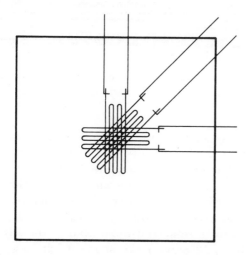

Figure 1-90. Three-element, 45° stacked, wire-gage rosette. (Courtesy of BLH Electronics, Inc.)

1.8.2.2 Metal-foil strain gages. Refinements in photoetching techniques permitted the development of low-cost metal-foil strain gages. This type of gage is now most widely used, not primarily because of the relatively low cost of general-purpose gages, but because foil gages offer a number of significant advantages over the wire gages. They can be made in a variety of sizes, including extremely small sizes (down to about 0.2 mm gage length); they exhibit greater stability during prolonged loading; they are also more stable during exposure to temperature extremes and, because of their relatively large surface area, are better able to follow the temperature variations of the measured surface.

The gages are usually made by photoetching thin, heat-treated, metal-alloy foil (a few μm thick); this process involves removal of unwanted metal by etching so that the desired grid shape is obtained. Materials of foil, carriers, and leads are essentially the same as those described for wire gages. Many types of foil gages are not furnished with leads; instead, they are provided with large *tabs*, integral with the grid pattern, and which sometimes are provided with solder dots, to which leads can then be attached by the user. Typical single-element gages are illustrated in Figure 1-91. Foil gages exist in a variety of geometries; the most common one, for general-purpose gages, has a grid pattern which is longer in the sensing axis (horizontal, in the illustration) so that transverse-strain effects are reduced.

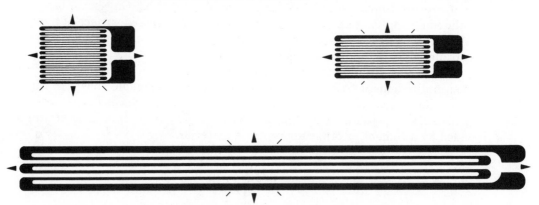

Figure 1-91. Metal-foil strain gages. (*Note:* For size comparison, the gage shown on the bottom is 5 cm long.) (Courtesy of Micro-Measurements Div., Vishay Intertechnology, Inc.)

Foil gages, and the processes used to form them, are particularly suitable for rosettes. Figure 1-92 shows some examples, all of which exist in a variety of sizes, down to 1 mm or a few mm for a complete rosette. The 90° rosettes measure axial and transverse strains simultaneously. A variation of this design is the "stress gage," in which the two elements have different resistances. The resistances are so selected that their ratio provides a sensor whose combined output is proportional to "stress" and the output of the axial element alone is proportional to "strain." Figure 1-92b shows a "shear gage," whose geometry enables the two elements to be aligned in the direction of shear strains, such as those encountered in torsion bars of torque transducers.

Three-element rosettes are particularly useful for determinations of the magnitude and direction of principal strains under complex loading conditions. The 45° rosettes provide greater angular resolution than the 60° rosettes; however, they are normally used where the approximate direction of the principal strains is known. Equations as well as computer programs have been developed for determinations of principal stresses and strains when such ro-

Figure 1-92. Examples of foil-gage rosettes: (a) two-element, 90° planar; (b) two-element, 90° shear planar; (c) two-element, 90° stacked; (d) three-element, 45° rectangular, stacked; (e) three-element, 45° planar; (f) three-element, 60° planar; (g) four-element, full-bridge diaphragm configuration. [(a), (b), (e), (f), courtesy of BLH Electronics, Inc.; (c), (d), (g), courtesy of Micro-Measurements, a Division of Vishay Intertechnology, Inc.]

settes are used. The "diaphragm gage" (Figure 1-92g) is intended for use on such sensing elements as the diaphragms of pressure transducers. Multielement gages are also available for other sensing elements such as bending beams.

1.8.2.3 Deposited-metal strain gages. *Thin-film* strain gages are applied directly to the measured surface, which is first coated with an insulating substrate, by evaporative or bombardment methods. They have been applied primarily to pressure-sensing diaphragms. The thin-film techniques provide gages, in four-active-arm configurations, which are not only very small in size but are also very uniform in their characteristics.

Flame-sprayed strain gages have been applied to structures which are to be exposed to extremely hostile environments, such as the exterior surfaces of rockets. A substrate is first flame-sprayed on the measured surface by propelling ceramic particles, at a high temperature and with high speed, onto it. A strain gage, typically a thin-metal-wire gage, is then applied to the substrate and bonded and encapsulated to it by a second application of flame-sprayed ceramic. Such gages have performed acceptably at operating temperatures up to about 1200 °C.

1.8.2.4 Semiconductor strain gages. When experiments during the early 1950s confirmed that the piezoresistive effect is much larger in semiconductors than in conductors, a number of government and commercial laboratories undertook the development of semiconductor strain gages. Since then a variety of such devices, with satisfactory and controllable performance characteristics, have become commercially available. The gage factors of semiconductor strain gages are between 50 and 200 and are typically around 125, whereas the gage factors of metal strain gages are no greater than 6 and are typically around 2. However, semiconductor gages tend to be more difficult to apply to measured surfaces and, since they are basically made of thin silicon, tend to be fragile. Their strain measuring ranges are usually limited to about 3000 $\mu\varepsilon$, whereas ranges of metal gages extend to about 40 000 $\mu\varepsilon$. The resistance change of semiconductor gages with applied strain is inherently nonlinear; maximum operating temperature is more limited, and temperature compensation is more laborious.

Because of their ability to provide relatively large output signals (when connected into a bridge circuit) in response to small strains, however, semiconductor gages have found quite a few applications, especially in transducers. In these (e.g., acceleration, force, and pressure transducers) they offer the very significant advantage of requiring much lower sensing-element (e.g., diaphragm, bending beam) deflections than metal gages. This permits the use of stiffer and generally more stable sensing elements, and stiffer sensing elements also provide a far higher frequency response. Also, transducer manufacturers can train personnel to install the gages properly, and their engineering staff can work out methods for nonlinearity and temperature compensation suitable for production operations. Compensation techniques, including those involving

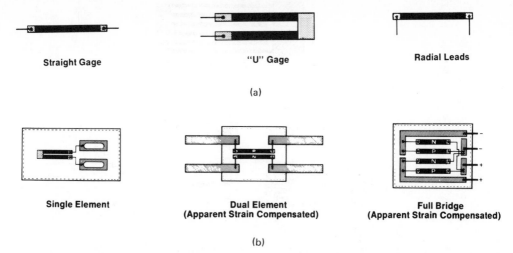

Straight Gage   "U" Gage   Radial Leads

(a)

Single Element   Dual Element
                        (Apparent Strain Compensated)

Full Bridge
(Apparent Strain Compensated)

(b)

Figure 1-93. Typical semiconductor-strain-gage configurations: (a) bare gages; (b) encapsulated gages. (Courtesy of Kulite Semiconductor Products, Inc.)

variations of doping and resulting carrier concentration in the semiconductor, are now quite well established.

Typical semiconductor strain gage configurations are shown in Figure 1-93. The gages can be bare (surface-transferable) or encapsulated on a carrier. Dual-element and full-bridge rosettes can be made so that they are self-compensating for apparent strain. Dimensions are typically very small; the overall lengths of bare gages are between about 1 and 5 mm, for example. Lead materials are typically gold or silver wire or nickel ribbon. Compensation for thermoelectric potentials generated at their junction with the (silicon) gage is quite important, since silicon develops very high thermoelectric potentials (see Table 4-2).

By diffusing the dopant directly into selected portions of silicon wafers or diaphragms (see Figure 1-94) it is possible to manufacture complete sensing/transduction elements. Because of the low density and high stiffness of silicon, such elements are characterized by a very high natural frequency. Gage matching and compensation can be effected by appropriate control of dopants and diffusion techniques and a number of manufacturers have applied their expertise to these materials and methods.

1.8.2.5 Special-applications gages. Post-yield gages, typically made of special annealed Constantan with a high-elongation carrier, are used when large post-yield strains are to be measured, that is, those occurring after the test specimen has been loaded beyond the yield point. Such gages have strain measuring ranges between 10 and 20% (between 100 000 and 200 000 με). They will exhibit substantial zero shifts, however, when subjected to cyclic strains of large magnitudes.

Fatigue-life gages have the appearance of foil strain gages, and are in-

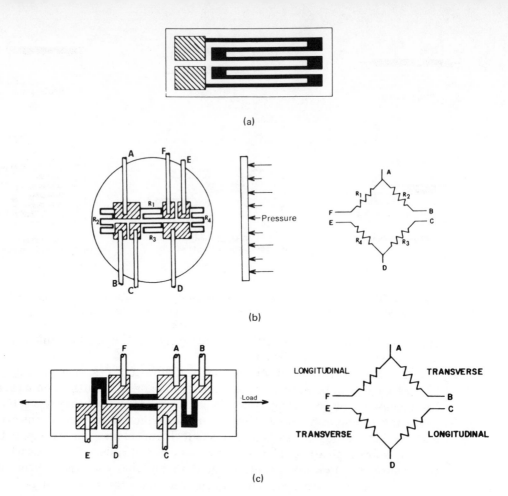

(a)

(b)

(c)

Figure 1-94. Diffused semiconductor-strain-gage sensors: (a) single-element gage; (b) integrated-bridge silicon pressure-sensing diaphragm; (c) integrated-bridge silicon bending beam. (Courtesy of Kulite Semiconductor Products, Inc.)

stalled in the same manner. The material of the foil, however, is chosen and treated to give this gage its unique characteristic: cyclic loading will cause irreversible changes of its resistance. The ohmic value of the resistance change depends on the magnitude of the strain applied during each loading cycle and on the number of loading cycles. If the strain is held to a constant amplitude over a complete test in which the specimen is subjected to cyclic loading, the resistance changes will accumulate and the cumulative change of gage resistance is a function of the number of loading cycles and, hence, the strain history of the specimen. The characteristics of the gage must be chosen so as to match the characteristics of the specimen material for the range of strains to be applied.

In many applications, such as in tests of large structures, it is necessary to have the fatigue-life gage experience a strain greater than that experienced by the measured surface. Mechanical multipliers (*strain multipliers*) can then

Solid-Mechanical Quantities

be used. These multipliers contain the fatigue-life gage on a center section of special design and are then bonded to the measured surface at their ends. Strain multiplication between $2\times$ and $20\times$, depending on choice of multiplier, is generally available. A regular strain gage may be included in the multiplier.

Data indicative of impending fatigue damage can be based on the results of a prior test in which the sensor is installed on an exact replica specimen of the measured surface, which is then cycled in a testing machine until cracking occurs, and noting the cumulative resistance change in the fatigue-life gage at the point where cracking starts.

Crack-propagation gages have very thin foil grids consisting of a number of closely spaced parallel conductors connected to a single common bus tab at each end. The gage is installed on a portion of measured surface where a crack is expected to occur, with the conductors bridging the expected crack. As the crack propagates under the gage, each of the conductors is broken sequentially. Since the conductors are connected in parallel, the resistance measured across the bus tabs increase as each of the strands breaks until a completely open circuit is seen after the last strand has broken.

1.8.3 Design and Performance Characteristics

Gage dimensions usually include not only the grid length (gage length) and grid width, but also the overall length and width, including terminals, of the gage itself. For gages bonded to, or encapsulated within, a carrier (matrix), either the overall size of the carrier is shown, or, if the carrier is provided with trim marks, dimensions between those marks are given. Tolerances should be included.

The materials and nature of the gage itself, of the carrier, and of either integral leads or of terminals should always be stated. For multielement gages (rosettes or active/dummy gage combinations) the nature and purpose of the gage pattern should be described. When gages are self-temperature-compensated for the thermal coefficient of expansion of a measured surface, the material of the measured surface the gage is matched to must be stated.

The gage resistance is shown, in ohms with a tolerance, for individual gages as well as for each gage in a rosette. The maximum excitation current allowable for a gage should be known, for a given application. For weldable gages and some encapsulated gages the insulation resistance is often stated.

The gage factor is always shown for a strain gage, together with its tolerance. The strain range should be shown (in percent, in microstrain, or in other units, such as $\mu in/in$), with the understanding that this is the range over which stated tolerances for linearity, hysteresis, and creep will apply. Additionally, an overrange capability can be specified ("strain limit"). Transverse sensitivity, where relevant, should also be stated. An operating temperature range is always specified for a gage or rosette and the thermal effects on gage factor, often also on gage resistance, are shown. Allowable maximum temperature limits, usually meant for short-term exposure, can be included.

The effects of thermal expansion of the strain gage and of differential thermal expansion between gage and measured surface, often referred to as "apparent strain," should be known, even for self-temperature-compensated (for thermal expansion) types of gages. Actually, the apparent strain as well as the temperature gradient error can be stated with reasonable accuracy only for a gage installed by a specified method on a well-defined specimen. The following definitions can be applied to strain gages in strain measuring systems:

1. *Indicated strain* is the output of an installed strain gage as indicated on the data display device and as corrected for all errors introduced by the measuring system except the installed gage.

2. *Real strain* is the deformation of the measured surface due to applied loads as well as thermal changes.

3. *Apparent strain* is the difference between real and indicated strains.

4. *Thermal strain* is the deformation of an unrestrained specimen due to a change in temperature alone.

5. *Mechanical strain* is the difference between real and thermal strains.

6. *Thermal output* is the indicated strain resulting only from apparent and thermal strains.

These definitions are useful to an understanding of the various phenomena occurring during an actual strain measurement but are not typical for those shown in gage specifications. In most of these, apparent strain is defined as the indicated strain produced by a gage mounted to an unrestrained specimen which is subjected to a change in temperature.

In addition to the foregoing characteristics, the cycling life of a gage is often shown (sometimes referred to as "fatigue life").

1.8.4 Gage Installation

Except for weldable and embeddable gages, the usual method of installing a strain gage is by means of an adhesive ("cement"). Recommendations for installing welded and embedded gages are usually stated by, or available from the gage manufacturer. Gage manufacturers also provide instructions for the bonding of gages by adhesives. Several manufacturers can furnish not only the various adhesives needed but also special installation tools. Some of them even offer training of installation technicians.

Strain gages differ from most other sensing devices in that their installation is intended to be permanent; they cannot be removed and reused. Proper installation is, therefore, essential. The following are generally the major steps in procedures for bonding strain gages by means of an adhesive:

1. *Surface preparation.* The surface to which the gage (or rosette) is to be bonded must be cleaned completely and should be roughened slightly; this is best done immediately before gage installation.

2. *Adhesive application.* The proper adhesive must first be selected; adhesives can be of the solvent-release type, contact-setting type, epoxy, phenolic, polyimide (or similar materials), or for high-temperature applications, ceramic cements; each of these requires different application methods and cure cycles; cure temperatures vary with type of adhesive used and can be as high as 320 °C (for ceramic cements); the cure time can be as short as 5 min and as long as 70 h, depending on adhesive, gage, and installation.

3. *Clamping and curing.* Most installations require clamping of the installed gage, using a metal plate, with a strip of nonadhesive plastic between gage and plate, and applying pressure to the plate; the pressure must be applied evenly over the entire gage installation; for installations on curved surfaces the plate may have to be preformed; while clamped, the installation is cured.

4. *Moisture-proofing.* After curing and removal of clamping devices, a moisture-proofing compound should be applied over the installed gage.

The electrical connections between the gage leads and system cabling are frequently made by affixing small insulated terminals to the measured surface near the gage. Such terminals can be welded to the surface, or they can be attached by an adhesive, in which case their installation is part of the gage installation.

1.8.5 Strain Measurement Circuits

The resistance changes in strain gages are converted into voltage changes by passive networks. The voltage is then amplified for signal transmission or display. Excitation is supplied to such networks from a well-regulated power supply. The output of networks used with semiconductor strain gages may be large enough, for some applications, to obviate the need for amplification.

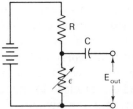

Figure 1-95. Simple voltage-divider circuit for dynamic-strain transduction.

A simple voltage-divider circuit (Figure 1-95) can be used when only the variable component of dynamic strains needs to be measured. The dc voltage drop across the strain gage (shown as variable resistor, with the symbol ε) is removed from the output since the coupling capacitor only passes the ac variation in this voltage drop.

Wheatstone-bridge (*strain-gage bridge*) circuits are used for all other types of strain measurements (i.e., static and dynamic or only static measurements). Excitation may be dc or ac. AC excitation is often preferred since the resulting ac bridge output tends to be simpler to amplify. The bridge network is normally balanced, externally or within the bridge, so that the bridge output is zero when the strain acting on the active gage(s) is zero.

A *one-active-arm* strain-gage bridge is shown in Figure 1-96. Only one strain gage is used in this bridge network; resistors (R_1, R_2, and R_3) comprise the other three legs of the bridge. A circuit of this type is sometimes used, but it is limited to metal gages and to operation at room temperature. Compensation for temperature effects can be achieved by using a *dummy gage* in the adjacent arm of the bridge (Figure 1-97). This is a gage made of the same

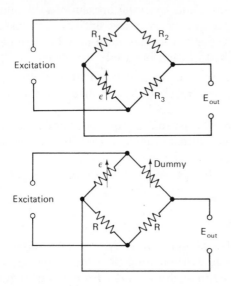

Figure 1-96. One-active-arm bridge.

Figure 1-97. Temperature compensation by use of dummy gage.

material as the active gage, and of the same resistance, mounted adjacent to the active gage so that it experiences the same temperature; the dummy gage, however, is isolated from mechanical strain. When connected into the bridge as shown, the increase in resistance due to temperature will be the same for both gages and will not cause a bridge unbalance (and its resulting output). Only the resistance change, due to strain, in the active gage will result in bridge unbalance, and bridge output proportional to strain will be observed. Dummy gages can compensate for slowly varying temperature changes, when mounted but mechanically isolated either close to the active gage, or mounted on a plate of the same characteristics as the measured surface and exposed to the same temperatures as the active gage; however, this technique usually will not compensate for temperature-gradient errors.

A *two-active-arm* strain-gage bridge (Figure 1-98) is sometimes used in applications such as on bending beams, where one gage will sense tensile strain whereas the gage on the opposite surface senses compression strain when a force is applied to the beam. Tensile strain causes gage resistance to increase and compression strain causes gage resistance to decrease, as indicated by the upward and downward, respectively, arrows in the schematic. The magnitude

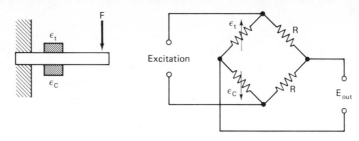

Figure 1-98. Two-active arm strain-gage bridge.

of these two strains is usually equal; hence, with the gages connected as shown, the bridge ouput will be double that obtained from a one-active-arm bridge. If the gages have identical characteristics and see the same temperature, they will also tend to compensate each other for thermal effects on gage resistance and for differential thermal expansion between gage and beam. The same compensation, but with bridge output four times that of a one-active-arm bridge, is provided by a *four-active-arm* bridge (see Figure 1-99), where two adjacent gages sense tensile strain (ε_t) and two gages on the opposite surface sense compression strain (ε_c) and are connected as shown in the schematic. The four-active-arm bridge is the most frequently used strain-gage bridge.

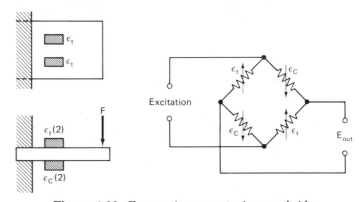

Figure 1-99. Four-active arm strain-gage bridge.

The use of bridge connection for linearizing the output of two or four matched semiconductor strain gages sensing strain in the same direction (all tensile or all compression) is illustrated in Figure 1-100. The increase and decrease in gage resistance, in this case, is due to the gage factor of one gage being positive (P) whereas the gage factor of the other gage is negative (N), as achieved by different doping techniques. The resistive legs (R) in the two-active-gage bridges are made up by matched resistors.

Strain-gage bridges used in transducers are almost invariably four-active-arm bridges. The passive networks used in conjunction with strain gages usually contain additional provisions to compensate for bridge unbalances and thermal effects, as illustrated in Figure 1-101. Temperature compensation is provided by temperature-sensitive resistive elements of which one (R_{ZC}) is

Stress and Strain   **167**

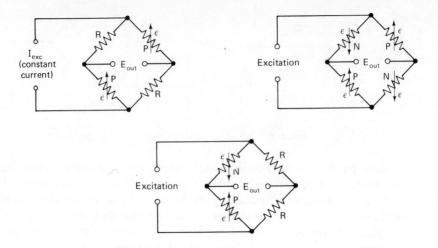

Figure 1-100. Compensation for nonlinearity of semiconductor gages.

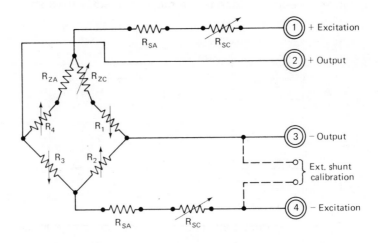

Symbol	Function
R_{ZA}	Zero balance adjustment
R_{ZC}	Compensation for thermal zero shift
R_{SA}	Sensitivity adjustment
R_{SC}	Compensation for thermal sensitivity shift
$R_1 - R_4$	Strain-gage bridge (transduction element)

Figure 1-101. Typical compensation and adjustment network used in strain-gage transducers.

intended to compensate for thermal zero shift, while the others (R_{sc}) are intended to compensate for thermal sensitivity shift. They are in close thermal contact with the strain-gaged mechanical element. Resistor R_{ZA} is selected to provide zero bridge output at zero measurand (*zero balance*). Resistors R_{SA} are selected to adjust the full-scale output of the transducer to a nominal value. These resistors and temperature-sensitive resistive elements are selected and installed after the behavior of the strain-gage bridge in combination with the sensing element is first established, when adherence to close specified tolerances is required. More than one resistor may have to be used for each of the adjusting and compensating elements shown, or one or more of the elements may be omitted and replaced by a jumper when the precompensation tests indicate that there is no need for them.

External *shunt calibration* can be used in measuring systems, using strain-gage bridges either as such or in transducers, for system-calibration purposes. This is achieved by connecting a resistor of appropriately selected value in parallel with one of the bridge arms (typically across the two terminals shown in Figure 1-101). Connecting this resistor in this manner causes a bridge unbalance which can be made to equal 50% (or a different specified percentage) of the nominal full-scale output of the bridge. The shunt calibration resistor is disconnected for the normal operation of the strain-gage bridge.

Bibliography

1. *Proceedings of the Society for Experimental Stress Analysis (SESA),* Vol. 1– , 1943– . Westport, CT: Society for Experimental Stress Analysis.
2. **Savet, P. H.,** *Gyroscopes: Theory and Design.* New York: McGraw-Hill Book Company, 1961.
3. **Dean, M., III** (Ed.), *Semiconductor and Conventional Strain Gages.* New York: Academic Press, Inc., 1962.
4. **Pitman, G. R., Jr.** (Ed.), *Inertial Guidance.* New York: John Wiley & Sons, Inc., 1962.
5. **Dove, R. C., and Adams, P. H.,** *Experimental Stress Analysis and Motion Measurement.* Columbus, OH: Charles E. Merrill Books, Inc., 1964.
6. **Slater, J. M.,** *Inertial Guidance Sensors.* New York: Reinhold Publishing Corp., 1964.
7. "Guide for Specifications and Tests for Piezoelectric Acceleration Transducers for Aero-Space Testing," *ISA Tentative Recommended Practice RP37.12.* Research Triangle Park, NC: Instrument Society of America, 1964.
8. **Canfield, E. B.,** *Electromechanical Control Systems and Devices.* New York: John Wiley & Sons, Inc., 1965.
9. **Dally, J. W., and Riley, W. F.,** *Experimental Stress Analysis.* New York: McGraw-Hill Book Company, 1965.
10. *The Journal of Strain Analysis,* Vol. 1– , Oct. 1965– . London: Institution of Mechanical Engineers.

11. **Durelli, A. J.,** *Applied Stress Analysis.* Englewood Cliffs, NJ: Prentice-Hall, Inc., 1967.

12. **Keast, D. N.,** *Measurements in Mechanical Dynamics.* New York: McGraw-Hill Book Company, 1967.

13. **Baeck, H. S.,** *Practical Servomechanism Design.* New York: McGraw-Hill Book Company, 1968.

14. **Farago, F. T.,** *Handbook of Dimensional Measurement.* New York: Industrial Press, 1968.

15. **Gates, R. L.,** *Inertial Guidance Systems.* Indianapolis, IN: Howard W. Sams & Company, Inc., 1968.

16. **Skudrzyk, E. J.,** *Simple and Complex Vibratory Systems.* University Park, PA: Pennsylvania State University Press, 1968.

17. **Snowdon, J. C.,** *Vibration and Shock in Damped Mechanical Systems.* New York: John Wiley & Sons, Inc., 1968.

18. *Shock and Vibration Digest,* Vol. 1– , 1969– . Washington, DC: Shock and Vibration Information Center, U.S. Dept. of Defense.

19. **Skolnik, M. I.** (Ed.), *Radar Handbook.* New York: McGraw-Hill Book Company, 1970.

20. **Blake, M. P., and Mitchell, W. S.,** *Vibration and Acoustic Measurement Handbook.* New York: Spartan Books, 1972.

21. **Herceg, E. E.,** *Handbook of Measurement and Control.* Camden, NJ: Schaevitz Engineering, 1972.

22. **Fertis, D. G.,** *Dynamics and Vibration of Structures.* New York: Wiley-Interscience, 1973.

23. **Lenk, A., and Rehnitz, J.,** *Schwingungsprüftechnik* (Vibration Test Technology). Berlin, GDR: VEB Verlag Technik, 1974.

24. **Colijn, H.,** *Weighing and Proportioning of Bulk Solids.* Bay Village, OH: Trans Tech Publications 1975.

25. **Meirovitch, L.,** *Elements of Vibration Analysis.* New York: McGraw-Hill Book Company, 1975.

26. **Roark, R. J.,** *Formulas for Stress and Strain* (5th ed.). New York: McGraw-Hill Book Company, 1975.

27. "Specifications and Tests for Strain-Gage Linear Acceleration Transducers," *ANSI Standard MC6.3-1975 (ISA S37.5).* Research Triangle Park, NC: Instrument Society of America, 1975.

28. "Specifications and Tests for Strain-Gage Force Transducers," *ISA Standard S37.8.* Research Triangle Park, NC: Instrument Society of America, 1975.

29. **Harris, C. M., and Crede, C. E.** (Eds.), *Shock and Vibration Handbook* (2nd ed.). New York: McGraw-Hill Book Company, 1977.

30. "Specifications and Tests for Potentiometric Displacement Transducers," *ISA Standard S37.12.* Research Triangle Park, NC: Instrument Society of America, 1977.

chapter two

Fluid-Mechanical Quantities

2.1 BASIC CONCEPTS

2.1.1 Flow, Density, and Viscosity

Flow is the motion of a fluid.

Flow rate is the time rate of motion of a fluid, expressed as fluid quantity per unit time.

Flowmeters are flow-rate transducers.

Volumetric flow rate is flow rate expressed as fluid volume per unit time.

Mass flow rate is flow rate expressed as fluid mass per unit time.

Total flow is the flow rate integrated over a (stated) time interval.

Laminar flow (streamline flow) is motion of fluid particles along lines parallel to the local direction of flow; it can be represented as layers *(lamina)* of fluid sliding steadily over one another.

Turbulent flow is motion of fluid whose velocity at a point of observation fluctuates with time in a random manner.

Density ("absolute density") is the ratio of the mass of a homogeneous substance or body to its volume (mass per unit volume).

Relative density is the ratio of the mass of a substance to the mass of a reference substance of the same volume.

Specific gravity is the ratio of the density of a substance at a given temperature to the density of a substance considered as standard; pure distilled water at 4°C or at 15.5°C (60.0°F) has been used as such a standard, for use with liquids and solids; specific gravity varies with temperature.

Viscosity is a fluid's resistance to the tendency to flow.

Kinematic viscosity is the ratio of the viscosity of a fluid to its density.

Relative viscosity is the ratio of the viscosity of a liquid to the viscosity of a liquid considered as standard; in the case of a solution, it is the ratio of its viscosity to the viscosity of the pure solvent of the solution.

The *Reynolds number* is a dimensionless number used to express the fluidity of a fluid in motion; it is given by the relationship $N_R = VD\rho/\mu$, where V is the mean flow velocity, D the internal diameter of the pipe through which the fluid is flowing, ρ the density and μ is the viscosity of the fluid, and N_R is the Reynolds number; Reynolds numbers below about 2000 indicate laminar flow, whereas those above 4000 generally indicate turbulent flow.

The *Prandtl number* of a fluid is the ratio of its kinematic viscosity to its thermal conductivity.

2.1.2 Humidity and Moisture

Humidity is a measure of the water vapor present in a gas.

Absolute humidity is the mass of water vapor present in a unit volume.

Relative humidity is the ratio of the water-vapor pressure actually present to the water-vapor pressure required for saturation, at a given temperature; this ratio is expressed in percent; relative humidity is temperature-dependent; it is the most commonly used quantity in humidity measurement, including in weather reports.

Specific humidity is the ratio of the mass of water vapor in a sample of gas to the total mass of the sample.

The *humidity mixing ratio* is the mass of water vapor per unit mass of the dry constituents.

Moisture is the amount of water (unless another liquid is specified) adsorbed or absorbed by a solid, or in a liquid, or chemically bound to a liquid.

The *dew point* is the temperature at which the saturation water-vapor pressure is equal to the partial pressure of the water vapor (in the atmosphere); any cooling of the atmosphere below the dew point would produce water condensation; it has also been defined as the temperature at which the actual quantity of water vapor (in the atmosphere) is sufficient to saturate this atmosphere (with water vapor); the relative humidity at the dew point is 100%.

2.1.3 Pressure, Vacuum, and Liquid Level

Pressure is a multidirectionally uniform type of stress, a force acting on a unit area; it is measured as force per unit area exerted at a given point.

Absolute pressure is measured relative to zero pressure (a "perfect vacuum").

Gage pressure is measured relative to ambient pressure.

Differential pressure is the pressure difference between two points of measurement, measured relative to a reference pressure or a range of reference pressures.

Partial pressure is the pressure exerted by one constituent of a mixture of gases not reacting chemically with each other. According to *Dalton's law,* the total pressure in the mixture equals the sum of the partial pressures.

Static pressure is the pressure of a fluid, exerted normal to the surface along which the fluid flows.

Impact pressure is the pressure in a moving fluid exerted parallel to the direction of flow (due to flow velocity).

Stagnation pressure (also called *total pressure*) is the sum of the static pressure and the impact pressure. According to *Bernoulli's equation* for horizontal flow, $p_s = p_0 + \frac{1}{2}\rho V_0^2$, where p_s is the stagnation pressure, p_0 the static pressure, ρ the density of the fluid, and V_0 the flow velocity upstream from the stagnation point. The flow velocity can, hence, be determined as $V_0 = \sqrt{2/\rho(p_s - p_0)}$.

Head is the height of a liquid column at the base of which a given pressure would be developed, for a given liquid; the pressure at a depth h below the surface of a liquid, p_L, is the product of the depth and the *specific weight* of the liquid, or $p_L = wh$. Specific weight is density multiplied by the acceleration due to gravity, or $w = \rho g$. *Liquid level,* the height of the surface above the point at which p_L is measured, can be determined from the above and from knowledge of the pressure p_S existing at the surface, as $h = (p_L - p_S)/w$.

Vacuum is, theoretically, the complete absence of any matter in a volume or a region of space; in practice, the term is applied to pressures significantly below 1 standard atmosphere (normal atmosphere).

2.1.4   Units of Measurement

Only generalized units will be described here and units are given only as SI units; however, Table 2-1 shows other units which have been or are still in use and their conversion to SI units.

Flow rate is expressed in either units of volume per unit time (volumetric flow rate) or units of mass per unit time (mass flow rate). Volumetric flow rate is expressed in m^3/s and mass flow rate is expressed in kg/s. The mass flow rate of gases is often expressed as equivalent volume flow at "standard conditions," 20°C and 1 standard atmosphere [i.e., as *standard m^3/s* (or other units that can be converted to m³/s)].

Density is expressed in units of mass per unit of volume, kg/m^3. *Specific gravity* is typically expressed in the form "t_f/t_s specific gravity," where t_f is the temperature of the fluid under consideration and t_s is the temperature of the fluid considered as standard (e.g., "the 20/20°C specific gravity"); it is a dimensionless number since it is a density ratio.

Viscosity is expressed in units of force per unit area per unit time, $N{\cdot}s/m^2$.

Kinematic viscosity is expressed in units of area per unit time, m^2/s.

Relative humidity is expressed in *percent* ("% RH").

Absolute humidity is typically expressed in units of mass per unit volume, kg/m^3 (very commonly in g/m^3).

Moisture is expressed in percent by "weight" (of either the total or the dry "weight") or in percent by volume.

Table 2-1   Conversion Factors for Fluid-Mechanical Quantities

To Convert from:	to:	Multiply by:
Density		
gram/centimeter^3	kg/m^3	1000
pound mass/inch^3	kg/m^3	2.768×10^4
slug/foot^3	kg/m^3	515.4
Flow		
foot^3/minute	m^3/s	4.7195×10^{-4}
inch^3/minute	m^3/s	2.732×10^{-7}
yard^3/minute	m^3/s	1.2743×10^{-2}
gallon/minute	m^3/s	6.309×10^{-5}
liter/second	m^3/s	10^{-3}
pound-mass/second	kg/s	0.4536
pound-mass/minute	kg/s	7.56×10^{-3}
Pressure		
atmosphere (normal)	Pa	$1.013\ 25 \times 10^5$
bar	Pa	10^5
dyne/centimeter^2	Pa	10^{-1}
foot of water (39.2 °F)	Pa	2.989×10^3
inch of mercury (0 °C)	Pa	3.3864×10^3
inch of water (4 °C)	Pa	2.491×10^2
kilogram-force/cm^2	Pa	$9.806\ 65 \times 10^4$
kilogram-force/meter^2	Pa	$9.806\ 65$
millibar	Pa	100
millimeter Hg (O °C)	Pa	133.32
pound-force/foot^2	Pa	47.88
pound-force/inch^2	Pa	6.895×10^3
torr	Pa	133.32
Viscosity		
centipoise	N·s/m^2	10^{-3}
poise	N·s/m^2	10^{-1}
pound-mass/foot second	N·s/m^2	1.4888
pound-force second/foot^2	N·s/m^2	47.88
slug/foot second	N·s/m^2	47.88
centistoke	m^2/s	10^{-6}
stoke	m^2/s	10^{-4}
foot^2/second	m^2/s	9.29×10^{-2}

Dew point is shown in units of temperature, *K* or °C.

Pressure is expressed in units of force per unit of area, N/m^2; in the special case of pressure the N/m^2 is called *pascal (Pa)* and the *Pa* is now the SI unit of pressure. A large variety of different units have been used to express pressure (see Table 2-1); relatively low pressures, for example, have been expressed in terms of liquid head (column height), such as millimeters of mercury (at 0 °C)—a unit also called *torr* in vacuum work—or centimeters of water (at 4 °C). A frequently used unit, the *normal atmosphere,* representing the ambient atmospheric pressure at earth sea level, was defined as the pressure indicated by a 760-mm-high column of mercury (at 0 °C, at a density of 13.595 g/cm^3, and at an acceleration due to gravity of 980.665 cm/s²). The most commonly used unit of pressure in the United States is the *pound force per square inch (psi),* which has been in use in the more specific forms denoting what pressure the expressed pressure is referenced to: *psia* (for *absolute*), *psig* (for *gage*), and *psid* (for *differential*); such a differentiation is often very important and no equivalent suffixes have been assigned to the Pa, nor are any expected. It is, therefore, important to remember that *Pa* is a unit of absolute pressure, unless otherwise stated (e.g., "tires are typically inflated to a *gage* pressure of 200 kPa," or "resulting in a *differential* pressure of 2.4 MPa"). Since the *Pa* is a very small unit of pressure (about 1.45×10^{-4} psi) its acceptance will meet considerable resistance, except for low-pressure measurements, especially in the United States. However, decimal multiples of the *Pa* offer more reasonable conversion magnitudes: 1 psi = 6.894 757 kPa or, where a very coarse approximation is adequate, 7 kPa; 1 kPa = 0.145 0377 psi, or very closely 0.145 psi. Megapascals (MPa) can be used for higher and very high pressures; 1 MPa = (very closely) 145 psi. Finally, in weather reports, atmospheric pressure is most commonly expressed in millibars (*mbar*); 1 bar = 10^5 Pa or 10^2 kPa and 1 mbar is 100 Pa. Hence, for meteorology the *kPa* also promises to be useful (e.g., 1013 mbar = 101.3 kPa).

Vacuum has traditionally been expressed in *torr* (mm Hg, at 0 °C), sometimes in "microns" [i.e., micrometers of Hg (at 0 °C)], also called "millitorr," or in millibars. Here, the conversion to *Pa* is already in various states of acceptance, since the conversion magnitudes are reasonable: 1 torr = 133.322 (or very close to 133) Pa, and 1 mbar is exactly 100 Pa.

Liquid level is usually expressed as a length dimension, the height of the liquid surface relative to a reference point; when the geometry of the vessel is known and entered into a calculation, liquid level can be expressed in units of volume; when the density of the liquid is known and additionally entered into a calculation, level can be expressed in units of mass. Such calculations can be done electronically.

2.1.5 Pressure-depth and pressure-altitude

The ambient pressure decreases with altitude and increases with depth below water surface. Pressure measurements are often used to determine altitude (e.g., on-board an aircraft), and standard pressure vs. altitude relationships are used for the correlation of such measurements; typical values are shown in Table 2-2.

Similarly, pressure measurements are used to determine depth underwater, below sea level, and below the surface of freshwater bodies. Pressure-depth readings are affected to varying degrees by water temperature, density, and salinity. When corrections for these parameters are not, or need not be considered, the average *seawater* depth can be calculated from pressure measurements on the basis of *10.066 kPa/m* (1.46 psi/m) or very nearly *10 kPa/m;* the average freshwater depth can be calculated on the basis of *9.817 kPa/m* (1.424 psi/m).

Table 2-2 Altitude (Above Mean Sea Level) vs. Atmospheric Pressure[a]

Altitude (km)	Pressure (kPa)	Altitude (km)	Pressure (kPa)
0	101.32	16	10.50
1	89.74	17	8.91
2	79.92	18	7.55
3	70.10	19	6.50
4	61.63	20	5.52
5	54.18	21	4.77
6	47.41	22	4.06
7	41.31	23	3.49
8	35.90	24	2.96
9	31.15	25	2.56
10	26.75	26	2.22
11	23.03	27	1.90
12	19.64	28	1.64
13	16.80	29	1.40
14	14.39	30	1.20
15	12.22		

[a]Pressure values shown are approximate and rounded-off; officially accepted values can be obtained from tables furnished by governmental aviation agencies.

2.2 DENSITY

2.2.1 Sensing Methods

Several different sensing methods have been successfully employed in density sensors (density transducers, "densitometers"). The buoyancy principle, used in the *hydrometer,* which is the most commonly used device for measuring density, is not used in electronic density-sensing devices. *Capacitive* sensors utilize the correlation between density and the dielectric constant of a given liquid. The dielectric constant of a liquid varies proportionally to the density of the liquid. If the temperature of the liquid is known, density can be obtained from the output of a fixed-plate, variable-dielectric capacitive sensing device. *Photoelectric* devices in the form of *refractometers* (see Section 5.4.2.4) are used for density determinations; the refractive index correlates with mass density. *Sonic* sensing is based on the variation of the propagation velocity of sound through a liquid with variations in the density (or specific gravity) of the liquid (at constant pressure and temperature). *Nucleonic* sensing devices rely on the increasing attenuation of gamma rays, passing through a liquid, with increasing density. *Vibrating-element* sensing devices use the changes in natural frequency of a mechanical element, located and maintained in vibration within a fluid, with the density of the fluid.

2.2.2 Design and Operation

Several density transducer designs employ the vibrating-element principle. The mechanical element which is set into oscillation can be a straight tube, in which the oscillation is circumferential, a U-shaped tube, twin tubes arranged in the shape of a tuning fork, or an end-fixed beam or vane positioned so that it is parallel to the flow direction, as used in the sensor shown in Figure 2-1. Various methods are used to drive the sensing element into oscillation and maintain the oscillation, and to detect the frequency of oscillation of the element. The sensor illustrated, for example, uses magnetostrictive drive and a crystal detector for sensing the oscillation of the vibrating vane. The output frequency decreases (or the period of the output frequency increases) with increasing density of the measured fluid.

Capacitive sensors typically employ two concentric cylinders as the two capacitor electrodes across which the ac excitation voltage is applied and whose changes in capacitance due to dielectric-constant variations with density produce the sensor output variations.

Density sensors often incorporate a temperature sensor whose output is either displayed separately or used to correct the density signal (or both). However, many designs are inherently temperature-compensated, by choice of sensing element material within reasonably close limits over certain temperature ranges.

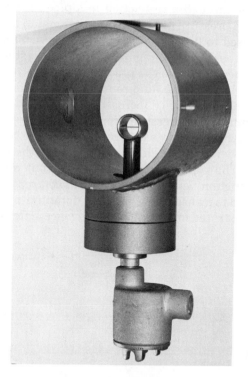

Figure 2-1. Vibrating-vane fluid-density sensor. (Courtesy of ITT Barton.)

2.2.3 Performance Characteristics

Essential characteristics of density sensors include the type of measured fluid it can be used for and the physical and chemical characteristics of these fluids, including viscosity and temperature range. Operation with cryogenic fluids has been demonstrated for several designs and their use for density determinations of, for example, liquified natural gas (LNG) is quite common. Other measured-fluid characteristics that must be considered are its pressure, or range of pressures, and corrosiveness.

The measuring ranges of density sensors extend from below 0 to 50 kg/m^3 to 0 to about 400 kg/m^3 for gases and to over 0 to 2000 kg/m^3 for liquids. Accuracy characteristics may be different for different measured fluids, but error bands between ± 0.2 and 0.5% FSO are typical for most fluids. Where the output is in terms of frequency, the output frequencies are usually in the order of 1 to a few kHz.

2.3 FLOW

2.3.1 Sensing Methods

2.3.1.1 Differential-pressure flow sensing. Flow is very commonly measured by forcing the fluid to flow through a restriction in a pipe so that its velocity changes at that point and a pressure difference proportional to flow is created. The fluid can also be caused to flow through curved pipe sections so that its velocity profile changes in the curvature region, causing a pressure differential to occur at a point in this region. Since the product of the cross-sectional area of the pipe and the flow velocity of the fluid remains the same when the fluid flows through a restriction, the velocity increases where the area is reduced because of the restriction, and the pressure drops accordingly. The resulting pressure difference is then measured by a differential-pressure transducer (see Figure 2-2). Volumetric flow rate is roughly proportional to the square root of the differential pressure. The point at which the pressure is minimum, in a pipe equipped with a restriction, is known as the *vena contracta*.

Sensing elements used to measure flow by the differential-pressure ("pressure head") method are illustrated in Figure 2-3. The *orifice plate* (a) is typically

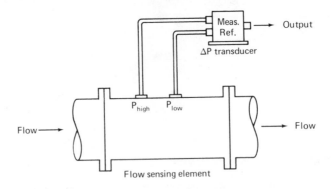

Figure 2-2. Measurement of differential pressure due to flow rate.

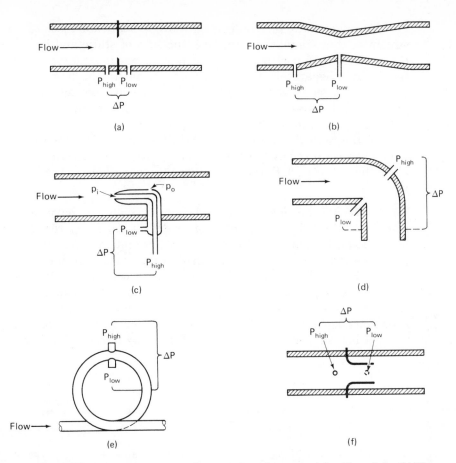

Figure 2-3. Differential-pressure flow-sensing elements: (a) orifice plate; (b) Venturi tube; (c) Pitot tube; (d) centrifugal section (elbow); (e) centrifugal section (loop); (f) nozzle.

inserted between two flanges. The opening in the orifice plate can be circular and either concentric or eccentric relative to the centerline of the pipe, or it can be segmented (i.e., other than a full circle). The opening can be square-edged (i.e., drilled straight through the plate) or conical at the outlet side ("sharp-edged"), the inlet side, or both sides. Pressure ports ("pressure taps") can be located in the flanges ("flange taps"), upstream of and directly at the vena contracta, respectively ("vena contracta taps"), or well upstream and downstream, respectively, of the orifice ("pipe taps").

The *Venturi tube* (b), whose external configuration is often barrel-shaped rather than following its internal configuration, usually has its pressure ports at the throat and just upstream of the entrance cone. The *nozzle* ("flow nozzle") (f) is typically clamped between two flanges. Its throat is shaped so as to cause the flow discharge to be parallel with the centerline of the downstream section of the pipe. In the *nozzle-Venturi* the cross section immediately downstream of the nozzle is configured as the exit cone of a Venturi tube.

The *Pitot-static tube* (c) is a right-angle-bent tube inserted into the fluid stream so that stagnation pressure (the sum of static and impact pressures, P_i) is sensed by a port in its upstream-pointing tip, and static pressure, P_o is sensed by a separately tubulated port normal to the flow direction. In the classical or basic *Pitot-tube* configuration the static pressure port is located in the pipe wall instead, facing the point at which the stagnation-pressure port of the bent tube, in the flow stream, is located.

In the *centrifugal sections*, either the elbow (d) or the loop (e), the centrifugal force caused by the change in flow direction causes a pressure gradient along the radius such that the pressure is higher where the radius of curvature is larger.

2.3.1.2 Mechanical flow sensing. Mechanical elements have been designed to respond to fluid flow by displacing or deflecting, or by rotating at a speed proportional to flow rate. *Variable-area* flowmeters use a float in a vertical, tapered section of pipe; the float displaces upward with increasing flow rate so that the weight of the float balances the upward-acting force on it (Figure 2-4a). The *spring-restrained plug,* in conjunction with an appropriately shaped restriction, also operates on the variable-area principle (Figure 2-4b). Flow acting on a spring-loaded *hinged vane* (Figure 2-4c) or on a *cantilever beam* to which a disk-shaped body is attached (Figure 2-4d) respond to flow-rate changes

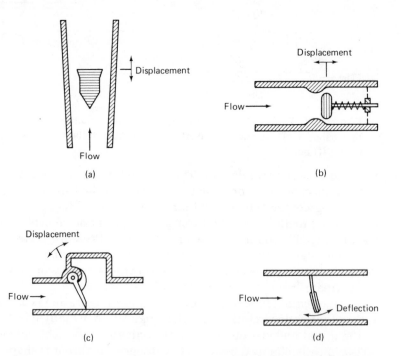

Figure 2-4. Mechanical-displacement flow-sensing elements: (a) float (variable area); (b) spring-restrained plug (variable area); (c) hinged vane; (d) cantilever vane.

with changes in deflection or in strain in the beam, respectively. The latter principle, where the flow acts with impact on a disk ("target") at the end of a beam is also used in *target flowmeters* operating in a force-balance mode. A related flow element is the *drag body,* supported in a pipe section so that its displacement due to flow causes deflection (or strain) in its supports or other mechanically linked members.

The mechanical flow sensing elements described above are not used as frequently as the rotating types, employing design variations of a propeller (used for wind-speed and ocean current sensing) or, most notably, a turbine wheel, or a rotating cup assembly (used in *anemometers,* wind-velocity sensing devices); these elements are illustrated in Figure 2-5.

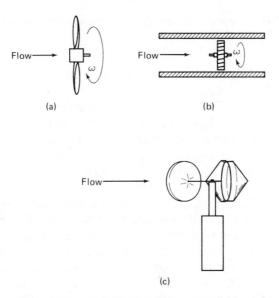

Figure 2-5. Rotating mechanical flow-sensing elements: (a) propeller; (b) turbine; (c) cup assembly.

2.3.1.3 Thermal flow sensing. The amount of heat transferred between two points in a moving fluid is proportional to mass flow rate. The first *thermal flowmeter* was described by C. C. Thomas in 1911, and later developments and design refinements did not substantially alter the basic components of this design (see Figure 2-6a): a heating element immersed in the fluid and two temperature sensors, one located upstream of the heater to sense the fluid temperature, t_1 for reference purposes, the other located downstream of the heater to sense the additional heat transferred from the heater by the moving fluid. The heat input (Q_H) and the mass flow rate (Q_M) are related by $Q_H = c(t_2 - t_1)Q_M$, where c is the specific heat of the fluid. Thermocouples, originally used for temperature sensing, are now largely replaced by resistive temperature sensors.

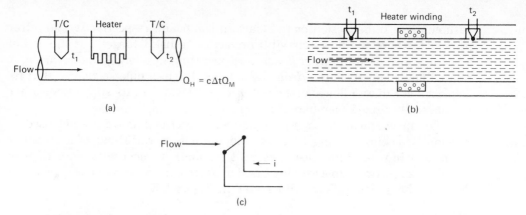

Figure 2-6. Thermal flow sensing: (a) Thomas flowmeter; (b) boundary-layer flow-meter; (c) hot-wire anemometer.

Since the heater power required in this type of design increases dramatically with pipe diameter, the use of such flowmeters is limited to relatively small pipe sizes. For larger pipe sizes, however, constant-ratio bypass sections of small diameter have been used to sample the fluid (typically gaseous) and sense its mass flow rate. Another way in which the heater power problem could be overcome is to inject the heat only into the very thin boundary layer of the fluid, adjacent to the pipe wall. In such a *boundary-layer flowmeter* the temperature sensors are installed flush with the inside pipe surface, and the heater is embedded in a groove flush with the inside pipe wall, but isolated from the fluid, or wound around the outside of the pipe (Figure 2-6b). The heat input varies with mass flow rate and temperature differential; however, the relationship is more complex than for the Thomas flowmeter.

The *hot-wire anemometer* (Figure 2-6c) consists basically of a thin heated wire whose cooling due to fluid flow is indicative of mass flow rate. Such designs also use thin conductive films in lieu of a wire. The cooling is detected in the form of a change in wire resistance. The hot-wire anemometer has been used primarily for air-flow measurements (the Greek word *anemos* means wind) but is now used increasingly for additional applications.

2.3.1.4 Magnetic flow sensing. A conductive (even mildly conductive) fluid flowing through a transverse magnetic field has an increasing electromotive force induced in it with increasing flow velocity (Figure 2-7). The magnetic field is typically created by an electromagnet, excited by sinusoidal ac or pulsed dc current, and two electrodes are used to detect the voltage signal.

2.3.1.5 Oscillating-fluid flow sensing. Devices can be introduced into a pipe or other conduit, through which a fluid is flowing, which will give the fluid an oscillatory motion proportional to volumetric flow rate. The two forms of oscillatory motion which are utilized for flow measurement can be classified as forced oscillation and natural oscillation. The type of forced oscillation used is that due to the generation of a vortex which causes the flow to become

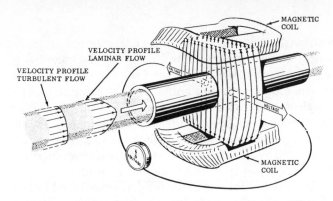

Figure 2-7. Magnetic flow sensing. (Courtesy of Fischer & Porter Co.)

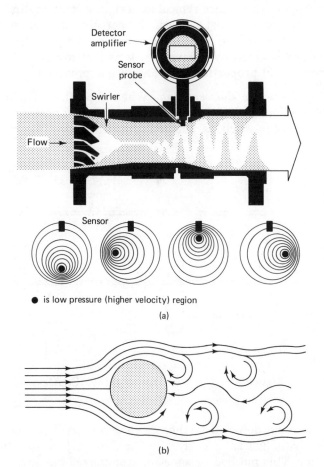

Figure 2-8. Oscillating-fluid flow sensing: (a) forced oscillation (vortex precession); (b) natural oscillation (vortex shedding). (Courtesy of Fischer & Porter Co.)

helical, with the velocity profile characterized by a higher velocity (lower pressure) along the centerline ("core") of the conduit, which is also the centerline of the sensing device. When the fluid then encounters an area enlargement, the axis of rotation shifts from a straight-line path to a helical path; this path itself rotates (precesses). The frequency with which the precessing vortex core passes a given point is proportional to the volumetric flow rate for the vortex-precession method of flow sensing (Figure 2-8a). This frequency is then detected by a sensor with fast time response, such as a piezoelectric sensor, and a frequency output, proportional to volumetric flow rate, is produced.

Natural oscillations in the fluid are generated by immersing a nonstreamlined *vortex-shedding* body into the flow stream. Vortices are produced (shedded) by this body due to surface frictional forces acting on the fluid boundary layer. The vortex pattern, a stable pattern of alternate shedding, is known as a *von Kármán vortex street* pattern. The pattern will be different for different body shapes; the pattern typical for a right circular cylinder is shown in Figure 2-8b. The vortex street patterns by certain other shapes of shedding bodies were, however, found to be more suitable. The periodic fluctuations in vortex forces are detected by a device such as a strain-gage force sensor and a frequency output proportional to flow rate is provided by it.

2.3.1.6 Nucleonic flow sensing. When a portion of a moving fluid is made mildly radioactive, either by injection of a radioisotope trace element or by other methods, such as neutron bombardment (Figure 2-9), the amount of

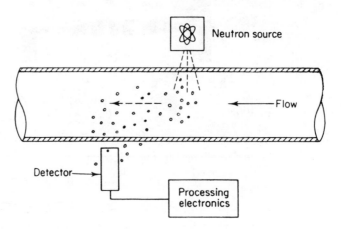

Figure 2-9. Nucleonic flow sensing. (Courtesy of Conrac Corp.)

radioactivity, detected farther downstream by a nuclear radiation sensor, is indicative of flow rate, as given by the changes in output counts of the radiation detector. This method is sometimes employed for flow measurements of "difficult" fluids (multiphase or variable-composition fluids, certain slurries and suspensions).

2.3.1.7 Dye-dilution flow sensing. This method is used mainly for flow meas- urements in open channels, ditches, sewers, and natural streams. A fluorescent tracer dye is injected into the stream, either at a constant rate or in a single burst ("slug injection") and a fluorescence sensing device *(fluorometer)*, placed downstream from the injection point, senses the amount of fluorescence in the liquid at that point. When the constant-rate method is employed, the fluoro- meter is used to measure dye concentration as a result of flow velocity. When the time-of-travel method is used, the time of arrival of fluorescent material, as referred to the time of slug injection, is measured. The general method is illustrated in Figure 2-10.

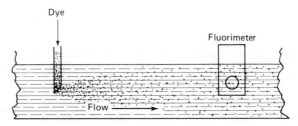

Figure 2-10. Dye-dilution flow sensing.

2.3.1.8 Ultrasonic flow sensing. Several different principles are employed in ultrasonic flow sensing. One or more pairs of "transducers" are employed by all but one method, an infrequently used "noise" method in which a sound- level transducer detects the variation in sound level in the pipe. The "trans- ducers" are emitters or receivers of ultrasonic energy or are operated so as to provide both of these functions in rapid succession. A transducer used for sound emission (full-time or half-time) is referred to as "active," whereas a transducer used only for sound reception is called "passive." The transducers can either be in contact with the measured fluid ("wetted") or attached to the outside of the pipe ("clamp-on").

One pair of transducers is the most common configuration, and deter- mination of flow rate by measurement of sound propagation velocity through the fluid is most frequently used. The changes in wave travel velocity, using either continuous or pulsed signals, can be measured in terms of travel-time difference, phase difference, or frequency difference. These are the differences in detected time, phase, or frequency. The basic principle for frequency-dif- ference ultrasonic flow rate sensing is illustrated in Figure 2-11 for wetted as well as clamp-on transducers. The difference between arrival frequencies f_1 and f_2, Δf, is related to flow velocity, v, by $v = k_v \, \Delta f$, where k_v, the flow-velocity scaling factor, is given by $k_v = S^2/2X$; S and X are the dimensions shown in Figure 2-11a. The orientation angle θ is, of course, given by $\cos \theta = X/S$. Since the flow velocity must be multiplied by the cross-sectional area, $\pi D^2/4$, to obtain volumetric flow rate, Q_v, the latter is given by $Q_v = k_Q \, \Delta f$, where k_Q, the volumetric flow scaling factor, equals k_v multiplied by the cross-sectional area, or $k_Q = \pi(S^2 D^2/8X)$.

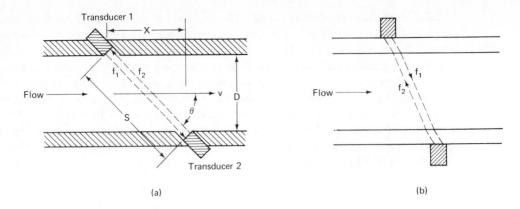

Figure 2-11. Ultrasonic flow sensing (frequency-difference principle): (a) wetted; (b) clamp-on.

Other ultrasonic flow sensing methods include the *Doppler method,* measuring flow velocity by Doppler shifts obtained from energy reflected by such scatterers as gas bubbles or solids in the measured fluid, and a *von Kármán vortex shedding method* involving ultrasonic detection of the vortex fluctuations explained in Section 2.3.1.5.

2.3.1.9 Special mass-flow sensing methods. Mass flow is usually determined from volumetric flow measurements with simultaneous measurement of density; electronic calculation can be used to provide real-time displays of mass flow rate. For gases, primarily, mass flow can also be measured by thermal sensing methods. Additional specialized methods have been employed for mass flow sensing. The *gyroscopic* mass-flow sensing method uses a circular loop of pipe (Figure 2-12) in a plane normal to the input line and output line. During flow of the measured liquid through the loop, the liquid develops angular momentum similar to that developed by the rotor of a gyroscope. The loop is mechanically vibrated through a small angle of constant amplitude about an axis in the plane of the loop. This vibration results in an alternating gyro-coupled torque about the orthogonal axis. The peak amplitude of this torque is directly proportional to mass flow rate. It can be detected in terms of an alternating angular displacement about the torque axis.

Another method uses a U-shaped pipe which is vibrated at its natural frequency. The *Coriolis-type acceleration* imparted by the fluid causes an angular deflection of the pipe section proportional to mass flow rate. A *dual-rotor turbine flowmeter* employs two rotors with different blade angles, connected by an elastic member which acts as a torsion bar, permitting transduction of the torque developed in it. A related method uses an upstream rotor driven by a synchronous motor which imparts *angular momentum* to the measured fluid; the angular momentum is removed from the fluid by a downstream turbine rotor, and the torque (which is transduced) exerted on the turbine is linearly proportional to mass flow rate.

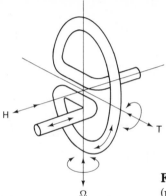

H

T

Ω

Figure 2-12. Gyroscopic (mass-)flow sensing.

2.3.2 Design and Operation

2.3.2.1 Differential-pressure flowmeters. These flow-sensing devices are really sensing systems comprising at least two major elements: (1) the orifice, Venturi tube, nozzle, Pitot tube, Pitot-static tube, or centrifugal section by which a differential pressure is developed; and (2) the differential-pressure transducer, which provides the output signal. Since flow rate is proportional to the square root of differential pressure, a "square-root extractor" is often added, in the form of electronic or electromechanical provisions. The pressure transducer can be separately installed and connected to the two pressure ports of the flow-sensing element by tubing, or it can be integrally packaged with the sensing device. Elements are added to refine the data presented by the output signal, such as a temperature transducer and an absolute-pressure transducer (both of these are needed when gas mass flow has to be determined). The computation of volumetric or mass flow rate, on the basis of the outputs of these transducers, is often performed by microprocessors ("flow computers").

The most common varieties of the sensing elements were described in Section 2.3.1.1. Additional design variations include a Pitot tube having a length essentially equal to the inside pipe diameter and provided with several appropriately spaced stagnation-pressure ports leading into a plenum tube in which a single port detects the average of the pressures. Another design, based on the eccentric-aperture orifice, is the segmented orifice/sliding valve combination shown in Figure 2-13. The variable dimension S, the orifice aperture size, is sensed by a displacement transducer at the upper stem of the sliding valve; its output is conditioned (1) and multiplied (3) with the output of a differential-pressure transducer with square-root extractor (2); "+" and "−" indicate the two pressure ports. The output of the multiplier is proportional to the actual flow rate and can be indicated (Q_i) on a display device such as a strip-chart recorder. When used for closed-loop flow control, as shown in the illustration, the output signal is also fed to a controller which causes the sliding valve to move, by means of an electrohydraulic actuator, until the flow rate corresponds to the set point (Q_s) selected on the dial of the controller.

Flow

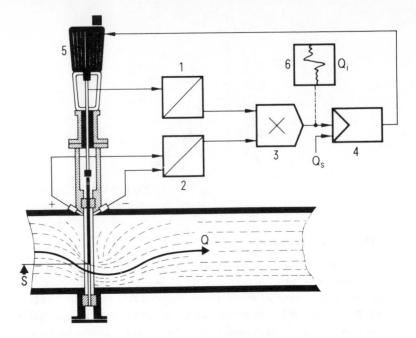

Figure 2-13. Sliding-valve/segmented-orifice flow measuring and control system: + (high) and − (low), pressure ports; 1, valve-stem displacement signal; 2, square-root-extracted differential-pressure signal; 3, multiplier; 4, controller; 5, sliding-valve actuator; 6, strip-chart recorder; S, opening travel of the slide; Q_i, indicated flow rate; Q_s, flow-rate set point. (Courtesy of Siemens A.G.)

2.3.2.2 Turbine flowmeters. Flowmeters using a turbine rotor as sensing element and an electromagnetic sensing coil ("pick-off") in conjunction with ferromagnetic turbine blades or blade tips as transduction element (sometimes replaced by electro-optical transduction) are widely used. The rotor is so designed that it converts the linear flow velocity into an equivalent angular velocity of the rotor (see Figure 2-14). Flow straighteners (flow conditioners) are always incorporated upstream of the rotor. The rotor is supported by a bearing, or bearings, and a variety of designs exist that minimize bearing friction. If pure electromagnetic transduction is used, a small amount of electromagnetic drag is created which tends to retard rotor motion. Transduction using inductive, eddy-current, RF-excited sensing coils overcome this minor problem, as does electro-optical transduction (see Sections 1.7.2.4 and 1.7.2.5). Viscous drag affects rotor velocity at low rotor speeds. The output signal is a frequency, proportional to volumetric flow rate; it can be sinusoidal or be in the form of pulses of various shapes, depending primarily on blade-tip geometry. The sensitivity of a turbine flowmeter is expressed as the flowmeter (or flow) coefficient K, in hertz ("cycles") per cubic meter (or per gallon or liter). This coefficient is applicable under specified conditions of measured-fluid density, viscosity, downstream temperature, back pressure (downstream absolute pressure) and flow rate, and for a specified line configuration (lengths of straight pipe run upstream as well as downstream, and flow straightener configuration).

Figure 2-15 illustrates two typical turbine flowmeter designs. The four cylindrical sections in front of the turbine constitute the flow straightener. Turbine flowmeter sizes (the size is given by the inside pipe diameter) range from about 0.6 cm (¼ in) to over 25 cm (10 in), with special designs to over 60 cm (24 in). Some turbine flowmeter designs incorporate compensation provi-

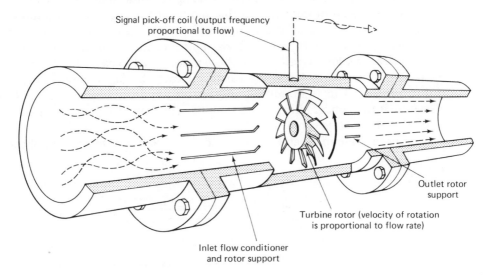

Figure 2-14. Basic elements of turbine flowmeter. (Courtesy of Fischer & Porter Co.)

Figure 2-15. Turbine flowmeters; large meter is designed for installation in 25-cm-diameter pipe; small meter was designed for rocket fuel-flow measurement. (Courtesy of ITT Barton.)

sions, for example, a rotating viscosity compensator drum in a case to which the measured fluid, filtered, is fed.

2.3.2.3 Other rotating-mechanical-element flowmeters. These devices are related to the turbine flowmeter but employ different rotor types. The flowmeter shown in Figure 2-16 contains a ring-shaped rotor supported by the fluid rather than by bearings. The measured liquid flows into the operating chamber through its circular periphery and forms tangential jets such that a spiral rotation is imparted to the liquid. This spiral rotation spins the rotor; it also stabilizes the spinning rotor in the middle of the chamber. The liquid makes a right-angle turn at the center of the chamber and exits from it. The rotor carries light-reflective marks. Fiber optics are used to carry a light beam to an optical window, located over these marks, and to carry back reflected light to a light sensor which produces an electrical pulse for each rotor mark passing the window. The light source and sensor are in a separate box which also contains the conditioning circuitry and which is connected to the flowmeter by the fiber-optics cable.

Rotating-cup assemblies form the rotor of *anemometers,* wind-speed sen-

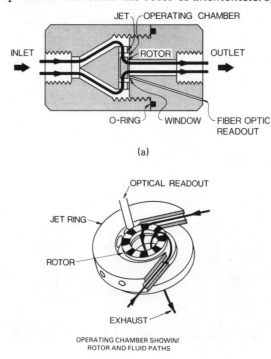

(a)

(b)

Figure 2-16. Bearingless-rotor flowmeter with electro-optical transduction: (a) cross section of typical flowmeter; (b) operating chamber, showing rotor and fluid paths. (Courtesy of Bearingless Flowmeter Co.)

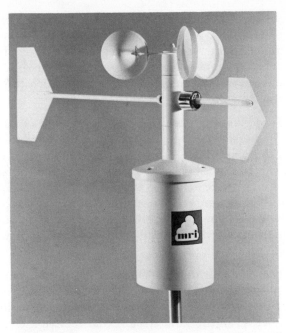

Figure 2-17. Rotating-cup wind-speed and wind-direction sensor. (Courtesy of Meteorology Research, Inc.)

sors which often also incorporate a rotatable vane assembly for the simultaneous measurement of wind direction using an angular-displacement transducer. Electromagnetic or electro-optical transduction can be used to produce output pulses whose frequency is proportional to wind speed. A typical anemometer of this type is illustrated in Figure 2-17.

Rotors having a shape similar to those of aircraft propellers are also used in some anemometers. Rotors whose shape resembles that of a ship's propeller are used in some types of ocean current (or other water current) meters. Electromagnetic sensing coils or cam-operated switch contacts provide a pulse-rate output proportional to water velocity. Propeller-shaped rotors have also been used in pipeline flowmeters; the propeller, shaft, and transduction element (e.g., magnetic-reed switch) form an assembly that is inserted into the pipe through a port which protrudes from the pipe wall at an angle; the assembly, with only the propeller end in the fluid stream, is sealed to, but removable from the port fitting. Similar insertable flow-sensing assemblies, which, however, are inserted perpendicular to the flow stream, use a turbine-shaped rotor.

Positive-displacement flowmeters such as the sliding-vane, nutating-disk, drum, or rotary-piston type employ rotary mechanical sensing elements which are designed to trap sequential volumes of fluid so that the fluid is "packetized" and then pass the "packets" to the exit port; the number of "packets" per unit time is proportional to volumetric flow rate. Such flowmeters have been in use for many years but normally have a mechanical rather than electrical output. A dial- or counter-type indicator is attached to the flowmeter and, driven by a shaft linked to the rotor, is used to provide a direct display of total flow (*flow totalizer*). However, positive-displacement flowmeters can also be provided with an angular-speed transducer (tachometer), which then provides an electrical output proportional to flow rate.

2.3.2.4 Target flowmeters. This category includes those flowmeters containing a body, immersed in the flow stream, and which is typically disk-shaped, attached to a mechanical link such that the force on the "target" due to flow velocity can be transduced. The associated force transduction is either of the strain-gage or a force-balance type. It is important for the target to be positioned at the pipe centerline and oriented normal to the flow direction, within close tolerances. The force exerted on the target is theoretically proportional to the square of the fluid velocity through the annular region formed between target and pipe wall.

2.3.2.5 Thermal flowmeters. Thermal flowmeters can be categorized in two groups: one group adds heat to a confined fluid stream and relates the resulting temperature rise in the fluid to the flow rate; the other group uses a heated body, immersed in the fluid stream, and relates the removal of heat from the body to flow rate.

The *heated-fluid flowmeter* was first developed by C. C. Thomas in 1911. It uses an electrical heater to raise the temperature of the measured fluid and two temperature sensors, one upstream, the other downstream of the heater to determine the temperature rise downstream of the heater as referred to the temperature upstream of the heater. The mass flow rate is related to the difference between the two temperatures by $Q_m = W/(c_p \, \Delta t)$, where Q_m is the mass flow rate, W the heater power, c_p the specific heat of the fluid at constant pressure, and Δt the temperature difference. This principle is illustrated in Figure 2-18a. If flow rate is to be expressed in terms of moles per unit time instead of units of mass per unit time, c_p is expressed in molar units instead of mass units. The primary application of thermal flowmeters is in measurements of mass flow rate (or "molar" flow rate) of gases.

Design variations of the *Thomas flowmeter* were developed subsequently, mainly to overcome the problem of high power consumption. One successful design was the boundary-layer flowmeter, in which only the "layer" of fluid closest to the inside pipe wall is heated and subjected to the two temperature determinations. Another design is the *heated-conduit flowmeter* (Figure 2-18b), in which heat is conducted along a conduit to heat sinks at each end. A differential thermocouple is arranged to measure the temperature distribution about the midpoint of the conduit. As the flow rate increases from zero, sensing junction TC-2 sees an increasingly higher temperature, whereas sensing junction TC-1 sees a decreasing temperature. The thermoelectric emf generated by the differential thermocouple is, therefore, proportional to mass flow rate, for a gas of given heat capacity, as indicated by the meter shown in the simplified schematic (additional signal-conditioning circuitry, including the means

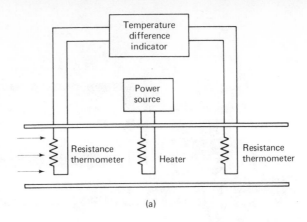

(a)

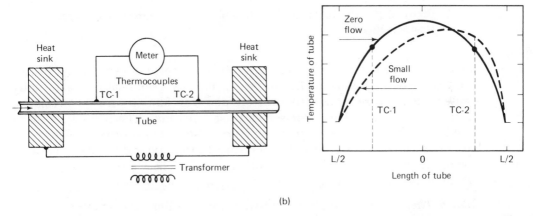

(b)

Figure 2-18. Heated-fluid thermal mass flowmeter: (a) basic operating principle (Thomas flowmeter); (b) simplified schematic of heated-conduit flowmeter with heat sinks at each end and associated temperature distribution. (Courtesy of Teledyne Hastings-Raydist.)

for eliminating the ac component in the output signal, is not shown; the full-scale thermoelectric potential, for the linear portion of the range, is about 8 mV). A typical flowmeter of this type, with associated display device, is shown in Figure 2-19.

The measuring range of the heated-conduit flowmeter is limited; however, it can be increased by shunting the main flow pipe with a small-diameter bypass section and either placing viscous restrictions in both of the lines or placing an orifice in the main as well as the bypass line (in which the measurement is made) such that the ratio of orifice discharge coefficients is constant for variations in flow rate, temperature, and pressure *(constant-ratio bypass section)*.

Related designs use resistance thermometers instead of a differential thermocouple, and they may employ different signal conditioning and display techniques, including providing a switch (discrete) output (flow/no flow).

The second group of thermal flowmeters is related to thermal anemo-

Figure 2-19. Thermal mass flowmeter for gases. (Courtesy of Teledyne Hastings-Raydist.)

meters (see Section 2.3.2.6) since they rely on removal of heat from a heated body by the flow stream. The heated body is usually a self-heated or externally heated temperature sensor (thermistors and thin-film or wire-type resistive temperature sensors lend themselves to self-heating). The heated sensor is operated either in a constant-current or constant-temperature mode. Most designs incorporate a second temperature sensor, typically connected as a compensating arm in a Wheatstone-bridge circuit if both sensors are resistive, which is also immersed in the flow stream but is not heated.

2.3.2.6 Thermal anemometers. Hot-wire and hot-film anemometers are used mainly to measure air velocity and flow velocities of other gaseous fluids; however, some designs are also usable in liquid fluids. Very small sensor size enables such anemometers to provide extremely fast frequency response, making them suitable for determinations of flow-velocity profiles in ducts and analyses of velocity microstructures in turbulent contained or free-stream flows.

The resistive sensing element consists of a thin metal wire or deposited film supported by electrical connections in such a manner that heat conduction from the element to its supports is minimized. The sensor is connected into a Wheatstone-bridge circuit to which sufficient excitation is provided to cause self-heating in the element. When immersed in the measured fluid the element loses heat, by convection, to the fluid stream. This convective heat loss varies approximately with the square root of fluid velocity. Two operating modes are used for heated-element anemometers (see Figure 2-20). The bridge circuit of the *constant-current anemometer* obtains its excitation from a constant-current supply (Figure 2-20a). The current is adjusted so that the sensor is heated to a temperature optimized for a given application. At increasing fluid velocities the sensor cools increasingly; the resulting resistance change causes a bridge unbalance and commensurate changes in the bridge output voltage. The *constant-temperature anemometer* has an unheated temperature-compensation

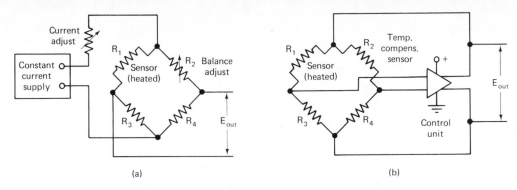

Figure 2-20. Heated-sensor anemometer circuits: (a) constant-current operation; (b) constant-temperature operation.

sensor connected into the bridge arm adjacent to the arm constituted by the heated sensor (the two sensors are in close physical proximity to each other). As the sensor cools due to flow velocity, its resistance change causes a bridge unbalance. The bridge output voltage is fed to a control unit containing a high-gain feedback amplifier whose output is the bridge excitation. The amplifier sees any bridge-unbalance voltage as error signal and causes its output (the bridge excitation) to change until the error signal is zero, under which condition the heated sensor is brought back to its initial temperature. Hence, the bridge-excitation changes also provide the output signal. The constant-temperature circuit is usually preferred for flow measurements.

Probe configurations have been developed for a variety of applications in anemometry. A probe consists of a sensor, the sensor support, probe body, and the electrical connections. Typical cylindrical sensors are either a thin (on the order of 5 μm in diameter) wire or a slightly thicker nonconductive rod on which a metal film is deposited. Wire materials include platinum-plated tungsten and platinum–rhodium alloy. For film sensors, a metal with a high temperature coefficient of resistance, such as nickel, is deposited on a temperature-stable substrate (e.g., quartz); the film sensor is then coated with a protective film, typically also of quartz; coating thickness varies between about 0.5 μm (for use in air) and 2 μm (for use in water). Active lengths of the element range between 0.2 and about 2 mm. The sensors in the probe configurations shown in Figure 2-21 are supported by sturdy prongs. The prongs can be straight and either of equal length, or of unequal length so as to place the sensor at an angle to the probe axis; they can be bent at a right angle so that the sensor is either parallel or perpendicular to the probe axis; they can also be double-bent so as to offset the sensor from the probe axis. Noncylindrical sensors are of the film type; they are used in wedge-shaped and conical probes (see Figure 2-22) as well as in flush-mounted and bondable probes used, for example, for skin-friction measurements. Two or three sensors, at specified angles to each other, can be incorporated at the tip of a single probe for measurements of flow direction and magnitude in a two-dimensional or three-dimensional flow field, respectively. The probe shown in Figure 2-23 contains three mutually orthogonal sensors.

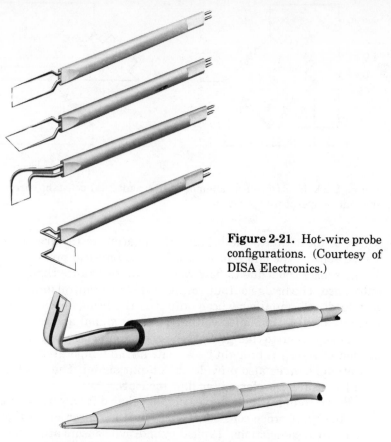

Figure 2-21. Hot-wire probe configurations. (Courtesy of DISA Electronics.)

Figure 2-22. Hot-film anemometer probes. (Courtesy of DISA Electronics.)

Figure 2-23. Triaxial triple-sensor hot-wire anemometer probe. (Courtesy of DISA Electronics.)

A temperature-compensation sensor of the wire or film type (usually of platinum) is often added at the probe tip, but with the velocity (heated) sensor protruding beyond the temperature sensor. Probes can have various body designs and are often protected by a sheath. Sheaths have been designed with a handle, for hand-held operation, or with mounting bosses, mounting chucks or pressure fittings for either fixed or rapidly removable installations. Figure 2-24 shows an air-velocity measuring system comprising an electronics box (operable from an ac power line) and an insertion probe connected to it by a cable. The probe is metal-sheathed and provided with a mounting chuck (permitting a variable immersion length). A cutout at the tip end of the sheath

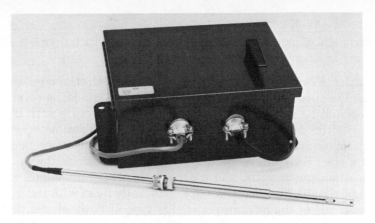

Figure 2-24. Constant-temperature anemometer system for air-velocity measurements; probe tip contains heated sensor and temperature compensation sensor. (Courtesy of Kurz Instruments, Inc.)

admits air flow to the heated velocity-sensing element and to the temperature-compensation sensor. Other anemometer-system designs use portable, battery-operated electronics and display devices and employ a variety of probe-body configurations, sheath designs, retractable sensor-protecting sheaths, and signal-conditioning circuitry of varying degrees of complexity. Since the output vs. velocity relationship is inherently nonlinear, some anemometers include a linearizer, either built in or as an optional accessory. For such determinations as turbulence studies, additional equipment is available to analyze the rapid output fluctuations, which can extend into the hundreds-of-kilohertz range.

2.3.2.7 Laser flow-sensing systems. Coherent-light techniques have been applied to flow measurement using methods similar to those explained for laser velocimeters (see Sections 1.7.1 and 1.7.2.2) and for certain types of nephelometers (see Section 5.4.2.3). The technique is based on coherent-light scattering from particles or inhomogeneities in fluids. The technique lends itself to remote sensing of flow of liquids, gases, and quasi-liquid solids, such as powdered and granular materials. Because it was first applied to air-velocity measurements, the laser flow sensor is known as *laser anemometer.* Most laser anemometers employ the Doppler effect, the frequency change that electromagnetic energy undergoes when it is back-scattered (reflected) or forward-scattered by a moving target. Such laser anemometers are referred to as *laser Doppler anemometers (LDA).* Two operating modes have been used more successfully than others: the *reference-beam mode* uses a single laser beam directed at the moving fluid and a reference beam directed only at the photodetector, which also senses the scattered light from the moving fluid; the *differential-Doppler mode* uses two laser beams which converge at a point in the moving fluid where they produce an interference-fringe pattern (see the discussion of the laser interferometer in Section 1.4.2.7). Because of the complexity of the equipment involved, laser anemometers have been used primarily for research; however, they may come into wider use for such applications as remote sensing of air turbulence, including the so-called clear-air turbulence (CAT) that presents a major hazard to aircraft.

2.3.2.8 Magnetic flowmeters. Magnetic (or electromagnetic) flowmeters are used to measure the flow rate of conductive liquids; however, the conductivity need not be very high: most meter designs operate with liquids having conductivities down to 5 μS/cm (microsiemens per centimeter) and special designs accept conductivities down to 0.1 μS/cm. A typical magnetic flowmeter consists of a steel body, an insulating liner through which the liquid flows, a set of electromagnetic coils, and a pair of electrodes in contact with the fluid (see Figure 2-25). The electrodes are essentially flush with the inside surface of the liner; one of the advantages of this type of flowmeter is that it offers no obstruction to the moving liquid. The electrodes are located at right angles to both the flow and the magnetic field, as explained in Section 2.3.1.4. The output signal, the voltage generated between the two electrodes, is related to fluid velocity by $E = Bdv$, where E is the output voltage, B the magnetic flux density, d the spacing between the electrode faces, and v the average fluid velocity. E is expressed in abvolts (10^{-8} V) when B is expressed in gauss, d in cm, and v in cm/s.

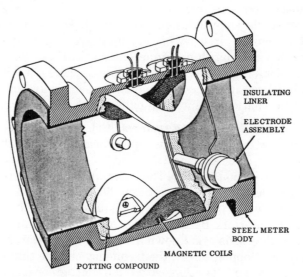

INSULATING LINER

ELECTRODE ASSEMBLY

STEEL METER BODY

MAGNETIC COILS

POTTING COMPOUND

Figure 2-25. Typical basic layout of a magnetic flowmeter. (Courtesy of Fischer & Porter Co.)

An ac voltage is usually applied to the magnetic coils, which can be connected in parallel, or, when lower power consumption at a cost in output signal level is acceptable, in series. Series connection also reduces the heat input from the coils into the fluid. Pulsed dc has been used for powering the coils in lieu of sinusoidal ac; this reduces power consumption and assures the absence of a quadrature voltage in the output signal. The output is inherently linear with flow rate.

Fluid-Mechanical Quantities

Different liner and electrode materials are available to fit the temperature and the physical (primarily abrasion) and chemical (notably corrosive) properties of the measured liquid. Glass or ceramic liners, for example, are usable at temperatures to 180 °C, fiberglas to about 150 °C, and polyurethane and synthetic rubbers to about 100 °C. Various stainless steels are commonly used for electrodes; other materials include nickel alloys, platinum, platinum–iridium, titanium, and zirconium.

The sizes of magnetic flowmeters (inside diameters) range from 0.25 cm to over 200 cm. For proper operation it is desirable that the fluid velocity is less than 10 m/s; for abrasive liquids it may have to be limited to about 2 to 3 m/s. Velocities somewhat above 2 m/s help to minimize coating of the electrode faces when the measured-liquid properties tend to cause such a coating problem.

The electromagnetic flow-sensing principle has also been applied to immersible water-current meters as well as to blood flow sensors.

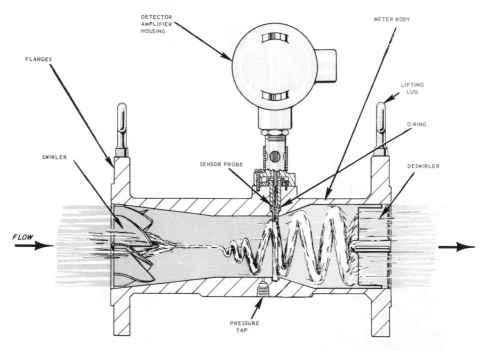

Figure 2-26. Oscillating-fluid flowmeter (vortex-precession type). (Courtesy of Fischer & Porter Co.)

2.3.2.9 Oscillating-fluid flowmeters. There are two types of oscillating-fluid flowmeters: the *forced-oscillation* type, in which the fluid is forced into oscillatory motion, and the *natural-oscillation* type, exemplified by the vortex-shedding flowmeter. The forced-oscillation flowmeter, which employs *vortex precession* to generate a frequency output proportional to flow rate, is intended for measurements of gaseous fluids. The vortex-shedding flowmeter is suitable for liquid fluids. The underlying principles are explained in Section 2.3.1.5.

The vortex-precession flowmeter (see Figure 2-26) uses a bladed entrance device to impart a swirling motion to the fluid, so that a vortex is generated. In the Venturi-shaped body this vortex is caused to precess: the axis around which the fluid is spinning changes from a straight-line path to a helical path. This oscillation is detected by a sensor located in the region where these oscillations occur. The swirling motion can then be removed by a deswirling

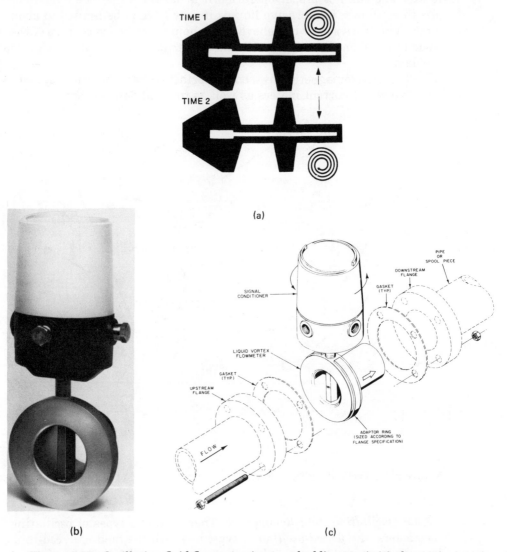

(a)

(b)   (c)

Figure 2-27. Oscillating-fluid flowmeter (vortex-shedding type): (a) alternating strain pattern on sensor body due to vortex (low-pressure region) alternation; (b) liquid-vortex flowmeter; (c) typical in-line installation. (Courtesy of Fischer & Porter Co.)

device at the exit of the flowmeter. The oscillation can be sensed as temperature fluctuations, using a thermistor, or as pressure variations, using a fast-response sensor (e.g., piezoelectric); it can also be detected ultrasonically. Signal conditioning can be added to convert the frequency output into an analog voltage or current output. Output frequencies are in the range 10 to 1000 Hz.

In the vortex-shedding flowmeter a pattern of vortices ("von Kármán street pattern") is generated by a nonstreamlined body immersed in the stream. The flowmeter shown in Figure 2-27 employs a vortex-shedding body of special (patented) design to create a stable vortex pattern. The vortices appear alternatingly across the downstream end of the shedding body, which incorporates the sensor. The flowmeter illustrated senses the oscillations in terms of strain. Other designs use thermal sensors, oscillating disks or cylinders, or pressure sensors. The frequency output from the sensor can be converted to other output forms, such as analog voltage or current signals.

2.3.2.10 Ultrasonic flowmeters. Since the 1950s and early 1960s, when attempts at designing and producing ultrasonic flowmeters were usually not too successful, a variety of good designs of this type of flow-rate sensor have been developed. Sensing principles are explained in Section 2.3.1.8. Ultrasonic flowmeters, unless specifically designated as "clamp-on" types, are usually of the wetted two-transducer design. As illustrated in Figure 2-28, they consist of a flanged pipe section with two piezoelectric "transducers" (sound transmitter/receivers) installed through openings in opposite sides of the pipe section so that they face each other at an angle of, usually, 45° with the pipe centerline. Each of the two transducers alternatingly functions as transmitter and receiver of electromagnetic energy in the ultrasonic range (the frequency of the "ultrasound" can actually lie in the megahertz range). Only one of the two transducers is visible in the illustration. The transducers are recessed into angled

Figure 2-28. Ultrasonic flowmeter. (Courtesy of Siemens A.G.)

ports protruding from the pipe wall so that their faces are essentially flush with the inside pipe surface; obstructionless flow is one of the advantages of ultrasonic flowmeters. Flow rate is directly proportional to the difference in frequency between the ultrasonic waves transmitted toward and against the direction of flow. The frequency-difference output can be converted into analog voltage or current signals as required. When necessitated by an application a pressure transducer and temperature sensor can also be incorporated in the pipe section. Ultrasonic flowmeters are usable for gases as well as liquids of essentially all types, including nonconductive liquids. Some ultrasonic flowmeters use four rather than two transducers, arranged in an X-shaped configuration, and one design using four pairs of transducers (whose output is integrated and averaged) has been reported.

Clamp-on ultrasonic flowmeters are quite useful for some applications such as semipermanent fixed installations and, especially, flow surveys in systems using either one pipe size or a number of different pipe sizes. Figure 2-29 shows a clamp-on ultrasonic flowmeter system whose electronics/display unit provides for plug-in modules needed for various ranges of pipe sizes. The two clamp-on transducers are shown attached to a sample of pipe. The pulses of ultrasonic energy pass through both pipe walls as well as the fluid flowing through the pipe. The use of clamp-on flowmeters requires some expertise on the side of the user (or assistance from a competent representative of the manufacturer). The basic operating principle is identical to that of the wetted-type ultrasonic flowmeter.

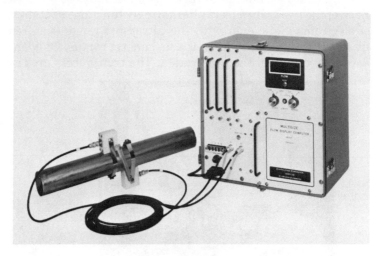

Figure 2-29. Clamp-on ultrasonic flowmeter. (Courtesy of Controlotron Corp.)

Other ultrasonic flowmeters include the vortex-shedding flowmeter (see Section 2.3.2.9) with ultrasonic vortex-oscillation detection and passive acoustic detectors responding to noise which increases, in a conduit, with flow rate; the latter are available primarily in the form of flow switches. The Doppler method, as explained for laser anemometers (see Section 2.3.2.7), has also been used with ultrasonic instead of light energy, using the back-scatter method to detect the velocity of moving targets (e.g., gas bubbles or solid particles) in fluids in terms of the resulting Doppler shift. Ultrasonic flowmeters based on flow noise and on Doppler shifts have found applications in blood flow measurements.

2.3.3 Design and Performance Characteristics

Flowmeter characteristics, to be considered when selecting and specifying such a device, will depend largely on the type of flowmeter selected. Certain characteristics, however, are applicable to all in-line flowmeters to approximately the same extent. The size of the pipe into which a flowmeter is to be inserted generally dictates the size of the flowmeter; for some applications some types of flowmeters may be larger or, more often, smaller than the pipe. The physical and chemical characteristics of the measured fluid influence flowmeter selection and design characteristics very strongly. The fluid can be gaseous or liquid; if liquid, it may contain some amounts of gas, or solids in solution, undissolved solids, or abrasive particles. The specific gravity and the viscosity (over the complete temperature range) of the fluid must be known. Its conductivity and relative corrosiveness must be established. The maximum fluid pressure and the minimum and maximum fluid temperatures must be known. Mechanical connections of the flowmeter can be by means of threads or flanges; dimensional standards exist for both. Specification drawings show the configuration and dimensions as well as materials of construction and the mass of the flowmeter. The location and type of external electrical connections must also be known or specified; codes or standards may apply to these and to the housing in which they are contained.

The sensing element of a flowmeter offers either no obstruction, a minor obstruction, or a major obstruction to the moving fluid, depending on type and operating principle. The flowmeter may also cause a pressure drop in the line. These characteristics are quite important in the selection of a flowmeter for a given application. Provisions for checking or servicing a flowmeter are sometimes provided or required; they can be mechanical (e.g., a spin port on a turbine flowmeter) or electrical in nature. Some designs permit servicing or replacement of the sensing assembly without removal of the flowmeter body.

Performance characteristics include the range of flow rates to be measured and the portion of this range over which the measurand vs. output relationship is linear within a specified tolerance. Where "accuracy" is shown, this term usually applies to repeatability. Sensitivity (such as the K factor of a turbine flowmeter) is expressed in terms of hertz per unit of volume (m^3, L*, gallon, etc.) when the flowmeter provides a frequency output; when the output is in analog form, sensitivity is shown in units of voltage or current per unit of flow rate. For dc analog outputs the amount of ripple or other ac component must

*Pending a further decision by the CGPM, the symbol for liter (litre) can be either a lowercase or a capital L.

be covered by tolerances. Frequency outputs should be shown not only in range of output frequency over the measuring range, but also in terms of their wave-shape (and total harmonic distortion if sinusoidal). Dynamic characteristics of a flowmeter are sometimes shown in terms of frequency response, more commonly in terms of time constant or response time.

2.3.4 Installation Precautions

Most flowmeters require a minimum length of straight pipe upstream and downstream, primarily to avoid random fluid swirl at the sensing element. For turbine flowmeters the recommended lengths are 20 diameters upstream and 5 diameters downstream. For other types these numbers may be different. When the flowmeter does not incorporate a flow straightener, such a device may have to be installed separately upstream of the flowmeter. Some installations may also require a strainer to be installed at some point upstream from the end of the straight pipe run.

Flowmeters are usually supported only by the pipe in which they are installed. They can be subject to case stresses introduced by bending, thermal deformation, vibration, or improper mounting. The operation of any mechanical sensing element may also be affected by earth-gravity effects when they are positioned in an attitude different from that in which the flowmeter was calibrated. Following the manufacturer's recommendations for mounting usually overcomes such problems; they should be followed, as should, of course, the direction of flow as indicated by an arrow marked on the case of unidirectional flowmeters. The maximum-speed rating for rotating mechanical elements, notably turbines, must not be exceeded. Not only can the rotor be damaged, but portions of the rotor may break off and cause damage to downstream equipment. Such overspeeding may be caused by the presence of gas in a supposedly always liquid measured fluid.

2.4 HUMIDITY AND MOISTURE

2.4.1 Sensing Methods

2.4.1.1 Hygrometric humidity-sensing methods. Hygrometric humidity sensors provide an output that is directly indicative of humidity. The earliest humidity-sensing elements were *mechanical* elements, and some of these are still in use. Various materials change their dimensions with adsorption and desorption of water. Two organic materials that exhibit this characteristic have been used extensively: hair, especially human hair, and certain types of animal membrane. When used for humidity sensing they are typically kept in tension by a spring; as they lengthen or otherwise expand with increasing humidity, a mechanical displacement is produced (see Figure 2-30a) which can be transduced. Since the displacement is quite small, reluctive or strain-gage transduction is most frequently employed. Certain inorganic materials (e.g., some plastics) also possess this characteristic and have found some applications as humidity-sensing elements.

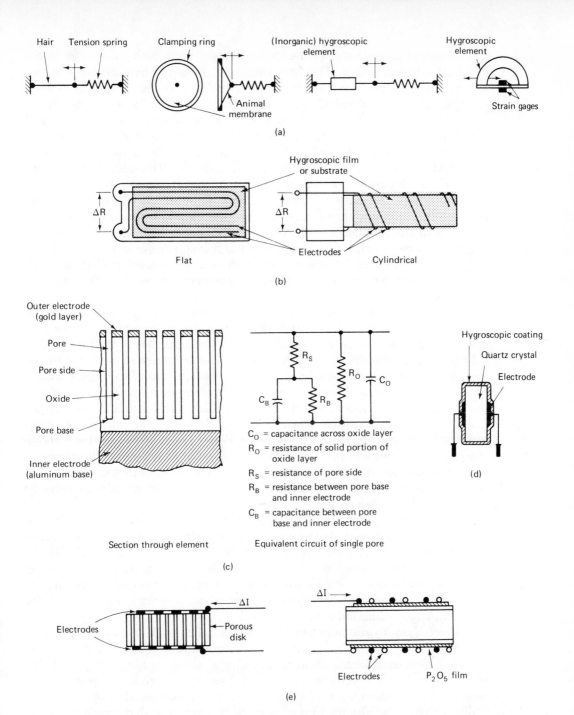

Figure 2-30. Humidity sensing elements: (a) mechanical hygrometer elements; (b) resistive hygrometer elements; (c) capacitive/resistive (aluminum oxide) hygrometer element; (d) oscillating-crystal hygrometer element; (e) electrolytic hygrometer elements.

Resistive hygrometer elements are widely used, both in a wafer and a cylindrical (probe) form. The first successful resistive hygrometer was one using a hygroscopic film consisting of a 2 to 5% aqueous solution of *lithium chloride* (LiCl) and provided with two electrodes so that the resistance change of the film, due to a change in humidity, could be measured. Such an element was first developed by F. W. Dunmore in 1938 at the National Bureau of Standards in Washington and, although the design has been refined since then, is still often referred to as "Dunmore element" or "Dunmore hygrometer." Bifilar wire electrodes, wound around an insulating (typically polystyrene) mandrel, or foil electrodes in a zigzag pattern on a substrate of similar material, are coated with the hygroscopic-salt film (see Figure 2-30b). Similar hygrometer elements use changes in surface resistivity of the substrate itself without employing a hygroscopic film. An example is polystyrene which is treated with sulfuric acid to obtain the desired surface-resistivity characteristics; such *sulfonated polystyrene* elements are sometimes referred to as "Pope elements" (or "Pope cells") after their developer.

Aluminum-oxide elements exhibit a change in resistance as well as capacitance, hence a change in impedance, with a change in humidity. This type of element consists, essentially, of aluminum whose surface is anodized so that a thin layer of aluminum oxide is formed. The structure of such a film has been determined to consist of a multitude of fibrous pores (see Figure 2-30c). A very thin film of gold, vacuum-deposited on the outside surface of the aluminum oxide layer, acts as one electrode (the film is thin enough to be porous) and the aluminum substrate acts as the other electrode. The equivalent circuit of a single pore is included in Figure 2-30c. Water vapor is transported through the gold layer and equilibrates on the pore walls in a manner functionally related to the vapor pressure of water in the ambient atmosphere. The number of water molecules absorbed on the oxide structure determines the change in impedance of the element.

Oscillating-crystal elements (Figure 2-30d) consist of a quartz crystal with a hygroscopic coating. The crystal is connected as the frequency-controlling element in an oscillator circuit. The mass of the crystal changes with the amount of water sorption on the coating. This results in changes in the frequency at which the crystal oscillates, and a frequency output proportional to humidity is produced by the circuit. Hygroscopic polymers appear to be the most suitable coating materials.

Electrolytic hygrometer elements are supplied with current sufficient to electrolyze water vapor into hydrogen and oxygen. The water vapor is usually absorbed by a desiccant such as a thin film of phosphorous pentoxide (P_2O_5) on which the bifilar electrodes are wound. Another design uses a porous glass disk with electrodes on both its surfaces; water vapor sorption occurs on the walls of the pores. The amount of current required for electrolysis varies as a function of water vapor absorbed, and hence of humidity, and the current itself provides the sensor output indicative of humidity.

A resistive hygrometer element which has been referred to as the *Brady array* differs from hygroscopic-film or hygroscopic-substrate elements in that it consists of an "array" of semiconducting crystal matrices which look electrically neutral to the water molecules. Vapor pressure then allows the molecules to drift in and out of the interstices, creating an energy exchange within the structure. The structure then becomes increasingly conductive (to ac excitation at about 1 kHz) as more electrons enter the structure. The use of ac excitation is typical for hygrometer elements.

2.4.1.2 Psychrometric humidity-sensing methods. The sensing elements of psychrometric sensors (i.e., those that measure humidity by the "wet- and dry-bulb" method) are temperature-sensing elements (see Chapter 4). Two separate elements are always used to provide readings from which relative humidity can be determined. One element (the "dry bulb") measures ambient temperature. The other element (the "wet bulb") is enclosed by a wick which is saturated with distilled water (see Figure 2-31). The air is made to ventilate

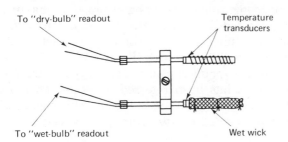

Figure 2-31. Psychrometric sensing element.

over the wick so that it cools the sensing element below ambient temperature by causing evaporation of water from the wick. This evaporation is dependent on the vapor pressure or moisture content of the air (or other fluid). Humidity (or moisture) is then determined from the two temperature readings using a table or chart *(psychrometric chart)*. To assure proper ventilation of the wet bulb, the air is usually forced around it by manually swirling the entire sensing assembly with a circular motion (as in the *sling psychrometer*) or by employing a small blower *(aspirated psychrometer)*. The wick is usually made from a textile material such as cotton; sometimes it takes the form of a porous ceramic sleeve, fitted over the temperature-sensing element. Resistive (e.g., platinum-wire or thermistor) temperature-sensing elements are used far more frequently than thermocouples. A psychrometric chart is shown in Figure 2-39.

2.4.1.3 Dew-point sensing methods. The *dew point* is that temperature at which the liquid and vapor phases of a fluid are in equilibrium (the temperature at which the vapor and solid phases are in equilibrium is usually called the *frost point*). At this temperature only one value of saturation (water) vapor pressure exists. Hence, absolute humidity can be determined from this temperature as long as the pressure is also known. The most commonly used method of measuring a dew point is to cool a surface, whose temperature is being measured, until dew (or frost) first condenses on it. As soon as this point in the cooling cycle is reached, the temperature of the surface is read out.

The sensing element used for this method of dew-point measurement must provide two functions: it must sense the temperature of the surface that is being artificially cooled, and it must sense the change from vapor to liquid (or solid) phase. Resistive or thermoelectric elements (see Section 4.2) are commonly used for the temperature measurement. Sensing the instant of condensation can be performed by various methods (see Figure 2-32). All methods require a condensing surface, which is typically a thin disk or plate in close thermal coupling with a cooling device, usually a thermoelectric (Peltier-effect) cooler. The photoelectric method (Figure 2-32a) is used most frequently. The condensation surface is polished to mirror-quality reflectivity. A light beam is aimed at the mirror and one or more light sensors receive the light reflected from the mirror; condensation is accompanied by an abrupt change in the amount of light reflected to the sensor(s). A resistive type of condensation detector employs a surface of insulating material with an inlaid metal-electrode pattern; a change in surface resistance occurs when condensation forms (see Figure 2-32b). In nucleonic condensation detectors an alpha- or beta-particle radiation source is located flush with the condensation surface and a radiation detector above the surface senses the drop in particle flux when condensation forms over the radiation source (Figure 2-32c).

A different method of dew-point sensing is employed in the *heated saturated-salt-solution* sensor; it has been referred to as an "energy-balance" method. Since the salt most commonly used is lithium chloride, such sensors are also known as *saturated heated lithium chloride* dew-point sensors. The

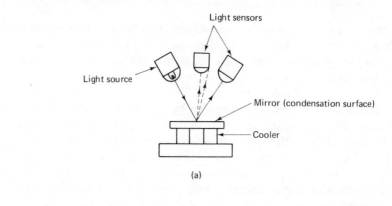

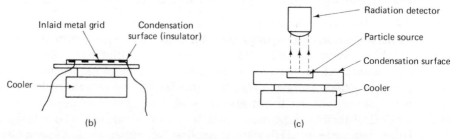

Figure 2-32. Dew-point condensation detection elements: (a) photoelectric; (b) resistive; (c) nucleonic.

Fluid-Mechanical Quantities

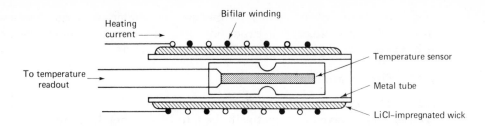

Figure 2-33. Saturated-solution dew-point sensing element.

sensor (see Figure 2-33) consists of a thin-walled metal tube, covered by a fabric sleeve which is impregnated with a lithium chloride solution. A bifilar winding around the impregnated sleeve is used for heating the sensor. A temperature transducer inside the tube, and in good thermal contact with it, is used to provide a dew-point reading. The sensor is heated until the vapor pressure of the LiCl solution is in equilibrium with the vapor pressure of the fluid (e.g., ambient air) whose dew point is to be determined. The resistance of the salt solution is indicative of the point at which equilibrium temperature is reached. The output of the temperature sensor is displayed and related to the corresponding (lower) water-vapor dew point (the vapor pressures for saturated LiCl are well established).

2.4.1.4 Remote-moisture-sensing methods. These methods generally involve the applications of electromagnetic energy in the radio-frequency, infrared, or ultraviolet regions of the spectrum. Devices employing such methods can be calibrated to read out in terms of volumetric (percent) or mass ratio (parts per million) of moisture content of solids, liquids, and gases. One device couples high-frequency (RF) power to a sample and determines moisture in terms of RF power loss, since moisture content is related to a dielectric constant, which, in turn, is related to electromagnetic admittance (impedance).

More commonly used devices are spectroscopic in nature. Their operation is based on the partial and selective absorbtion of radiation, due to moisture content, at specific wavelengths. These wavelengths are located in many portions of the spectrum extending from ultraviolet (UV) through infrared (IR) and including visible light. In developmental devices and some research instruments the spectrum extends down into the gamma-ray range. Commercially available moisture-sensing systems are primarily based on the use of infrared absorption spectra. In some, the IR absorption at a specific wavelength (characteristic of H_2O) is measured for a sample volume of the measured fluid and for a volume of a reference fluid with known moisture content and the two readings are compared. Another system looks at two specific wavelengths in the measured fluid and compares the attenuation (in IR energy incident on a photodetector) at the two "dips" in the spectral curve, at only one of which significant changes due to absorption occur, but with the "dip" at the other wavelength used as reference. Absorption bands characteristic of moisture content can also be observed at microwave and submillimeter-wave frequencies, and equipment using such frequencies (e.g., microwave radiometers) has been used for remote sensing (from satellites) of atmospheric moisture content; it has potential applications for commercial moisture sensing.

2.4.2 Design and Operation

2.4.2.1 Hygrometers. The production of hygroscopic-salt resistive humidity transducers received its impetus in the late 1930s when humidity sensors with enhanced accuracy and reliability characteristics were required for balloon-carried meteorological *radiosondes,* small telemetry packages that transmit data on temperature, pressure, and humidity to the ground. The telemetry circuit used with the resistive humidity sensor was so designed that a resistance from about 5MΩ at 15% RH to about 5 kΩ at 100% RH was needed from the sensor. This range of resistances is still typical for lithium-chloride humidity sensors. It was also found that improved performance could be obtained when sensor designs were optimized for each of several portions of the total (10 to 100% RH) range.

Hygroscopic-salt humidity sensors have been fabricated in the form of rectangular wafers as well as cylindrical elements. The wafer is typically made of a plastic material such as polystyrene. Electrodes are printed on both sides of the wafer. A humidity-sensitive coating consisting of an aqueous solution of the hygroscopic salt in a plastic binder is applied to both surfaces. The printed electrodes have a zigzag pattern to optimize detection of the resistance changes. Probe-type elements have been constructed with a bifilar winding of

Figure 2-34. Relative-humidity/temperature sensor probe; sulfonated-polystyrene hygrometer element is mounted on rear of element assembly, which shows the platinum resistance thermometer mounted to its front side. (Courtesy of General Eastern Corp.)

palladium wire over a polystyrene bobbin, with the hygroscopic-salt coating then applied over the winding. Hygrometric sensors using the resistance changes, due to ion exchange, of the surface of a sulfonated polystyrene substrate can also be wafers with zigzag electrodes printed on one or both surfaces, or they can be cylindrical. The probe shown in Figure 2-34 uses such an element, which incorporates a temperature-compensating thermistor. A platinum resistance thermometer is integrally packaged with the humidity-sensing element so that simultaneous measurements of temperature and relative humidity can be obtained. A perforated stainless-steel cover protects both sensing elements.

A *carbon-film* resistive hygrometer has been used for radiosonde applications. The wafer-shaped or cylindrical element was made from acrylic plastic, provided with metallized electrodes and coated with a carbon-powder suspension in a gelatinous cellulose carrier. The resistance of such sensors increases with increasing relative humidity, whereas it decreases in hygroscopic-salt sensors. However, the carbon-film sensors were still capable of meeting the same kilohms-to-megohms resistance change required for radiosonde use, but with the lowest resistance (about 15 kΩ) at 10% RH. Development was also started on other types of resistive hygrometer elements, such as lead iodide on glass, polyelectrolyte combinations with ion-exchange resins, and cerium titanate, but these developments have apparently not resulted in satisfactory production designs.

The *aluminum-oxide* (resistive–capacitive) hygrometer element has seen additional development since its original conception prior to 1960. Typical designs now use very small wafer-shaped elements (see Figure 2-35). Associated signal-conditioning and readout equipment can indicate dew point/frost

Figure 2-35. Aluminum-oxide hygrometer; *top:* probe assembly with sintered stainless-steel end cap protecting the sensor assembly; *bottom:* sensing element, with lead wires on its mechanical mount. (Courtesy of Panametrics, Inc.)

point or moisture content in parts per million by weight. The sensor is unaffected by variations in pressure over wide ranges and can be used for in situ measurements in gases as well as liquids.

Electrolytic hygrometers are used for measurements of moisture content of a variety of gases. Those using a phosphorous pentoxide (P_2O_5) sensor for electrolyzing the water vapor in a gas sample, such as the unit shown in Figure 2-36, can be used for most gases except corrosive gases, alcohols, ammonia, and unsaturated hydrocarbons (i.e., fluids that combine or interact with P_2O_5). The unit illustrated has gas inlet and outlet ports in its rear panel and a flow-control valve on its front panel. The sensor, internal to the unit, is connected to the ports, valve, and an internal differential-pressure regulator by plumbing.

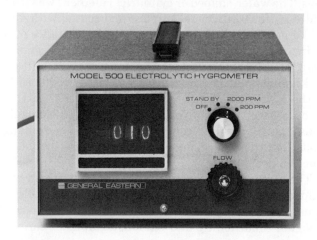

Figure 2-36. Electrolytic hygrometer system with internal P_2O_5 sensor. (Courtesy of General Eastern Corp.)

The sensor consists of a bifilar winding of inert electrodes on a fluorinated hydrocarbon capillary coated with a thin film of partially hydrated P_2O_5. Direct current is applied to the electrodes so that the water absorbed by the P_2O_5 is dissociated into hydrogen and oxygen; this current is directly proportional to the number of water molecules electrolyzed. The current can then be displayed as parts per million by volume, at a specified sample-gas flow rate.

Oscillating-crystal humidity sensors rely on changes in the frequency of oscillation of a quartz crystal, coated with a hygroscopic material, for their operation. The crystal is connected into an oscillator circuit, normally mounted together with the crystal. The crystal case can be equipped with inlet and outlet ports for sample-gas flow. The oscillator frequency is either read out directly, or the frequency is mixed with that of a reference crystal and the beat frequency is then read out.

Electromechanical hygrometers are mostly used for the direct display or recording of humidity; however, some versions are of the type that produces an electrical output. The deformation of the humidity-sensitive element, such as the lengthening of human hair kept under a small amount of tension, is detected by a transduction element typically of the reluctive or strain-gage type. Human hair rolled into an elliptical cross section or chemically treated has been used in such hygrometer elements, as have certain plastics and animal-membrane diaphragms.

2.4.2.2 Psychrometers. The development of many types of direct-indicating electronic hygrometers and dew-point sensors has caused a reduction in the number of practical and available electronic psychrometer designs. Psychrometers require consulting a table or chart *(psychrometric chart)* to determine relative humidity or moisture from two simultaneously measured temperatures, the "wet bulb" and "dry bulb" temperatures. The term "bulb" is a carryover from the days when liquid-filled thermometer systems were used in psychrometers. The dry-bulb thermometer senses the ambient temperature. The wet-bulb thermometer is covered with a water-saturated wick and measures a temperature lower than ambient, due to evaporative cooling. The difference between the two temperatures is called *wet-bulb depression,* and relative humidity, at 1 standard atmosphere barometric pressure, can be determined from a *psychrometric table* which, for given dry-bulb temperatures, shows % RH as a function of wet-bulb depression. At other barometric pressures corrections to the humidity values are required or alternative tables can be consulted.

To obtain a meaningful wet-bulb temperature reading, some means of forced ventilation must be used. For the *sling psychrometer,* which dates back to the late nineteenth century in its original form employing mercury-in-glass thermometers, this is done simply by holding the assembly by an attached hand sling and swinging it around. The ventilation rate should be in the order of 300 m/min. For electronic psychrometers this function is often performed by a blower or fan. When such a device is integrally packaged with the sensing assembly, the package is referred to as an "aspiration" or "aspirated" psychrometer.

In most electronic psychrometers the wet-bulb and dry-bulb temperatures are obtained by resistive temperature sensors (platinum-wire, nickel wire, or thermistors). One design uses a resistive element for dry-bulb temperature in conjunction with a differential thermopile to measure wet-bulb depression; one set of thermopile junctions is covered with a wick, the other set is placed close to the dry-bulb resistive element. A small water reservoir is sometimes included in electronic psychrometers for wetting the wick.

2.4.2.3 Dew-point sensors. Most electronic dew-point sensors are either of the cooled-condensation-surface type or of the saturated-lithium-chloride-solution type. The concept underlying the former type is based on techniques developed during the nineteenth century involving polished silver condensation surfaces, visual observation of the condensation, and surface temperature measurements with mercury-in-glass thermometers. Modern devices based on this concept cannot only detect very accurately the surface temperature at which condensation first occurs upon cooling (the dew point), they can also track the dew

(a)

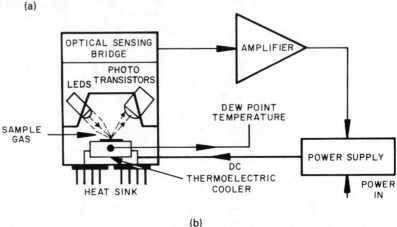

(b)

Figure 2-37. Dew-point sensor with electro-optical condensation detection: (a) sensor configurations; (b) sensing-system block diagram. (Courtesy of E G & G Environmental Equipment Div.)

point, as it varies, by using closed-loop cooler control. The measured fluid can be any of a large variety of gases at pressures to about 2000 kPa.

The operation of such dew-point sensors is illustrated in Figure 2-37. The thermoelectrically cooled (Peltier effect) mirror reflects light from light-emitting diodes (LEDs) to light sensors (phototransistors) when the mirror surface is dry. The mirror is cooled until condensate forms on it. The appearance of condensate on the surface causes light scattering. An optical sensing bridge detects the resulting change in light level and produces a signal that is used for closed-loop proportional control of cooler temperature. The mirror temperature is stabilized at the dew point, and variations in dew point are continuously tracked. The temperature of the mirror is sensed by a platinum-wire resistance thermometer embedded in it. The output of the temperature sensor, with appropriate signal conditioning, provides a continuous display of dew point. Peltier-effect coolers offer the advantage of also being usable as heaters by simply reversing the polarity of the dc current supplied to it. Other, related designs use a separate resistive heating element to provide this function. The two sensor configurations shown each have inlet and outlet ports for the sample gas. The sensor at the left, which is provided with a threaded spin-off cover, is equipped with a coolant jacket (whose two ports are visible at the extreme left), an optional accessory. The power supply and control circuitry are contained in the electronics/display unit. The system can be augmented by an ambient-temperature sensor assembly and a microprocessor used to compute % RH, which can be displayed additionally and separately on the panel of the electronics unit.

The electro-optical method of chilled-mirror condensation detection is the most popular one. Other designs have used an inlaid metal grid in a mirror of insulating material; condensation is detected by monitoring the resistance across the grid. A mildly radioactive mirror surface (or integral portion thereof), in conjunction with semiconductor radiation detectors, has also been used for condensation detection. Partial absorption of the (alpha or beta) radiation occurs in the condensate, resulting in a drop in output counts of the detector. This output change can be used for closed-loop Peltier-cooler control and dew-point tracking.

Figure 2-38 illustrates an example of a dew-point sensor of the saturated-lithium-chloride-solution type. Bifilar electrodes are wound on a wick covering a hollow bobbin. The wick is impregnated with a saturated solution of lithium chloride. When a current is caused to flow through the electrodes, and flows through the solution, the wick is heated by I^2R heating. As moisture evaporates

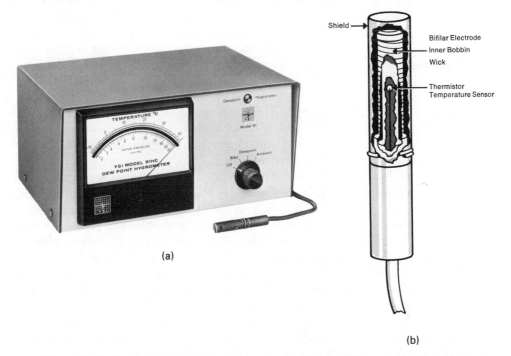

(a)

(b)

Figure 2-38. Dew-point sensing system using saturated-lithium-chloride-solution sensor: (a) electronics/display unit with probe; (b) probe construction. (Courtesy of Yellow Springs Instrument Co., Inc.)

due to heating, the resistance of the wick increases and evaporation is reduced since heating is reduced. The wick (and bobbin) then start to cool and take on water again, and the heating increases. The cycle repeats until a heat/moisture equilibrium condition is reached. This equilibrium temperature can be directly related to dew point. A thermistor thermometer inside the bobbin senses this temperature and its resistance changes are electronically converted to output variations that are displayed in terms of dew-point temperature. Other such designs can use a platinum resistance thermometer instead of a thermistor thermometer. Thermal shielding of the bobbin from flow-induced heat loads is an important design characteristic. An additional (sometimes optional) measurement of ambient temperature is often provided by such sensing systems.

2.4.3 Design and performance characteristics

The essential characteristics of moisture and humidity sensors are partly dependent on whether a hygrometer, a psychrometer, or a dew-point sensor is to be considered. *Mechanical characteristics* that should be shown include the sensor configuration and, for fixed-mounted sensors, all pertinent overall and mounting dimensions, including, for duct- or pipe-mounted probe-type sensors, dimensions of the pressure-tight fitting. For measured fluids other than open air, fluid pressures and sensor compatibility with the fluids must be established. *Electrical characteristics* such as element-resistance range (and nominal resistance at a given humidity and temperature), power supply requirements, warm-up time, and output characteristics must be shown for sensors that are intended to be connected into the user's signal-conditioning and excitation circuitry. More commonly the sensors are procured in conjunction with circuitry, and often also complete excitation/conditioning/display equipment, furnished by the manufacturer. In this case only line-voltage power requirements are shown (or type of battery, if only battery-operated). However, any significant limits on electrostatic and electromagnetic environmental conditions (conducted or radiated) should be stated.

Performance characteristics comprise primarily range, measured-fluid temperatures, and output and accuracy characteristics. For hygrometric sensors the range is usually shown in % RH (percent relative humidity), for psychrometric sensors in terms of wet-bulb and dry-bulb temperatures, and for dew-point sensors in terms of dew point (temperature). For many dew-point sensors and some hygrometers, as well as for moisture sensors of other types (e.g., infrared, microwave) the range may be shown in terms of moisture content, in "ppm" (parts per million) or units equivalent to grams of water per kilogram of dry air. For psychrometric and, sometimes, dew-point sensors, the wet-bulb depression range (dry-bulb minus wet-bulb temperatures) is also shown, for a given operating temperature range. Range is sometimes also expressed in terms of volume ratio or specific volume.

The various quantities used for range are interrelated as shown in the *psychrometric chart* of Figure 2-39. The chart, applicable at 1 standard at-

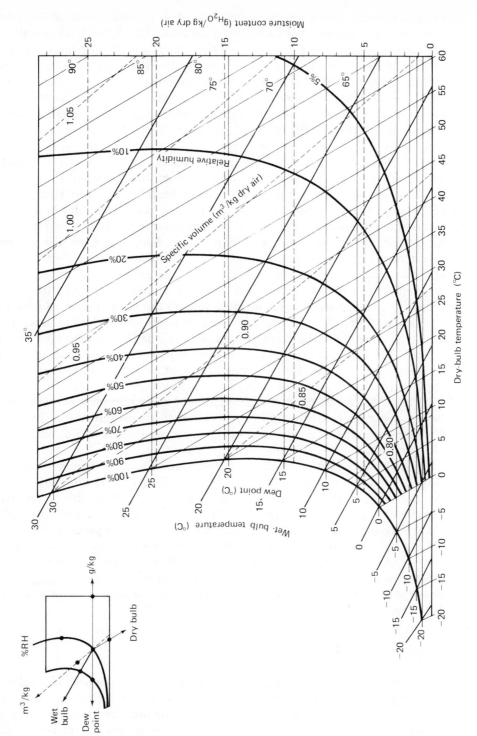

Figure 2-39. Psychrometric chart (at 101.32 kPa barometric pressure).

mosphere barometric pressure, shows how other quantities can be determined from the knowledge of two measured quantities. Examples: the dry-bulb temperature (measured-fluid temperature) was 35 °C and the dew point was measured as 15 °C. From the point where the two lines intersect, the humidity can be read off as 30% RH. Had a wet-bulb temperature been taken instead of dew point, that temperature would have been approximately 21.5 °C (psychrometric charts in actual use are more finely graduated than the example shown, but some interpolation is still required for them). It can further be seen that the moisture content, based on the two measured quantities, would be 10.8 g/kg. Dew point (at the stated barometric pressure) relates directly to moisture content. For example, following the dew-point line horizontally across the chart, a dew point temperature of $-10°C$ translates into a moisture content of 1.6 g/kg (or 1600 ppm). Further, for this dew point and a dry-bulb temperature of approximately $+8$ °C, the specific volume can be read off as 0.8 m³/kg, for air, at the stated barometric pressure. Measured frost points have to be converted to dew points. The output of the sensor can be shown in terms of the intrinsic transduction characteristic (i.e., resistance of the element, or impedance at a stated carrier frequency, or current or voltage) for a stated humidity or moisture range. For most sensors the range limits, to which end points apply, are not at 0% and 100% RH (or equivalent values in other units). For some types of hygrometers, ranges such as 5 or 10% to 90 or 95% are more typical. Those are, of course, the ranges over which stated accuracy characteristics apply; for the same sensor, different accuracy characteristics may apply to portions of the measuring range above and below those limits. Since the output vs. measurand characteristics of most humidity sensors are not linear, accuracy characteristics are limited to repeatability and hysteresis. Only for some types of mechanical-element hygrometers is resolution or threshold specified.

Dynamic performance characteristics are shown in terms of time constant, sometimes rise time or response time. This time is typically different for increasing and decreasing humidity or moisture; it is also temperature-dependent and often strongly dependent on flow (or ventilation) rate; all applicable conditions should be stated. Measured-fluid temperature ranges are always shown; additionally, limits of temperature ambient to the head of an immersion probe (immersed in a pressurized fluid) should be shown, as should other ambient conditions that may affect probe performance. Storage conditions for hygrometers usually involve keeping the sensor in its packaged condition together with a desiccant such as silica gel.

2.5 LIQUID LEVEL

This section describes sensing devices for determining the *level* of liquids and quasi-liquids (e.g., slurries and powdered or granular solids) in vessels such as open or closed tanks, hoppers, and ducts. The measurement can be *continuous* or it can be discrete *(point level)*. One, two, or more point-level sensors may be used in an installation. From level measurements the *volume* of the liquid in a tank can be determined if the tank geometry and dimensions are known and the *mass* of the liquid can be established if its density is additionally known. Point-level sensors can also be used to detect the presence or absence of a liquid in a pipe or duct. The *interface* between a liquid and a gas, or between two different liquids, is another parameter detectable by level sensors.

Electronic level-sensing systems have been gradually replacing two devices with a long history of use: the dipstick and the sight glass; both of these are still in use. Units of level measurements are either in terms of height, in terms of volume, or (if density is either constant and known or if it is measured simultaneously) in terms of mass.

2.5.1 Sensing Methods

2.5.1.1 Pressure methods of level sensing. A very common method of measuring level is in terms of *head,* the height of a liquid column at the base of which a pressure is developed (see Figure 2-40). When the specific weight, w, of the liquid is known, the level, h, above the point at which the pressure, p_L, is measured relative to the pressure above the liquid's surface, p_H, by

$$h = \frac{p_L - p_H}{w}$$

When the tank is closed, the pressure difference (p_D) must be measured by a differential-pressure transducer, whose ports are connected with plumbing to the top and bottom of the tank. For a liquid of a given specific weight, the output of the transducer is then directly proportional to level. When the gas above the liquid is pressurized (so as to force the liquid to flow from a port at the bottom of the tank), the gas pressure is known as *ullage pressure.*

Two other pressure methods are also shown in Figure 2-40. When vessels

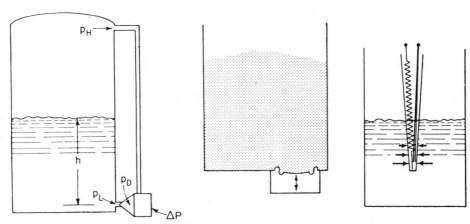

Figure 2-40. Pressure methods of level sensing.

contain powdered or granular solids and the vessel is open at its top (or otherwise vented to the ambient atmosphere), a level measurement in terms of head can be made by making a sensing diaphragm integral with the bottom of the tank and transducing the deflection of the diaphragm. A different method is employed in a proprietary device which relies on the compression of an immersible flexible sleeve to press a portion of a continuous electrical contact against a continuous strip-type electrical resistance element so that the resistance between strip and contact terminals decreases with rising level.

A number of techniques of varying complexity are illustrated for head measurements, used for level sensing, in Figure 2-41. The simplest measure-

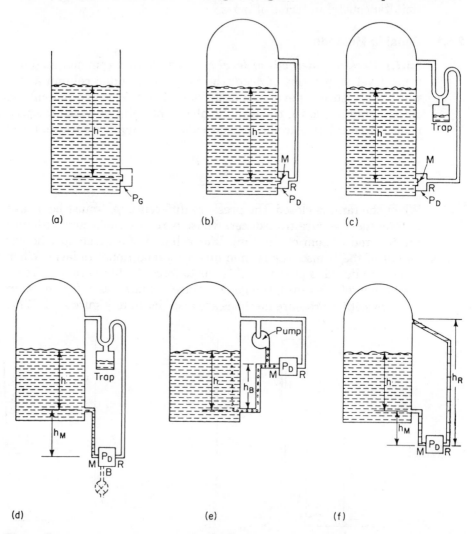

Figure 2-41. Level sensing by differential-pressure measurement: (a) open tank; (b) flush-mounted transducer; (c) moisture trap in reference line; (d) lines to both ports; (e) bubbler; (f) transfer fluid in reference line.

Fluid-Mechanical Quantities

ment is that which can be made in a stationary open tank by flush-mounting a gage-pressure transducer close to the bottom of the tank (Figure 2-41a), so that the sensing element of the transducer is always wetted by the liquid. The pressure, P_G, sensed in this manner is directly equal to hw. In the other examples illustrated, differential pressure, P_D, is measured by a transducer whose measurand port is identified by M, and whose reference port is identified by R. The head of any gas in either line is assumed to have a negligible effect on measurement accuracy. The specific weight of the liquid is assumed to be much larger than that of the gas; when this assumption cannot be made, the gas head must be accounted for in the total measurement. The configuration shown in Figure 2-41b, in which the measurand port is flush-mounted to the tank, can be used where there is no possibility of moisture condensation in the reference-pressure line. When vapor in the ullage gas may enter and condense in the reference line, a moisture trap can be inserted in this line (Figure 2-41c) to prevent a liquid head of unknown height from building up in the line.

In many installations the pressure transducer cannot be flush-mounted to the tank; both of its ports must be connected to the appropriate points in the tank by means of plumbing. A simple scheme for accomplishing this is shown in Figure 2-41d. The transducer is located below the level of the lower measuring point *(tap)* in the tank. The transducer is often equipped with a *bleed port* (B) so that any air or gas in the line can be bled off and only liquid then fills the line. The differential pressure sensed by the transducer is now $(h + h_m)w$, where h_m is the (fixed) head of liquid in the measurand line and the level measurement must account for this fixed head. *Bubbler* systems are useful when the transducer is located above the measurand tap in the tank, or when its sensing element should not come in contact with the liquid. For open tanks, purge air is bubbled, at low flow, into the tank through a standpipe; the (gage) pressure transducer is connected to the top of the standpipe and senses a back-pressure proportional to level (at constant density). For closed tanks, a pump (Figure 2-41e) can be used to bubble ullage gas through the measurand line, or a separate gas supply can be used for this purpose. The differential pressure is then equal to $hw - h_B w_B$, where w_B is the specific weight of the gas.

When it is undesirable to have the ullage gas come in contact with the reference port of the transducer (e.g., when the gas is corrosive or contaminating), the reference line can be filled with a *transfer fluid* having a specific weight (density) equal to or greater than that of the liquid in the (closed) tank. An elastic membrane is located at the reference tap to isolate the transfer fluid. Since the head in the reference line, h_R, is always greater than the head seen by the measurand port of the transducer (when the latter is installed below the bottom tap of the tank), a negative differential pressure will be sensed, varying from zero, when the liquid is at the reference tap, to a maximum value, when it has decreased to the measurand tap (Figure 2-41f). In all applications where a differential-pressure transducer is used and the ullage pressure can vary, the *reference-pressure error* of the transducer must be negligible (or known and accounted for in level determinations).

2.5.1.2 *Level sensing by weighing.* By weighing a tank of known geometry, subtracting the weight of the empty tank *(tare)*, and allowing for the specific weight of the liquid, the level in the tank can be determined (see Figure 2-42). Such mass determinations are usually made by load cells. The tank can also be mounted in a weighing arrangement in which its tare weight is balanced by a ballast mass equivalent to the tare weight of the tank.

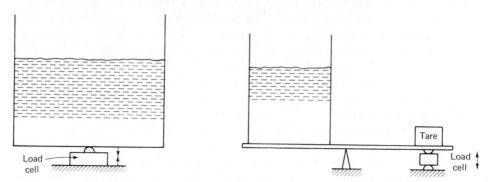

Figure 2-42. Level determination by weighing.

2.5.1.3 *Buoyancy level sensing.* Archimedes' principle—a body submerged wholly or partially in a fluid is buoyed up by a force proportional to the mass of the fluid displaced—is put to use in level sensors whose sensing element is a float, either hollow or made of a material lighter than the measured fluid (Figure 2-43). The up/down motion of the float relative to the (fixed) case of the sensor is converted into an output, indicative of level, by a transduction element in the case. Potentiometric or reluctive transduction is typically used in continuous-level sensors. A magnetic reed switch in combination with a permanent magnet, which can be embedded in the float, has been popular in

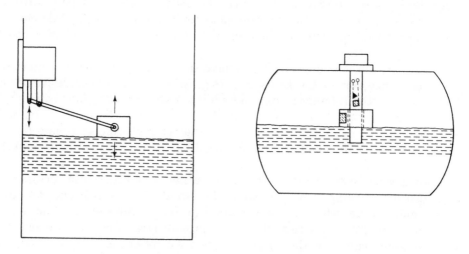

Figure 2-43. Level sensing using floats.

point-level sensors. When the transducer case can be wetted by the measured liquid, the case as well as the actuation mechanism must be hermetically sealed. In a related sensing method, the float *(displacer)* does not actually move; the force acting on it due to buoyancy is transduced by an appropriate transduction element, typically of the strain-gage or force-balance type.

2.5.1.4 Conductivity level sensing. The level of electrically conductive liquids can be sensed by two electrodes in contact with the liquid, by monitoring the change in resistance between the electrodes (Figure 2-44). The conductivity of the liquid can be used for continuous-level as well as for discrete-level indications. The tank wall, if metallic, can be used as one of the two electrodes.

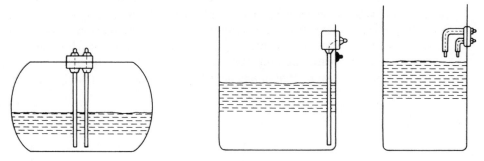

Figure 2-44. Conductivity level sensing.

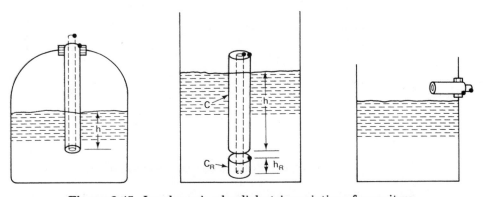

Figure 2-45. Level sensing by dielectric variation of capacitors.

2.5.1.5 Capacitive level sensing. The dielectric constant of a liquid is usually different from that of the air, or other gas, above it. When one or more pairs of electrodes (Figure 2-45) are immersed into a liquid, the variation in dielectric due to rising or falling liquid level will cause a change in capacitance between electrode pairs. The tank wall, if metallic, can be used as one electrode of a pair. This principle is applicable to continuous-level as well as point-level sensing. The sensing element can be configured as two or four coaxial tubes, with alternate tubes ganged together when more than one pair of electrodes is used. A four-arm ac bridge network is typically used, with the level-sensing capacitive element constituting one arm of the bridge. Accuracy can be improved by placing a second capacitive element, which remains submerged, below the level-sensing element to compensate for changes in characteristics of the liquid. As indicated in the illustration, this reference capacitive element, C_R, sees a fixed head, h_R, which constitutes a small fraction of the head, or capacitive-element height, h, sensed by capacitive element C. The tank level is measured between the top of C_R and the top of C, and the level is then determined by $h/h_R = \Delta C/\Delta C_R$.

2.5.1.6 Heat-transfer level sensing. The rate of heat transfer is generally larger from a heated element to a liquid than to a gas. This principle is applied in various discrete-level sensors (Figure 2-46). Resistive elements are often used for this purpose, with a current through them sufficient to cause some self-heating (thermistors are popular for such applications). When the level rises so that it comes in contact with the warm element, the element will be cooled and the resulting step change in its resistance is used for a point-level indication. The same principle is used by thermocouples attached to wirewound heaters.

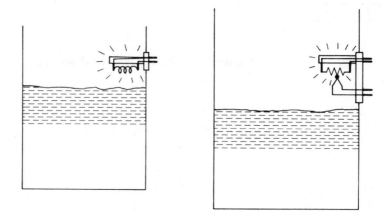

Figure 2-46. Heat-transfer level sensing.

2.5.1.7 Photoelectric level sensing. Photoelectric sensing methods are used for point-level sensing in two different modes (Figure 2-47). In the transmittance mode the light beam from a source to a sensor, installed either in the opposite tank wall or immediately below the source, is attenuated when the level of the liquid rises into the optical path. In the reflection mode, an optical prism is so arranged that less light is reflected back to a light sensor when the prism is immersed in liquid, due to the change in the index of refraction, then when it is immersed in gas.

2.5.1.8 Damped-oscillation level sensing. The change in damping of an oscillating element, when its ambient fluid changes from gas to liquid, is used in two types of point-level sensors (Figure 2-48). One type uses a vibrating paddle

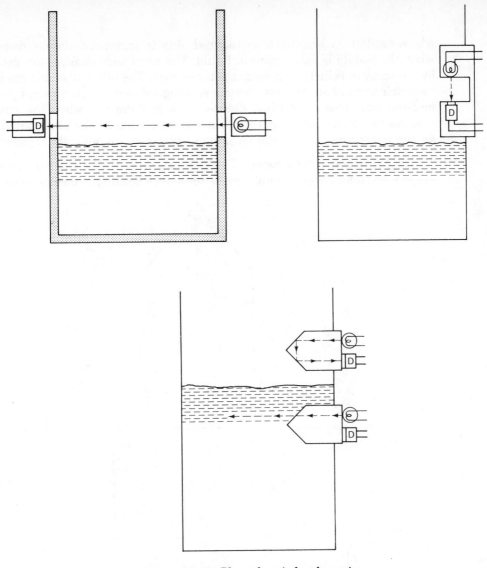

Figure 2-47. Photoelectric level sensing.

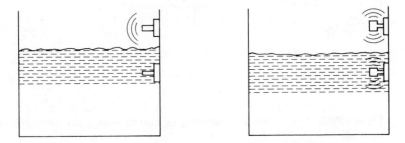

Figure 2-48. Level sensing by oscillation damping.

whose oscillation amplitude is reduced, due to increased viscous damping, when the paddle is submerged in liquid. The amplitude changes are detected by a (typically reluctive) transduction element. The other type utilizes a piezoelectric or magnetostrictive element so designed that it oscillates in a gaseous medium but stops oscillating, due to acoustic damping, when the medium changes to liquid. Oscillation frequencies are chosen in the ultrasonic range for the latter type, and in the low audio-frequency range for the former type.

2.5.1.9 Ultrasonic level sensing. Two categories of ultrasonic sensing methods are employed for level sensing: cavity-resonance sensing and sonic-path sens-

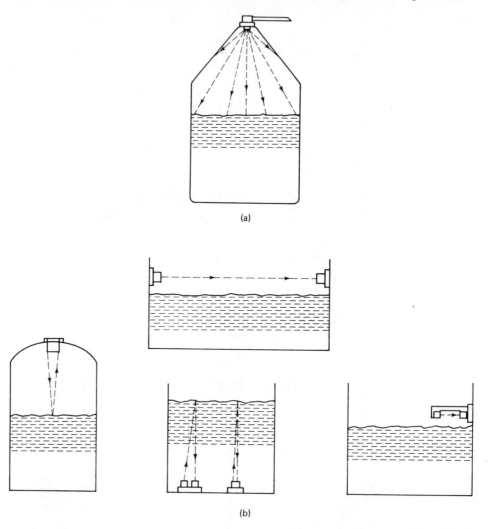

Figure 2-49. Ultrasonic level sensing: (a) cavity-resonance method; (b) ultrasonic-path method.

Fluid-Mechanical Quantities

ing (Figure 2-49). The damped-oscillation ultrasonic sensors, described above, could be considered a third category but deserve separate treatment.

The cavity-resonance method (Figure 2-49a) is a volume-sensing technique from which level can be derived. Electromagnetic oscillations at ultrasonic or radio frequencies are excited within the cavity bounded by tank walls and liquid surface from a coupling element at the top of the tank. As the liquid rises the cavity volume shrinks and its resonant frequency changes accordingly. When the resonant frequency of the empty tank is known and a scaling factor is applied, the volume or level of the liquid can be determined. Variable-frequency oscillators can be used for the resonant-frequency search. The radio-frequency method can be used with dielectric liquids.

Sonic-path methods can be used for continuous-level as well as discrete-level sensing; the reflectance mode is commonly used for the former and the transmittance mode for the latter (see Figure 2-49b). For continuous-level sensing either a separate transmitting and receiving element or a single element, operating alternatingly in the transmitting and receiving mode, can be employed. Pulsed ultrasonic energy is directed at the liquid/gas interface and the travel time of the pulse, reflected back by this interface, is measured. When the velocity of sound in the fluid through which the pulse travels is known, the distance between the transmitting/receiving element(s) and the interface, and hence the liquid level, can be determined. Discrete-level sensors normally use a transmitter and a receiver. When liquid enters the sonic path between the two, the amount of sound energy at the receiver is attenuated significantly (circuit elements can even be adjusted so that the receiver output drops to zero). With the exception of the *gap* type of point-level sensor, transmitting and receiving elements can be either of the wetted or externally mounted type; the latter may not be feasible in some installations or its use may be precluded by characteristics of the measured fluid.

2.5.1.10 Nucleonic level sensing. Radiation emanating from a radioactive source at a constant rate will reach one or more detectors located at the opposite wall of the tank to a lesser degree when the path is through liquid than when it is through gas. Figure 2-50 shows typical sensing configurations, in which S indicates the source and D indicates a detector. Gamma radiation from a source such as ^{137}Cs, ^{60}Co, ^{226}Ra is most commonly used. Its attenuation by liquid is caused mainly by absorption. Single or multiple point-level sensing is accomplished by one source and one or more detectors located at horizontally opposite tank walls. Continuous-level sensing can be achieved by using a vertical radiation path and monitoring the detector output, which will decrease with rising level. Other means of continuous-level sensing involve either the use of long vertical sources and detectors in the form of strips or an electro-mechanical servo control system which raises and lowers source and detector simultaneously so that they follow the liquid/gas interface. In most installations nucleonic level-detection systems can be installed or placed at the outside of the tank (or other vessel); this is their major advantage.

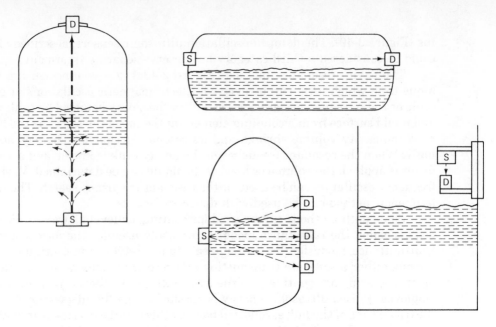

Figure 2-50. Nucleonic level sensing.

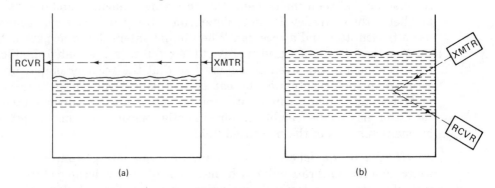

(a)   (b)

Figure 2-51. Microwave level sensing: (a) transmittance; (b) reflectance.

2.5.1.11 Microwave level sensing. The changes of transmittance or reflection of microwave energy when the fluid between a transmitter and a receiver changes from gas to liquid (or quasi-liquid) have been used for point-level sensing (Figure 2-51). When the container wall material is relatively transparent to microwaves, the transmitter and receiver can be mounted external to the container walls. The attenuation of the microwave energy, used for level indication, is dependent on the interaction between instrument characteristics (angle of incidence, wavelength, polarization) and material characteristics (conductivity, permittivity, permeability, surface quality). Pulsed energy at a frequency around 10 GHz is typically employed.

2.5.1.12 Superconductive cryogenic level sensing. Certain metals become superconductive at low cryogenic temperatures; that is, their resistance drops to zero. This principle has been applied to level determinations of liquid helium. Point-level sensing has been achieved with, for example, a niobium film on a quartz substrate. Its resistance becomes zero when in contact with helium at a temperature slightly above its boiling point; hence the niobium film is superconductive when wetted by liquid helium. Use of this principle for continuous-level indications has also been demonstrated, using a niobium–titanium wire connected to a low-capacity constantan-wire heater which is located in the region in which helium is expected to remain in its vapor phase. A portion of the vertically suspended wire is thus sufficiently heated to be nonsuperconductive ("normal"), whereas the portion submerged in liquid helium dissipates this small amount of heat rapidly enough to become superconductive. As the level of the liquid helium rises, an increasing portion of the wire becomes superconductive and the resulting change in the wire's end-to-end resistance can be converted into an IR change (i.e., can be read out as a varying voltage).

2.5.1.13 Variable-coupling liquid-metal level sensing. The variation in mutual inductance between two windings of a transformer due to the relative presence of a conductive liquid has been used for sensing levels of liquid metals. An example of a device employing this technique is a ceramic mandrel, intended for vertical immersion and continuous level sensing, wound bifilarly with primary and secondary windings of nickel-alloy wire. The wound element is protected by a metallic sheath or thermowell. When excited by an ac current, the primary winding causes eddy currents in everything that is adjacent and metallic, including the liquid metal that is wetting the sheath or thermowell. These eddy currents increase as the level of liquid metal rises and wets more of the thermowell. As a result the amount of current induced by coupling into the secondary winding decreases. The output of the secondary winding is, therefore, inversely proportional to liquid level. Levels of metals having boiling points up to about 700 °C have been measured using this technique.

2.5.2 Design and Operation

This section covers typical designs of the more commonly used level sensors and their operation. The gage-pressure and differential-pressure transducers used for level sensing, using the methods described in Section 2.5.1.1, are described in Section 2.6.

2.5.2.1 Float-type level sensors. Level sensors using the buoyancy force acting on a float are usually designed for point-level sensing. A switch is actuated when the float attains a certain position. Some continuous-level sensors exist as well, using either a continuous displacement derived from float motion to actuate a potentiometric or reluctive transduction element, or sensing the continuously variable force acting on a float ("displacer") and employing strain-gage or force-balance transduction to provide an analog output signal proportional to level.

The majority of point-level sensor designs use the interaction between a permanent magnet and a magnetic reed switch to provide their discrete (on/

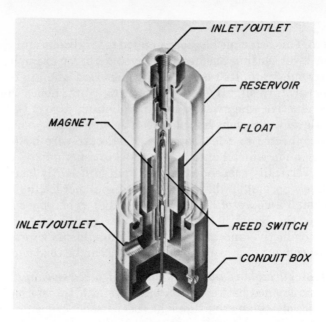

INLET/OUTLET

RESERVOIR

MAGNET

FLOAT

INLET/OUTLET

REED SWITCH

CONDUIT BOX

Figure 2-52. Float-actuated liquid-level switch. (Courtesy of Compac Engineering, Inc.)

off) output signal. In vertically mounted, either immersed or flow-through sensors, a magnet is embedded in an annular float which rides up and down along a sealed (from the measured fluid) tube containing the magnetic reed switch (see Figure 2-52). When the float attains a vertical position such that it is adjacent to the switch, the switch is actuated magnetically. The switch can be normally open or normally closed.

Flow-through sensors are used when access inside the tank is not feasible or not practical. They are connected to appropriate ports in the tank by plumbing. Shutoff valves in the plumbing can be used to permit servicing of the sensor without losing tank pressure or needing to empty the tank first. Directly immersed sensors can be installed from the top (for a "high" level signal) or from the bottom (for a "low" level signal). They can also be installed as a single assembly with two or more floats, with the tube extending from the top to near the bottom of a tank. One float can be limited in travel to a region near the top of the tank and a second float can be limited in travel near the bottom of the tank. One or more additional travel-limited floats can also be placed at intermediate points. A magnetic switch is furnished, within the tube, for each float and their wiring is brought out through the tube. Floats are normally made of a material lighter than the measured liquid; however, a few designs have used a heavier displacer, restrained by a spring which pulls it up when a rising level reduces its "weight."

Side-mounted sensors use the angular displacement at the fulcrum of a lever arm to the end of which a float is attached. The angular motion can be used to bring a permanent magnet into sufficiently close proximity to the magnetic switch to cause actuation, either directly or by employing a cam to provide horizontal linear motion of an annular body containing the magnet. Cylindrical or spherical floats are used in side-mounted sensors. A related design uses a conical float, weighted on one side and connected by a weighted cable to a mounting head. As the level changes, the angular attitude of the float changes accordingly, and one or more mercury switches, each placed at a different angle, are actuated at one or more specified angular attitudes corresponding to various liquid levels.

2.5.2.2 Electromechanical plumb-line-type level sensors. This category of continuous-level sensors is related to the float type but uses a completely different operating principle (see Figure 2-53). An angular-position transducer, typically of the toothed rotor type, is used to indicate the number of turns of a drum as a plumb line, wound on the drum, is unwound until a weight (for granular solids) or a float (for liquids) touches the surface. When this occurs the plumb line loses tension. A tension sensor (force transducer) detects the loss in tension and sends a signal to a direction-changing device (e.g., polarity-reversing relay) that controls a drum-drive motor. The motor then rotates the drum in the opposite direction, winding up the plumb line again and pulling up the weight. The motor stops when the plumb line is wound up completely and the sensor is then ready for repeating the level-sensing cycle. The resolution of the sensor depends strongly on the number of output pulses generated per turn of the drum.

Flexible steel tape is often used as plumb line, and angular encoders have been used as turns-counting transducers. One design uses a disk-shaped float

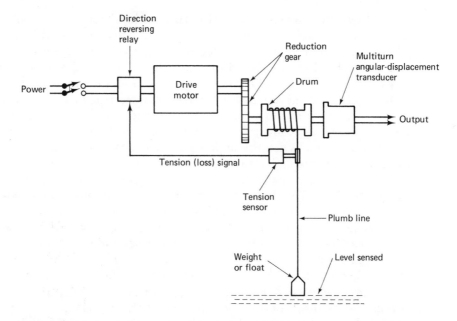

Figure 2-53. Operating principle of plumb-line-type electromechanical level sensors.

balanced by a counter-weight at the opposite end of the tape (float and counter-weight both hang down) and thus operates without motor, tension sensor, and direction-reversal drive. A different but related design employs both, a permanent magnet in an annular float, and a plumb-line turns-counting device. A magnet is mounted to the end of the string instead of a weight or float. This magnet, within a sealed guide tube, moves up and down with the annular float due to flux linkage between the plumb-line magnet and float magnet.

2.5.2.3 Conductivity level sensors. Conductivity probes (which are described in Section 8.2.1) are used for point-level sensing when the liquid is electrically conductive. A typical probe consists of a threaded or flanged mounting head and a metal rod, insulated from the head, of the required length. Dual-level probes contain two such rods, one short (for "high" level sensing) the other long (for "low" level sensing). Conductivity probes are normally installed vertically, from a mounting boss in the top of the tank. The tank wall usually forms one conductive path so that the resistance of the liquid between tank wall and point of immersion is sensed. Metals such as stainless steel or titanium are typically used as electrode rods. Most of the upper portion of the electrode is usually coated with glass, ceramic, or plastic insulation. The probe is typically connected as one leg of an ac-excited Wheatstone bridge. The bridge can be adjusted to allow for the conductivity, or range of conductivities, of the measured fluid. The current through the liquid must be sufficiently small to prevent electrolysis or a potential explosion hazard. Conductivity probes should be designed for ease of removal and reinstallation since they require relatively frequent cleaning.

2.5.2.4 Capacitive level sensors. Continuous-level and point sensors, whose capacitance changes as the dielectric between one or more pairs of electrodes changes, exist in a number of different configurations. Capacitance increases with rising level of the liquid or quasi-liquid, whose dielectric constant is greater than the air or other gas it replaces. A single probe, in the form of a metal (typically steel) rod, insulated from its mounting head, can be immersed vertically downward into a tank and act as one electrode of a capacitor when the tank walls are conductive and the measured fluid has a reasonably high dielectric constant. When the tank walls are nonconductive or when the measured fluid has a low dielectric constant, the metal rod can be mounted within a coaxial metallic cylinder which acts as the second electrode. This cylinder is partly perforated or slotted to permit free flow of liquid and gas. Two or four concentric cylinders can be used for liquids (e.g., some liquified gases) having very low dielectric constants. When severe foaming or sloshing is expected, a stillwell can be built into the tank and the probe immersed into the stillwell.

Single-electrode probes can also be dagger-shaped or provided with rectangular extension plates to increase the surface area when a greater capacitance change is needed. Probes used for point-level sensing are often covered with an anti-fouling coating for a portion of their length. For very long immersion depths the electrode can take the form of a weight at the end of a cable ("cable probe" or "rope probe"). Point-level probes are best side-mounted so that the entire probe length becomes the active electrode sensing the capacitance change when the probe becomes wetted by the measured liquid. Probe design, material, and finish should minimize any adherence of liquid when the level falls. Plate- and blade-type probes are often more suitable for this reason than rod-probes when the measured material is a granular solid. Completely coated insulated probes can be used in conductive liquids; the liquid then acts as the grounded electrode whose height, relative to the probe, increases with rising level. In such cases the changes in capacitance as well as liquid resistance can be measured as changes in impedance (or admittance).

The capacitive element formed by the probe, or by probe and tank wall, is usually connected into one arm of an impedance-bridge circuit excited by low-voltage ac at frequencies between about 400 Hz and over 10 kHz. The output due to bridge unbalance is then amplified and conditioned to either actuate a relay, provide a gated pulse, or furnish an analog or digital continuous display. The cable between probe and electronics should be low-capacitance coaxial shielded cable which should also be constrained as to its length. Many capacitive level sensors overcome the cable problem by packaging the bridge circuit and amplifier, and sometimes further signal conditioning, into the mounting head of the probe.

2.5.2.5 Heat-transfer level sensors. The principle of heat transfer to the measured fluid from a heated element in a probe is used in some point-level sensor designs. Heat transfer is more rapid when the fluid is a liquid than when it is a gas. Thermistors (see Section 4.2), operated at sufficient current to produce some self-heating when they are in air (or another gas), are quite suitable for such applications. As the thermistor comes in contact with liquid its resistance undergoes a step change due to cooling. This resistance change can be converted into a voltage change by such means as a voltage-divider or bridge circuit.

Various heat-balance designs are also used for point-level sensing. In one design a heated resistive element is connected into a bridge circuit with another resistive element connected into an adjacent bridge arm so as to form a differential-temperature sensing circuit. When the probe is immersed in liquid the temperature difference between the two elements will be significantly less than when the probe is in gas. Another design employs a heated thermocouple sensing junction at the probe tip with its reference junction (see Section 4.2) located a small distance away from it but still within the probe envelope. When immersed in liquid, the sensing and reference junctions are at approximately the same temperature. When immersed in gas, the sensing-junction temperature rises above that of the reference junction; as a result, a measurable thermal emf is produced and can be amplified for display or control purposes. Another heat-balance design uses the thermal coefficient of expansion to cause a relay-type contact to be held open when a heated metal rod, provided with a good heat conduction path to the measured fluid, remains heated because the probe is in air. When the probe is in liquid, the metal rod cools due to the increased heat transfer into the liquid, and its contraction causes the contact to close.

Besides thermistors, wirewound resistive elements which are excited to produce self-heating when in gas ("hot-wire probes") have been used for liquid-level sensing, notably for cryogenic liquids. Exposed-element probes, either wound around a hollow mandrel or wound, as planar winding, in the form of a grid supported by small insulating studs, have been used in such applications. The amount of self-heating must be carefully controlled to cause only *nucleate boiling,* that is, the formation of vapor bubbles, at various points of the element, which leave the element and rise to the surface (usually recondensing into liquid before they reach the surface). With further heating the *film boiling* phase is reached, in which an unstable film of vapor is formed along the wire surface, greatly reducing heat transfer from probe to liquid since the film forms an insulating layer. Hot-wire probes can be connected into a Wheatstone-bridge circuit or they can be excited from a constant-current source so that the voltage across their terminals changes when their resistance changes.

2.5.2.6 *Photoelectric level sensors.*

Photoelectric sensors, in the form of a light source installed in one wall and a light sensor installed in the opposite wall, have been used for the detection of fill levels in hoppers and other vessels, mostly with granular solids. When the material reaches the level at which the light beam crosses the vessel, the *transmittance* is either interrupted or greatly used and this causes a drop in the output of the photosensor. The resulting output change can then be used for level indication or control.

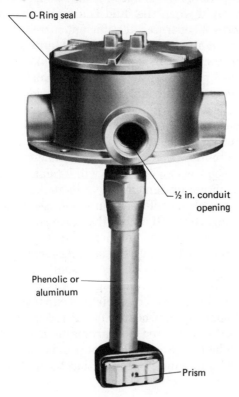

O-Ring seal

½ in. conduit opening

Phenolic or aluminum

Prism

Figure 2-54. Photoelectric point-level sensor using light refraction. (Courtesy of MICRO SWITCH, A Division of Honeywell.)

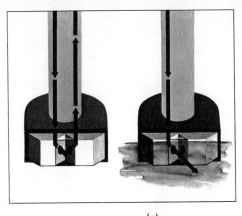

(a)

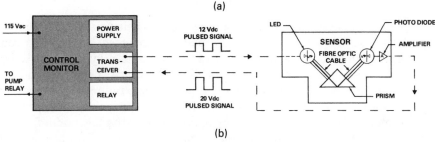

(b)

Figure 2-55. Operation of light-refraction-type photoelectric level sensor: (a) operating principle; (b) block diagram for typical application. (Courtesy of MICRO SWITCH, A Division of Honeywell.)

More commonly used are point-level sensors using the index of refraction of the measured liquid to change *reflectance*. This sensing method is employed in the sensor illustrated in Figure 2-54. The operating principle is shown in Figure 2-55. An optical prism is so designed that a light beam, from source to sensor, is reflected back to the sensor when immersed in gas. When immersed in liquid, however, the index of refraction of the liquid in contact with the prism causes most of the light energy to be directed into the liquid (see Sections 5.4.1 and 5.4.2.4) so that virtually no light is reflected back onto the light sensor (Figure 2-55a). The mounting head of the sensor contains the LED light source and the photodiode light sensor and its associated amplifier. Fiber optics conduct the light beam to and from the prism; hence, the prism and probe stem conduct only light and are nonelectrical in nature, an advantage when the measured fluid is potentially explosive. An electronics unit is connected to the sensor by cabling. It generates a pulsed current to the LED and receives the pulsed signal from the photodiode/amplifier combination. The two pulse streams have different characteristics to avoid erroneous indications. The signal from the sensor is then conditioned into an actuating voltage for the relay (see Figure 2-55b).

2.5.2.7 Electromechanical vibrating-element level sensors. Viscous damping will cause the oscillation amplitude of a vibrating mechanical element to be reduced when the ambient fluid around the element changes from gas to liquid.

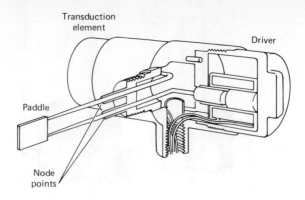

Transduction
element

Driver

Paddle

Node
points

Figure 2-56. Vibrating-paddle point-level sensor.

A simplified typical design of a sensor using this principle is shown in Figure 2-56. The vibrating element is a paddle supported by two thin rods held by seals at their node points (points of minimum oscillation amplitude). One rod is driven so that it causes the paddle to oscillate. The other rod leads to the (reluctive) transduction element, which detects reductions in paddle vibration amplitude when the paddle sees liquid and then provides an appropriate output signal. The oscillation frequency is typically in the low audio-frequency range and can be at or near the line-voltage frequency. Damped-oscillation level sensors operating at ultrasonic frequencies are discussed below.

2.5.2.8 Ultrasonic level sensors. Ultrasonic level sensors employ one of three basic sensing methods: cavity-resonance, damped-oscillation, or sonic-path sensing (see Section 2.5.1). The sensors share one characteristic: their operating frequency is in the ultrasonic range, that is, above the audio-frequency range (and generally well into the radio-frequency, or RF, range). Sensors specifically designed for the cavity-resonance method (acoustic-resonance) are relatively rare and have been used only for specialized applications.

Damped-oscillation ultrasonic point-level sensors can be of the piezoelectric or magnetostrictive type. *Piezoelectric* sensors employ a quartz or ceramic crystal mounted in the tip of a hermetically sealed probe sheath. The crystal, driven by an oscillator circuit, resonates at normal amplitude when immersed in gas and at a significantly reduced amplitude when immersed in liquid. The amplitude change is detected and the detection elements of the circuit provide the discrete output signal. *Magnetostrictive* sensors use an assembly consisting of a drive coil and a feedback coil, both wound on the same ferromagnetic rod, whose tip is in physical contact with the inside surface of the tip of a hermetically sealed probe sheath. The rod (and probe tip, as in piezoelectric sensors) are set into vibration by an oscillator connected to the drive coil. Two effects are employed in the magnetostrictive assembly with its associated circuitry to maintain the rod in longitudinal elastic vibration at a frequency controlled by the characteristics of the rod (typically around 40 kHz): when an iron rod is subjected to a longitudinal magnetic field, it increases slightly in length, whereas a nickel rod would decrease in length under these conditions *(Joule effect);* a change of magnetic induction occurs within the ferromagnetic rod under longitudinal stress *(Villari effect)*. The drive and feedback coils are connected in a current-driven feedback oscillator, with signal levels so adjusted as to maintain oscillation in the rod only when the probe tip is exposed to a compressible fluid such as air, froth, or foam. As soon as the probe tip encounters a noncompressible fluid (a liquid), the vibration is damped and the oscillation stops; output-conditioning circuitry provides a resulting discrete output signal. The circuitry can be contained in a separate box, with interconnecting cables kept short to minimize their capacitance, or it can be packaged into the probe head. The liquid sensed by such point-level sensors should not contain any material that may remain on the probe tip and dry and then harden.

Sonic-path ultrasonic sensors are used for continuous-level sensing in the reflectance mode and for point-level sensing in the transmittance mode. For both types of sensing either a single element (usually a piezoelectric crystal), acting alternatingly as transmitter or receiver, or a pair of elements, one acting as transmitter, the other as receiver, can be employed. Continuous-level sensors generally see the surface of the liquid from the top of the tank, sometimes (particularly when the level of an interface between two dissimilar liquids is to be sensed) from the bottom of the tank. Typically, the transmitter is excited by repetitive pulses of ultrasonic energy which are then reflected back to the receiver, and the time elapsed between pulse transmission and reception is a measure of the distance between sensors and surface and, hence, of level.

Point-level ultrasonic sensors can be installed from the top of a tank (when the surface rises close enough to the top that the probe need not be too long) or from the side. Many such sensors are of the gap type; that is, a single assembly contains both receiver and transmitter separated by a relatively small distance and a discrete output signal is generated when liquid (or granular solids) fill the gap. A sensor of this type, for use with liquids, is shown in Figure 2-57. The gap is sized by the thin metal rod between the probe body and probe tip. Body and tip contain the transmitter and receiver, respectively, facing each other across the gap. All associated excitation and signal conditioning, including the relay actuated by output-conditioning circuitry, is contained in an assembly mounted under the cover. The electronics assembly operates directly off the line voltage (a power supply is also included in the package). Terminals are also provided for a normally open as well as a normally closed relay contact. A variation of this design is used in the cryogenic level sensor shown in Figure 2-58. Again, transmitting and receiving crystals face each other across the gap (which should be kept vertical when the probe is side-mounted). This sensor is usable for liquids whose temperature can be as low as 60 K (below the nitrogen boiling point). The associated circuitry is in a separate box. The small gap used in both of the sensors illustrated allows very small crystals and very low power to be used.

Somewhat larger crystals and more power are needed for the level detection of granular solids. A side-mounted gap-type sensor for such applications is shown in Figure 2-59 (a similar design is available for top mounting). The transmitting crystal and receiving crystal face each other across a 10-cm gap.

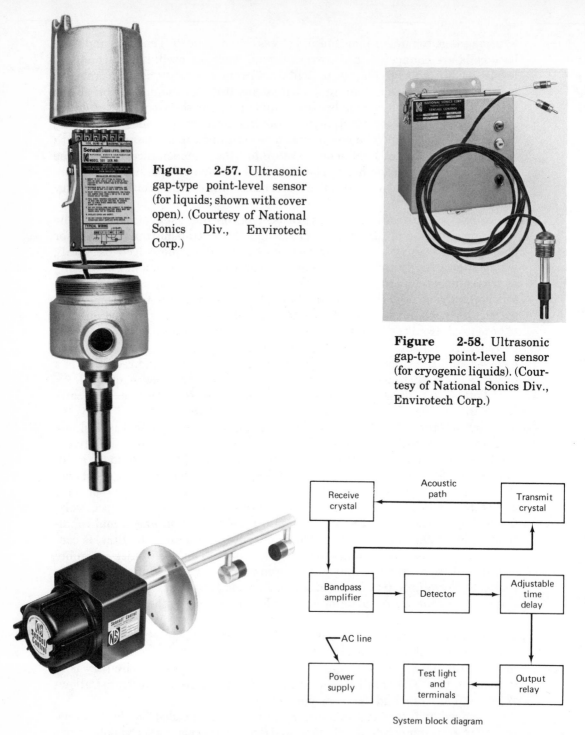

Figure 2-57. Ultrasonic gap-type point-level sensor (for liquids; shown with cover open). (Courtesy of National Sonics Div., Envirotech Corp.)

Figure 2-58. Ultrasonic gap-type point-level sensor (for cryogenic liquids). (Courtesy of National Sonics Div., Envirotech Corp.)

System block diagram

Figure 2-59. Ultrasonic gap-type point-level sensor (for dry products). (Courtesy of National Sonics Div., Envirotech Corp.)

The sensor illustrated has integrally packaged circuitry, whose elements are shown in the block diagram. Separate circuitry packages are also available. Interconnecting cables should be protected by conduit.

Sensor pairs installed separately and facing each other across the inside of a pipe, hopper, tank, or open duct are used in many applications. Long gap-type probes can be equipped with two gaps, with a crystal pair associated with each gap, where one gap corresponds to a "low" level and the other to a "high" level. Special sensor designs are used for point-level detection of the interface between two liquids. Some applications permit the use of externally mounted (cemented or clamp-on) sensors.

2.5.2.9 Nucleonic level sensors. Nucleonic level sensing systems are usable when the level inside containers must be sensed and neither openings in the container are permitted nor the use of clamp-on sensors is feasible. Such sensor systems consist of three major elements: a source of nuclear radiation, usually gamma rays; one or more radiation detectors; and the electronics associated with the detector. For point-level sensing a source emitting a narrow conical beam is typically used, mounted opposite the radiation detector. For multi-point-level and continuous-level sensing a source emitting a fan-shaped beam is used in conjunction with either a long detector (see Figure 2-60) or two or more individual detectors.

The *radiation source* contains the radioactive isotope that emits the gamma rays. Americium (^{241}Am, energy 0.066 MeV, half-life 455 years) and radium (^{226}Ra, energy 1.5 MeV, half-life 1620 years) have been used in some sources; however, cobalt (^{60}Co, energy 1.25 MeV, half-life 5.5 years) and, es-pecially, cesium (^{137}Cs, energy 0.66 MeV, half-life 30 years) are most commonly used. The source is always enclosed in a *source holder,* which not only provides shielding of the activated source in all directions except the viewing direction and must meet rigid radiation safety standards, but also provides for a (usually mechanical) "shutter" or positioning device that either rotates the source away from its viewing port or places a radiation shield between it and the viewing port. A source holder with the source in the "off" position must be capable of meeting radiation safety standards in all directions, so that it is completely safe during shipping, handling, installation, and maintenance.

The *detector* is usually a Geiger–Mueller tube (Geiger counter) or an ionization chamber (see Chapter 6). The *electronics* are those necessary to provide excitation potentials to the detector and condition the output of the detector. Ion chambers, with their associated electronics, have been used to form the "long" detector needed for continuous-level monitoring. Level sensing is based on the amount of radiation absorbed in the path between source and detector. The thickness and density of the material in this path are usually expressed in terms of *half-value thickness* (inversely proportional to material density), or "half-value layer," the thickness of a material necessary to reduce incident radiation by 50%. Hence, two half-value thicknesses reduce the ra-diation by 75%; for example, for a ^{137}Cs source, the half-value of thickness of steel is 1.5 cm and two such thicknesses (or layers), 3 cm of steel, would reduce

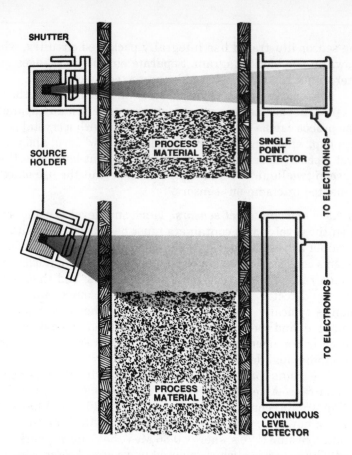

Figure 2-60. Schematic presentation of nucleonic point-level and continuous-level sensor systems. (Courtesy of Kay-Ray Inc.)

an incident radiation of 10 milliroentgens per hour (mR/h) to 2.5 mr/h. Safety of the installation can be determined from this (the radiation penetrates two wall thicknesses and no additional material when only air or gas is in the transmission path). The required radiation at the source, in millicuries, also depends on the container half-value thickness as well as on the measured material, the detector threshold (dosage required at the detector), a dosage constant given by type of radioactive material used, and the square of the distance between source and detector. When more than one point-level detector is used, the difference in transmission path length due to angle must be considered in sizing the source and adjusting the gain of each detector.

2.5.3 Design and Performance Characteristics

Mechanical characteristics of level sensors are given by their specification drawing supplemented by statements of such items as operating and proof-pressure rating, materials in contact with measured fluid, recommended installation method, and rating of probe and head in terms of applicable industrial or governmental codes (e.g., explosion-proof, corrosive atmosphere, radiation safety). The latter also applies to any separately mounted electronics unit. Outline and mounting dimensions and details of mounting provisions are shown for electronics boxes as well as probe assemblies; additionally, for the latter, relative locating dimensions of the sensing element relative to the level sensed as well as any plumbing connections should be stated. The physical and chemical characteristics of the measured fluid must be known, of course, since they are of primary criticality to the selection of a particular type of sensor.

Electrical characteristics include type of line voltage and power, any limitations on cable length and protection, insulation resistance of the probe, and output characteristics, including, for continuous-level systems, the output impedance. Intrinsic safety in accordance with applicable codes, if provided, should also be stated. All external connections must be identified.

Performance characteristics for point-level sensors are essentially limited to level-sensing accuracy (expressed in terms of unit of height, e.g., " ± 0.5 cm") and time constant or (typically 98%) response time; if the latter is different for rising and falling level, both values should be shown. Repeatability is often shown, with a tolerance smaller than the overall accuracy tolerance. For continuous level sensors (and their associated electronics) the measuring range and output range are shown, together with tolerances on sensitivity or end points and on linearity, hysteresis, and repeatability.

Environmental characteristics comprise, primarily, the operating temperature range (the fluid temperature range is part of measured-fluid characteristics, of course) of the probe head and the electronics unit as well as cabling; secondarily, they should include all other significant environmental conditions, such as atmospheric conditions, vibration, shock, noise level, magnetic fields, electromagnetic interference, and nuclear-radiation levels if such conditions are expected to occur and to have potentially deleterious effects on sensor system operation.

2.6 PRESSURE

Basic concepts underlying the measurement of pressure are described in Section 2.1.3, and units of measurement in Section 2.1.4. The SI unit for pressure is the *pascal (Pa);* however, it is the *kilopascal* that has become accepted as a more convenient unit to use (1 kPa = 1000 Pa). Table 2-1 shows all applicable conversion factors. Again for convenience, the conversions can often be rounded off as follows (the Pa is the name for the unit N/m^2):

$$1 \text{ psi} = 6.895 \text{ kPa (approx. 7 kPa)}; \quad 1 \text{ kPa} = 0.145 \text{ psi (approx. 0.15 psi)}$$
$$1 \text{ atm} = 101.3 \text{ kPa (approx. 101 kPa)}; \quad 1 \text{ kPa} = 0.00987 \text{ atm}$$
$$1 \text{ bar} = 100.00 \text{ kPa (exactly 100 kPa)}; \quad 1 \text{ kPa} = 0.01 \text{ bar} = 10 \text{ mbar}$$
$$1 \text{ in Hg} = 3.386 \text{ kPa (approx. 3.4 kPa)}; \quad 1 \text{ kPa} = 0.295 \text{ (approx. 0.3) in Hg}$$
$$1 \text{ in H}_2\text{O} = 0.249 \text{ kPa (approx. 0.25 kPa)}; \quad 1 \text{ kPa} = 4 \text{ in H}_2\text{O}$$

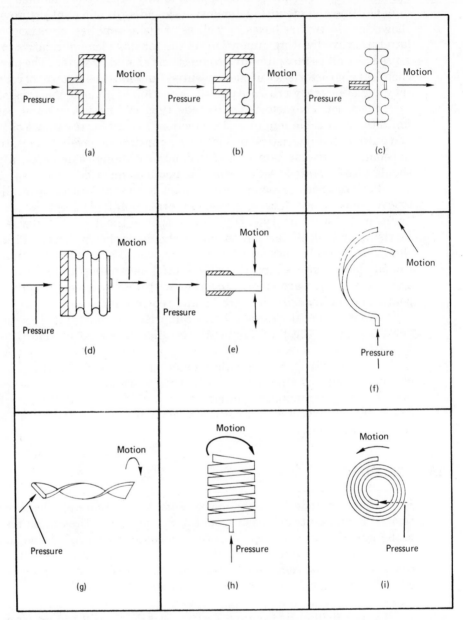

Figure 2-61. Pressure sensing elements: (a) flat diaphragm; (b) corrugated diaphragm; (c) capsule; (d) bellows; (e) straight tube; (f) C-shaped Bourdon tube; (g) twisted Bourdon tube; (h) helical Bourdon tube; (i) spiral Bourdon tube.

Refer to Section 2.1.5 for explanations of pressure–depth and pressure–altitude.

2.6.1 Sensing Methods

Pressure is essentially always sensed by a mechanical sensing element, an elastic member such as a plate, shell, or tube, which offers the pressure *(force)* a surface *(area)* to act upon. Pressure is measured as force per unit area (N/m²). When this force is not balanced by an equal force acting upon the opposite surface of the sensing element, the element is caused to deflect. This deflection is then transduced (by a transduction element) as either displacement or strain. The most commonly used sensing elements are illustrated in Figure 2-61. The motion produced by the deflection of a flat diaphragm, a straight tube, and, to a large extent, also of a corrugated diaphragm are typically not transduced as a displacement (except by transduction elements that can respond to such very small deflections, e.g., a capacitive element) but, more frequently, as strain (hoop strain in the case of the straight tube).

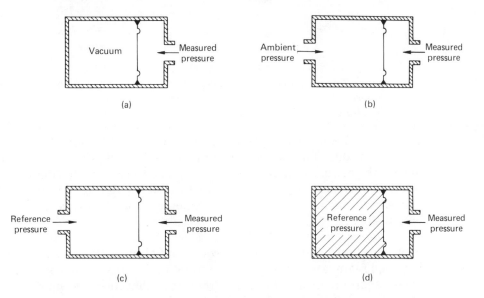

Figure 2-62. Pressure reference configurations: (a) absolute pressure; (b) gage pressure; (c) differential pressure; (d) differential pressure, sealed reference.

Although all pressure-sensing elements really respond to a change in differential pressure across them, transducers can be designed to measure either differential, gage, or absolute pressure, depending on the *reference pressure* maintained in, or admitted to, the reference side of the element. The basic pressure reference configurations are shown in Figure 2-62, with a diaphragm used to examplify the sensing element. The reference side of an *absolute-pressure* sensing element is evacuated and sealed. *Gage pressure* is measured when the reference side is vented to ambient pressure. A *differential-pressure* sensing element deflects with an increasing difference between two pressures, both of which may vary. It has become customary to call the normally lower and less-varying pressure the *reference pressure* and the other pressure the *measured pressure* (although the latter may vary between levels lower as well as higher than the reference pressure). In a special version of the differential-pressure configuration (Figure 2-62d) a fixed pressure which is greater than zero is permanently maintained on the reference side.

The measured pressure applied to hollow sensing elements is traditionally shown as entering the sensing element. Equivalent operation can usually be obtained by using the inside of such an element as the reference side and applying the measured pressure to the cavity surrounding the element (Figure 2-63). Except for the absolute-pressure configuration, sensing elements can normally be used for measurements of pressure above as well as below the pressure maintained or existing at the reference side.

Figure 2-63. Application of measured pressure to sensing element (shown for absolute-pressure transducer): (a) pressure into sensing element; (b) pressure into cavity.

A *diaphragm* is essentially a thin circular plate fastened continuously around its edge. Two basic types of diaphragms are used in pressure transducers: the flat diaphragm (Figure 2-61a) and the corrugated diaphragm (Figure 2-61b). Exact calculations are required for diaphragm design; recent developments include the use of computer-assisted design for diaphragm optimization.

Flat diaphragms (Figure 2-64) deflect in accordance with laws generally applicable to circular plates under conditions of symmetrical loading. The basic flat diaphragm is an uninterrupted straight circular web supported at its edge. Diaphragms are either machined from stock that includes their edge support as well as additional portions of the transducer, or they are formed separately and then welded (sometimes brazed) to their support. In the *spherical diaphragm* the web is slightly concave. The *catenary diaphragm* (Latin: *catena*, chain) is additionally supported by the edge of an inner ring or tube concentric with the structure to which the web is fastened. *Drum-head diaphragms* are bent around and fastened to the outside of their supporting structure while radial tension is applied to stretch the diaphragm. An *annular diaphragm*, which can be flush or recessed, is a diaphragm with a central reinforcement ("boss") to facilitate the translation of its deflection into a secondary mechanical displacement.

Corrugated diaphragms contain a number of concentric corrugations

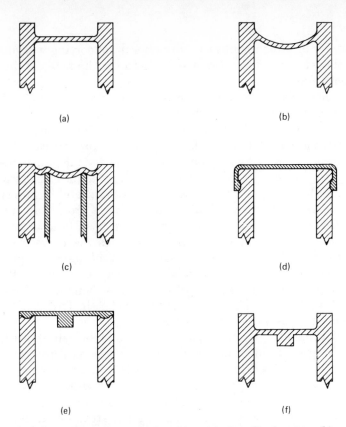

Figure 2-64. Flat diaphragms: (a) flat diaphragm; (b) spherical diaphragm; (c) catenary diaphragm; (d) drumhead diaphragm; (e) annular diaphragm (flush); (f) annular diaphragm (recessed).

Figure 2-65. Corrugated diaphragm.

(Figures 2-61b and 2-65). These increase the stiffness as well as the effective area of the diaphragm, thus providing a larger useful deflection than that of a flat diaphragm. The corrugations become progressively shallower from the periphery toward the center because bending is maximum near the periphery and minimum at the center.

The deflection of a diaphragm varies inversely to the 1.2 to 1.6 power of its thickness and approximately the fourth power of its diameter. Within the limits of deflection that changes linearly with pressure (usable deflection), deflection is proportional to pressure; it is also influenced by the design of the corrugations (if any), the material and its preparation and treatment, the manner of attachment to its peripheral supporting wall (and its fillet radius at the wall interface, if machined) and the diameter of the central reinforcement (if any).

Materials used for diaphragms are elastic metal alloys such as brass, bronze, phosphor bronze, beryllium copper, stainless steel (a predominant material), and such proprietary alloys as Monel, Inconel-X, and Ni-Span-C (a ferrous nickel alloy with good thermal properties). Choice of diaphragm material is strongly influenced by the chemical properties of the measured fluid that comes in contact with the diaphragm. Heat treating and pressure cycling help reduce elastic after-effects (drift) and hysteresis in diaphragms.

Membranes are soft diaphragms made from thin metal sheet or from rubber, neoprene, or plastics. They have been used as pressure-sensing elements, backed by a spring which provides the necessary elastic properties. More often they are used as *isolation diaphragms,* to prevent incompatible fluids from coming in contact with the sensing element; the volume between sensing element and isolation diaphragm is then filled with a compatible liquid such as silicon oil *(transfer fluid)* to transfer the force due to pressure from the membrane to the sensing element.

A *capsule* (sometimes called "aneroid") consists of two annular corrugated diaphragms, formed into shells of opposite curvature and sealed together at their peripheries (Figures 2-61c and 2-66). In a single capsule, one diaphragm is provided with a pressure port, the other with a boss from which the mechanical displacement originates. Alternatively, one diaphragm is provided with an internal boss to which a pushrod is attached; the pushrod leads through a port in the opposite diaphragm at which pressure (usually reference pressure) is admitted into the capsule. The use of two diaphragms in the form of a capsule

Figure 2-66. Capsules (left: triple; right: single).

nearly doubles the deflection obtained from a single diaphragm. Additional multiplication of deflection can be obtained by ganging two or more capsules together (Figure 2-66).

Bellows (Figures 2-61d and 2-67) are typically made from thin-walled tubing formed into deep convolutions and sealed at one end, which displaces axially when pressure is applied to a port in its opposite end. The number of convolutions can vary from less than 10 to over 20, depending on pressure range and displacement *(stroke)* requirements and on outside diameter. Since inside diameters of bellows range between 50 and 90% of outside diameter, the effective area of one convolution is substantially less than that of a capsule. Bellows have been used mainly for low pressure ranges and when no significant vibration exists in their environment. They have also been used for isolation, in the same manner as described for membranes, above, incorporated within a transducer. Additionally, they have found use as *expansion bellows,* sealed at both ends and containing an inert gas at low pressure, to compensate for

Figure 2-67. Bellows.

changes in the volume of damping oil, due to temperature changes, in viscous-damped transducers.

The *straight-tube* sensing element has been used in a limited number of transducer designs. The tube, of circular cross section, is sealed at one end; it expands and contracts with changes in the pressure admitted into its open end. These minute displacements are transduced either as strain or as changes in the resonant frequency of the tube (in a vibrating-element transducer).

The Bourdon tube (Figures 2-61f–i and 2-68) is a curved or twisted tube, oval or elliptical in cross section, which is sealed at one end (the *tip*). When pressure is applied into its open end, the tube tends to straighten. This results

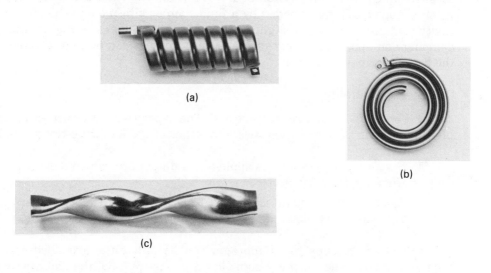

(a)

(b)

(c)

Figure 2-68. Bourdon tubes: (a) helical; (b) spiral; (c) twisted.

in an angular tip deflection in a twisted tube and in a curvilinear tip deflection *(tip travel)* in curved tubes. The Bourdon tube is named after the French inventor Eugene Bourdon, who patented it in 1849, although it was reportedly built and used by a German locomotive engineer prior to that date.

The *C-shaped Bourdon tube* (Figure 2-61f) has an angle of curvature between 180 and 270° and tip travel is outward with increasing pressure. A related element is the *U-shaped Bourdon tube,* which has its pressure port at the center of its about 270° curve; both tips are sealed and travel outward and away from each other with increasing pressure. The *helical Bourdon tube* is similar in deflection behavior to a C-shaped tube. Since it is coiled into a multiturn helix, with a total angle of curvature of 1800 to 3600°, its tip travel is proportionately greater. The *spiral Bourdon tube* also amplifies tip travel due to its multiturn configuration (typically between four and eight turns). The *twisted Bourdon tube* is a flattened tube, twisted along its length (about two to five twists), with the centerline of the tube straight throughout its length.

The deflection of a Bourdon tube varies with the ratio of its major to minor cross-sectional axes, the tube length, the radius of curvature and total angle (rate of twist of a twisted tube), and with applied pressure; it also varies inversely to tube wall thickness and to the modulus of elasticity of the tube material after processing (including heat treating). Materials are similar to those used (and described) for diaphragms; additionally, quartz has been used in at least one design. Metal tubes can be machined from bar stock or drawn, flattened, and then formed into the desired configuration. Great care is taken to achieve a leakproof seal at the tip and at the pressure port. Pressure cycling as well as temperature cycling is needed to provide long-term stability and a repeatable thermal behavior. Multiturn Bourdon tubes tend to be vibration-sensitive and, when their environment will include vibration, are often damped using viscous damping provided by a fluid such as silicone oil. The oil fills a cavity containing, and just slightly larger than, the tube. Thermal effects on damping and apparent changes in reference pressure can be counteracted by the use of expansion bellows.

2.6.2   Design and Operation

2.6.2.1 Capacitive pressure transducers. The capacitive transduction principle is utilized in pressure transducers in either of the following two designs:

1. *Single-stator:* pressure is applied to a diaphragm which moves to and from a stationary electrode *(stator)*.

2. *Dual-stator:* pressure is applied to a diaphragm supported between two stationary electrodes.

In single-stator designs the diaphragm can be either the grounded or the ungrounded electrode. In the design shown in Figure 2-69, the diaphragm is integrally machined with its support member; it moves toward the stator

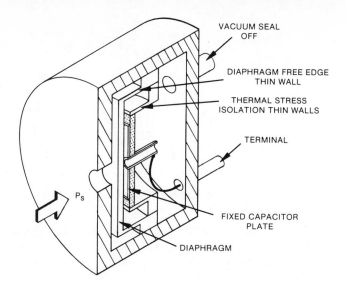

VACUUM SEAL
OFF

DIAPHRAGM FREE EDGE
THIN WALL

THERMAL STRESS
ISOLATION THIN WALLS

TERMINAL

P_s

FIXED CAPACITOR
PLATE

DIAPHRAGM

Figure 2-69. Single-stator capacitive absolute-pressure transducer. (Courtesy of Rosemount Inc.)

electrode (on an insulating substrate); full-scale diaphragm deflection is about 0.1 mm; a lead connects the stator to an external terminal; the case acts as the other terminal. The internal cavity of the absolute-pressure transducer shown is evacuated and then sealed. The diaphragm is of the (patented) "free-edge" type: the free edge acts as a hinge when pressure is applied to the diaphragm, reducing stress levels by a factor of about 5 over typical prestressed flat diaphragms; this reduces hysteresis and nonrepeatability.

Insulated stators, or, as used in other designs, insulated diaphragms are now frequently made of quartz or ceramic with the electrode vacuum-deposited or sputtered onto the substrate.

Dual-stator designs offer the advantage of a multiplication of the capacitance change, since, as the diaphragm deflects, its capacitance to one stator increases while it simultaneously decreases to the other stator. This effect is best utilized by connecting the two halves of the sensor as two arms in an ac bridge (Figure 2-72). In the transducer shown in Figure 2-70, the diaphragm is grounded by a welded seal to the case and the two metallized electrodes on ceramic substrates have external lead connections. This design also uses two isolating diaphragms (isolating membranes) and a transfer fluid to isolate the sensing cavity from the measured fluid as well as reducing shock and vibration effects and providing a fluid with a known and invariable dielectric constant between the capacitor electrodes. Use of appropriate metal alloys for the isolation diaphragms also enables the transducer to be used for corrosive measured fluids. Figure 2-71 shows the dual-stator sensor in a rugged housing intended for industrial applications. The cylindrical box on top of the transducer contains the excitation- and signal-conditioning circuitry; the latter can provide the frequently required two-wire, 4 to 20 mA or 10 to 50 mA dc output signal.

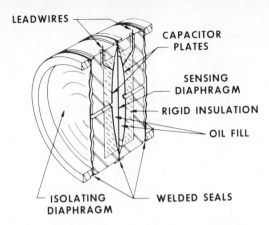

LEADWIRES

CAPACITOR PLATES

SENSING DIAPHRAGM

RIGID INSULATION

OIL FILL

ISOLATING DIAPHRAGM

WELDED SEALS

Figure 2-70. Dual-stator capacitive differential-pressure transducer. (Courtesy of Rosemount Inc.)

Figure 2-71. Capacitive differential pressure transducer in industrial-type configuration. (Courtesy of Rosemount Inc.)

Circuitry associated with capacitive sensors typically include the oscillator, which applies ac (in the audio-frequency range, sometimes in the RF range) to the sensor, which can be connected into a bridge circuit (Figure 2-72) or other circuit, an amplifier and detector or demodulator for the output signal so that a dc output signal can be furnished, and temperature-compensation as well as output-adjustment (gain, zero, linearity) stages. Capacitive pressure transducers are typically used for relatively low pressure ranges (to about 800 kPa), and some designs are suitable for vacuum measurements (see Section 2.7.2); at least one design, however, is available in ranges up to 70 MPa.

2.6.2.2 Inductive pressure transducers. In an inductive pressure transducer (Figure 2-73) the self-inductance of a single coil is varied by pressure-induced

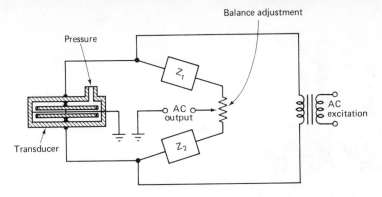

Figure 2-72. Basic bridge connection schematic for dual-stator capacitive pressure transducer.

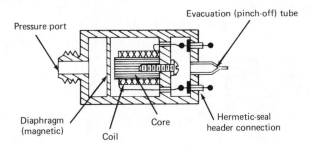

Figure 2-73. Inductive pressure transducer.

changes in displacement of a metallic diaphragm in close proximity to the coil. Past designs used a diaphragm of magnetic material and its motion to and from the ferric core around which the coil is wound, or actuation of a movable ferromagnetic core within a coil, to obtain the inductance changes. Such designs are still in use. Some more recent designs use a metallic diaphragm and a coil excited by ac current at RF frequencies to use the changes in eddy currents in the diaphragm for obtaining the self-inductance changes; a second (reference) coil is often included in the same housing; it remains unaffected by pressure variations and provides compensation for temperature changes. Inductive pressure transducers are used much less than the related reluctive transducers (see Section 2.6.5).

2.6.2.3 Potentiometric pressure transducers. Potentiometric transduction was used in some of the earliest pressure transducers developed. Over the many intervening years a large variety of designs have been produced for a multitude of applications. Since their output varies between 0 and 100% of the applied excitation voltage, they are inherently high-level-output devices needing no amplification in most applications.

Single or multiple capsules are used for relatively low pressure ranges and Bourdon tubes (helical, spiral, or twisted) are used for high-pressure ranges; the region of overlap (where either type of sensing element can be used) is around 3.5 MPa (500 psi). Although units with a range below 7 kPa

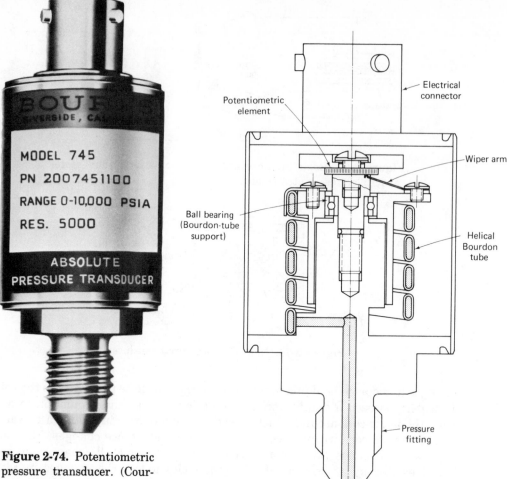

Figure 2-74. Potentiometric pressure transducer. (Courtesy of Bourns, Inc.)

Figure 2-75. Internal layout of potentiometric pressure transducer. (Courtesy of Bourns, Inc.)

(1 psi) have been produced, the ranges of the more commonly used production models extend from 100 kPa (15 psi) to 70 MPa (10 000 psi). A high-pressure transducer is shown in Figure 2-74; this configuration mounts directly into a boss at the point of measurement (with a compression-type washer or O-ring used as seal). As illustrated in Figure 2-75, a helical Bourdon tube is used as sensing element in this transducer. The tube tip is attached to a rotary support, which rides on ball bearings. The (electrically insulated) wiper arm is attached to this support and slides over an exposed strip on the (otherwise insulated-wire) resistance element. The entire cavity, containing Bourdon tube and transduction element, is usually filled with silicone oil for purposes of vibration damping.

High-pressure transducers using multiturn or multitwist Bourdon tubes usually need no amplification linkage to drive the wiper arm over the potentiometric element, which varies in length between about 5 and 20 mm. Low-pressure transducers, however, often require some mechanical amplification, since the displacement obtained from a single capsule is only in the order of 1 mm. Lever or flexure linkages have been used for this purpose, and jewel pivots as well as ball bearings have been employed in such mechanisms. Mechanical overpressure stops are often included to limit the displacement of the sensing element and keep the wiper arm from traveling beyond the end of the resistance element. Some overrange can be handled by winding the element a little longer than its nominal resistance requires and then shorting a number of turns at the "high" end with solder to form a short bus bar.

Vibration damping has been effected by other means besides filling the close-fitting cavity with silicone oil (or similar viscous damping liquid); counterbalance weights and pneumatic dashpots have also been used for this purpose.

The potentiometric resistance elements can be wirewound, or they can be made of conductive plastic; conductive ceramics (cermets), carbon-film, and metal-film elements have also been used but have been found to be generally less producible or satisfactory. Wirewound elements are typically made by winding between 300 and 600 turns of precious-metal or nickel-alloy wire, 0.008 to 0.05 mm diameter (platinum alloy is often used) around a flat, oval, or round mandrel which should be of a material that matches the wire in temperature coefficient of expansion. Epoxy or ceramic cements are sometimes used to fix the winding in position on the mandrel. Use of bare wire requires very precise spacing between turns to avoid turns shorting to each other. Wire coated with a thin insulation is frequently used. After completion of all processes on the element, the insulation is then carefully abraded so that a thin strip of bare wire contacts are provided for the wiper arm to slide over. Wipers are usually stamped from spring alloy and grooved or dimpled to provide a narrow contact surface. Other wiper designs include a slim spring-alloy arm to the bottom of which a precious-metal wire is attached to provide the required narrow contact surface. Wiper contact pressure must be carefully controlled; it must be high enough to prevent lift-off or noise and low enough to minimize friction error that can be caused by wiper drag and, generally, minimize friction, which reduces wiper or element life.

Potentiometric pressure transducers may incorporate more than one transduction element; two separate wiper arms can be caused to move over their respective resistance elements by the same sensing element. The elements can be identical or one can be linear while the other provides a specific type of nonlinearity or one or more discrete-level outputs (switch outputs). Other such transducers incorporate a nonlinear sensing element or potentiometric element (or both) to provide an output linear with altitude (pressure–altitude, see Table 2-2) or with airspeed (derived from a Pitot-static tube and using a differential-pressure transducer to obtain an output linear with indicated airspeed on aircraft).

The sensing element of an absolute or gage pressure transducer can be exposed to a variety of measured fluids, depending on choice of element material (some materials withstand corrosive fluids). The cavity of a differential-pressure transducer (which also contains the transduction element) can be filled with a transfer fluid such as silicone oil and sealed by an isolation membrane to which an otherwise incompatible fluid can then be applied. Gage pressure transducers usually vent their reference side to the ambient atmosphere through a filter or porous plus (*gage vent*) to protect the cavity from atmospheric contaminants (to a limited extent; severe contaminant levels may dictate the use of an absolute-pressure transducer).

2.6.2.4 Resistive pressure transducers. A number of different designs were developed that use resistance changes in certain conductive materials when pressure acts directly on the material. Thus, carbon powder has been used in some designs (the earliest microphones were based on this material and principle) and stacked carbon disks were used similarly, with a diaphragm or bellows as force-summing member. Carbon resistors have also been used in this manner with two resistors, in opposite arms of a Wheatstone bridge, exposed to the measured fluid and the other two resistors, also carbon, shielded from this pressure. Carbon undergoes a decrease of resistance when pressurized. A similar phenomenon was observed in resinous mixtures of rare earths (lanthanide-series elements) and zirconium tetrachloride; this material has also been used in pressure transducers.

The only material that is used in commercially available sensors, however, is *manganin,* an alloy of approximately 84% Cu, 12% Mn, and 4% Ni. This material is used in the form of wire, loosely coiled or shaped in a grid pattern (similar to a metal-wire strain gage), or as foil (photoetched in a pattern resembling a metal-foil strain gage) which can be purchased as such and installed by the user or as incorporated in a complete transducer assembly; in either form they are often referred to as *manganin gages.* The pressure sensitivity of manganin wire and foil is usually between 2.1 and 2.8 microhms/ohm/kPa (0.0021 to 0.0028 ohms/ohm/kbar). Manganin gages are probably the most suitable sensors for very high pressures. Pressures to about 1400 MPa (14 kbar) are commonly measured with manganin gages and transient pressures (e.g., in high-pressure shock-wave studies) to over 40 TPa (400 kbar) have been measured experimentally. Research has also been reported on high-pressure sensors using resistance changes in monocrystalline tellurium and indium antimonide (performance improved when the two materials were connected in series and both exposed to the pressure), and current or voltage changes in planar transistors on which the pressure is caused to act directly.

2.6.2.5 Reluctive pressure transducers. This category includes two major types of reluctive transduction elements used in pressure transducers: the differential transformer (usually the linear variable differential transformer or LVDT) and the two-coil inductance bridge. The former uses capsules, bellows, or Bourdon tubes as sensing elements, and the latter uses diaphragms or Bourdon tubes as sensing elements.

Inductance-bridge reluctive pressure transducers use a magnetically permeable member to increase the inductance of one coil while decreasing the inductance in the second coil. The coils are connected in a bridge circuit so that the increase and decrease in inductance of the two coils, respectively, are additive in the resulting bridge-output voltage change. When a diaphragm is used (Figure 2-76), the diaphragm itself is the magnetically permeable inductance-changing member. When a Bourdon tube is used as the sensing element, as in the transducer illustrated in Figure 2-78, it is usually a twisted Bourdon tube to whose tip a strip of magnetically permeable material (an *armature*) is attached; the armature is located between the two coils and their inductances change simultaneously in opposite directions as the flux gaps of the two coils are changed by the armature moving away from one coil and toward the other coil.

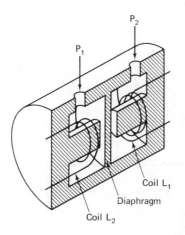

Figure 2-76. Reluctance change by diaphragm deflection.

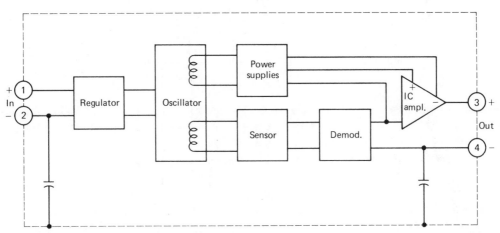

Figure 2-77. Typical dc-to-dc reluctive pressure transducer block diagram. (Courtesy of Bourns, Inc.)

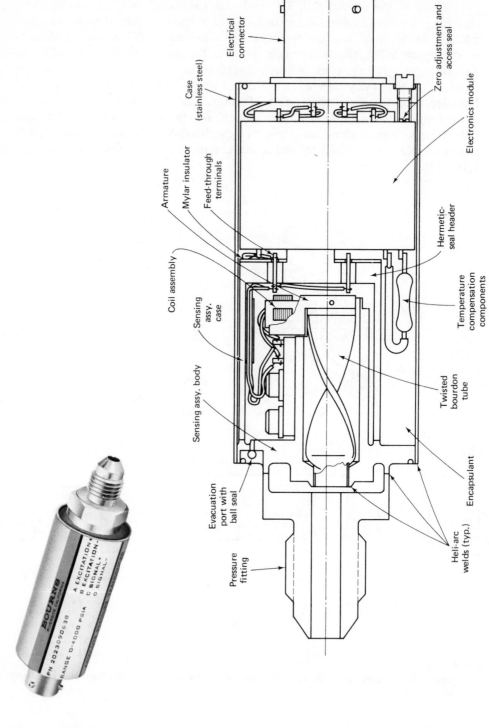

Figure 2-78. Reluctive, dc output pressure transducer with twisted-Bourdon-tube sensing element. (Courtesy of Bourns, Inc.)

Electrical connector

Case (stainless steel)

Armature

Mylar insulator

Feed-through terminals

Coil assembly

Sensing assy. case

Sensing assy. body

Evacuation port with ball seal

Pressure fitting

Zero adjustment and access seal

Electronics module

Hermetic-seal header

Temperature compensation components

Twisted bourdon tube

Encapsulant

Heli-arc welds (typ.)

BOURNS
PRESSURE CALIFORNIA
PN 202390638
RANGE 0-1000 PSIA
A EXCITATION+
B EXCITATION-
C SIGNAL+
D SIGNAL-

Many pressure transducers of the inductance-bridge type (as well as of the LVDT type, described below) incorporate circuitry that enables the transducer to be powered by dc and provide a dc output voltage. Typical circuitry (Figure 2-77) includes a regulator (so that fairly large variations in power-supply voltage can be accepted); an oscillator, which provides the required ac voltage for the transduction coils (sensor) and can also feed a small transformer–rectifier module that supplies regulated voltages to internal elements; a demodulator for converting the bridge-output voltage to dc; and an operational (differential) amplifier that boosts the dc output signal to the required level (e.g., 0 to 5 or 0 to 10 V dc); circuitry can also be included for transducer operation on a two-wire system where its output is in the form of a current change (e.g., 4 to 20 mA). Figure 2-78 illustrates a complete inductance-bridge transducer design with an integrally packaged electronics module containing the circuitry described. The twisted-Bourdon-tube sensing element is usable for pressure ranges between 0 and 350 kPa (50 psi) and 0 and 35 MPa (5000 psi), when used in conjunction with the armature and coil assembly designed for this transducer model. Resistive temperature-compensation components are connected to the electronics module.

In LVDT-type reluctive pressure transducers (Figure 2-79), an assembly of three coils, one acting as primary winding and the other two acting as the secondary windings of a transformer that is differentially connected, is all wound on a hollow mandrel in which a core of magnetic material moves axially, actuated by a Bourdon-tube or capsule sensing element. Displacement of the core toward either of the secondary windings, from a center (null) position,

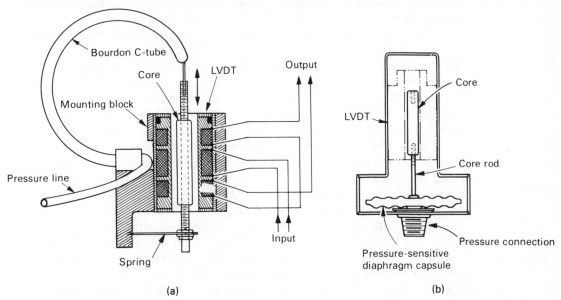

(a)   (b)

Figure 2-79. Operating principles of LVDT (reluctive) pressure transducers: (a) with Bourdon-tube sensing element; (b) with capsule sensing element. (Courtesy of Schaevitz Engineering.)

decreases the reluctance path and hence increases the coupling between that winding and the ac powered primary winding. In the most commonly used winding configuration, core motion toward either secondary produces an output change that increases in amplitude equally for both directions of motion from the null position, but differs in phase; the phase changes, together with the amplitude changes, can then be converted into a unidirectionally varying dc output voltage by appropriate circuitry. C-shaped as well as U-shaped Bourdon tubes have been used for pressure ranges having an upper limit of 1.5 MPa and higher, and single or multiple capsules are used for pressure ranges with an upper limit below about 3.5 MPa (500 psi); both types of sensing elements have been used in the region of overlap. Use of the capsule tends to improve producibility and reduce cost.

In addition to the widely produced designs described above, a different approach has also been employed in pressure transducers, involving the change in permeability due to a change in stress of a straight-tube sensing element. This element is used as a fixed (but variable-permeability) core in conjunction with a differential-transformer winding configuration.

2.6.2.6 Strain-gage pressure transducers. The conversion of pressure changes into changes of resistance due to strain in two or, much more commonly, four arms of a Wheatstone bridge has been used in commercial pressure transducers for many years. Unbonded wire gages were used in many of the earlier models. Bonded metal-foil gages are used in many current designs. Deposited-metal-film *(thin-film)* gages are used increasingly. Advances in semiconductor technology led, first, to the use of bonded semiconductor gages, later to integrally diffused gages (diffused directly into a silicon diaphragm).

The diaphragm is the most frequently used sensing element in these transducers. The gages are applied either directly to the inside of the diaphragm or to a secondary sensing member that is, in turn, deflected by diaphragm deflection by means of a pushrod or other linkage. The sensing diaphragm is either located at the surface of the transducer that sees the measured fluid (in *flush-mounted* transducers, used where high-frequency response is required) or recessed in a cavity provided with a pressure port.

Figure 2-80 shows three typical bonded-metal-gage pressure transducer designs. The absolute (or gage) pressure design shown in Figure 2-80b contains a number of machined pieces and assemblies that are bolted together. The pressure-fitting end cap admits the measured fluid into a narrow cavity, where it acts upon an integrally machined diaphragm. The center of the diaphragm is in contact with a pushrod that is part of a double-cantilever beam (see Figure 2-80a). The thin, flat portions of the beam have foil gages bonded to them so that two gages are on top of the beam and two gages are on the bottom of the beam; hence, two gages see compression strain, whereas the other two see tension strain. A header, with terminal pins, seals the sensing cavity. The reference cavity (between header and receptacle) is evacuated, for absolute pressure transducers, or provided with a gage vent, for gage pressure transducers.

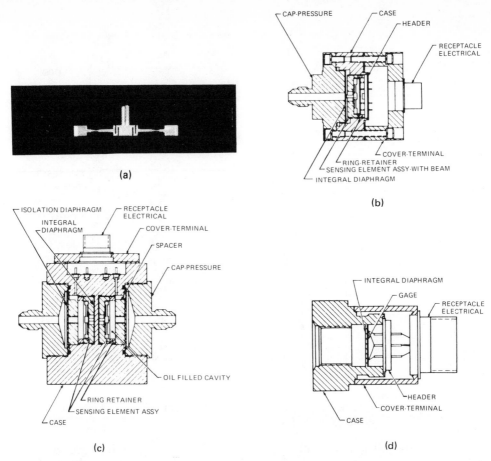

Figure 2-80. Bonded-strain-gage pressure transducer designs: (a) gaged double-cantilever beam; (b) absolute-pressure configuration with gaged beam; (c) wet/wet differential-pressure configuration with two gaged beams; (d) gaged-diaphragm configuration. (Courtesy of Genisco Technology Corp., Instrument Div.)

Compensation and adjusting resistors are usually connected to the pins in the header (to which the leads from the gages are connected internally); such resistors typically compensate for thermal zero and sensitivity shifts and provide adjustments for zero balance and for sensitivity (see Figure 2-81).

The transducer illustrated in Figure 2-80c uses two integrally machined diaphragms to deflect two separate double-cantilever beams. It also contains two soft isolation diaphragms and transfer fluid (silicone oil) in each of the two sensing cavities; this type of design allows two fluids (e.g., liquids that would be incompatible with the materials of the sensing assembly) to be applied to such a differential-pressure transducer. Transducers including such provisions are known as "wet/wet differential" pressure transducers, as opposed to the "wet/dry differential" types, which require that the fluid applied to the reference ("low") port be a dry gas compatible with the sensing assembly.

The gage (or absolute) pressure transducer illustrated in Figure 2-80c

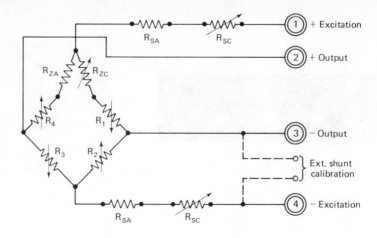

Symbol	Function
R_{ZA}	Zero balance adjustment
R_{ZC}	Compensation for thermal zero shift
R_{SA}	Sensitivity adjustment
R_{SC}	Compensation for thermal sensitivity shift
$R_1 - R_4$	Strain-gage bridge (transduction element)

Figure 2-81. Typical compensation and adjustment network for strain-gage transducer.

has its foil gages bonded directly to the sensing diaphragm. Such multiple circular gage configurations, constituting a four-arm active bridge when bonded to a diaphragm, are commercially available. Two gages are oriented radially, the other two circumferentially.

Secondary sensing elements (that produce strain when acted upon by diaphragm deflection) include, besides single and double cantilever beams, such force-sensing elements as proving rings, proving frames, and columns, such as the hollow cylindrical column *(strain tube)*.

The force-sensing element (sensing beam) in the transducer shown in Figure 2-82 is a special design. It, too, is actuated by a pushrod (linkage pin); the pushrod is integrally machined with the pressure-sensing diaphragm. The beam design provides some mechanical amplification, which makes the transducer usable for low pressure ranges (under 700 kPa). The thin-film gages are vacuum-deposited on the highly polished rear surface of the beam on which an insulating ceramic film has first been deposited. After the strain-gage metal is deposited, a different metal is used for the deposition of interconnecting strips, to which gold leads are then attached by microcircuit welding techniques. A vacuum-sealed header encloses the sensing cavity. The rear portion of the case accommodates the compensation/adjustment resistors or an electronics module which includes an amplifier to provide a high-level dc output.

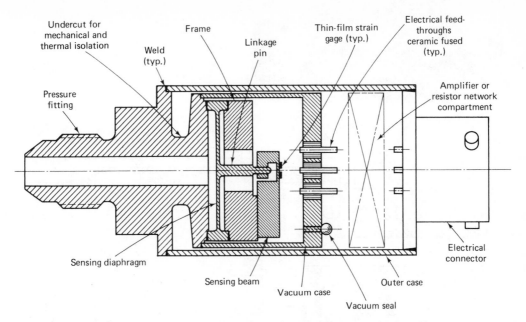

Undercut for mechanical and thermal isolation

Frame

Weld (typ.)

Linkage pin

Thin-film strain gage (typ.)

Electrical feed-throughs ceramic fused (typ.)

Pressure fitting

Amplifier or resistor network compartment

Sensing diaphragm

Sensing beam

Vacuum case

Vacuum seal

Outer case

Electrical connector

Figure 2-82. Strain-gage absolute-pressure transducer with thin-film strain gages applied to cantilever beam. (Courtesy of Gould/Statham.)

In the transducer shown in Figure 2-83 the thin-film gages are vacuum-deposited directly to the inside surface of the pressure-sensing diaphragm, also on an insulating ceramic substrate. This design, as well as the one shown in Figure 2-82, provide for good mechanical and thermal isolation of the sensing assembly. Mechanical contact (and the heat conduction path) is limited to the small area where the case is welded to the pressure-fitting end cap. This tends to isolate the sensing assembly from the thermal and mechanical environment seen by the case (outer case). Sputtering of thin-film gages is an alternative process to vacuum deposition. Semiconductor strain gages have been used in the same manner as metal-foil gages, using special bonding techniques. Such gages provide a much greater sensitivity, and hence a much higher bridge-output voltage, than metal wire or foil gages; however, temperature compensation is more critical. They are useful in applications where the now more common integrally diffused silicon diaphragm cannot be used (some measured fluids are not compatible with silicon; use of isolation membranes and transfer fluid to circumvent such noncompatibility problems is feasible and has been implemented, but it adds to design complexity). Silicon diaphragms into whose rear surface a four-arm strain gage bridge is diffused are manufactured using techniques employed for the manufacture of integrated-circuit chips. A typical wafer consists of a circular slice of n-type silicon into which strain-sensitive p-type areas have been diffused using an appropriate dopant; interconnecting strips and tabs for lead attachment are vacuum-deposited or diffused. Photo-lithographic techniques allow the production of very small sensors (as small

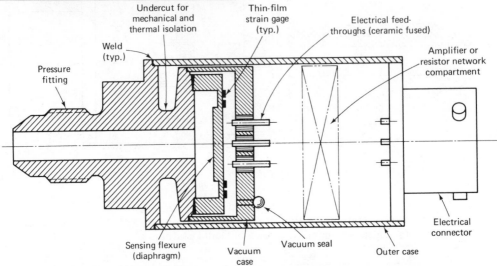

Undercut for
mechanical and
thermal isolation

Thin-film
strain gage
(typ.)

Electrical feed-
throughs (ceramic fused)

Weld
(typ.)

Amplifier or
resistor network
compartment

Pressure
fitting

Sensing flexure
(diaphragm)

Vacuum
case

Vacuum seal

Outer case

Electrical
connector

Figure 2-83. Strain-gage absolute-pressure transducer with thin-film strain gages applied to inside of diaphragm. (Courtesy of Gould/Statham.)

as 0.75 mm diameter). In some designs temperature compensation and adjustment "resistors" are also diffused into the diaphragm and interconnected. Two complete strain-gage circuits can be created in a single diaphragm, with either one or the other used in the final sensor on the basis of test results. In a few designs an integrally diffused force-sensing beam is deflected by a pushrod extending from a metal diaphragm. Most transducers, however, have the pressure acting directly on the silicon diaphragm.

Integrally diffused pressure sensors have been developed and produced

Figure 2-84. Diffused-silicon-sensor pressure transducer for automotive applications. (Courtesy of Fairchild Semiconductor Components Group, Fairchild Camera and Instrument Corp.)

for a wide variety of pressure ranges (between 25 kPa and 200 MPa) and in many configurations, including flush-diaphragm and cavity types and specialized versions such as a thin (1 mm thick), flat sensor for use on airfoils and turbine blades. Such sensors have also reached a stage of high producibility, resulting in low-cost pressure transducers such as the automotive type shown in Figure 2-84, which incorporates a supply-voltage regulator as well as two operational amplifiers in addition to the silicon diaphragm.

2.6.2.7 Servo-type pressure transducers. Servo pressure transducers incorporate a closed servo loop. These designs are generally more complex than other transducer types but provide very close accuracy. Figure 2-85 shows

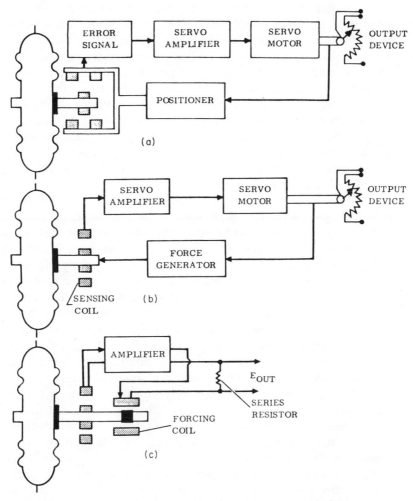

Figure 2-85. Basic block diagrams of servo-type pressure transducers: (a) null-balance pressure transducer; (b) force-balance pressure transducer (with shaft-output); (c) force-balance pressure transducer (with direct voltage-output).

simplified block diagrams for the three basic types of servo pressure transducers.

In the *null-balance* transducer (Figure 2-85a) the sensing element (capsule or bellows usually) is allowed to deflect freely. The displacement is detected by a null-type transduction element such as a differential transformer. Any unbalance output due to the displacement (e.g., of a pushrod attached to the sensing element) becomes an error signal in the servo loop. The signal is amplified and applied to a servo motor, which drives the coil system to its new null position while simultaneously driving an output device. The latter can be a rotary potentiometer, a synchro or other reluctive device, or a shaft-angle encoder.

A motor-driven output device is also used in the *force-balance* transducer illustrated in Figure 2-85b. However, the sensing element is not allowed to deflect freely but is restrained by a force generator. When the sensing element tries to deflect in response to applied pressure a transduction element detects the beginning of displacement and produces an error signal. The transduction element can be inductive (as implied by "sensing coil"), reluctive, or capacitive. The error signal is amplified and applied to a motor which drives an output device while simultaneously causing a (mechanically linked) force generator to apply sufficient force to the sensing element to restore a balance condition. The transducer output (from the output device; at least one such system uses a shaft-angle encoder) is proportional to the force required to restrain the sensing element from displacing.

The operation of the force-balance transducer illustrated in Figure 2-85c is less complex and, therefore, used more frequently in production designs. The error signal that is produced by the (inductive, capacitive, etc.) transduction element is amplified. The output of the amplifier is applied to a forcing coil which operates electromagnetically to keep the sensing element from displacement. The current through the forcing coil is proportional to applied pressure. The forcing coil circuit is completed by a series resistor and the *IR* drop across this resistor is the output voltage produced by the transducer; it can be further amplified or conditioned if required. A pressure transducer of this type is shown schematically in Figure 2-86. A pair of bellows are attached to a beam, to extensions of which two capacitor plates are mounted. These are part of a dual capacitive transduction element in conjunction with two fixed capacitor plates. When a pressure differential is applied between the two ports and into the bellows, the beam will deflect toward the bellows carrying the lower pressure, causing an unbalance condition in the capacitive elements. A force-balance (forcing) coil is also attached to the bellows/beam assembly. It is positioned in the field of a permanent magnet. The output from the capacitive element is detected and amplified and the output of the amplifier (not shown) is fed to the forcing coil. Due to interaction of the flux produced by the coil, with a soft iron ring providing a magnetic return path, the bellows/beam assembly is forced back into its balance position. The current through the force balance (forcing) coil also produces the transducer output signal. The design shown has a measuring range of 0 to 200 kPa in its absolute-pressure version

Fluid-Mechanical Quantities

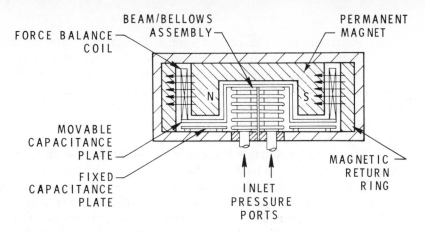

Figure 2-86. Force-balance differential-pressure transducer. (Courtesy of Sundstrand Data Control, Inc.)

and a range of ± 1 bar in the differential-pressure version shown. Repeatability is reported as within 0.02% of the pressure excursion, and the threshold (smallest detectable pressure change) is reported as 0.1 Pa.

2.6.2.8 Piezoelectric pressure transducers. Piezoelectric pressure transducers are widely used for pressure measurements where a very high frequency response (up to 500 kHz in some designs) is required or where an equivalently short response time is required. Piezoelectric crystals are made of quartz or of a variety of proprietary ceramic mixtures; ceramic crystals acquire their piezoelectric characteristics by exposure to an orienting electric field during cooling after first being heated.

A typical piezoelectric pressure transducer using quartz crystals is shown in Figure 2-87. The pressure-sensing diaphragm acts against a stack of quartz

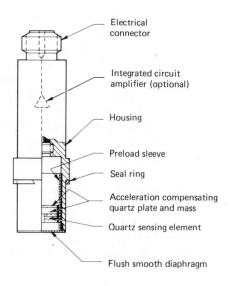

Figure 2-87. Piezoelectric pressure transducer. (Courtesy of PCB Piezotronics, Inc.)

disks which produce the output signal. The crystals are mechanically pre-loaded. The design shown also includes a small seismic mass with an associated quartz crystal which senses acceleration and produces a signal that is used for compensating the pressure-generated signal for simultaneously experienced acceleration. The housing may contain an (optional) IC amplifier, a device very useful in providing a low-impedance output; the output impedance of the quartz crystal is very high.

The crystal materials originally developed for use in transducers, such as barium titanate and lead zirconate, are no longer used in production designs and the single quartz crystal, formerly used, is now almost invariably replaced by stacked crystals. Quartz crystals are usable to temperatures up to about 350 °C. Some recently developed types of ceramic crystals can withstand higher temperatures; others have lower temperature limits. The limiting temperature of ceramic crystals is the *Curie point;* when heated above this point they lose their piezoelectric characteristics. Pressure ranges extend up to 150 MPa, although most transducers capable of measuring such a high range may only be calibrated for a portion of the range. Ranges to 50 or 100 MPa are more common; on the other hand, experimental sensors using a lithium niobate crystal have been reported to be usable for very short pressure transients up to 1.7 TPa.

Piezoelectric pressure transducers exist in many general-purpose as well as specialized configurations; the latter include designs that can replace a spark plug in an engine, those that fit into a small cavity in a fuel-injection line, also for automotive testing, and those that fit against a cartridge in a gun chamber, for ballistic measurements. Water-cooling adaptors are available for many configurations.

2.6.2.9 Vibrating-element pressure transducers. Pressure transducers using the change in the resonant frequency of a vibrating mechanical member, due to pressure changes, are capable of providing extremely close repeatability. They also produce a frequency output or frequency-modulated output (frequency deviation from a center frequency) which lends itself to digitization without conversion error (or direct display on a frequency counter). In some FM/FM telemetry systems such transducer outputs were fed directly into the system as one of the subcarrier channels. A significant number of vibrating-wire pressure transducers were built and used primarily in aerospace and oceanography. They were found to be difficult to produce. A vibrating-diaphragm transducer was designed and used experimentally. Vibrating-cylinder transducers were produced in several countries but suffered from high temperature sensitivity as well as producibility problems. These problems were finally overcome and the vibrating-cylinder pressure transducer is now commercially available. Further development may bring similar results for other types of vibrating-element transducers.

The vibrating-wire pressure transducer uses a pressure-sensing diaphragm to the center of which a very thin wire (typically tungsten) is attached. The other end of the wire is mechanically anchored and electrically insulated

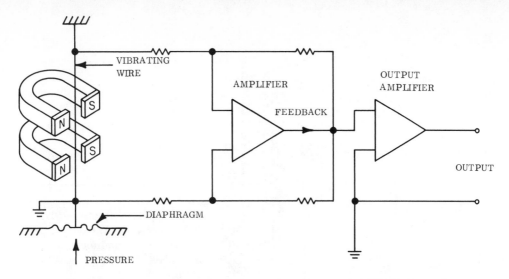

Figure 2-88. Vibrating-wire pressure transducer: simplified schematic.

(see Figure 2-88). The wire is located in a magnetic field usually obtained from a permanent magnet. When a current is passed through the wire, the wire moves within this field sufficiently to have a current induced in it. The emf due to this induced current is amplified and fed back to the wire to sustain its oscillation. The output of this oscillator circuit is then further amplified, with the output amplifier also acting as buffer.

The transducer is normally so designed that increasing pressure results in decreasing wire tension and hence in a reduction of its frequency of oscillation. The frequency of vibration of a stretched wire is given by the relationship

$$f = \frac{n}{2L}\sqrt{\frac{F}{Ad}}$$

where n = any integer expressing mode of oscillation

(1 for the fundamental, 2 for the second mode, etc.)

L = wire length

F = tension force acting on wire

A = cross-sectional area of wire

d = density of wire material

Second-mode wire oscillation is obtained by establishing two opposing magnetic fields, as indicated by the two magnets in Figure 2-88. It can be noted from this relationship that vibrating-wire transducers are inherently nonlinear; however, they are capable of repeating points on their calibration curve within very close tolerances. The minute deflection of the stiff sensing diaphragm poses a requirement for very close tolerances in the diaphragm/wire/magnet assembly as well as for near-perfect matching of thermal coefficients

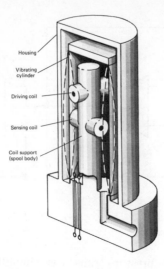

Housing

Vibrating cylinder

Driving coil

Sensing coil

Coil support (spool body)

Figure 2-89. Vibrating-cylinder pressure transducer. (Courtesy of Hamilton Standard Div. of United Aircraft Corp.)

of expansion to minimize thermal effects on performance. Thermal effects can be reduced further by enclosing the sensing assembly in a proportionally controlled heater jacket.

The vibrating-cylinder pressure transducer (Figure 2-89) uses a sensing element of the straight-tube type; the cylindrical wall of this tube undergoes changes in hoop stress as pressure is applied to it. When the cylinder is set into oscillation, its frequency of oscillation (natural frequency) will increase with increasing hoop stress due to increasing pressure. The cylinder is maintained in oscillation by a feedback amplifier/limiter combination which is connected to the driving coil and receives its input from the sensing coil. The output of this amplifier/limiter is also fed to another amplifier followed by circuitry that converts the sinusoidal signal into a square-wire output signal (pulse-frequency output) which can then be converted into a digital output by conventional means.

The cavity between cylinder and housing is evacuated so that absolute pressure is measured. The mode of oscillation is given by the length of the cylinder. The cylinder configuration is chosen so that a four-lobed symmetrical hoop mode is obtained. The magnetic pickup coil is mounted orthogonal to the drive coil in the spool body and their spatial relationship helps in setting the cylinder into this oscillatory mode. The repeatability of this type of transducer is reported as within 0.0001%. The temperature error is on the order of 0.01%/°C; it can be reduced by a factor of about 5 by incorporating a proportionally controlled heater within the transducer. Other options include linearization circuitry to improve the end-point linearity from the inherent ±5% to ±0.04%, and to ±0.008% when additional circuitry provides a binary (linear) output, according to the manufacturer.

A few other types of vibrating-element pressure transducers were also developed. One uses the force obtained from a deflecting sensing element to actuate a lever linkage which causes the oscillating frequency of a quartz crystal to vary in proportion to pressure. Another design, developed for very low pressure measurements, uses capacitor plates as well as electrostatic forcing in a feedback network to maintain a diaphragm in oscillation while increasing gas density within the sensing chamber tends to dampen such oscillations.

2.6.2.10 Other types of pressure transducers. Several pressure transducer designs have been developed in which conventional sensing elements drive transduction elements other than those described for the major transducer categories described in preceding sections. *Photoelectric* pressure transducers use the deflection of a diaphragm to actuate a double-knife-edge shutter through a short pushrod. Shutter motion then varies the amount of illumination from a miniature ruggedized lamp on two phototransistors connected in a feedback-controlled bridge circuit. This design has an inherently high-level output signal. Other forms of sensing varying amounts of illumination effected in this manner can be used, too, but have not been reported in commercially produced sensors. *Direct-digital-output* pressure transducers use the tip travel of a multiturn Bourdon tube to drive an angular encoder; various output codes can be produced depending on the disk pattern in the encoder (e.g., binary or BCD). *Pressure-sensitive transistors* have been produced for use in low-pressure measurement. The column height in a *mercury manometer* can be sensed by a variety of means (other than visual observation); among the sensing methods employed are ultrasonic techniques (as described for liquid-level sensing) and reluctive devices (with the tip of the mercury column acting as core) used for vernier column-height determinations.

2.6.2.11 Pressure switches. Pressure switches are probably the most abundant type of all pressure sensors. Millions of them are used in residential and automotive applications, besides their widespread industrial use. Most of these devices share the following design features: a pressure-sensing element, often counterbalanced by one or two adjustable-tension springs, a mechanical linkage actuated by the sensing element, and a push-button type switch (typically with snap action). The sensing element can be a bellows but is most frequently a diaphragm made of a metallic or nonmetallic (e.g., silicone rubber, Buna N) material. The counterbalancing spring is used to set the switching point. Many units include an externally accessible adjustment to set spring tension and switching point. A variety of lever linkages are used, some with provisions for dead-band adjustment. The basic electromechanical switch is of the type that requires a very small amount of plunger motion to actuate it. Several types of switching configurations are available: normally open only, normally closed only, make/break separate pairs of contacts, or, most commonly, a single switch which provides a normally closed as well as a normally open contact. Many types of housings are used for pressure switches, ranging from simple plastic-molded enclosures with slip-on terminals to explosion-proof and corrosion-resistant metallic housings incorporating a terminal block and provided with threads for conduit couplings.

2.6.3 Design and Performance Characteristics

Specification characteristics for pressure transducers start with the *range* and type of pressure reference (absolute, gage, differential, sealed-reference differential, and, if gage or differential, a unidirectional or bidirectional range which may or may not be symmetrical). When the application requires it, the range of the transducer can be expressed in terms of water depth or altitude, provided that the transducer's calibration curve uses such units rather than units of pressure. The U.S. Customary system of units permits identification of the pressure reference by the name and symbol of the unit *(psia, psig, psid)*. The SI does not as yet make allowance for such differentiation; the *pascal* is a unit of absolute pressure. It should be remembered that the pascal is as "new" to the countries that have been using the "metric" system as it is to the United States. In such countries the kilogram-force *(kilopond)* per square centimeter *(kp/cm^2)* has been the most commonly used *(1 kp/cm^2 = 9.806 65 $\times$ 10^4 Pa = approximately 100 kPa = 1 standard atm = 14.7 or approximately 15 psi)*. The suffixes "a" for absolute and "d" for differential should present no problem since very similar Latin-derived words are used in most European languages; however, there is no equivalent word starting with "g" (for gage) in those languages. No ambiguity will exist as long as complete wording is used (e.g., "a *differential* pressure of ± 50 kPa").

Mechanical characteristics to be considered include: configuration, mountings and all pertinent dimensions; flush mounting or location of pressure ports and their pertinent dimensions, including threads; location and type of electrical connections; measured fluids (and any limitations on their physical and chemical characteristics); sealing of case or housing (e.g., hermetically sealed, explosion-proof, waterproof); isolation of sensing element(s), if any, by isolation membrane and transfer fluid; mounting or pressure-coupling torque; mass; location of nameplate, and nameplate contents; and type of damping (and of damping fluid) if used. If the transducer is expected to be solvent-cleaned, the cleaning fluid should be considered as a "measured fluid." If a transducer must be hermetically sealed, details of the type of sealing should be stated; gaskets and O-rings may deteriorate, and brazed joints may have flux entrapped in the braze, with the entrapped material subject to outgassing and creation of small voids in the joint. Special sealing of transducer and electrical cable is needed for water-depth transducers, of course.

Electrical characteristics include: nominal and maximum excitation (voltage or current or both); output impedance and, for some types of transduction elements, also input impedance; insulation resistance or breakdown-voltage rating; electrical input/output isolation; wiper noise (in potentiometric transducers); output noise (when an amplifier is incorporated in the transducer); and any integrally provided provisions for simulated calibration.

Additional specifications of design characteristics are necessary or desirable for certain types of transducers or certain applications. For differential-pressure transducers it is, of course, necessary to identify the two pressure ports as either "HIGH" and "LOW" or, more correctly, as "M" or "MEAS." and

"R" or "REF.," since these transducers measure one pressure with reference to another pressure (the "M" and "R" designations make sense in many languages besides English as well). When a fairly high frequency response is required of a non-flush-mounted transducer, the total volume of the sensing cavity *(dead volume)*, and its change over the measuring range, can become important. Details of sensing and transduction elements are often shown and can provide information useful to the application. External electrical connections are best identified, by function vs. connector pin or lead color, on the nameplate. For some applications it is useful that the axis in which the transducer is most vibration-sensitive is known. For high-pressure transducers it is useful to specify a case-burst-pressure rating in addition to that rating as it applies to the sensing element. Leakage of pressure into the case may build up a high enough pressure to rupture the case eventually; the end plate carrying the electrical connector may then become a dangerous projectile.

Performance characteristics include those generally applicable to most transducers and explained in Chapter II. Accuracy characteristics are often specified in terms of error band instead of in terms of such individual characteristics as linearity (and type of linearity), hysteresis, repeatability, zero balance, and zero shift. Warm-up period is sometimes specified, as is creep. For certain types of pressure transducers their sensitivity is shown as primary performance characteristic. *Reference-pressure* range and reference-pressure error (effects) must be specified for differential-pressure transducers, and overrange *(proof pressure)* must be specified for all types of pressure transducers. (*Note:* Reference pressure is sometimes called "line pressure.")

Dynamic performance characteristics are usually shown in terms of "flat" frequency response (with a tolerance applied to the flatness of the response curve), sometimes as natural frequency (lowest-frequency resonant peak should be used) and damping ratio, and sometimes (for overdamped transducers) as time constant and (when damping is close to critical damping so that a small amount of underdamping may occur) overshoot.

Environmental performance characteristics comprise those defined in general for transducers in Chapter II. Limits on thermal effects are shown in terms of temperature error band or individual specifications for thermal zero and sensitivity shifts, over the operating temperature range (ambient temperature) or the measured-fluid temperature range, whichever is more severe (some specifications lack clarity in this respect). In some specifications error limits are shown as applicable over a "compensated temperature range," with no limits on performance shown between limits of this range and a maximum (or "safe") temperature or, similarly, a minimum temperature. Thermal effects on damping should be shown for artificially damped transducers. The frequency response at specified elevated or cold temperatures is sometimes shown for wide-response transducers. Temperature-gradient error may need to be considered (and pyroelectrically induced thermal errors in piezoelectric transducers). Errors due to acceleration, shock, and vibration (the latter can induce errors significant only at certain vibration frequencies) are shown where such environments are expected. Errors and defects can also be introduced in the output of many types of transducers by high sound-pressure levels, high-intensity magnetic fields, and nuclear radiation and, in some designs, by changes in ambient pressure.

Reliability characteristics include operating and cycling life, errors and defects seen after long periods of storage, and stability.

Although various groups of characteristics can be of major importance in selecting a pressure transducer for a given application, the characteristics that most often govern such a selection are range, accuracy, output, frequency response, nature of measured fluids, and environmental conditions.

2.7 VACUUM

Vacuum measurements are treated separately from pressure measurements here, because vacuum technology is a specialized field, and because vacuum-sensing devices differ radically from virtually all pressure-sensing devices. The most widely used unit of pressure in the vacuum range is the *torr,* which is equivalent to $^1/_{760}$ standard atmosphere.

1 torr = 133 Pa = 1.33 mbar = 1 mm Hg;   1 Pa = 7.5 × 10⁻³ torr

By convention (not by any formal standard) the vacuum range is the range of pressures extending from 1 standard atm (110.32 kPa, 7.6 × 10² torr) down to zero pressure (for practical purposes, down to the lowest measurable pressures). In vacuum terminology, a *low* pressure is a *high* vacuum. By the same convention the vacuum range is divided into the following regions:

Low vacuum: 760 to 25 torr (110 to 3.3 kPa)

Medium vacuum: 25 to 10^{-3} torr (3300 to 0.133 Pa)

High vacuum: 10^{-3} to 10^{-6} torr (1.33 × 10^{-1} to 1.33 × 10^{-4} Pa)

Very high vacuum: 10^{-6} to 10^{-9} torr (1.33 × 10^{-4} to 1.33 × 10^{-7} Pa)

Ultra high vacuum (UHV): below 10^{-9} torr (below 1.33 × 10^{-7} Pa)

2.7.1 Sensing Methods

2.7.1.1 Pressure-diaphragm vacuum sensing. Sensors using the same basic operating principles and some of the same design features as capacitive pressure transducers (see Sections 2.6.1 and 2.6.2.1) have been designed for vacuum measurements down to 10^{-4} to 10^{-5} torr. Sufficient deflection can be produced in a pressure-sensing diaphragm to vary the capacitance between it and one or two electrodes at such very low pressures. Diaphragms and capsules are also used as sensing elements in conjunction with other transduction elements (e.g., reluctive) for low-vacuum measurements down to about 1 torr and with an upper limit of 760 torr or higher.

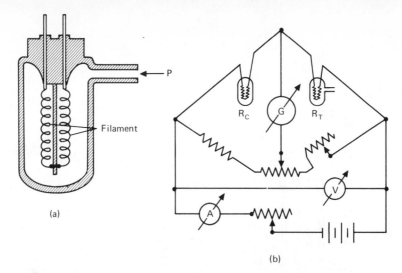

Figure 2-90. Thermal-conductivity vacuum sensing—resistive: (a) transducer; (b) typical bridge circuit.

2.7.1.2 Thermal-conductivity vacuum sensing. The flow of heat from a source to the wall surface of a small chamber will decrease with a decreasing number of gas molecules in the chamber and, hence, with increasing vacuum. At low pressures the thermal conductivity of a gas decreases linearly with pressure. If the heat source is a filament excited by constant current, the reduction in heat transfer from the filament, with increasing vacuum, will cause the temperature of the filament to rise. This effect is employed in *resistive* devices by measuring the increase in the resistance of the filament due to heating (Figure 2-90). The sensor is usually connected so that the hot filament forms one arm of a Wheatstone bridge. This type of sensor is commonly referred to as a *Pirani gage*.

A second sensor of the same configuration, but sealed so as not to respond to vacuum changes, can be connected into a second arm of the bridge as reference. The filament is typically heated to a temperature of about 200 °C (at the lower end of the measuring range). A variation of this design employs a thermistor instead of a filament *(thermistor gage)*. In a *thermoelectric* device based on thermal conductivity *(thermocouple gage),* the temperature rise of the filament is sensed by a thermocouple welded to the center of the filament (Figure 2-91). Use of a thermopile instead of a single-junction thermocouple increases the output signal.

2.7.1.3 Ionization vacuum sensing. In this general category of vacuum sensors, vacuum is measured as a function of gas density by measuring ion current. The ion current results from positive ions which are collected at a negatively charged electrode when the gas is ionized by a stream of electrons or other particles. The ion current is proportional to gas molecular density and, hence, inversely proportional to vacuum, when the number of electrons and their

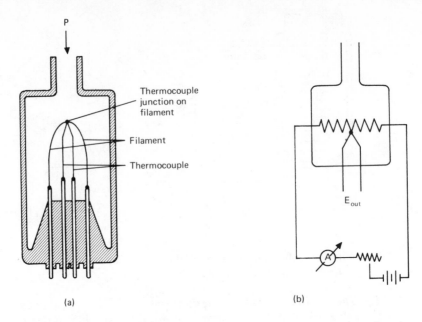

P

Thermocouple
junction on
filament

Filament

Thermocouple

E_{out}

(a)   (b)

Figure 2-91. Thermal-conductivity vacuum sensing—thermoelectric:
(a) transducer; (b) typical circuit.

average path length are constant and all ions are collected. Because such
sensors respond to variations in gas density, which is different for different
gases, the calibrations of the sensors will also be different for different gases.

Ionization gages (ion gages) represent the simplest form of *thermionic
vacuum sensors.* An ionization gage (Figure 2-92a) resembles a triode-type
vacuum tube that has an opening in its envelope. A filamentary cathode is
surrounded by a helical grid around which a cylindrical anode is placed. Positive ions are collected at the anode, which is kept at a low negative voltage
with respect to the filament. A basic measuring circuit is shown in Figure 2-
92c. Switching in the grid outgas supply allows heating the grid electrically
to drive off gas molecules from the grid surface and thus to avoid any *outgassing*
during the operation of the sensor. Outgassing products are detected just like
the measured gas; hence they cause errors. Commonly used accessories, which
take the place of some of the elements shown in the basic circuit, include an
ion-current amplifier for the output current and a feedback-controlled power
supply for the filament.

Various techniques and design modifications have been developed to extend the range of the basic ionization gage, which extends between about
10^{-8} and 10^{-3} torr. At pressures above 0.1 Pa (about 10^{-3} torr) the space-charge
effect, as well as recombination of ions due to a reduction in their mean free
path, cause extreme nonlinearity and effectively limit the usable range. In the
Shulz–Phelps gage a second electron collector electrode is added to minimize
space-charge effects and thus yield a usable range up to about 1 torr.

The lower end of the triode-type's measuring range is limited to about

10^{-8} torr because of X-ray effects. The electron stream produces soft X-rays at the grid. When these X-rays strike the collector electrode, they drive electrons from it by secondary emission. The resulting ion current is of the same polarity as the normally produced ion current. At about 10^{-8} torr, then, the calibration curve of the sensor becomes asymptotic to this residual X-ray current. This phenomenon is substantially reduced in the *Bayard–Alpert gage* (Figure 2-92b). The arrangement of filament, grid, and anode is inverted. The anode is a thin wire. Its surface area is very small and only a small number of the X-rays produced at the grid strike the collector. The resultant much lower X-ray current extends the usable range down to 10^{-10} torr.

Because the Bayard–Alpert gage does not contain the large outer anode

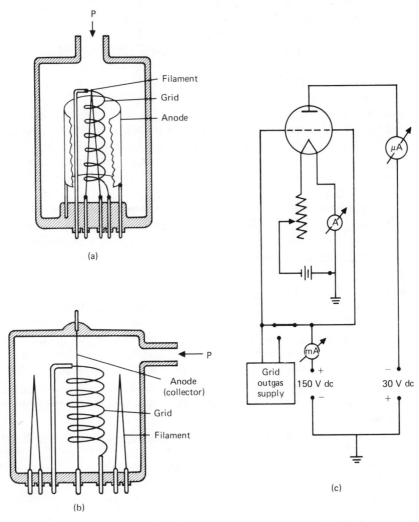

(a)

(b)

(c)

Figure 2-92. Ionization vacuum sensing—thermionic: (a) triode type; (b) Bayard-Alpert type; (c) typical circuit.

plate of the basic triode type, more electrons and ions strike the inside wall of the glass envelope, where they build up an electrostatic charge that can cause erratic operation of the sensor. In the *Nottingham gage* this problem is minimized by a metallic coating which is applied to the inside of the glass envelope and electrically connected into the circuit of the sensor. Also, the grid is provided with end shields. The Nottingham modifications to the Bayard–Alpert gage extend the usable range down to 10^{-11} torr.

Additional modifications to the Bayard–Alpert gage have resulted in further extensions of the low end of the range, mainly by effecting further reductions of the X-ray effects. Suppression of photoelectrons in the *Schuemann modification* (W. C. Schueman, 1962) extends the range close to 10^{-12} torr. The use of *modulation techniques* (P. A. Redhead, 1963, and J. P. Hobson, 1964) extends it to 8×10^{-13} torr (with use of an aluminosilicate glass envelope), and to 7×10^{-15} torr with a portion of the measuring system immersed in liquid helium. The *buried collector gage* (F. P. Clay and L. T. Melfi, 1966, and L. T. Melfi, 1969) also extends the range to below 10^{-12} torr. Use of a low geometry and obtaining a high sensitivity by means of ion optics in the *extractor gage* (P. A. Redhead, 1966) extends the range to 5×10^{-13} torr. A range extension to close to 10^{-13} torr was achieved in the bent-beam *Helmer gage* (J. C. Helmer and W. H. Hayward, 1966). Use of a *photomultiplier** in place of a single-electrode anode allows the ion current to be amplified; hence, much lower electron currents can be used for the formation of positive ions, with a resulting decrease in the production of X-rays permits additional low-range limit extensions. Employing a *channel electron multiplier* instead of a photomultiplier has been reported to extend the range to about 10^{-15} torr (D. Blechschmidt, 1973). Using the *deflected-beam* technique in conjunction with a channel electron multiplier has reportedly resulted in a range limit near 10^{-14} torr (D. Blechschmidt, 1975).

Note: In the discussion above of methods of extending the lower range limit of the Bayard–Alpert gage by modifications, the modifications extend over a considerable range of complexity; some experimental results were much easier to achieve and proved more repeatable than others. The names and dates in parentheses are an attempt to indicate the original developer who published a paper on the modification and results, and the year the report was published in conference proceedings or professional journals. Range limits are shown in *torr (equivalent nitrogen),* as is customary in ultra-high-vacuum work (i.e., the range limit that would apply had nitrogen been used as calibration gas).

The addition of a *magnetic field* to ionizing vacuum sensors increases the electron path length at very low pressures. This increases the ionization obtainable, since the probability of electron collisions with gas molecules is now increased. Two basic versions of such a *magnetron gage* have been developed, one using hot-cathode electron emission, the other cold-cathode electron emission.

---

*Only the dynode-type electron multiplier portion is used.

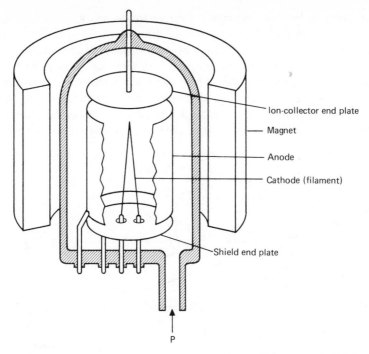

Ion-collector end plate

Magnet

Anode

Cathode (filament)

Shield end plate

P

Figure 2-93. Ionization vacuum sensing with magnetic field—
hot cathode.

In a *hot-cathode magnetron gage,* such as the *Lafferty gage* (Figure 2-93), the electric and magnetic fields are crossed. The electrons emitted from the filamentary cathode, and accelerated radially toward the anode, are also subjected to an axial magnetic field, which forces them into a helical path; this path is much longer than the basic linear path. The shield and collector and plates are negative, and the anode is positive with respect to the cathode. Ion current is measured between collector and cathode. A range of 10^{-14} to 10^{-5}, extendable down to 10^{-17} torr by adding an electron multiplier, has been reported for this type of vacuum sensor.

The cold-cathode magnetron gage is illustrated by the design example shown in Figure 2-94. In this *Penning gage* (sometimes called *Philips gage* after its first manufacturer) the electrons are accelerated by a high-voltage field between the cathodes and the anode. When the cathode surfaces are bombarded by high-energy ions, these surfaces emit electrons which join the total electron stream and produce additional ions, which, in turn, produce additional electrons *(avalanche effect).* The transverse magnetic field forces the electrons to travel along a helical path. The total current, as seen by a microammeter (Figure 2-94b) between cathodes and anode, is the sum of the ion current and the electron current and, hence, not linear with pressure. The sensitivity of this type of sensor is about 0.5 A/torr. The usable range, 10^{-7} to 10^{-3} torr, can be extended downward to nearly 10^{-12} torr by the addition of a flash filament which triggers the discharge at very low pressures when the filament is briefly activated. Cold-cathode designs require a large-diameter pressure port and plumbing *(tubulation)* because of their relatively high ionic pumping speed. An advantage of such sensors is the absence of a hot filament which could burn out (some ionization vacuum sensors contain a standby filament that can be turned on and used when the other filament has burnt out).

In a design variation of the cold-cathode magnetron, the *Redhead gage* (named after its developer, as is frequent practice for vacuum sensors), the field emission and ion collection are separated by means of an auxiliary cathode

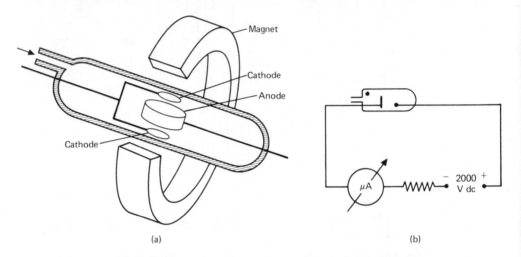

Figure 2-94. Ionization vacuum sensing with magnetic field—cold cathode: (a) transducer; (b) typical circuit.

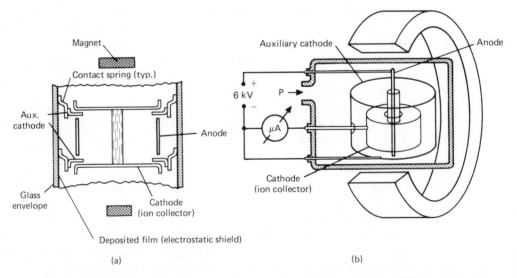

Figure 2-95. Use of auxiliary cathode in cold-cathode, magnetic field, ionization vacuum sensors: (a) magnetron type (sectional view); (b) inverted magnetron type.

Fluid-Mechanical Quantities

(Figure 2-95). The normal magnetron type uses a magnetic field of about 0.1 T and the ion current vs. pressure relationship is a straight line on a log-log plot. The inverted magnetron type uses a field of about 0.2 T and its calibration is linear down to about 5×10^{-10} torr and exponential below that level to the range limit (about 10^{-13} torr; the upper limit is about 10^{-4} torr). The auxiliary cathode acts as electrostatic shield and prevents field emission from the edges of the opening in, or at, the collector electrode. The sensitivity of the Redhead gage is approximately 4.5 A/torr.

The use of particles other than electrons to ionize the measured gas is exemplified by the alpha-particle ionizing sensor illustrated in Figure 2-96.

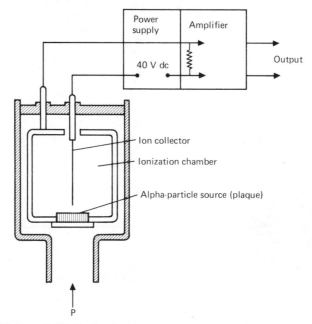

Figure 2-96. Ionization vacuum sensing using radioisotope source.

An appropriate radioisotope source provides a steady alpha-particle flux. The particles cause ionization of the gas molecules and their flow to the ion collector electrode. The principle employed is similar to that of the ionization chamber used for particle detection (see Chapter 6) except that in the vacuum sensor the particle flux is constant and the pressure of the gas varies in the chamber. This type of sensor is normally used for a measuring range in the low and medium vacuum regions (10^{-1} to 100 torr) but is capable of measuring between 10^{-5} and 1000 torr. The use of a beta source instead of an alpha source has also shown promising results, and could extend the measuring range down to about 10^{-8} torr.

2.7.1.4 Vacuum sensing by partial-pressure determination. Ultra-high-vacuum measurements, below about 10^{-12} torr, are often performed by measuring the abundance of molecules of each gas that is a constituent of the gas mixture

DOUBLE-SIDED CONSTRUCTION   SINGLE-SIDED CONSTRUCTION

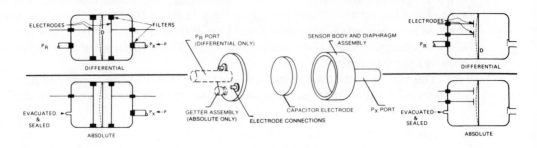

(a)

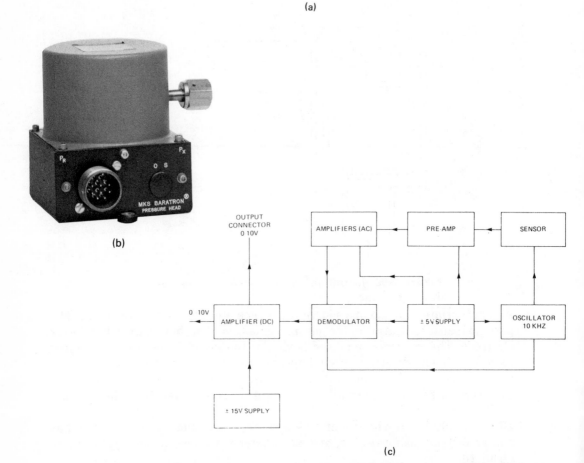

(b)

(c)

Figure 2-97. Capacitance manometer: (a) Construction alternatives; (b) typical transducer design; (c) excitation- and signal-condition block diagram. (Courtesy of MKS Instruments, Inc.)

measured. The molecule of each gas (e.g., O_2, N_2, Ar) is identified by its mass number, and the density at each of the mass numbers can be determined by a device such as a mass spectrometer, notably one of the quadrupole type, which provides very good sensitivity and is readily available commercially (see Section 8.10). The partial pressure can then be determined for each constituent and the total pressure can then be calculated (the molecular density of air is approximately 3×10^{10} molecules/cm^3 at 10^{-6} torr and in the order of 10^3 molecules/cm^3 at 10^{-14} torr, at a temperature of 300 K).

2.7.2   Design and Operation

2.7.2.1 Capacitance manometers. Capacitive pressure transducers (see Section 2.6.2.1) have been developed for vacuum measurements down to about 10^{-5} torr, using special techniques and materials for construction of the sensing assembly, and using sophisticated electronics to detect the very small capacitance changes (in the order of 10^{-5} pF) provided by diaphragm deflections of a fraction of a nanometer. Figure 2-97a depicts two types of sensor construction, in absolute and differential pressure configurations. In the "double-sided" version the stretched (prestressed) welded diaphragm is positioned between two parallel electrodes, typically ceramic disks to which a metal layer has been applied. Leads from the electrodes are connected to the associated electronics. The excitation circuitry (see Figure 2-97c) drives the sensor, which acts as the variable element in a phase-sensitive *LC* bridge arrangement, at a carrier frequency of 10 kHz. The diaphragm displacement modulates the carrier and a synchronous demodulator receives the amplified signal and provides dc output signals (which are bipolar for bidirectional differential-pressure sensors) which are then amplified to a 10-V full-scale output. Filters keep any electrically conductive or contaminating particles out of the sensing chamber. In the absolute-pressure configuration, the reference cavity is evacuated and then sealed. The vacuum is usually maintained by incorporating a *getter,* a metallic deposit (e.g., titanium) which absorbs gas molecules.

In the "single-sided" version (Figure 2-97a) the electrode assembly is removed from the measured-pressure cavity; a small baffle assembly replaces the filter and acts to keep high-speed particles from impinging on the diaphragm. A center electrode and an off-axis electrode are both placed in the reference side. One of the advantages of this type of design is that the measured gas, whose dielectric constant may vary, does not enter the gap between diaphragm and electrode. The two electrodes are used in a "curvature-sensing" mode: the diaphragm deflects much more at its center than at the off-axis location of the second electrode, hence the differences in capacitance sensed by the two electrodes will be more pronounced with increasing diaphragm curvature due to its deflection. Developmental efforts have also resulted in a single-electrode single-sided design which operates in capacitance/frequency-change circuitry and appears to have the capability of vacuum measurements down to 10^{-7} torr.

Figure 2-97b shows a typical capacitive vacuum transducer in its absolute-pressure configuration (the same design also exists in a differential-pressure configuration). Its measuring range extends from 10^{-5} torr to 15 000 torr. It employs the single-sided design explained above. The sensing assembly is temperature-controlled at 50 °C, by a proportionally controlled heater, to minimize temperature errors. The transducer contains a solid-state follower and preamplifier and operates in conjunction with a separate electronics/display unit.

The differential-pressure designs lend themselves to use for precision molecular flow measurement when used in conjunction with a flow element across which a pressure drop, proportional to flow, is developed. Capacitive vacuum sensing heads are available in nonbakeable as well as bakeable versions. Many applications require *bake-out* of elements that come in contact with the measured fluid so that gas molecules are driven off surfaces prior to operation of the measuring system and will not then *outgas* (and introduce errors by increasing the molecular density of the fluid) during operation. Bake-out is performed at high temperatures.

2.7.2.2 Other mechanical-element vacuum sensors. In the overlap region between low-pressure ranges and low and medium vacuum ranges (0 to 760 torr or 0 to 100 kPa full scale) pressure transducers other than the capacitive type can be used. They typically use a diaphragm or capsule sensing element and a differential-transformer reluctive transduction element (see Section 2.6). Sensors of this type exist for ranges as low as 1 to 50 torr full scale.

2.7.2.3 Pirani gages. This version of thermoconductive (heat-loss) vacuum sensors uses a heated resistive element. Its resistance varies with varying heat loss due to varying vacuum. The element is made of a pure-metal wire characterized by a high-temperature coefficient of resistance; nickel or tungsten is frequently used. One design uses a gold-plated tungsten wire heated to 125 °C. Filament temperatures can run up to 400 °C in some designs but tend to be closer to 200 °C. The element is typically connected as one arm of a Wheatstone bridge with a second temperature-sensitive resistor, not exposed to the vacuum, used as a second (compensating) arm of the bridge. The sensor also contains the two fixed-resistance arms of the bridge. It is connected to an electronics/display unit, which also provides excitation and signal conditioning, by a cable. Bakeable sensing heads are available. Thermistors have been used, in a few designs, as the heated resistive element. Most Pirani gages have a usable measuring range from 10^{-3} torr (1 millitorr) to about 10 torr; however, at least one modified design is capable of an extended upper range to 1000 torr.

2.7.2.4 Thermocouple gages. The basic thermoconductive vacuum sensor employing a thermocouple used it to detect the temperature changes (varying with heat loss) of a heated filament. Newer designs do away with the filament and heat the thermocouple itself. Also, the single-junction thermocouple is often replaced by a thermopile of two or more junctions. In the design shown schematically in Figure 2-98a, two thermocouples are connected in series (but with polarities bucking) across the secondary of a transformer which supplies ac heating power to them. Since thermocouples are self-generating they provide a dc output voltage that is proportional to temperature. The temperature increases with increasing vacuum due to decreasing heat loss from the thermocouples. An unheated thermocouple, connected between the center of the two-junction thermopile and the transformer's center tap, provides compensation for changes in ambient temperature.

In the full-bridge thermopile circuit (Figure 2-98b) two dissimilar noble-metal wires, welded in the center, form two thermocouples. A constant alternating current from a dual-secondary transformer heats each wire independently to the same temperature rise above ambient temperature. The dc thermoelectric emf caused by this temperature rise is dependent on the applied heating power as well as the heat loss through the surrounding gas (measured fluid). Since the reference junctions are all at the same (ambient) temperature

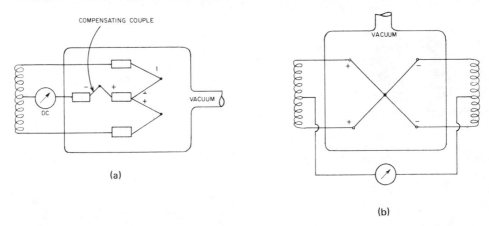

Figure 2-98. Thermocouple gage schematics (thermopile type): (a) compensated half-bridge thermopile; (b) full-bridge thermopile. (Courtesy of Teledyne Hastings-Raydist.)

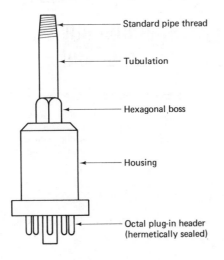

Figure 2-99. Typical thermocouple gage configuration.

and the hot thermopile junction is the hottest spot on any of the four wires, the bridge is symmetrical and is inherently temperature-compensated.

Figure 2-99 shows a configuration typical for most thermocouple gages. The pins in the octal header provide all external electrical connections. The housing is usually metal but can be a high-temperature glass. Measuring ranges are usually in the region 10^{-4} to 10^{-2} torr; some extend close to 10^{-5} torr; others are available for medium vacuum ranges, 10^{-3} to 1 torr, or 0.1 to 100 torr.

2.7.2.5 Hot-cathode ion gages. Hot-cathode triode-type ion gages are usually Bayard–Alpert gages in that the anode (positive-ion collector electrode) is a central wire, surrounded by the coiled grid, and with the filament (cathode) located outside the grid. Many designs incorporate a second filament which can be switched in when the first filament burns out. A typical design is shown in Figure 2-100. The small-diameter grid, made of platinum–iridium alloy, the

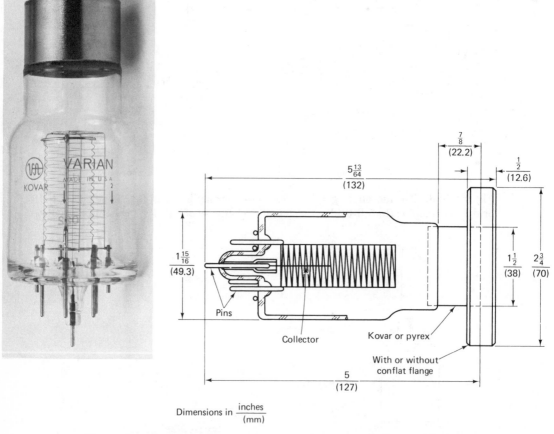

Figure 2-100. Bayard-Alpert ion gage. (Courtesy of Varian Associates, Vacuum Division.)

closed grid structure, and the thin (0.1 mm diameter) collector are design features that aid in minimizing the X-ray limiting current (it is equivalent to an indication of 2×10^{-11} torr). The gauge is enclosed in a glass envelope that is bakeable at 400 °C. The gage *tubulation* (equivalent to the pressure port in a pressure transducer) is 38 mm in diameter and can be either glass or Kovar alloy (the latter lends itself to sealing by heliarc welding), or it can be furnished

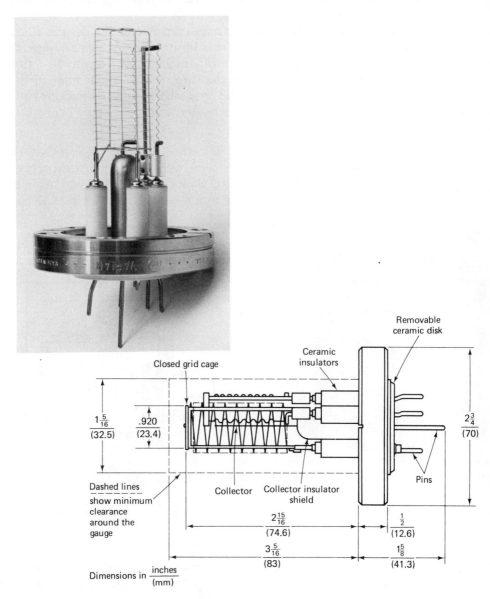

Figure 2-101. Nude ion gage (Bayard-Alpert type). (Courtesy of Varian Associates, Vacuum Division.)

with a flange. A backup filament is included. Such gages typically use a thoria-coated filament made of a high-temperature metal (e.g., iridium) wire.

In some applications it is desirable that all tubulation be eliminated. This requirement can be filled by using a *nude gage* (Figure 2-101). The nude ion gage illustrated is similar in internal design to the gage shown in Figure 2-100, except that it has no glass envelope and the internal elements are mounted on ceramic insulators, so that the gage can be baked out at 450 °C. The filament is easy to replace in a nude ion gage.

The range of hot-cathode ion gages typefied by the designs illustrated is from 10^{-3} to 2×10^{-11} torr (the X-ray limit). In many other designs the range is shifted upward in pressure; such ranges 0.6 to 10^{-6} torr or 10^{-3} to 10^{-9} torr are often encountered. Ion gages that incorporate one or more of the modifications discussed in Section 2.7.1.3, and whose range extends to 10^{-13} torr or lower, are rarely available commercially; they tend to be "hand-built" for a specific application.

2.7.2.6 Cold-cathode ion gages. Cold-cathode ionization gages that use a magnetic field for their operation have been developed in many experimental and some practical designs. Figure 2-102 shows a practical design using this principle. A high dc voltage discharge in a magnetic field ionizes the particles of

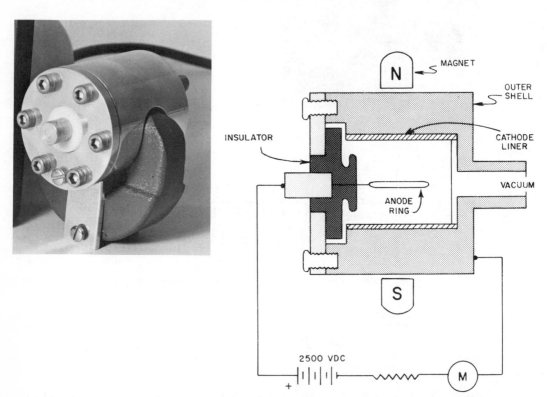

Figure 2-102. Cold-cathode ion gage. (Courtesy of Teledyne Hastings-Raydist.)

the measured gas (*residual gas* particles), producing an ionization current inversely proportional to the density (pressure) of the residual gas. The high-voltage potential is applied between an elliptical-ring-shaped anode and the cathode liner of the outer shell. The magnetic field is supplied by a strong permanent magnet. The measuring range of this design is from 10^{-2} to 10^{-6} torr, with some visibility down to 10^{-7} torr. The associated signal conditioning and display equipment provides an expanded scale (10^{-6} to 5×10^{-5} torr) as well as a single-scale indication from 10^{-5} to 10^{-2} torr.

2.7.3 Performance Characteristics

The most essential *performance characteristics* of vacuum sensors are measuring range, sensitivity, and provisions for degassing and bake-out. Typical measuring ranges are as follows:

> *Reluctive diaphragm gages:* from over 10^3 to 1 torr
>
> *Capacitive diaphragm gages:* from over 10^3 to 10^{-4} torr
>
> *Pirani gages:* from 10 to 10^{-3} torr
>
> *Thermocouple gages:* from 1 to 10^{-4} torr
>
> *Cold-cathode ionization gages* (discharge gages): from 10^{-2} to 10^{-6} torr
>
> *Hot-cathode ionization gages:* 10^{-3} to 10^{-10} torr

Some designs of most of the above-listed sensor types are capable of measuring beyond the typical limits shown, or have a range whose limits are shifted upward from those shown. Not included are sensor types that are either built only by one manufacturer or that are produced only occasionally and in small quantities. Generally, however, ionization gages using an alpha radioisotope source have ranges from 10^3 to 10^{-3} torr, cold-cathode magnetron gages from 10^{-5} to 10^{-13} torr, and hot-cathode magnetron gages from 10^{-7} to 10^{-13} torr. Mass spectrometers, especially the quadrupole type, can be used for measurements from about 10^{-6} to 10^{-14} torr. Such "partial-pressure gages" are produced by several manufacturers. Most development efforts have been directed at extending the lower range limit of hot-cathode ionization gages; similar efforts, directed at capacitive diaphragm gages (capacitance manometers), have already resulted in significant extensions of the lower range limit.

Vacuum sensors are usually procured together with their electronics/display unit. The readout device shows pressure units in terms of "equivalent nitrogen." For most types of sensors (diaphragm gages in which the transduction element does not come in contact with the measured gas are a notable exception) the readings have to be corrected for gases other than nitrogen or air. Manufacturers will usually furnish conversion charts for other commonly measured gases, such as helium, krypton, argon, neon, oxygen, Freon, carbon dioxide, and methane.

The sensitivity of a vacuum sensor is customarily shown in amperes per torr (A/torr) or A/Pa for sensors whose output is an ionization current. When the output is another quantity (e.g., a voltage), the sensitivity is shown in units of that quantity per unit pressure. The torr is still the most commonly used unit of pressure; however, the SI unit, the pascal (Pa) is used increasingly (some readout scales have markings in both units). Scales are also frequently marked in submultiples of the torr (or the mm Hg), notably the millitorr (10^{-3} torr) and, sometimes, the "micron," actually 1 μm Hg, which is also equal to 10^{-3} torr.

Sensors for the high to ultrahigh vacuum ranges usually incorporate provisions for degassing in situ, by applying a potential across one element or between two elements. Specifications for such sensors also show the temperature at which bake-out can be performed.

2.8 VISCOSITY

A limited number of sensing devices have been developed for the direct measurement of viscosity. The generic sensor types are described here briefly. Some sensor types measure *absolute viscosity,* whose SI unit is the $N \cdot s/m^2$ and whose U.S. Customary unit is the *poise* ($= 0.1$ N·s/m²), whereas other types measure *kinematic viscosity* (the ratio of absolute viscosity to density), whose SI unit is the m^2/s and whose U.S. Customary unit is the *stoke* ($= 1.0$ cm²/s $= 1 \times 10^{-4}$ m²/s). The ranges of viscosity sensors *(viscometers)* are typically shown in *centipoise* or *centistokes,* respectively.

Torque sensing is employed in *rotating element* devices, such as rotating-cone, gyrating-cone, rotating-disk, and rotating-spindle types. The element is made to rotate in the measured fluid and a torque, or a reaction torque, developed due to viscosity (viscous drag) is detected by a torque or reaction-torque transducer. One rotating-spindle design uses a radial spring to couple the spindle mechanically to the motor shaft; the angular displacement of the spring, due to torque, is then transduced. Different measuring ranges are obtainable for this device by using spindles of different sizes.

Differential-pressure flow-rate sensing is used in *capillary flow* devices in which the measured fluid is forced to flow through a restriction, typically a capillary tube, and the pressure differential across the restriction, at a constant flow rate, and under laminar flow conditions, is measured by a differential-pressure transducer, whose output is then proportional to kinematic viscosity. When the pressure drop is due to a fixed force (e.g., positive displacement pump or fixed high-pressure source) that is independent of density, the transducer output is proportional to absolute density.

Time measurement is employed in *falling-piston* and *falling-ball* devices. A piston or ball, of known density, is first lifted, then permitted to drop (due to gravity) through a sample of the measured fluid (the sample can be contained in the process line). The time it takes the piston or ball to drop to the bottom of the measuring chamber, with its final position sensed, for example, by a magnetic switch, is measured and is indicative of viscosity.

Oscillation damping is sensed in *vibrating-element* viscosity transducers.

288   *Fluid-Mechanical Quantities*

The amplitude of a vibrating reed, paddle, or sphere is reduced with increasing viscosity of the measured fluid. The element is driven electromechanically and a transduction element detects the amplitude changes. Such devices respond to changes in viscosity as well as density; however, effects of density variations can be eliminated by maintaining the measured liquid as well as the transducer at a closely controlled constant temperature.

Linear-displacement sensing is used in *float-type* viscometers. This device consists of a variable-area flowmeter with a viscosity-sensitive float. With the flow rate held constant (by a separate flow control system), the linear displacement of the float is indicative of kinematic viscosity.

Range, accuracy, and warm-up time are essential performance characteristics of viscosity sensors. The physical and chemical characteristics of the measured fluid must be well understood. Response time varies for different designs and types.

Bibliography

1. *Journal of Vacuum Science and Technology,* Vol. 1– . New York: American Vacuum Society, 1964– .

2. **Schlichting, H.,** *Boundary-Layer Theory.* New York: McGraw-Hill Book Company, 1968.

3. **Spink, L. K.,** *Principles and Practice of Flow Meter Engineering,* 9th ed. Foxboro, MA: The Foxboro Company, Publications Division, 1967.

4. **Liptak, B. G.,** *Instrument Engineers' Handbook.* Radnor, PA: Chilton Book Company, 1969.

5. Tentative Standards of the American Vacuum Society, New York, 1969–1976:
   "Procedure for Calibrating Gas Analyzers of the Mass Spectrometer Type," *AVS 2.3-1972.*
   "Procedure for Calibrating Vacuum Gages of the Thermal Conductivity Type," *AVS 6.2-1969.*
   "Procedure for Calibrating Hot Filament Ionization Gages against a Reference Manometer in the Range 10^{-2} to 10^{-5} Torr," *AVS 6.4-1969.*
   "Procedure for the Calibration of Hot Filament Ionization Gage Controls," *AVS 6.5-1971.*

6. **Brombacher, W. G.,** "Survey of Micromanometers," *NBS Monograph 114.* Washington, DC: U.S. Government Printing Office, June 1970.

7. **Bean, H. S.,** "Fluid Meters—Their Theory and Applications," *ASME Handbook.* (6th ed.) New York: American Society of Mechanical Engineers, 1971.

8. **Geary, P. J.,** *Measurement of Moisture in Solids.* Chislehurst, Kent, England: Sira Institute, 1971.

9. **November, M. H.,** "Electronic Density Measuring System," *ITT Barton Technical Paper.* Monterey Park, CA: ITT Barton, 1971.

10. **Streeter, V. L.,** *Fluid Mechanics* (5th ed.). New York: McGraw-Hill Book Company, 1971.

11. "Specification, Installation and Calibration of Turbine Flowmeters," *ISA RP31.1* (ANSI approved Jan. 1977). Research Triangle Park, NC: Instrument Society of America, 1972.

12. "A Guide for the Dynamic Calibration of Pressure Transducers," *ANSI Standard B88.1-1972*. New York: American Society of Mechanical Engineers, 1972.

13. **Fanger, P. O.,** *Thermal Comfort*. New York: McGraw-Hill Book Company, 1973.

14. **Considine, D. M.,** *Process Instruments and Controls Handbook*. New York: McGraw-Hill Book Company, 1974.

15. **Schommartz, G.,** *Induktive Strömungsmessung,* (Inductive Flow Measurement). Berlin, GDR: VEB Verlag Technik, 1974.

16. **Strickert, H.,** *Hitzdraht- und Hitzfilmanemometrie,* (Hot Wire and Hot Film Anemometry). Berlin, GDR: VEB Verlag Technik, 1974.

17. "Relative Humidity by Wet- and Dry-Bulb Psychrometer, Method of Test for," *ANSI Standard Z110.3 (ASTM E337)*. Philadelphia: American Society for Testing and Materials, Apr. 26, 1974.

18. *Flow, Its Measurement in Science and Industry* (Proc. 1971 Conf.). Research Triangle Park, NC: Instrument Society of America, 1974.

19. **Hinze, I. O.,** *Turbulence*. New York: McGraw-Hill Book Company, 1975.

20. **Soisson, H. E.,** *Instrumentation in Industry*. New York: Wiley-Interscience, 1975.

21. "Specification Forms for Process Measurement and Control Instruments," *ISA Standard S20*. Research Triangle Park, NC: Instrument Society of America, 1975.

22. "Specifications and Tests for Piezoelectric Pressure and Sound Pressure Transducers," *ANSI Standard MC6.4-1975* (ISA S37.10). Research Triangle Park, NC: Instrument Society of America, 1976.

23. "Specifications and Tests of Potentiometric Pressure Transducers," *ANSI Standard MC6.5-1976* (ISA S37.6). Research Triangle Park, NC: Instrument Society of America, 1976.

24. "Specifications and Tests for Strain-Gage Pressure Transducers," *ANSI Standard MC6.2-1975* (ISA S37.3). Research Triangle Park, NC: Instrument Society of America, 1976.

25. **Durst, F., Melling, A., and Whitelaw, J. H.,** *Principles and Practice of Laser Doppler Anemometry*. New York: Academic Press, 1976.

26. **Benedict, R. P.,** *Fundamentals of Temperature, Pressure and Flow Measurements*. New York: John Wiley & Sons, Inc., 1977.

27. *Proceedings of the Dynamic Flow Conference 1978*. Skovlunde, Denmark (PO Box 121): DFC'78, 1979.

chapter three

Acoustic Quantities

3.1 BASIC CONCEPTS

3.1.1 Basic Definitions

Sound is an oscillation in pressure, stress, particle displacement, particle velocity, or density that is propagated in an elastic or viscous medium or material, or it is the superposition of such propagated oscillations *(sound wave);* it is also the auditory sensation evoked by such oscillations *(sound sensation).*

Sound energy of a portion of a medium is the total energy in that portion minus the energy that would exist if no sound waves were present.

Sound pressure is the total instantaneous pressure, at a given point, in the presence of a sound wave, minus the static pressure at that point.

Peak sound pressure is the maximum absolute value of the instantaneous sound pressure within a specified time interval.

Effective sound pressure is the root-mean-square value of the instantaneous sound pressures, over a specified time interval, at a given point.

Sound pressure level is normally expressed, in decibels, as 20 times the logarithm to the base 10 of the ratio of the rms (effective) sound pressure to an rms reference pressure, or

$$L_p = \text{SPL} = 20 \log_{10} \frac{p(\text{rms})}{p_{\text{ref}}(\text{rms})}$$

where L_p and SPL are both acceptable symbols for sound pressure level, expressed in dB. The reference pressure must be stated. It is usually taken as either 2×10^{-4} μbar (2×10^{-5} Pa) or 1 μbar (1 dyne/cm², 0.1 Pa).

Sound level is a weighted sound-pressure level (in dB), at a point in a sound field, averaged over the audible frequency range, and as displayed on a *sound-level meter* that complies with a prescribed national and/or international standard. Examples of such standards are: international: IEC R 179; U.S.: ANSI S1.4-1971; Germany: DIN 45 633.

Impulsive sound is sound that consists of short bursts (rather than sustained tones).

Sound intensity is the average rate of sound energy transmitted in a specified direction through a unit area normal to this direction at a given point.

Sound power (of a source) is the total sound energy radiated by the source per unit of time.

Sound absorption is the process by which sound energy is diminished by being partially changed into some other form of energy, usually heat, while passing through a medium or striking a surface.

A *simple sound source* is a source that radiates sound uniformly in all directions under free-field conditions.

A *sound field* is a region containing sound waves.

A *free sound field* is a sound field in a homogeneous medium free of any acoustically reflecting boundaries.

Noise (in acoustics) is any unwanted sound.

Noise dose is the accumulated noise exposure a person is subjected to, with reference to a specified sound level [typically 90 dB(A)] and over a specified period of time (e.g., 8 h).

Propagation velocity is a vector quantity that describes the speed and direction with which a sound wave travels through a medium.

Reverberation time is the time required for the average sound-energy density, at a given frequency, to decrease, when the source has been in a steady state and is stopped, to 10^{-6} (-60 dB) of its initial value.

Pressure frequency response (of a sound-pressure measuring transducer) is the ratio, as a function of frequency, of the transducer output to sound pressure which is equal in phase and amplitude over the entire sensing-element surface of the transducer.

Free-field frequency response (of a sound-pressure measuring transducer) is the ratio, as a function of frequency, of the output of the transducer in a sound field to the free-field sound pressure that would exist at the transducer location were the transducer not present.

Free-field normal incidence response is the free-field frequency response when sound incidence at a specified sensing surface of the transducer is from a direction normal to that surface.

Free-field grazing incidence response is the free-field frequency response when sound incidence at a specified sensing surface of the transducer is from the direction parallel to that surface.

Random incidence response is the diffuse-field frequency response (of a sound-pressure measuring transducer) where sound incidence at a specified sensing surface of the transducer is from random directions.

Diffuse sound is sound, in a given region, which has uniform sound-energy density and is such that all directions of sound-energy flux, at all points in the region, are equally probable.

Directivity (of a sound-pressure measuring transducer) is the solid angle, or the angle in a specified plane, over which sound incident on the sensing element is measured (within specified tolerances) at a specified sound frequency or in a specified band of sound frequencies.

The *directivity factor* is the ratio of the square of the output (of a sound-pressure measuring transducer) produced in response to sound incident from a specified direction to the mean-square output that would be produced in a perfectly diffuse sound field, of the same frequency or band of frequencies and of the same mean-square sound pressure.

A *directional response pattern (directivity pattern)* of a sound-pressure measuring transducer is a description, usually in graphical form, of the transducer's response as a function of direction of incidence of sound waves in a specified plane, and at a specified frequency or band of frequencies.

The *equivalent volume* of a sound-pressure measuring transducer is its acoustic input impedance expressed in terms of the acoustic impedance of an equivalent volume of a gas enclosed in a rigid cavity.

3.1.2 Defining Relationships

Sound Pressure (considered as pressure, in general terms)

$$p_s = \frac{F_s}{A}$$

where p_s = sound pressure

F_s = force due to sound acting on a surface

A = area of the surface

Acoustic Impedance and Volume Velocity

$$Z_a = \frac{p_s}{Su} \qquad Z_a = R_a + jX_a \qquad U = Su$$

where Z_a = acoustic impedance

p_s = rms sound pressure

S = area of surface (through which the sound waves act)

u = rms particle velocity (of an infinitesimal portion of the medium)

R_a = acoustic resistance

X_a = acoustic reactance

U = volume velocity

Sound-Energy Flux   *Sound Intensity*

$$J = \frac{p^2 S}{\rho c} \cos \theta \qquad I = \frac{p^2}{\rho c}$$

where J = sound-energy flux (for one period)

$\quad\ \ I$ = sound intensity (in the direction of propagation)

$\quad\ \ p$ = rms sound pressure

$\quad\ \ \rho$ = density of medium

$\quad\ \ c$ = velocity of propagation of free (plane or spherical) sound wave

$\quad\ \ S$ = area (of surface through which the flux acts)

$\quad\ \ \theta$ = angle between the normal to area S and the direction of travel of the sound wave

Total Acoustic Power Radiated from a Point Source

$$W_p = 4\pi r^2 I$$

where W_p = acoustic power

$\quad\ \ r$ = distance from point source

$\quad\ \ I$ = sound intensity

Spectrum Level (for a given band of frequencies)

$$S(f) = L_p - 10 \log_{10} \Delta f$$

where $S(f)$ = spectrum level at center (of band) frequency, dB

$\quad\ \ L_p$ = SPL = sound pressure level, dB

$\quad\ \ \Delta f$ = bandwidth, Hz

3.1.3 Units of Measurement

Sound pressure can be expressed in *pascals (Pa)* or in equivalent non-SI units such as the *dynes/cm² (= 0.1 Pa);* however, it is generally expressed as *sound-pressure level*, in *decibels (dB)*, as explained, above, in the definition of sound-pressure level. Sound-pressure level (*SPL* or L_p) is usually referenced to (referred to a reference pressure of) 2×10^{-4} μbar ($= 0.0002$ dyne/cm² $= 20$ μPa) unless a different reference pressure is specified.

Sound power is expressed in *watts (W)*.

Acoustic impedance, resistance, and reactance are expressed in N·s/m⁵; this unit is also referred to as the *mks acoustic ohm.*

3.2 SENSING METHOD

Sound is sensed by *pressure-sensing* elements; the *flat diaphragm,* or design variations thereof (see Section 2.6.1), is used in virtually all sound sensing devices. In some cases the transduction element itself provides the sensing function and the diaphragm then acts as isolation membrane. The diaphragm responds to variations in sound pressure. The sensing element is usually configured for gage-pressure sensing, that is, ambient pressure is admitted to the reference side of the diaphragm. Hence, sound pressure is measured with respect to ambient static pressure, while static pressures acting on the outer and inner diaphragm surfaces are equalized. The gage vent can also be made to act as a "low-pass filter" acoustic leak which prevents the sound pressure variations to be seen by the reference side of the diaphragm. Some sensing elements exist in sealed-reference differential pressure configurations, with their reference side sealed and sometimes partly evacuated.

3.3 DESIGN AND OPERATION

3.3.1 Microphones

Sound-pressure sensors are commonly referred to as *measuring microphones,* or just *microphones.* They are, essentially, special-purpose dynamic pressure transducers (see Sections 2.6.2.1 and 2.6.2.8). Considered as pressure transducers, microphones have a relatively low pressure measuring range but a high frequency response. The latter requirement limits the transducer designs usable for sound-pressure measurements to those few types having stiff, low-mass sensing elements with very small deflection and high natural frequency and having transduction elements capable of following high-frequency changes in sensing-element deflection. The two most commonly used transduction methods are piezoelectric and capacitive.

3.3.1.1 Piezoelectric microphones. The design and operation of piezoelectric sound-pressure transducers (the term "microphone" is less commonly applied to this type than to the capacitive type) is very similar to the design and operation of piezoelectric pressure transducers (see Section 2.6.2.8). Ceramic as well as quartz crystals are used in modern sound-pressure transducers. A typical design is shown in Figure 3-1. The cylindrical housing allows hand-held use as well as clamping in a fixed location. Designs with a partly threaded housing are also available, for flush-mounting into a threaded port in the wall of a chamber, duct, or pipe. The incorporation of a preamplifier, as in the unit illustrated, is quite common. It not only provides a signal amplitude sufficient to drive many types of display, analysis, and recording devices, it also has a low output impedance (about 1000 Ω) which is much easier to handle by associated cabling and signal-processing equipment than the inherently high output impedance (megohms) of the crystal itself. Transducers with such built-

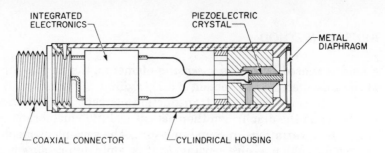

INTEGRATED
ELECTRONICS

PIEZOELECTRIC
CRYSTAL

METAL
DIAPHRAGM

COAXIAL CONNECTOR

CYLINDRICAL HOUSING

Figure 3-1. Piezoelectric sound-pressure transducer. (Courtesy of BBN Instruments Co.)

in solid-state preamplifiers require only an external power supply (often battery-operated) which also contains a simple passive network for extracting the output signal from the (typically 15 V) positive lead between power supply and transducer. The design and mounting of the diaphragm/crystal combination is such that vibration effects are minimized. Some piezoelectric designs incorporate a separate vibration-compensating element.

Piezoelectric microphones designed for underwater use are known as *hydrophones* (most hydrophones are piezoelectric). Their sensing portion is enclosed in a waterproof sheath (e.g., neoprene) and they are usually furnished with a waterproof cable whose sheath is sealed, at the transducer connection, to the transducer housing. The piezoelectric effect is reversible; that is, a crystal will emit sound when excited by an ac voltage, at the frequency of that voltage. Hydrophones are often designed to provide the sound-transmission as well as the sound-reception functions.

3.3.1.2 Condenser microphones. Condenser microphones are capacitive sound-pressure transducers whose design is optimized for acoustic measurements. A typical design is shown in Figure 3-2. The metallic diaphragm acts as one electrode, and the backplate acts as the other electrode of the capacitive sensing/transduction element. The diaphragm is electrically and mechanically bonded to the housing, and the housing is also used as the ground terminal of the sensor. The backplate is retained in a silicone-treated quartz (or synthetic ruby) insulator which forms the rear wall of the sensing cavity and provides an acoustic reference surface. The perforations in the backplate equalize the pressure within this cavity. A capillary duct provides equalization between sensing cavity and ambient pressure in a controlled manner. A silver wire is used for adjusting this "acoustic leak" so as to give a well-defined and low low-frequency limit. Electrical contact with the backplate is provided through the (gold) output terminal. An end cap with a symmetrical protecting grid is mounted, by threading, over the diaphragm.

The unit illustrated is intended for mounting to a housing which provides for operation either hand-held or clamped and also contains a preamplifier. When so installed, a contact on the preamplifier module comes in firm electrical contact with the output terminal of the "microphone cartridge." A cable (or rigid or flexible conduit) is furnished integrally with the preamplifier. The cable is then connected to an amplifier/display unit (which contains the re-

296

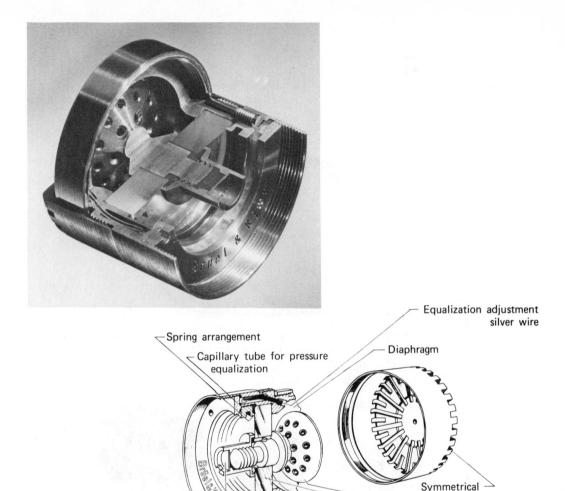

Labels in figure:
- Equalization adjustment silver wire
- Spring arrangement
- Capillary tube for pressure equalization
- Diaphragm
- Symmetrical protection grid
- Quartz insulator
- Backplate
- Output terminal gold

Figure 3-2. Cutaway and sectional view of condenser microphone. (Courtesy of Brüel & Kjaer Instruments, Inc.)

quired power supply) or to a power supply unit which also includes a line-drive amplifier (Figure 3-3). The basic condenser microphones require a stable dc polarization voltage, applied, through a high resistance, across the two capacitor electrodes in order to maintain a constant charge on the electrodes. This polarization voltage (usually 200 V, although lower voltages can also be used for certain microphone designs) is furnished by the power supply unit (or built-in power supply in other associated equipment) together with the power required by the preamplifier. The preamplifier also provides the low output impedance needed by the measuring system.

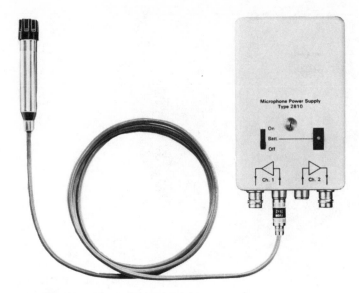

Figure 3-3. Condenser microphone system, consisting of preamplifier with microphone cartridge and integrally attached cable, and (two-channel) power supply unit. (Courtesy of Brüel & Kjaer Instruments, Inc.)

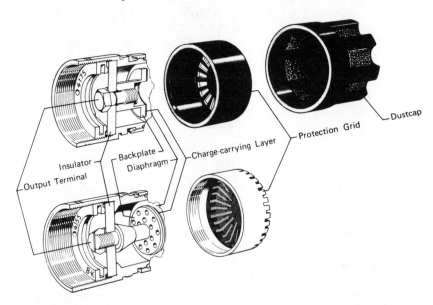

Figure 3-4. Prepolarized (electret) condenser microphones, with frequency response to 12 kHz (upper unit) and 20 kHz (lower unit). (Courtesy of Brüel & Kjaer Instruments, Inc.)

The need for a stabilized polarization voltage is obviated in condenser microphones incorporating a permanently polarized dielectric layer (electret) between the capacitor electrodes. Two microphone designs provided with such a charge-carrying layer are illustrated in Figure 3-4. There are various approaches to producing an electret. Barium titanate/lead titanate ceramic layers can be polarized by first raising their temperature above the Curie point, then cooling the layer, while exposing it to a high-voltage electric field. Another approach uses a metallized plastic foil processed through a high-voltage electric field at a high temperature. The use of a solid dielectric also permits closer spacing between the electrodes, which increases the capacitance of the sensor.

Some condenser microphones are specifically designed to operate with a high-frequency carrier system instead of a power supply. The carrier (typically 10 MHz) is modulated by the capacitance variations. This type of system extends the lower limit of the frequency response from the usual 2.5 to 7 Hz downward, to as low as 0.01 Hz.

The protecting-grid end caps on condenser microphones are usually designed for free-field measurements. For diffuse-field measurements this end cap can be replaced by one having a different grid configuration appropriate for such measurements ("random incidence corrector"). A dust cap is normally kept over the microphone when it is not in use. For use in certain environments, umbrella-like rain covers, spherical sponge windscreens, or other specialized protective devices can be placed over the microphone. Microphones with quartz coatings over their (nickel or nickel alloy) electrodes are available for use in humid, salty, or corrosive atmospheres. Silica gel dehumidifiers can be mounted between microphone cartridge and preamplifier to keep the sensing element dry. Other accessories include floor stands (tripods) and rotating booms.

3.4 MICROPHONE PERFORMANCE CHARACTERISTICS

Essential *mechanical design characteristics* include configuration and overall dimensions, mounting means and dimensions, and a description of any protecting-grid end cap. For hydrophones, in which the sensing element is concealed by the waterproof sheath, the location of the center of the acoustic field should be defined on the outline drawing. Housing and sensing element materials and type of sealing should be described. Limitations on constituents and contaminants of the ambient atmosphere should be stated. A statement of equivalent volume (due to sensing element compliance) is often desirable. Any enclosed or semienclosed volume associated with the sensing element, and its effect on frequency response, should be described in adequate detail.

The location and type of external electrical connections should be explained. If the microphone (or microphone/preamplifier assembly) is furnished with an integral cable, the type and characteristics of cable and connector should be described.

Electrical design characteristics include polarization voltage requirements or carrier voltage amplitude and frequency requirements for condenser microphones, and power supply requirements for integrally packaged or integrally assembled preamplifiers. Other characteristics to be stated include output impedance, insulation resistance, output noise, grounding, and permissible range of load impedance of user-furnished associated equipment.

Performance characteristics are stated either for the basis sensor ("microphone cartridge") or for an integrally packaged (not disassemblable) microphone/preamplifier combination. The conditions under which the performance characteristics are applicable (e.g., excitation supply voltage and stability, load impedance) must be explained.

Range (dynamic range) is usually specified in terms of sound-pressure level (SPL or L_p) together with a statement of the reference pressure (e.g., "Range: 48 to 170 dB re 20 µPa"). In some cases range has also been expressed in units of pressure (Pa, µbar, psi, dynes/cm²). *Overrange* capability or maximum sound pressure are often stated additionally.

Linearity (independent linearity unless otherwise specified) is often shown in conjunction with the range over which a specified linearity applies ("linear dynamic range"). It is expressed in percent or in dB. Since nonlinearity in an acoustic system produces harmonic distortion, the linear dynamic range is sometimes defined by sound-pressure levels at which a specified percent distortion occurs.

Sensitivity is usually shown in *mV/Pa* (pressure sensitivity). It is also often shown in terms of *sensitivity level,* expressed in decibels referred to a stated reference sensitivity, typically 1 V/µbar (e.g., "−94 dB re 1 V/µbar"). The sensitivity (level) in dB is equal to $20 \log_{10} (V/p_s)$, where V is the output in volts rms and p_s is the effective sound pressure in µbar. Sensitivity can also be shown (for piezoelectric transducers without integral preamplifier) as *charge sensitivity level* (e.g., "____dB re 1 picocoulomb per microbar"). Sensitivity, regardless of the manner in which it is expressed, is always the *nominal* sensitivity. Its statement should be accompanied by a set of tolerances; however, microphones are usually accompanied by an individual calibration chart which includes a statement of their actual measured sensitivity.

Frequency response specifications should state whether pressure response, random incidence response, or free-field response is meant; when free-field response is indicated, normal incidence is implied unless grazing incidence is specified. Preferably, the frequency response should be referred to a specific amplitude and frequency. The flatness of frequency response is expressed in dB as a tolerance on the sensitivity, over a stated frequency range [e.g., "Free-field normal-incidence frequency response: within ±2 dB from 4.2 Hz to 40 kHz (as referred to the response at 100 Hz and at 160 dB SPL)"].

The pressure frequency response is generally equal to the free-field random- or grazing-incidence response at wavelengths which are long compared to the maximum dimension of the microphone. Frequency response can sometimes be calculated from the microphone's response to transient pressure, or from its geometry and mechanical properties when these are relatively simple;

when determined in this manner it must be stated as "calculated frequency response." If the microphone is intended for use in fluids other than air (or if it is a hydrophone) and its frequency response and other specification characteristics are applicable when used in such a fluid, the specification must be annotated appropriately.

Directivity can be specified as directivity factor or as solid angle symmetrical about (bisected by) the principal axis of the microphone. It is often shown, in manufacturers' literature, as one or more typical directional response patterns, based on test data, and plotted on circular graph paper.

Threshold is sometimes specified. Resolution is not included in specifications since all commonly used measuring microphones have continuous resolution.

Temperature sensitivity is shown either as a tolerance, in ±dB, on sensitivity, over a specified operating temperature range, or as thermal sensitivity shift, in dB/°C, for such a temperature range. *Temperature gradient error* is often shown, especially for piezoelectric microphones (which can exhibit pyroelectric-effect potentials); this is sometimes called "transient temperature response." Some microphone designs can be equipped with a water cooling jacket, for high-temperature operation.

Acceleration and vibration effects have been covered, in specifications, in terms of the output, due to acceleration, equivalent to an output corresponding to a stated sound-pressure level. The acceleration error is then shown in dB per rms g (or per m/s^2). Vibration error is also shown in this manner, with an additional statement of the vibration frequency range. Both of these specifications should indicate along which microphone axis the tolerances are applicable (when not stated, acceleration acting along the longitudinal axis, normal to the sensing diaphragm, is implied, as worst-case condition). Vibration and acceleration error can also be specified in terms of equivalent sensitivity level, expressed as equivalent SPL per g, and determined as $20 \log_{10}$ of the ratio of the apparent rms sound pressure due to acceleration to the rms applied acceleration (vibration) amplitude.

Ambient-pressure error is specified as a tolerance on sensitivity, in ±dB, over a stated range of ambient pressures or, as "altitude error," over a stated range of altitude above sea level. For hydrophones, this type of error can be shown for a stated range of pressures or depths below sea level.

Other environmental effects on performance may include those due to contaminating or corrosive atmospheres, due to shock, or due to exposure to nuclear radiation or electromagnetic fields.

3.5 SOUND-PRESSURE MEASUREMENTS

A basic sound-pressure measuring system consists of a microphone with its preamplifier and an amplifier which has a flat frequency response matched as closely as possible to that of the microphone. For sound-pressure telemetry applications the compact, ruggedly packaged amplifier has a fixed gain setting such that full-scale output, as accepted by the telemetry set, is produced at the upper SPL range limit. Voltage amplifiers are used in all cases except when the output of a piezoelectric microphone without built-in preamplifier must be amplified, in which case a charge amplifier is used instead. Since a wide band of frequencies must be examined, a wide-band telemetry channel is needed for the transmission of analog signals. In digital telemetry systems this requirement translates into a very high data rate for a single measurement. When a reduced data rate is required and a reasonable approximation of the measured signal is acceptable for reconstruction at the data reception, processing and display facility, a *spectrum analyzer* can be used with the amplifier. Such an analyzer typically contains a number of narrow-band-pass filters to which the signal is applied. The output of each filter is then an analog signal representative of the amount of acoustic energy in the respective narrow band of frequencies. The filter outputs are then read out sequentially.

Most sound-pressure measuring systems, however, are in the form of bench-test setups and controllable by human operators. The amplifier is equipped with a calibrated attenuator so that selected portions of the overall measuring range can be displayed. The amplifier may also be equipped with one or more filters (or provisions for connecting an external filter or filter set). The output of the amplifier can either be applied directly, as ac signal, to display or analysis equipment, or it can be rectified into a dc signal. This signal can also be passed through a linear-to-logarithmic converter to provide a logarithmic display of sound-pressure level. The signal, in either of its forms, can also be recorded for non-real-time analysis. Analog as well as digital analyzers are available for obtaining a cathode-ray tube (CRT) or other graphic display of the frequency characteristics of the measured signal.

There are many applications in sound-pressure measurement where either the continuous or short-term sounds of a sound-producing source or the sound field existing at a particular location are measured and characterized as to amplitude vs. frequency distribution. Continuous sounds are emitted by propulsion systems (automotive, ship, rail, aircraft and rocket engines) and by essentially all types of machinery. Measurements of *sound power* of machinery or other equipment are made by an array of microphones placed around the equipment or by a single microphone at the end of a rotating boom. Use of a sound source of known characteristics in conjunction with one or more microphones allows measurements of the *sound-insulating* qualities of walls, of *reverberation time* and *sound distribution* (e.g., in rooms, auditoriums, and concert halls), and of *sound absorption*.

Measurements of the *acoustic emissions* from materials undergoing stress, and the characterization of such emissions, have become a useful tool in stress and fatigue analysis. Such characterizations are related to the "signatures" of rotating parts and assemblies, from which such factors as bearing wear can be determined, that are obtained by vibration analysis techniques (see Section 1.2.3.2).

3.6 SOUND-LEVEL MEASUREMENTS

Sound level is a weighted sound-pressure level; the signal from the microphone preamplifier is fed to an amplifier which incorporates a *weighting network* that emphasizes certain frequencies while deemphasizing others. Weighting networks carry a reference designation letter (A, B, C) and the characteristics of each network are defined in national and international standards. A sound-pressure level measuring system that incorporates one or more weighting networks is called a *sound-level meter*. A typical instrument is shown in Figure 3-5. It is a compact, hand-held, battery-operated device which contains a measuring condenser microphone and preamplifier in the necked-down stem at its

Figure 3-5. Sound-level meter. (Courtesy of Brüel & Kjaer Instruments, Inc.)

top, two selectable weighting networks (A and C) as well as selectable linear response (unweighted), and a calibrated attenuator (range selector) which shifts the range of the displayed reading by 10-dB increments. Since many noise level measurements are based on the "A" weighting network, some sound-level meters include only that network and then provide a display in "dB(A)" (sometimes simply shown as "dBA").

Sound-level measurements are specifically related to human sound sensation and the characteristics of aural perception form the basis of the weighting networks. The frequency response of networks, A, B, and C is fairly flat between about 1 and 10 kHz; however, the response of the A network drops off sharply below 1 kHz, the response of the B network drops off only moderately below 400 Hz, and the response of the C network is essentially flat between 100 Hz and 3 kHz and drops off only by 5 dB between 100 and 20 Hz and between 3 and 10 kHz.

Sound-level meters can include a number of additional features. *Impulse* sound-level meters are specifically designed for impulse sound (short bursts) measurement (e.g., for sounds produced by a punch press or forge hammer). Other features include adjustable response time, octave (or octave-fraction) filter sets (or provisions for interconnection with external filter sets), peak value hold, overload indication, and determination and calculation of L_{eq}, the integrated ("equivalent continuous") sound level over adjustable periods of time. Extension cables can often be inserted between the microphone/preamplifier and the meter.

Noise dose meters measure accumulated noise exposure over a specified period of time (typically an 8-h working day). Such meters are usually compact enough to be worn in a worker's breast pocket. The meter is not resettable except by a supervisor, who reads and records the worker's noise dose reading at the end of the day. Some models provide a noise hazard warning to the worker when a specified sound level such as 140 dB(A) is exceeded.

Sound-level measurements are the basis of noise control. With increased awareness of the hazards of "noise pollution," which range from hearing impairment and nervous disorders to interference with speech and the creation of sales resistance to a product, government agencies in many countries (e.g., OSHA in the United States) have been specifying limits on noise in work areas and have been enforcing such regulations. Additionally, manufacturers of a large variety of products have been encouraged to reduce the amount of noise made by their products. These range from industrial equipment to home appliances and cars. All this has increased the importance and use of sound-level meters substantially. Noise is measured, designs are modified, or insulation is added to reduce the noise to acceptable levels; noise is then remeasured and often monitored continuously thereafter. As a result, work areas, highways, airports, and even homes have been getting quieter.

There are, of course, many applications of sound-level meters in areas other than noise control. They are used to obtain proper acoustical designs of studios, classrooms, and other architectural work. They are used by musical performers and performing groups and in many commercial establishments, such as department stores.

3.7 UNDERWATER SOUND DETECTION

The underwater version of the microphone, the *hydrophone*, is commonly used as an underwater listening device. Analysis of the frequencies, amplitudes, and waveshapes of its output signals can be interpreted to obtain information about the nature of the object from which the sound emanates. Two or more hydrophones can be used for *ranging,* that is, obtaining information about the location of the sound source.

Many hydrophone designs are also capable of operating in the transmit mode (using the inverse piezoelectric effect) as well as the receive mode. They can then be used in such systems as the *echo-ranging sonar* (the acronym "sonar" is derived from "*sound navigation and ranging*"). The usual operating mode of such a system involves the generation of a pulse of sound energy and its transmission by the hydrophone. The hydrophone is then immediately switched into its receive mode and the travel time of the pulse *(ping)* to and from the target is measured by the equipment. The travel time, combined with knowledge of the directional characteristics of the hydrophone, provides range information about the target. Further analysis of the "echo" from the target can yield additional information about the target (e.g., configuration, material). Most hydrophones are piezoelectric, some are magnetostrictive, in transduction principle.

Besides its many military applications, sonar is widely used for the detection of schools of fish, in salvage operations, for ocean-floor mapping, and in other oceanographic research.

3.8 ULTRASONICS

Ultrasonic waves are elastic waves, above the audio-frequency range in frequency, propagated through gaseous, liquid, or solid media. The frequencies of ultrasonic waves extend from the upper limit of the audio-frequency range (15 to 20 kHz) into the high-frequency range as used in telecommunications (see Figure 3-6). However, the term "ultrasonic" is not applied to frequencies

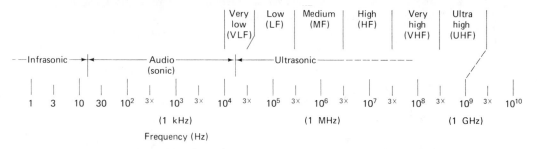

Figure 3-6. Frequency-band nomenclature below 3 GHz.

used for telecommunications purposes; the other terms shown in Figure 3-6 apply instead. It is primarily the propagation velocity of ultrasonic waves and the effects on this velocity by the density, viscosity, and elasticity of the gaseous, liquid, or solid medium through which the sound waves propagate that establish the most useful characteristics of ultrasound for measurement purposes.

The theory and applications of ultrasound and ultrasonic equipment are well covered in available technical literature. Ultrasonic devices used for the measurement of specific types of quantities, such as flow and liquid level, are discussed in applicable sections of this book. The ultrasonic *transducers* (piezoelectric or magnetostrictive) are related to hydrophones (see Section 3.4.4) in that they can operate in either the receive or the transmitting mode or, alternatingly, in both modes. Ultrasonic measuring techniques are related to echo-ranging sonar techniques in that a pulse of ultrasonic energy is transmitted and the echo from the medium or target is analyzed.

The interaction of ultrasonic waves with substances is similar to the interaction of light with substances (see Section 5.4). Besides the reflectance mode that allows a comparison with sonar techniques, the transmission mode is used in some applications. In materials testing, for example, the reflectance mode is commonly used for flaw detection in solids and other materials; however, the transmission mode, in combination with ultrasonic emissions from a reference transducer, are used in *acoustic holography imaging* systems for nondestructive testing. Ultrasonic scanning, using reflectance, is used for subcutaneous mapping of biological organisms, sometimes in combination with computerized image processing techniques. Since the penetration depth of ultrasonic energy, including into nonhomogeneous solids, is largely dependent on frequency, empirically defined strata of tissues and organs of the body can be scanned sequentially and three-dimensional images can be derived from the data.

Bibliography

1. **Beranek, L. L.,** *Acoustics.* New York: McGraw-Hill Book Company, 1954.

2. **Albers, V. M.,** *Underwater Acoustics Handbook.* University Park, PA: Pennsylvania State University Press, 1960.

3. **Kinsler, L. E., and Frey, A. R.,** *Fundamentals of Acoustics* (2nd ed.). New York: John Wiley & Sons, Inc., 1962.

4. **Keast, D. N.,** *Measurements in Mechanical Dynamics.* New York: McGraw-Hill Book Company, 1967.

5. **Morse, P. M., and Ingard, K. U.,** *Theoretical Acoustics.* New York: McGraw-Hill Book Company, 1968.

6. **Sessler, G. M., and West, J. E.,** "Foil Electrets and Their Use in Condenser Microphones," *Journal of the Electrochemical Society,* Vol. 115, pp. 836–841, 1968.

7. **Goldman, R. G.,** *Ultrasonic Technology.* New York: Van Nostrand Reinhold Company, 1962.

8. **Gayford, M. L.,** *Electroacoustics: Microphones, Earphones, and Loudspeakers.* London: Butterworth, 1970.

9. **Beranek, L. L.,** *Noise and Vibration Control.* New York: McGraw-Hill Book Company, 1971.

10. "Occupational Noise Exposure," Article 1910.95, Occupational Safety and Health Administration, *Federal Register,* Vol. 36, No. 105. Pt. II, May 29, 1971.

11. **Goodfriend, L. S.,** *Noise Pollution.* Cleveland OH: CRC Scientific Publications, 1972.

12. **Junger, M. C., and Feit, D.,** *Sound, Structures and Their Interactions.* Cambridge, MA: MIT Press, 1972.

13. **Fry, F. J.** (Ed.), *Ultrasound, Its Applications in Biology and Medicine.* New York: American Elsevier Publishing Co., 1975.

14. **Yerges, L. F.,** *Sound, Noise and Vibration Control.* New York: Van Nostrand Reinhold Company, 1978.

Commercial Publications

1. *Measuring Sound, Community Noise Measurements* and other simplified brochures; *Architectural Acoustics, Frequency Analysis* and other handbooks; and *Brüel & Kjaer Technical Review,* a quarterly periodical—all available from: B & K Instruments, Inc., Marlborough, MA, USA, or Brüel & Kjaer, Naerum, Denmark.

Selected Specifications and Standards

1. ANSI Standards, available from American National Standards Institute, New York: "Specification for Sound Level Meters," *ANSI S1.4-1971.*
"Preferred Frequencies for Acoustical Measurements," *ANSI S1.6-1967.*
"Preferred Reference Quantities for Acoustical Levels," *ANSI S1.8-1969.*
"Methods for the Measurement of Sound Pressure Levels," *ANSI S1.13-1971.*
"Procedures for Calibration of Underwater Electroacoustic Transducers," *ANSI S1.20-1972.*
"Methods for the Determination of Sound Power Levels of Small Sources in Reverberation Rooms," *ANSI S1.21-1972.*
"Specifications and Tests for Piezoelectric Pressure and Sound Pressure Transducers (ISA S37.10)," *ANSI MC6.4-1975.*
"Methods for Sound Power Determination," *ANSI S1.31 through S1.36-1980.*

2. ISO Standards (S), Recommendations (R) and Draft Standards (D) (expected to become Standards in the near future), available from Secretariat, International Organization for Standardization, Geneva, Switzerland (or from ANSI, in the USA): "Measurement of Sound Insulation in Buildings and of Building Elements," Parts I through VIII, *ISO D 140, May 1976.*
"Measurement of Absorption Coefficient in a Reverberation Room," *ISO R 354, Dec. 1963.*
"Measurement of Noise Emitted by Vehicles," *ISO R 362, Feb. 1964.*
"Standard Reference Zero for the Calibration of Pure Tone Audiometers," *ISO S 389, Jan. 1975.*
"Standard for Sound Level Meters," *ISO S 651, 1979.*
"Rating of Sound Insulation for Dwellings," *ISO R 717, May 1968.*
"Test Code for the Measurement of the Airborne Noise Emitted by Rotating Electrical Machinery," *ISO R 1680, July 1970.*
"Assessment of Noise with Respect to Community Response," *ISO R 1996, May 1971.*

"Assessment of Occupational Noise Exposure for Hearing Conservation Purposes," *ISO S 1999, Aug. 1972.*

"Measurement of Airborne Noise Emitted by Compressor/Primemover Units Intended for Outdoor Use," *ISO S 2151, June 1972.*

"Guide to the Measurement of Airborne Acoustical Noise and Evaluation of its Effects on Man," *ISO S 2204, May 1973.*

"Description and Measurement of Physical Properties of Sonic Booms," *ISO S 2249, Mar. 1973.*

"Measurement of Noise Emitted by Vessels on Inland Waterways and Harbors," *ISO S 2922, Sept. 1975.*

"Measurement of Noise on Board Vessels," *ISO S 2923, Sept. 1975.*

"Measurement of Noise Emitted by Railbound Vehicles," *ISO S 3095, Sept. 1975.*

"Measurement of Noise Inside Railbound Vehicles," *ISO S 3381, Feb. 1976.*

"Measurement of Reverberation Time in Auditoria," *ISO S 3382, Dec. 1975.*

"Determination of Sound Power Levels of Noise Sources—Guidelines for the Use of Basic Standards and for the Preparation of Noise Test Codes," *ISO D 3740, May 1976.*

"Precision Methods for Broad Band Sou‍ ‍es in Reverberation Rooms," *ISO S 3741, July 1975.*

"Precision Methods for Discrete Frequency and Narrow Band Sources in Reverberation Rooms," *ISO S 3742, Dec. 1976.*

"Engineering Methods for Special Reverberation Test Rooms," *ISO S 3743, Dec. 1976.*

"Engineering Methods for Free Field Conditions over a Reflecting Plane," *ISO D 3744, May 1975.*

"Precision Methods for Anechoic and Semi-anechoic Rooms," *ISO S 3745, Nov. 1975.*

"Survey Method" (for determining the A-weighted sound power level of a device or machine), *ISO D 3746, June 1976.*

"Laboratory Tests on Noise Emission by Appliances and Equipment Used in Water Supply Installations; Part I: Methods of Measurement," *ISO S 3822, July 1977.*

"Procedure for Describing Aircraft Noise Heard on the Ground," *ISO D 3891* (no date given).

chapter four

Thermal Quantities

4.1 BASIC CONCEPTS

4.1.1 Definitions

The *temperature* of a body is its thermal state considered with reference to its power of communicating heat to other bodies; it is a measure of the kinetic energy of the molecules of a substance due to heat agitation; it is the potential of heat flow.

Heat is energy, specifically energy in transfer, due to temperature differences, between a system and its surroundings or between two systems, substances, or bodies. It has also been defined as the energy contained in a sample of matter comprising potential energy resulting from interatomic forces as well as kinetic energy associated with random motion of molecules in the sample.

Heat transfer is the transfer of heat energy by one or more of the following methods:

1. *Conduction*: by diffusion through solid material or through stagnant fluids (liquids or gases).
2. *Convection*: by the movement of a fluid (between two points).
3. *Radiation*: by electromagnetic waves.

Heat capacity is the quantity of heat required to raise the temperature of a system, substance or body by one degree of temperature (in a specified manner).

Specific heat is the ratio of the heat capacity of a body to the mass (or to the volume, as specified) of the body. An earlier definition made specific heat the (dimensionless) ratio of the quantity of heat required to raise the temperature of a material (without change of phase) by one degree to the quantity of heat required to raise the temperature of water, having the same mass as the material, by one degree (in temperature), under specified conditions.

Thermal conductivity is the ratio of the time rate of heat flow, per unit area, to the negative gradient of the temperature per unit thickness in the heat-flow direction (see Fourier's law, Section 4.1.2.2).

Thermal diffusivity is the ratio of the thermal conductivity to the product of specific heat and density; the magnitude of thermal diffusivity determines how fast temperature differences, existing in a body or substance, will equalize.

Thermal resistance is a measure of a body's ability to prevent heat from flowing through it; it is equal to the difference in temperature between opposite faces of the body divided by the heat-flow rate.

Thermal equilibrium is a condition of a system and its surroundings (or of two or more systems, substances or bodies) when no temperature differences exist between them (i.e., no more heat transfer occurs between them).

The following definitions apply to fixed points of the temperature scale:

The *boiling point* is the temperature of equilibrium between the liquid and vapor phases of a substance (at 1 standard atmosphere unless otherwise specified).

The *freezing point* is the temperature of equilibrium between the solid and liquid phases of a substance (at 1 standard atmosphere unless otherwise specified).

The *triple point* is the temperature of equilibrium between the solid, liquid, and vapor phases of a substance.

The *ice point* (273.15 K, 0 °C, 32.0 °F) is the temperature at which ice is in equilibrium with air-saturated water at a pressure of 1 standard atmosphere.

The *sublimation point* is the temperature at which a substance changes from its solid phase directly to its vapor phase without passing through a liquid phase.

Absolute temperature is temperature measured on the thermodynamic scale; it is temperature measured from *absolute zero* (0 K, −273.15 °C).

A *blackbody* (ideal black body) is an ideal body that would absorb all and reflect none of the radiation incident on it (its *absorbtivity* would be 100% and its *reflectivity* would be 0%); it is also the ideal radiator.

Emissivity is the ratio of the radiation emitted by a given surface to the radiation emitted by the surface of a blackbody heated to the same temperature as the surface, under the same conditions, and within the same solid angle.

The *emissive power* of a blackbody is the total hemispherical radiation from it per unit area of radiation surface (see the Stefan–Boltzmann law, Section 4.1.2.3).

Heat flux is the amount of heat transferred across a surface of unit area per unit time.

4.1.2 Related Laws

4.1.2.1 *Gas temperature*

Boyle's Law. In a given quantity of gas, the product of pressure and volume remains constant as long as the temperature is held constant.
Charles' Law: In a given quantity of gas, the ratio of the absolute temperature to the volume remains constant if the pressure is held constant, and the ratio of the absolute temperature to the pressure remains constant if the volume is held constant.

Ideal-gas Law

$$\frac{pv}{T} = R = \frac{p}{\rho T}$$

where p = pressure
   v = specific volume
   T = absolute temperature
   ρ = density
   R = gas constant

4.1.2.2 *Heat conduction*

Fourier's Law

$$\frac{dQ}{dt} = -kA\frac{dT}{dx}$$

where Q = quantity of heat transferred across a body
   t = time
   k = thermal conductivity of the body
   A = cross-sectional area of the body
   T = temperature
   x = distance, in the direction of heat flow (taken as normal to A)

In this equation, dQ/dt is the time rate of heat flow and dT/dx is the *temperature gradient*.

4.1.2.3 Thermal radiation

Stefan–Boltzmann Law

$$Q_T = \sigma A T^4$$

where Q_T = total heat radiated from the surface of an ideal blackbody
(total hemispherical emission in all wavelengths)

σ = Stefan–Boltzmann constant

A = area of emitting surface (see below)

T = absolute temperature of emitting surface

Units of Q_T	Units of A	Units of T	Value of σ
W	m^2	K	5.67×10^{-8}
W	cm^2	K	5.67×10^{-12}
Btu/h	ft^2	°R	1.72×10^{-7}

Wien's Displacement Law

$$T\lambda_{\mathrm{max}} = 2.8978 \times 10^{-3} \quad \text{(Wien's constant)}$$

where T = absolute temperature, K

λ_{max} = wavelength of maximum radiance from blackbody, m

Note: When the wavelength is expressed in μm rather than in m, Wien's constant becomes 2898 μm·K.

Planck's Radiation Formula

$$W_\lambda = \frac{C_1 \, \Delta\lambda\varepsilon_\lambda}{\lambda^5 \, (e^{C_2/\lambda T} - 1)}$$

where W_λ = radiation intensity (radiant excitance), per unit area of source, at wavelength λ, over a spectral range $\Delta\lambda$, W/m^2

λ = wavelength, m

ε_λ = emissivity of source at wavelength λ (emissivity = 1.0 for a blackbody)

e = Naperian base (2.71828)

C_1 = First radiation constant, 3.7413×10^{-16} W·m^2

C_2 = Second radiation constant, 1.4388×10^{-2} m·K

T = absolute temperature, K

Note: This formula can also be shown for radiation intensity per $\Delta\lambda$, expressed in W/cm^2/μm, with the wavelength expressed in μm (and $\Delta\lambda$ deleted from the numerator); when so expressed, $C_1 = 37\,413 \times 10^{-12}$ and $C^2 = 14\,388$.

4.1.3 Temperature Scales and Units of Measurement

Temperature scales were originally established on an arbitrary basis; much later international agreement was reached on an appropriately defined temperature scale. The *Fahrenheit* scale is based on the mercury-in-glass thermometer, with the ice point defined as 32 °F and the *steam point* (boiling point of water) defined as 212 °F; the ice point − steam point difference is 180 °F. The *Rankine* scale is an absolute temperature scale, with the same difference (180 °R) between ice point and steam point as the Fahrenheit scale, but with the *absolute zero* of temperature defining 0 °R; hence, the ice point is 491.7 °R and the steam point is 671.7 °R. Since both of these temperature scales have the same difference in degrees between ice point and steam point, 1 °F = 1 °R. The *Réaumur* scale was used in some European countries but is now essentially obsolete; on this scale the ice point was 0 ° and the steam point was 80 °. The *Celsius* scale (a now obsolete name for which was the *centigrade* scale) is also based on the mercury-in-glass thermometer, but with the ice point defined at 0 °C and the steam point at 100 °C. This scale is still widely used and the °C is considered a unit of the "metric system."

The unit of temperature in the International System of Units (SI) is the *kelvin (K)*. It should be noted that the word "degree," or its symbol, is not used in conjunction with this unit. The kelvin is the unit of *thermodynamic* temperature and is defined as the fraction 1/273.16 of the thermodynamic temperature of the triple point of water. The triple point of water is 0.01 K above the ice point; hence, on the kelvin scale, the ice point is 273.15 K and the steam point is 373.15 K. The difference between these two temperatures is 100.00 K, and 1 K = 1 °C, exactly. Absolute zero is 0 K.

An International Temperature Scale was adopted in 1948. Between the oxygen point (boiling point of oxygen, − 183 °C) and the antimony point (freezing point of antimony, + 630 °C) it was based on the resistance of a standard platinum resistance thermometer; temperatures within this range were determined by calculations based on measured resistance values at 0 °C and at the temperature to be determined. The relationship used was the *Callendar–VanDusen equation:*

$$R_t = R_0 + R_0\alpha[t - \delta(0.01t - 1)(0.01t) - \beta(0.01t - 1)(0.01t)^3]$$

where R_t = resistance at temperature t, °C

R_0 = resistance at 0 °C (ice point)

α, δ, β are constants; typical values for a winding of pure, strain-free, annealed platinum are:

α = 0.003925 (temperature coefficient of resistance near 0 °C)

δ = 1.49

β = 0.11 (if t is negative)

β = 0 (if t is positive)

This equation is still used as the resistance vs. temperature relationship for platinum resistance thermometers, although the constants, which are empirical, may differ somewhat from those shown above for a "standard" thermometer.

Between 630 °C and the gold point (freezing point of gold, 1064 °C), the 1948 Temperature Scale was based on the emf vs. temperature relationship of a "standard" platinum/90% platinum–10% rhodium thermocouple. Above the gold point, the Temperature Scale was based on the optical pyrometer.

In 1968 The International Committee on Weights and Measures (CIPM) adopted a revised temperature scale, the International Practical Temperature Scale of 1968 *(IPTS-68)*. The main reasons for devising the new scale were to extend a unified scale down to about 10 K (instead of 90 K, the oxygen point) and to reflect more accurately measured temperatures between the oxygen point and the gold point.

The IPTS-68 is based on the assigned values *(defining fixed points)* of the temperatures of a number of equilibrium states (freezing points, boiling points, triple points) and on standard instruments calibrated at those temperatures. These points are established by realizing specified equilibrium states between phases of pure substances. All except one of these points (the 17.042-K point, the boiling point of equilibrium hydrogen at $^{25}/_{76}$ standard atmosphere) are included in Table 4-1. Interpolation between the fixed points is provided by formulas establishing the relationship between standard-instrument indications and temperature values. Formulas and reference functions are available in the applicable documents published by the BIPM, 92 Sèvres, France, and reproduced by governmental standards agencies. The standard instrument used from 13.81 K (triple point of equilibrium hydrogen) to 630.74 °C (freezing point of antimony) is the platinum resistance thermometer, with a winding of pure, strain-free, annealed platinum. For the range between 630.74 and 1064.43 °C (freezing point of gold), the standard instrument is the platinum–10% rhodium/platinum thermocouple. Above 1064.43 °C the IPTS-68 is defined by Planck's radiation formula (see Section 4.1.2.3), with this temperature (which equals 1337.58 K) as reference temperature. Secondary reference points, to supplement the defining fixed points, are available and virtually all the points on Table 4-1 not identified as defining fixed points are usable as such additional reference points (except the melting points of niobium, molybdenum, tantalum, and rhenium, which are shown for general informational purposes).

The estimated uncertainties of defining fixed points are 0.01 K for points between 13.81 and 19.188 K; the triple point of water is exact by definition; above this point the uncertainties increase from 0.005 K (boiling point of water) to 0.2 K (freezing points of silver and gold). Recent research efforts have been directed at reducing such uncertainties. They have already resulted in a new Provisional Temperature Scale *(EPT-76)* which redefines values between 0.5 and 30 K on the basis of the temperatures of onset of superconductivity. This scale will probably replace temperature determinations below the limit of the IPTS-68 (13.81 K) performed on the basis of vapor-pressure vs. temperature relations for equilibrium hydrogen and for helium (^{3}He and ^{4}He). Other research is being carried on in improving platinum resistance thermometers so that they can be used as standard instruments up to the gold point. However, it is not probable that the IPTS-68 will be considered for a formal revision until about 1986.

The following relationships are used for temperature scale conversions:

$$°C = (°F - 32) \times {}^5/_9 \quad \text{and} \quad °F = {}^9/_5 \times °C + 32$$

$$K = °C + 273.15$$

$$°R = °F + 459.67 \quad \text{(which can usually be rounded off to 459.7)}$$

A convenient scale conversion table is given as Table 4-1.
The following units are used for thermal quantities other than temperature:

Quantity	US Customary Unit[a]	Multiply by:	to get: SI Unit
Heat flux	Btu/ft^2·s	1.136×10^4	J/m^2·s
Heat flux	cal/cm^2·s	4.184×10^4	W/m^2
Heat energy	Btu	1.055×10^3	J
Heat quantity	cal	4.1868	J
Thermal conductivity	Btu·in/s·ft^2·°F	5.192×10^2	W/m·K
Heat power	Btu/h	0.293	W
Specific heat	Btu/lb$_m$·°F	4.1868×10^3	J/kg·K
Heat-transfer coefficient	Btu/s·ft^2·°F	2.044×10^4	W/m^2·K
Thermal resistance	°F·h·ft^2/Btu	0.1761	K·m^2/W
Thermal diffusivity	ft^2/h	2.58×10^{-5}	m^2/s

[a]Conversion factors for *British thermal units (Btu)* and *calories (cal)* are based on the International Tables; conversion factors for *thermochemical Btu* and *cal* differ from those shown by about 0.07%.

4.2 THERMOMETRY

This section covers sensing methods and devices for in situ (contacting) temperature measurements. Remote-sensing (noncontacting) thermometers are described in Section 4.3.

4.2.1 Sensing Methods

Temperature sensors (temperature transducers), or (electric) *thermometers,* are characterized by having their sensing element also perform the transduction. Such sensing/transduction elements are referred to here simply as "sensing elements."

Celsius	Fahrenheit	Kelvin		°C	°F	K
Absolute Zero				Boiling Point of Neon (d)		
− 273.15	− 459.67	0		− 246.05	− 410.9	27.10
− 273.1	− 459.7	− 0.		− 241.1	− 402.0	32.0
− 272.0	− 457.6	1.1		− 240.0	− 400.0	33.1
− 270.0	− 454.0	3.1				
				− 238.9	− 398.0	34.3
Boiling Point of Helium				− 238.0	− 396.4	35.1
− 268.9	− 452.0	4.2		− 237.2	− 395.0	35.9
				− 236.0	− 392.8	37.1
− 268.3	− 451.0	4.8		− 235.0	− 391.0	38.1
− 268.0	− 450.4	5.1		− 234.0	− 389.2	39.1
− 267.2	− 499.0	5.9		− 233.3	− 388.0	39.8
− 266.0	− 446.8	7.1		− 232.0	− 385.6	41.1
− 265.0	− 445.0	8.2		− 231.1	− 384.0	42.0
− 264.0	− 443.2	9.1		− 230.0	− 382.0	43.1
− 263.3	− 442.0	9.8				
− 262.0	− 439.6	11.1		− 228.9	− 380.0	44.3
− 261.1	− 438.0	12.0		− 288.0	− 378.4	45.1
− 260.0	− 436.0	13.1		− 227.2	− 377.0	45.9
				− 226.0	− 374.8	47.1
Triple Point of Hydrogen (d)				− 225.0	− 373.0	48.1
− 259.34	− 434.8	13.81		− 224.0	− 371.2	49.1
				− 223.3	− 370.0	49.8
− 258.9	− 434.0	14.3		− 222.0	− 367.6	51.1
− 258.0	− 432.4	15.1		− 221.1	− 366.0	52.0
− 257.2	− 431.0	15.9		− 220.0	− 364.0	53.1
− 256.0	− 428.8	17.1				
− 255.0	− 427.0	18.1		Triple Point of Oxygen (d)		
− 254.0	− 425.2	19.1		− 218.79	− 361.8	54.36
− 253.3	− 424.0	19.8				
				− 218.0	− 360.4	55.1
Boiling Point of Hydrogen (d)				− 217.2	− 359.0	55.9
− 252.87	− 423.2	20.28		− 216.0	− 356.8	57.1
				− 215.0	− 355.0	58.1
− 252.2	− 422.0	20.9		− 214.0	− 353.2	59.1
− 252.0	− 421.6	21.1		− 213.3	− 352.0	59.8
− 251.1	− 420.0	22.0		− 212.0	− 349.6	61.1
− 250.0	− 418.0	23.1		− 211.1	− 348.0	62.0
− 248.9	− 416.0	24.3		− 210.0	− 346.0	63.1
− 248.0	− 414.4	25.1				
− 247.2	− 413.0	25.9		− 208.9	− 344.0	64.3
				− 208.0	− 342.4	65.1
Boiling Point of Neon (d)				− 207.2	− 341.0	65.9
− 246.05	− 410.9	27.10		− 206.0	− 338.8	67.1
				− 205.0	− 337.0	68.1
− 245.0	− 409.0	28.1		− 204.0	− 335.2	69.1
− 244.0	− 407.2	29.1		− 203.3	− 334.0	69.8
− 243.3	− 406.0	29.8		− 202.0	− 331.6	71.1
− 242.0	− 403.6	31.1		− 201.1	− 330.0	72.0

Table 4-1 (continued)

°C	°F	K		°C	°F	K
Triple Point of Oxygen *(d)*				**Boiling Point of Oxygen** *(d)*		
−218.79	−361.8	54.36		−182.96	−297.3	90.19
−200.0	−328.0	73.1		−167.2	−269.0	105.9
				−166.0	−266.8	107.1
−198.9	−326.0	74.3		−165.0	−265.0	108.1
−198.0	−324.4	75.1		−164.0	−263.2	109.1
−197.2	−323.0	75.9		−163.3	−262.0	109.8
−196.0	−320.8	77.1				
				−162.0	−259.6	111.1
Boiling Point of Nitrogen				−161.1	−258.0	112.0
−195.8	−320.4	77.3		−160.0	−256.0	113.1
				−158.9	−254.0	114.3
−195.0	−319.0	78.1		−158.0	−252.4	115.1
−194.0	−317.2	79.1		−157.2	−251.0	115.9
−193.3	−316.0	79.8		−156.0	−248.8	117.1
−192.0	−313.6	81.1		−155.0	−247.0	118.1
−191.1	−312.0	82.0		−154.0	−245.2	119.1
−190.0	−310.0	83.1		−153.3	−244.0	119.8
				−152.0	−241.6	121.1
Triple Point of Argon				−151.1	−240.0	122.0
−189.3	−308.8	83.8		−150.0	−238.0	123.1
				−148.9	−236.0	124.3
−188.9	−308.0	84.3		−148.0	−234.4	125.1
−188.3	−307.0	84.8		−147.2	−233.0	125.9
−188.0	−306.4	85.1		−144.0	−227.2	129.1
−187.2	−305.0	85.9		−143.3	−226.0	129.8
−186.0	−302.8	87.1		−140.0	−220.0	133.1
−185.0	−301.0	88.1		−138.9	−218.0	134.3
−184.0	−299.2	89.1		−136.0	−212.8	137.1
−183.3	−298.0	89.8		−135.0	−211.0	138.1
				−132.0	−205.6	141.1
Boiling Point of Oxygen *(d)*				−131.1	−204.0	142.0
−182.96	−297.3	90.19				
				−128.0	−198.4	145.1
−182.2	−296.0	90.9		−127.2	−197.0	145.9
−181.1	−294.0	92.0		−124.0	−191.2	149.1
−180.0	−292.0	93.1		−123.3	−190.0	149.8
−178.9	−290.0	94.3		−120.0	−184.0	153.1
−178.0	−288.4	95.1		−118.9	−182.0	154.3
−177.2	−287.0	95.9		−116.0	−176.8	157.1
−176.0	−284.8	97.1		−115.0	−175.0	158.1
−175.0	−283.0	98.1		−112.0	−169.6	161.1
−174.0	−281.2	99.1		−111.1	−168.0	162.0
−173.3	−280.0	99.8				
				−108.0	−162.4	165.1
−172.0	−277.6	101.1		−107.2	−161.0	165.9
−171.1	−276.0	102.0		−104.0	−155.2	169.1
−170.0	−274.0	103.1		−103.3	−154.0	169.8
−168.9	−272.0	104.3		−100.0	−148.0	173.1
−168.0	−270.4	105.1				

Table 4-1 (continued)

°C	°F	K		°C	°F	K
Boiling Point of Oxygen *(d)*				**Sublimation Point of**		
−182.96	−297.3	90.19		**Carbon Dioxide**		
				−78.5	−109.3	194.7
−98.9	−146.0	174.3				
−96.0	−140.8	177.1		−15.6	4.0	257.6
−95.0	−139.0	178.1		−12.0	10.4	261.1
−92.0	−133.6	181.1		−11.7	11.0	261.5
−91.1	−132.0	182.0		−8.0	17.6	265.1
−88.0	−126.4	185.1		−7.8	18.0	265.4
−87.2	−125.0	185.9		−4.0	24.8	269.1
−84.0	−119.2	189.1		−3.9	25.0	269.3
−83.3	−118.0	189.8				
−80.0	−112.0	193.1		**Ice Point**		
−78.9	−110.0	194.3		0.0	32.0	273.15
Sublimation Point of				**Triple Point of Water** *(d)*		
Carbon Dioxide				0.01	32.02	273.16
−78.5	−109.3	194.7				
				4.0	39.2	277.1
−77.8	−108.0	195.4		4.4	40.0	277.6
−76.0	−104.8	197.1		8.0	46.4	281.1
−75.0	−103.0	198.1		8.3	47.0	281.5
−72.0	−97.6	201.1		12.0	53.6	285.1
−71.1	−96.0	202.0		12.2	54.0	285.4
−68.0	−90.4	205.1		16.0	60.8	289.1
−67.2	−89.0	205.9		16.1	61.0	289.3
−64.0	−83.2	209.1		20.0	68.0	293.1
−63.3	−82.0	209.8				
−60.0	−76.0	213.1		24.0	75.2	297.1
−58.9	−74.0	214.3		24.4	76.0	297.6
−56.0	−68.8	217.1		28.0	82.4	301.1
−55.0	−67.0	218.1		28.3	83.0	301.5
−52.0	−61.6	221.1		32.0	89.6	305.1
−51.1	−60.0	222.0		32.2	90.0	305.4
−48.0	−54.4	225.1		36.0	96.8	309.1
−44.0	−47.2	229.1		36.1	97.0	309.3
−43.3	−46.0	229.8		40.0	104.0	313.1
−40.0	−40.0	233.1		44.0	111.2	317.1
−38.9	−38.0	234.3		44.4	112.0	317.6
−36.0	−32.8	237.1		48.0	118.4	321.1
−35.0	−31.0	238.1		48.3	119.0	321.5
				52.0	125.6	325.1
−32.0	−25.6	241.1		52.2	126.0	325.4
−31.1	−24.0	242.0		56.0	132.8	329.1
−28.0	−18.4	245.1		56.1	133.0	329.3
−27.2	−17.0	245.9		60.0	140.0	333.1
−24.0	−11.2	249.1		64.0	147.2	337.1
−23.3	−10.0	249.8		64.4	148.0	337.6
−20.0	−4.0	253.1		68.0	154.4	341.1
−16.0	3.2	257.1		68.3	155.0	341.5

Table 4-1 (continued)

°C	°F	K		°C	°F	K
Triple Point of Water *(d)*				**Triple Point of Benzoic Acid**		
0.01	32.02	273.16		122.4	252.3	395.5
72.0	161.6	345.1		152.0	305.6	425.1
72.2	162.0	345.4		152.2	306.0	425.4
				156.0	312.8	429.1
76.0	168.8	349.1				
76.1	169.0	349.3		**Freezing Point of Indium**		
80.0	176.0	353.1		156.6	313.9	429.8
84.0	183.2	357.1				
84.4	184.0	357.6		160.0	320.0	433.1
88.0	190.4	361.1		164.0	327.2	437.1
88.3	191.0	361.5		164.4	328.0	437.6
92.0	197.6	365.1		168.0	334.4	441.1
92.2	198.0	365.4		168.3	335.0	441.5
96.0	204.8	369.1		172.0	341.6	445.1
				172.2	342.0	445.4
96.1	205.0	369.3		176.0	348.8	449.1
				176.1	349.0	449.3
Boiling Point of Water *(d)*				180.0	356.0	453.1
100.0	212.0	373.15		184.0	363.2	457.1
				184.4	364.0	457.6
104.0	219.2	377.1				
104.4	220.0	377.6		188.0	370.4	461.1
108.0	226.4	381.1		188.3	371.0	461.5
108.3	227.0	381.5		192.0	377.6	465.1
112.0	233.6	385.1		192.2	378.0	465.4
112.2	234.0	385.4		196.0	384.8	469.1
116.0	240.8	389.1		196.1	385.0	469.3
116.1	241.0	389.3		200.0	392.0	473.1
				204.0	399.2	477.1
120.0	248.0	393.1		204.4	400.0	477.6
				208.0	406.4	481.1
Triple Point of Benzoic Acid						
122.4	252.3	395.5		208.3	407.0	481.5
				212.0	413.6	485.1
124.0	255.2	397.1		212.2	414.0	485.4
124.4	256.0	397.6		216.0	420.8	489.1
128.0	262.4	401.1		216.1	421.0	489.3
128.3	263.0	401.5		220.0	428.0	493.1
132.0	269.6	405.1		224.0	435.2	497.1
132.2	270.0	405.4		224.4	436.0	497.6
136.0	276.8	409.1		228.0	442.4	501.1
136.1	277.0	409.3		228.3	443.0	501.5
140.0	284.0	413.1				
				Freezing Point of Tin *(d)*		
144.0	291.2	417.1		231.97	449.55	505.12
144.4	292.0	417.6				
148.0	298.4	421.1		232.2	450.0	505.4
148.3	299.0	421.5		232.0	449.6	505.1

Table 4-1 (continued)

°C	°F	K		°C	°F	K
Freezing Point of Tin (d)				**Freezing Point of Cadmium**		
231.97	449.55	505.12		321.1	610.0	594.3
232.2	450.0	505.4		324.0	615.2	597.1
236.0	456.8	509.1		324.4	616.0	597.6
236.1	457.0	509.3				
240.0	464.0	513.1		**Freezing Point of Lead**		
244.0	471.2	517.1		327.5	621.5	600.7
244.4	472.0	517.6				
248.0	478.4	521.1		328.0	622.4	601.1
248.3	479.0	521.5		328.3	623.0	601.5
				332.0	629.6	605.1
252.0	485.6	525.1		332.2	630.0	605.4
252.2	486.0	525.4				
256.0	492.8	529.1		336.0	636.8	609.1
256.1	493.0	529.3		336.1	637.0	609.3
260.0	500.0	533.1		340.0	644.0	613.1
264.0	507.2	537.1		344.0	651.2	617.1
264.4	508.0	537.6		344.4	652.0	617.6
268.0	514.4	541.1		348.0	658.4	621.1
268.3	515.0	541.5		348.3	659.0	621.5
				352.0	665.6	625.1
Freezing Point of Bismuth				352.2	666.0	625.4
271.4	520.5	544.6		356.0	672.8	629.1
272.2	522.0	545.4				
276.0	528.8	549.1		**Boiling Point of Mercury**		
276.1	529.0	549.3		356.7	674.0	629.8
280.0	536.0	553.1				
284.0	543.2	557.1		360.0	680.0	633.1
284.4	544.0	557.6		364.0	687.2	637.1
288.0	550.4	561.1		364.4	688.0	637.6
288.3	551.0	561.5		368.0	694.4	641.1
292.0	557.6	565.1		368.3	695.0	641.5
292.2	558.0	565.4		372.0	701.6	645.1
296.0	564.8	569.1		372.2	702.0	645.4
296.1	565.0	569.3		376.0	708.8	649.1
300.0	572.0	573.1		380.0	716.0	653.1
304.0	579.2	577.1				
304.4	580.0	577.6		384.0	723.2	657.1
308.0	586.4	581.1		384.4	724.0	657.6
308.3	587.0	581.5		388.0	730.4	661.1
312.0	593.6	585.1		388.3	731.0	661.5
				392.0	737.6	665.1
312.2	594.0	585.4		392.2	738.0	665.4
316.0	600.8	589.1		396.0	744.8	669.1
316.1	601.0	589.3		396.1	745.0	669.3
320.0	608.0	593.1		400.0	752.0	673.1
				404.0	759.2	677.1

Thermal Quantities

Table 4-1 (continued)

°C	°F	K		°C	°F	K
Boiling Point of Mercury				Boiling Point of Sulfur		
356.7	674.0	629.8		444.7	832.5	717.8
404.4	760.0	677.6		484.4	904.0	757.6
408.0	766.4	681.1		488.0	910.4	761.1
408.3	767.0	681.5		488.3	911.0	761.5
412.0	773.6	685.1		492.0	917.6	765.1
412.2	774.0	685.4		492.2	918.0	765.4
416.0	780.8	689.1		496.0	924.8	769.1
416.1	781.0	689.3		496.1	925.0	769.3
Freezing Point of Zinc (d)				500.0	932.0	773.1
419.58	787.24	692.73		504.0	939.2	777.1
				504.4	940.0	777.6
420.0	788.0	693.1		508.0	946.4	781.1
424.0	795.2	697.1		508.3	947.0	781.5
424.4	796.0	697.6		512.0	953.6	785.1
428.0	802.4	701.1		512.2	954.0	785.4
428.3	803.0	701.5		516.0	960.8	789.1
432.0	809.6	705.1		516.1	961.0	789.3
432.2	810.0	705.4		520.0	968.0	793.1
436.0	816.8	709.1				
436.1	817.0	709.3		524.0	975.2	797.1
440.0	824.0	713.1		524.4	976.0	797.6
444.0	831.2	717.1		528.0	982.4	801.1
444.4	832.0	717.6		528.3	983.0	801.5
				532.0	989.6	805.1
				532.2	990.0	805.4
Boiling Point of Sulfur				536.0	996.8	809.1
444.7	832.5	717.8		536.1	997.0	809.3
				540.0	1004.	813.1
445.0	833.0	718.1		544.0	1011.	817.1
448.0	838.4	721.1				
448.3	839.0	721.5		544.4	1012.	817.6
452.0	845.6	725.1		548.0	1018.	821.1
452.2	846.0	725.4		548.3	1019.	821.5
456.0	852.8	729.1		552.0	1026.	825.1
456.1	853.0	729.3		552.2	1026.	825.4
460.0	860.0	733.1		556.0	1033.	829.1
464.0	867.2	737.1		556.1	1033.	829.3
464.4	868.0	737.6		560.0	1040.	833.1
				564.0	1047.	837.1
468.0	874.4	741.1		564.4	1048.	837.6
468.3	875.0	741.5				
472.0	881.6	745.1		568.0	1054.	841.1
472.2	882.0	745.4		568.3	1055.	841.5
476.0	888.8	749.1		572.2	1062.	845.4
476.1	889.0	749.3		576.0	1063.	849.1
480.0	896.0	753.1		576.1	1069.	849.3
484.0	903.2	757.1		580.0	1076.	853.1

Table 4-1 (continued)

°C	°F	K		°C	°F	K
Boiling Point of Sulfur				**Freezing Point of Aluminum**		
444.7	832.5	717.8		660.4	1220.7	933.6
584.0	1083.	857.1		676.0	1249.	949.1
584.4	1084.	857.6				
588.0	1090.	861.1		676.1	1249.	949.3
588.3	1091.	861.5		680.0	1256.	953.1
				684.0	1263.	957.1
592.0	1098.	865.1		684.4	1264.	957.6
592.2	1098.	865.4		688.0	1270.	961.1
596.0	1105.	869.1		688.3	1271.	961.5
600.0	1112.	873.1		692.0	1278.	965.1
604.0	1119.	877.1		692.2	1278.	965.4
604.4	1120.	877.6		696.0	1285.	969.1
608.0	1126.	881.1		696.1	1285.	969.3
608.3	1127.	881.5		700.0	1292.	973.1
612.0	1134.	885.1		704.0	1299.	977.1
612.2	1134.	885.4		704.4	1300.	977.6
616.0	1141.	889.1		708.0	1306.	981.1
616.1	1141.	889.3		708.3	1307.	981.5
620.0	1148.	893.1		712.0	1314.	985.1
624.0	1155.	897.1		712.2	1314.	985.4
624.4	1156.	897.6		716.0	1321.	989.1
628.0	1162.	901.1		716.1	1321.	989.3
				720.0	1328.	993.1
Freezing Point of Antimony						
630.7	1167.3	903.9		724.0	1335.	997.1
				724.4	1336.	997.6
632.2	1170.	905.4		728.0	1342.	1001.
636.0	1177.	909.1		728.3	1343.	1002.
636.1	1177.	909.3		732.0	1350.	1005.
640.0	1184.	913.1		732.2	1350.	1005.
644.0	1191.	917.1		736.0	1357.	1009.
644.4	1192.	917.6		736.1	1357.	1009.
648.0	1198.	921.1		740.0	1364.	1013.
648.3	1199.	921.5		744.0	1371.	1017.
652.0	1206.	925.1		744.4	1372.	1018.
652.2	1206.	925.4		748.0	1378.	1021.
656.0	1213.	929.1		748.3	1379.	1022.
656.1	1213.	929.3		752.0	1386.	1025.
660.0	1220.	933.1		752.2	1386.	1025.
				756.0	1393.	1029.
Freezing Point of Aluminum						
660.4	1220.7	933.6		756.1	1393.	1029.
				760.0	1400.	1033.
664.0	1227.	937.1		764.0	1407.	1037.
664.4	1228.	937.6		764.4	1408.	1038.
668.0	1234.	941.1		768.0	1414.	1041.
668.3	1235.	941.5		768.3	1415.	1042.
672.0	1242.	945.1		772.0	1422.	1045.
672.2	1242.	945.4		776.0	1429.	1049.

Table 4-1 (continued)

°C	°F	K	°C	°F	K
Freezing Point of Aluminum			Freezing Point of Aluminum		
660.4	1220.7	933.6	660.4	1220.7	933.6
776.1	1429.	1049.	876.1	1609.	1149.
780.0	1436.	1053.	880.0	1616.	1153.
			884.0	1623.	1157.
784.0	1443.	1057.	884.4	1624.	1158.
784.4	1444.	1058.	888.0	1630.	1161.
788.0	1450.	1061.			
788.3	1451.	1062.	888.3	1631.	1162.
792.0	1458.	1065.	892.0	1638.	1165.
792.2	1458.	1065.	892.2	1638.	1165.
796.0	1465.	1069.	896.0	1645.	1169.
796.1	1465.	1069.	896.1	1645.	1169.
800.0	1472.	1073.	900.0	1652.	1173.
804.0	1479.	1077.	904.0	1659.	1177.
			904.4	1660.	1178.
804.4	1480.	1078.	908.0	1666.	1181.
808.0	1486.	1081.	908.3	1667.	1182.
808.3	1487.	1082.			
812.0	1494.	1085.	912.0	1674.	1185.
812.2	1494.	1085.	912.2	1674.	1185.
816.0	1501.	1089.	916.0	1681.	1189.
816.1	1501.	1089.	916.1	1681.	1189.
820.0	1508.	1093.	920.0	1688.	1193.
824.0	1515.	1097.	924.0	1695.	1197.
824.4	1516.	1098.	924.4	1696.	1198.
			928.0	1702.	1201.
828.0	1522.	1101.	928.3	1703.	1202.
828.3	1523.	1102.	932.0	1710.	1205.
832.0	1530.	1105.			
832.2	1530.	1105.	932.2	1710.	1205.
836.0	1537.	1109.	936.0	1717.	1209.
836.1	1537.	1109.	936.1	1717.	1209.
840.0	1544.	1113.	940.0	1724.	1213.
844.0	1551.	1117.	944.0	1731.	1217.
844.4	1552.	1118.	944.4	1732.	1218.
848.0	1558.	1121.	948.0	1738.	1221.
848.3	1559.	1122.	948.3	1739.	1222.
852.0	1566.	1125.	952.0	1746.	1225.
852.2	1566.	1125.	952.2	1746.	1225.
856.0	1573.	1129.	956.0	1753.	1229.
856.1	1573.	1129.	956.1	1753.	1229.
860.0	1580.	1133.	960.0	1760.	1233.
864.0	1587.	1137.			
864.4	1588.	1138.	Freezing Point of Silver (d)		
868.0	1594.	1141.	961.93	1763.47	1235.08
868.3	1595.	1142.			
872.0	1602.	1145.	961.1	1762.	1234.
872.2	1602.	1145.	964.0	1767.	1237.
876.0	1609.	1149.	964.4	1768.	1238.

Table 4-1 (continued)

°C	°F	K		°C	°F	K
Freezing Point of Silver (d)				**Freezing Point of Copper**		
961.93	1763.47	1235.08		1084.5	1984.1	1357.7
968.0	1774.	1241.		1100.	2012.	1373.
968.3	1775.	1242.				
972.2	1782.	1245.		1110.	2030.	1383.
976.0	1789.	1249.		1120.	2048.	1393.
976.1	1789.	1249.		1130.	2066.	1403.
980.0	1796.	1253.		1140.	2084.	1413.
984.0	1803.	1257.		1150.	2102.	1423.
984.4	1804.	1258.		1160.	2120.	1433.
988.0	1810.	1261.		1170.	2138.	1443.
988.3	1811.	1267.		1180.	2156.	1453.
992.0	1818.	1265.		1190.	2174.	1463.
992.2	1818.	1265.		1200.	2192.	1473.
996.0	1825.	1269.				
996.1	1825.	1269.		1210.	2210.	1483.
1000.	1832.	1273.		1220.	2228.	1493.
1004.	1839.	1277.		1230.	2246.	1503.
1008.	1846.	1281.		1240.	2264.	1513.
1012.	1854.	1285.		1250.	2282.	1523.
				1260.	2300.	1533.
1016.	1861.	1289.		1270.	2318.	1543.
1020.	1868.	1293.		1280.	2336.	1553.
1024.	1875.	1297.		1290.	2354.	1563.
1028.	1882.	1301.		1300.	2372.	1573.
1032.	1890.	1305.		1310.	2390.	1583.
1036.	1897.	1309.		1320.	2408.	1593.
1040.	1904.	1313.		1330.	2426.	1603.
1044.	1911.	1317.		1340.	2444.	1613.
1048.	1918.	1321.		1350.	2462.	1623.
1052.	1926.	1325.		1360.	2480.	1633.
1056.	1933.	1329.		[b]1370.	2498.	1643.
1060.	1940.	1333.		1380.	2516.	1653.
				1390.	2534.	1663.
Freezing Point of Gold (d)				1400.	2552.	1673.
1064.43	1947.97	1337.58		1410.	2570.	1683.
				1420.	2588.	1693.
1064.	1947.	1337.		1430.	2606.	1703.
1068.	1954.	1341.				
1072.	1962.	1345.		[b]1440.	2624.	1713.
1076.	1969.	1349.		1450.	2642.	1723.
1080.	1976.	1353.				
1084.	1983.	1357.		**Melting Point of Nickel**		
				1454	2650	1727
Freezing Point of Copper						
1084.5	1984.1	1357.7		1460.	2660.	1733.
				1470.	2678.	1743.
1088.	1990.	1361.		1480.	2696.	1753.
1092.	1998.	1365.		1490.	2714.	1763.
1096.	2005.	1369.		1500.	2732.	1773.

Table 4-1 (continued)

°C	°F	K		°C	°F	K
Melting Point of Nickel				**Freezing Point of Platinum**		
1454	2650	1727		1772	3222	2045
1510.	2750.	1783.		1900.	3452.	2173.
1520.	2768.	1793.		1910.	3470.	2183.
1530.	2786.	1803.		1920.	3488.	2193.
				1930.	3506.	2203.
1540.	2804.	1813.		1940.	3524.	2213.
1550.	2822.	1823.		1950.	3542.	2223.
				1960.	3560.	2233.
Freezing Point of Palladium						
1554	2829	1827		**Freezing Point of Rhodium**		
				1963	3565	2236
1560.	2840.	1833.				
1570.	2858.	1843.		1970.	3578.	2243.
1580.	2876.	1853.		1980.	3596.	2253.
1590.	2894.	1863.				
1600.	2912.	1873.		1990.	3614.	2263.
1610.	2930.	1883.		2000.	3632.	2273.
1620.	2948.	1893.		2010.	3650.	2283.
1630.	2966.	1903.		2020.	3668.	2293.
				2030.	3686.	2303.
1640.	2984.	1913.		2040.	3704.	2313.
1650.	3002.	1923.		2050.	3722.	2323.
1660.	3020.	1933.		2060.	3740.	2333.
1670.	3038.	1943.		2070.	3758.	2343.
1680.	3056.	1953.		2080.	3776.	2353.
1690.	3074.	1963.				
1700.	3092.	1973.		2090.	3794.	2363.
1710.	3110.	1983.		2100.	3812.	2373.
1720.	3128.	1993.		2110.	3830.	2383.
1730.	3146.	2003.		2120.	3848.	2393.
1740.	3164.	2013.		2130.	3866.	2403.
1750.	3182.	2023.		2140.	3884.	2413.
1760.	3200.	2033.		2150.	3902.	2423.
				2160.	3920.	2433.
Freezing Point of Platinum				2170.	3938.	2443.
1772	3222	2045		2180.	3956.	2453.
1780.	3236.	2053.		2190.	3974.	2463.
1790.	3254.	2063.		2200.	3992.	2473.
1800.	3272.	2073.		2210.	4010.	2483.
1810.	3290.	2083.		2220.	4028.	2493.
1820.	3308.	2093.		2230.	4046.	2503.
1830.	3326.	2103.		2240.	4064.	2513.
1840.	3344.	2113.		2250.	4082.	2523.
1850.	3362.	2123.		2260.	4100.	2533.
1860.	3380.	2133.		2270.	4118.	2543.
1870.	3398.	2143.		2280.	4136.	2553.
1880.	3416.	2153.				
1890.	3434.	2163.		2290.	4154.	2563.

Table 4-1 (continued)

°C	°F	K		°C	°F	K
Freezing Point of Rhodium				**Melting Point of Molybdenum**		
1963	3565	2236		2610	4730	2883
2300.	4172.	2573.		2650.	4802.	2923.
2310.	4190.	2583.		2660.	4820.	2933.
2320.	4208.	2593.				
2330.	4226.	2603.		2670.	4838.	2943.
2340.	4244.	2613.		2680.	4856.	2953.
2350.	4262.	2623.		2690.	4874.	2963.
2360.	4280.	2633.		2700.	4892.	2973.
2370.	4298.	2643.		2710.	4910.	2983.
2380.	4316.	2653.		2720.	4928.	2993.
				2730.	4946.	3003.
				2740.	4964.	3013.
2390.	4334.	2663.		2750.	4982.	3023.
2400.	4352.	2673.		2760.	5000.	3033.
2410.	4370.	2683.				
2420.	4388.	2693.				
2430.	4406.	2703.		2770.	5018.	3043.
2440.	4424.	2713.		2780.	5036.	3053.
				2790.	5054.	3063.
Freezing Point of Iridium				2800.	5072.	3073.
2447		2720		2810.	5090.	3083.
				2820.	5108.	3093.
2450.	4442.	2723.		2830.	5126.	3103.
2460.	4460.	2733.		2840.	5144.	3113.
				2850.	5162.	3123.
Melting Point of Niobium (Columbium)				2860.	5180.	3133.
2468	4474	2740				
				2870.	5198.	3143.
2470.	4478.	2743.		2880.	5216.	3153.
2480.	4496.	2753.		2890.	5234.	3163.
2490.	4514.	2763.		2900.	5252.	3173.
2500.	4532.	2773.		2910.	5270.	3183.
2510.	4550.	2783.		2920.	5288.	3193.
2520.	4568.	2793.		2930.	5306.	3203.
2530.	4586.	2803.		2940.	5324.	3213.
2540.	4604.	2813.		2950.	5342.	3223.
2550.	4622.	2823.		2960.	5360.	3233.
2560.	4640.	2833.				
				2970.	5378.	3243.
2570.	4658.	2843.		2980.	5396.	3253.
2580.	4676.	2853.		2990.	5414.	3263.
2590.	4694.	2863.				
2600.	4712.	2873.		**Melting Point of Tantalum**		
				2996	5425	3269
Melting Point of Molybdenum						
2610	4730	2883		3000.	5432.	3273.
				3010.	5450.	3283.
2620.	4748.	2893.		3020.	5468.	3293.
2630.	4766.	2903.		3030.	5486.	3303.
2640.	4784.	2913.		3040.	5504.	3313.

Thermal Quantities

Table 4-1 (continued)

°C	°F	K		°C	°F	K
Melting Point of Tantalum				Melting Point of Rhenium		
2996	5425	3269		3180	5756	3453
3050.	5522.	3323.		3280.	5936.	3553.
3060.	5540.	3333.		3290.	5954.	3563.
3070.	5558.	3343.		3300.	5972.	3573.
3080.	5576.	3353.		3310.	5990.	3583.
3090.	5594.	3363.		3320.	6008.	3593.
3100.	5612.	3373.		3330.	6026.	3603.
3110.	5630.	3383.		3340.	6044.	3613.
3120.	5648.	3393.		3350	6062.	3623.
3130.	5666.	3403.		3360.	6080.	3633.
3140.	5684.	3413.		3370.	6098.	3643.
3150.	5702.	3423.		Melting Point of Tungsten		
3160.	5720.	3433.		3387	6128	3660
3170.	5738.	3443.				
				3390.	6134.	3663.
Melting Point of Rhenium				3400.	6152.	3673.
3180	5756	3453		3410.	6170.	3683.
				3420.	6188.	3693.
3190.	5774.	3463.		3430.	6206.	3703.
3200.	5792.	3473.		3440.	6224.	3713.
3210.	5810.	3483.		3450.	6242.	3723.
3220.	5828.	3493.		3460.	6260.	3733.
3230.	5846.	3503.		3470.	6278.	3743.
3240.	5864.	3513.		3480.	6296.	3753.
				3490.	6314.	3763.
3250.	5882.	2523.		3500.	6332.	3773.
3260.	5900.	3533.		3510.	6350.	3783.
3270.	5918.	3543.				

[a](d) = defining fixed point of the IPTS-68. °R = °F + 459.7.

[b]Melting points of commonly used stainless steels are between about 1370 and 1440 °C (2500 and 2600 °F, 1640 and 1710 K).

4.2.1.1 Thermoelectric temperature sensing.

The sensing and transduction of temperature by thermoelectric means is based on the *Seebeck effect* (Thomas J. Seebeck, 1770–1831, German physicist): When two dissimilar conductors A and B (see Figure 4-1) comprise a circuit (by being joined at both of their ends), a current will flow in that circuit as long as the two junctions are at different temperatures, one junction at a temperature T, the other at a higher temperature $T + \Delta T$. The current will flow from A to B at the colder junction when conductor A is positive with respect to B. Two other effects are related to the Seebeck effect. When a current flows across a junction of two dissimilar conductors, heat is absorbed or liberated at the junction, dependent upon the direction of current flow *(Peltier effect)*. When a current flows through a con-

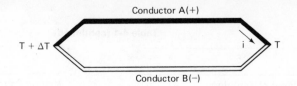

Figure 4-1. Seebeck effect.

ductor along which a temperature gradient exists, heat is absorbed or liberated in the wire *(Thomson effect)*.

The *thermocouple circuit* is based on the Seebeck effect. Two dissimilar conductors are joined at the point where temperature is to be measured *(sensing junction)* and are terminated at a point where both terminals are at the same temperature, which must be known *(reference junction)*. Although the temperature, t_{ref}, of the reference junction can be any temperature, it is usually kept at the ice point (0 °C). Thermocouple calibration curves are normally based on this being the reference-junction temperature, and the conductors are designated as positive *(P)* and negative *(N)* when the measured temperature, t, is higher than the reference temperature (see Figure 4-2). The connecting leads between the reference junction and the load (across which a voltage as a function of temperature is obtained), represented as R_L, can be copper wire.

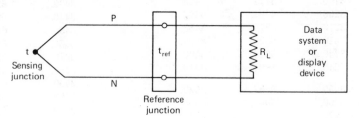

Figure 4-2. Basic thermocouple circuit.

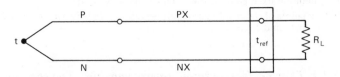

Figure 4-3. Thermocouple circuit with extension wire.

When the load (display device or data system) is located some distance away from the sensing junction it is often economical to use *thermocouple extension wire* between the measuring thermocouple and the load. This type of wire is made of materials that match the emf vs. temperature characteristics of the thermocouple very closely and, in effect, transfer the reference junction from the thermocouple side to the load side of the extension wires (see Figure 4-3).

The magnitude of the *thermoelectric potential (thermal emf)* produced by a thermocouple depends on the wire materials and on the temperature difference between the two junctions. Table 4-2 shows the thermal emf of a number of different wire materials that would be produced if the material would be formed into a thermocouple with platinum as the other conductor and with a reference-junction temperature of 0 °C. It can be seen that the polarity of some materials is negative, for temperatures above 0 °C, whereas it is positive for other materials. Since the physical and chemical characteristics as well as the cost of some materials are more suitable for their use in thermocouples than others, only a limited number of materials are used for thermocouples and most of those materials are alloys that were developed specifically for such use. Materials which, in combination with platinum, exhibit an increasingly positive potential are used as the positive (P) leg of thermocouples, whereas those exhibiting an increasingly negative potential are used as the negative (N) leg. The thermal emf produced by a thermocouple, then, is the algebraic difference of the two potentials that would be produced if each material would be combined with platinum; for example, the emf produced by a Type K (Chro-

TABLE 4-2   Thermal emf (in mV) of Conductors Relative to Platinum at t_{ref} = 0° C

Conductor Material	Junction Temperature, t (°C)					
	−200	0	+200	+500	+1000	+1400
Pure metals						
Aluminum (Al)	+0.45	0	+1.06	+3.93		
Antimony (Sb)		0	+10.14	+25.10		
Bismuth (Bi)	+12.93	0	−13.57			
Cadmium (Cd)	−0.04	0	+2.35			
Cobalt (Co)		0	−3.08	−9.35	−14.21	
Copper (Cu)	−0.19	0	+1.83	+6.41	+18.16	
Germanium (Ge)	−46.0	0	+72.4	+63.5		
Gold (Au)	−0.21	0	+1.84	+6.29	+17.05	
Iridium (Ir)	−0.25	0	+1.49	+4.78	+12.57	+20.47
Iron (Fe)	−2.92	0	+3.54	+6.79	+14.28	
Molybdenum (Mo)		0	+3.19	+10.20	+27.74	
Nickel (Ni)	+2.28	0	−3.10	−6.16	−12.11	
Palladium (Pd)	+0.81	0	−1.23	−3.84	−11.61	−20.40
Rhodium (Rh)	−0.20	0	+1.61	+5.28	+14.02	+22.99
Silicon (Si)	+63.13	0	−80.57			
Silver (Ag)	−0.21	0	+1.77	+6.36		
Tantalum (Ta)	+0.21	0	+0.93	+4.30	+15.15	
Tungsten (W)	+0.43	0	+2.62	+9.30	+27.73	
Standard thermocouple alloys (see Table 4.3)[a]						
Chromel (KP, EP)	−3.36	0	+5.96	+16.21	+32.47	+44.04
Alumel (KN)	+2.39	0	−2.17	−4.43	−8.78	−11.77
Constantan (JN, EN, TN)	+5.35	0	−7.45	−20.79	−43.85	
Pt–13% Rh (RP)		0	+1.47	+4.47	+10.50	+16.04
Pt–10% Rh (SP)		0	+1.44	+4.23	+9.58	+14.37

[a]See the upper portion of the table for iron (JP) and copper (TP); platinum (RN, SN) is the reference conductor in this table.

mel–Constantan) thermocouple at 500 °C is $+16.21 - (-4.43) = 16.21 + 4.43 = 20.64$ mV.

The integrity of the thermocouple material in a thermocouple circuit, between sensing and reference junctions, must be maintained; that is, the material of each leg must either be the same for the entire run of the circuit, or it must be a material having the same (or very close to the same) temperature vs. emf characteristics. When electrical connections are made between sections of a thermocouple leg, they must bring the same materials into good electrical contact with each other. Lead–tin solder and silver solder have thermal emfs different from those of most thermocouple materials and so do materials typically used for contacts in electrical connectors, such as beryllium–copper, brass, or phosphor bronze; all these materials exhibit a thermal emf (relative to platinum, at a t_{ref} of 0 °C) in the order of $+0.6$ mV.

It can be noted, from Table 4-2, that a silicon/germanium thermocouple would provide the highest output voltage (152 mV at $+200$ °C). For many practical considerations this material combination is not used for temperature measurement; however, silicon/germanium combinations, with controlled impurities (different for each of the two legs) are used as voltage generators in radioisotope thermoelectric generators (RTGs). The most commonly used and available thermocouples have been standardized. In the United States, American National Standard (ANSI) MC96.1 establishes type designations for thermocouples, thermocouple wire, and thermocouple extension wire as well as such characteristics as wire-insulation colors and recommended practices for fabrication; this standard, "Temperature Measurement Thermocouples," was sponsored and published by the Instrument Society of America (ISA); salient characteristics of these "standard" thermocouples are shown in Table 4-3. This standard is also used in many other countries; a number of countries have, instead, similar standards (for thermocouples) of their own. It should be noted that trade names other than Chromel, Alumel, and Constantan exist for these alloys, depending on their manufacturer. An important thermocouple characteristic, also covered in ANSI MC96.1, is a set of limits of error which the various types must meet in order to be able to be referred to by their respective type designation. These limits of error are expressed in terms of temperature reading (indicated temperature), as ± tolerances in °C or percent of reading, whichever is greater. Two sets of limits of error are given for most thermocouple types, one set referred to as "standard," the other (with closer tolerances) as "special," for ordering and verification purposes primarily. The limits of error apply under specified conditions including those of wire size and temperature range.

Reference tables which show the electromotive force (emf) generated by the "standard" thermocouples over their applicable range of temperatures have been published (in the United States) by the National Bureau of Standards at various times. The tables, shown for temperatures in °F as well as °C, were updated after the revised International Practical Temperature Scale IPTS 68 was adopted and are currently contained in National Bureau of Standards (NBS) Monograph 125 (available from the U.S. Government Printing Office,

TABLE 4-3 Standard Types of Thermocouple Wire and Thermocouple Extension Wire[a]

Type Designation	Designation of: Positive Wire	Negative Wire	Typical Material of: Positive Wire	Negative Wire	Duplex-wire Insulation Colors: Overall	Positive Wire	Negative Wire	Maximum Temp.[b] (°C) No. 14 AWG (1.63 mm)	No. 24 AWG (0.51 mm)
T	TP	TN	Copper	Constantan[c]	Brown-blue trace[d]	Blue	Red	370	200
J	JP	JN	Iron[e]	Constantan[c]	Brown-white trace[d]	White	Red	590	370
E	EP	EN	Chromel[f]	Constantan[c]	Brown-purple trace[d]	Purple	Red	650	430
K	KP	KN	Chromel[f]	Alumel[g]	Brown-yellow trace[d]	Yellow	Red	1090	870
S	SP	SN	Platinum (90%), rhodium (10%)	Platinum				1480	
R	RP	RN	Platinum (87%), rhodium (13%)	Platinum				1480	
B	BP	BN	Platinum (70%), rhodium (30%)	Platinum (94%), rhodium (6%)				1700	
TX[h]	TPX	TNX	Copper	Constantan[c]	Blue	Blue	Red[i]		
JX[h]	JPX	JNX	Iron[e]	Constantan[c]	Black	White	Red[i]		
EX[h]	EPX	ENX	Chromel[f]	Constantan[c]	Purple	Purple	Red[i]		
KX[h]	KPX	KNX	Chromel[f]	Alumel[g]	Yellow	Yellow	Red[i]		
SX[h]	SPX	SNX	Copper	Cu–Ni alloy[j]	Green	Black	Red[i]		
BX[h]	BPX	BNX	Copper[k]	Copper	Gray	Gray	Red[i]		

[a]As shown in Standard MC 96.1, "Temperature Measurement Thermocouples," © Instrument Society of America, 1975. Refer to text for discussion of "limits of error."

[b]Recommended upper temperature limit for protected thermocouples, shown for two typical wire sizes.

[c]An alloy of 55% Cu, 45% Ni; other names (trade names) exist for this material.

[d]Tracer is optional.

[e]99.9 + % pure.

[f]Trade name (Hoskins Mfg. Co.); other trade names exist for this material; typical composition: 90% Ni, 10% Cr.

[g]Same as in note f, except typical composition: 95% Ni, and about 2% Al, 2% Mn, 1% Si.

[h]Extension wire for thermocouple of type indicated by first letter, except that "SX" is used with "R" and "S."

[i]A tracer color (same as the color of the positive wire) is optional.

[j]A specific alloy, designated by various manufacturers' trade names.

[k]When head junction temperature exceeds 100 °C, certain (proprietary) alloys can be used to reduce errors.

Washington, DC). Favorable results have also been reported for Nicrosil/Nisil thermocouples, which are similar in output to Type K but seem to have better stability.

The outputs of standard and two not-yet-standardized thermocouples are shown in Figure 4-4, for comparison purposes, for the medium-, high-, and low-

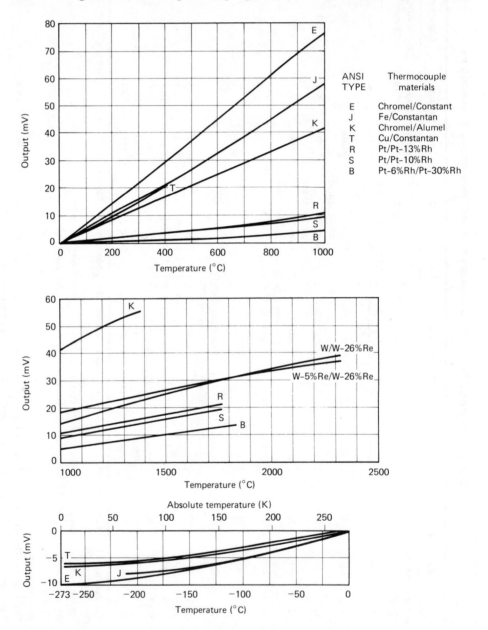

Figure 4-4. Output voltage (thermoelectric emf) of thermocouples ($t_{ref} = 0$ °C).

Thermal Quantities

temperature regions. The tungsten–rhenium combinations have come into common use for high-temperature measurements. The original pure-metal thermocouple (W/Re) is rarely used since higher output at high temperatures can be obtained by the alloy combinations, notably W/W–26% Re, W–5% Re/W–26% Re, and W–3% Re/W–25% Re. Considerable research has been done on other high-temperature thermocouples, but most of the combinations developed and tested are not generally available commercially and stability characteristics are, in most cases, not yet well enough established. Developments have included combinations of iridium with iridium–rhodium alloys (e.g., Ir/Ir–40% Rh) which are usable to about 2100 °C, molybdenum–rhenium alloys in combination with alloys of the same materials but in different proportions (e.g., Mo–10% Re/Mo–50% Re) and in combination with tungsten–rhenium alloys (e.g., Mo–3% Re/W–25% Re) which seem to be usable to about (and possibly somewhat above) 2000 °C, and nonmetallic thermocouples. The latter are combinations of carbides, carbon, graphite, and oxides and include such combinations as graphite/titanium carbide, columbium carbide/zirconium carbide, and carbon/titanium carbide; usable maximum temperatures for such materials range from 1800 to over 3000 °C, depending largely on the environment in which they are applied. Some thermocouples were also developed for the purpose of obtaining higher sensitivities in the low cryogenic range; low-temperature thermocouples include Chromel/gold–0.07 at. % iron and Cu/Au–2.1% Co.

When a higher output is required from a point of measurement, a number of thermocouples of the same material combination can be connected in series to form a *thermopile* (see Figure 4-5). The output of a thermopile is equal to

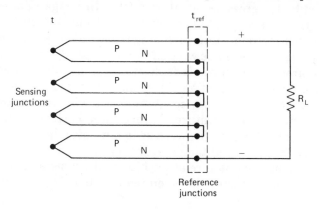

Figure 4-5. Thermopile circuit.

the emf produced by a thermocouple of the material combination chosen, multiplied by the number of thermocouples in the thermopile. A common reference junction is used for all sensing junctions in the thermopile. When averaging of temperatures at a number of measurement points is required, thermocouples can be connected in parallel and, provided that they are made from identical wire materials, sizes, and lengths, the emf generated will be indicative of the

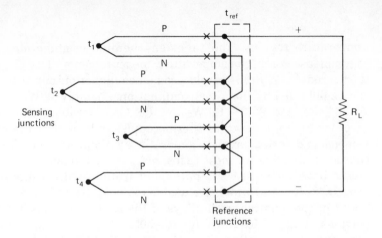

Figure 4-6. Parallel connection of thermocouples for temperature averaging. When used, swamping resistors are inserted at all points marked X.

mean of the temperatures at the sensing junctions (see Figure 4-6). When such identity cannot be assured, "swamping resistors" can be added, with one such (about 200 to 500 Ω) resistor connected in series with each wire.

4.2.1.2 Resistive temperature sensing using conductors. Conductors generally exhibit an increase in resistance with temperature. The change in resistance is given by the conductor's *temperature coefficient of resistance* (α) and the *base resistance* of a conductive temperature sensing element (usually its resistance at the ice point, sometimes at another specified temperature) is given by the cross-sectional area (the wire gage in case of a wire conductor) and the *resistivity* (ρ) of the material. Table 4-4 shows values of α and ρ for some typical conductors, including those which have been used for temperature sensing as well as some who exhibit particularly small alphas. For temperature measurement purposes it is desirable to have a conductor which has a reasonably high α, so that a substantial resistance change is obtained, which has an α that remains fairly constant over a wide temperature range, so that the resistance vs. temperature characteristic is close to linear, and which has a reasonably high resistivity, so as to minimize the amount of material required for use in a practical temperature sensor.

An approximate relationship for the resistance vs. temperature characteristics of conductors between 0 and 100 °C is given by the equation

$$R_t = R_0(1 + \alpha t)$$

where R_t = resistance at temperature t, °C

R_0 = resistance at 0 °C

α = temperature coefficient of resistance

Originally, copper wire was used in such resistance elements; its main dis-

TABLE 4-4 Resistance Properties of Pure, Annealed Metals and Alloys[a]

Material	Temperature Coefficient of Resistance, α, between 0 and 100 °C ($\Omega/\Omega/°C$)	Resistivity, at 20 °C ($\mu\Omega\cdot cm$ or $10^8\ \Omega\cdot m$)
Aluminum	0.0042	2.69
Constantan (55% Cu, 45% Ni)	± 0.00002	49.0
Copper	0.0043	1.673
Gold	0.0039	2.3
Indium	0.0047	9.0
Iron	0.00651	9.71
Manganin (86% Cu, 12% Mn, 2% Ni)	− 0.00002	43.0
Nickel	0.00681	6.844
Nichrome (60% Ni, 16% Cr, 24% Fe)	0.0002	109.0
Palladium	0.00377	10.8
Platinum	0.00392	10.6
Rhodium	0.00457	4.7
Silver	0.0041	1.63
Tungsten	0.0046	5.5

[a]Selected from various recent sources.

advantage was the low resistivity of copper and the resulting impractically long wire needed for winding a practical element. Later, platinum came into use increasingly; it is now used to the virtual exclusion of all other conductors except for some specialized applications. Elements made of nickel wire and some nickel–alloy wire were used for measurements over a relatively narrow temperature range; they were increasingly replaced by platinum elements but are still used occasionally because of their lower cost and acceptably high base resistance values. Attempts at using tungsten wire have been essentially discontinued. Certain alloys have been found usable for measurements in the low cryogenic range, notably a rhodium–0.5 at. % iron alloy wire which exhibits a higher sensitivity than platinum below 20 K. For all wirewound elements it is important that they be annealed after they are wound; annealing is essential to obtaining a stable R vs. T (resistance vs. temperature) relationship.

Platinum is used in both wire and film elements. Wire elements are used most frequently because of their predictable and calculable R vs. T relationship. Elements wound of pure platinum, wound so that they are strain free, and which are annealed after winding, are used to define the interpolation between fixed points of the IPTS 68 between the triple point of hydrogen (13.81 K) and the freezing point of antimony (630.74 °C). They have been found usable to temperatures above 800 °C and may, with additional development, be usable in reference thermometers at temperatures above the antimony point. Where less than reference-grade accuracy is acceptable and measurements are made for relatively short periods, some platinum-wire-element transducer designs have been used up to about 1050 °C.

The R vs. T relationship of a platinum-wire element, between -183 and $+630$ °C, is given by the *Callendar–Van Dusen equation*, shown below; however, a correction must be applied to the temperature values in order to conform to the IPTS 68.

$$R_t = R_0 + R_0\alpha[t - \delta(0.01t - 1)(0.01t) - \beta(0.01t - 1)(0.01t)^3]$$

where R_t = resistance at temperature t, °C

$\quad R_0$ = resistance at 0 °C

$\quad\alpha, \delta, \beta$ are constants; α is usually determined by measuring the element's resistance at $+100$ °C and β from a resistance measurement below 0 °C, usually at the oxygen point (-182.96 °C);

$\quad\quad\delta$ is determined by a resistance measurement well above 100 °C such as the boiling point of sulfur ($+444.7$ °C); typical values are:

$$\alpha = 0.00392$$
$$\beta = 0 \text{ (if } t \text{ is positive) and } 0.11 \text{ (if } t \text{ is negative)}$$
$$\delta = 1.49$$

The temperature values of the relationship established by this equation can be corrected for IPTS 68 by adding to them a small temperature value (Δt), which is generally less than 0.05 °C and can be calculated, if necessary, as

$$\Delta t = 0.045(0.01t - 1)(0.01t)(t/419.58 - 1)(t/630.74 - 1)$$

The constant α is given by the purity of the platinum used in the element. It increases with purity and values of up to 0.003927 have been obtained. A value of 0.003925 is acceptable for reference-standard grade elements and this value is used for reference tables of R vs. T in the United States. For industrial resistance thermometers a value of 0.00390 is usually acceptable. For the so-called "European curve" (shown, e.g., in DIN standards) a value of 0.003850 is used. Resistance values obtained by the two curves are shown in the typical values of Table 4-5. A version of the "European curve" is under consideration as an international standard and possibly also a U.S. standard. When platinum is used in the form of a film, deposited on an insulated (typically glass or ceramic) substrate, the Callendar–Van Dusen equation can usually not be used to establish a precise R vs. T relationship; however, highly repeatable R vs. T relationships can be established by other means and the "European curve" is often met. Other metals that have been used for specialized applications in the form of such a film are aluminum (superconductive, at temperatures around 1 K) and gold (for high temperatures). Temperature-sensing elements are also made in the form of foil grids, photoetched or die cut from very thin foil stock; metal alloys such as Manganin/nickel alloy combinations are typically used.

TABLE 4-5   Resistances of a Platinum Resistance Thermometer Having a $R_{0°C}$ = 100.00 Ω, between −200 and +800 °C (ohms)

Temperature (°C)	"U.S. Curve" (α = 0.003925)	"European Curve" (α = 0.003850)
−200	17.02	18.61
−100	59.49	60.26
0	100.00	100.00
+100	139.25	138.50
+200	177.33	175.84
+300	214.24	212.03
+400	249.97	247.08
+500	284.53	280.99
+600	317.93	313.73
+700	350.15	345.26
+800	381.19	375.56

4.2.1.3 Resistive temperature sensing using semiconductors. The most widely used semiconductor temperature sensing elements are *thermistors*. Their measuring range is typically between −50 and +300 °C, although some designs have been developed for temperatures in the low cryogenic range. The semiconductive materials, usually sintered mixtures of sulfides, selenides, or oxides of nickel, manganese, cobalt, copper, iron, and uranium, are formed into small beads, disks, or rods which are then encapsulated (e.g., in glass). Thermistors are characterized by high resistivities and high negative temperature coefficients of resistance. Their R vs. T characteristics are nonlinear (see Figure 4-7). Their characteristics are stated as "zero-power" characteristics, including the base resistance, which is normally shown as $R_{25°C}$ rather than at 0 °C, and the R vs. T relationship. The term "zero power" refers to a power dissipation low enough that self-heating is negligible; the excitation current for temperature-measurement thermistors is typically below 100 μA.

The basic resistance vs. temperature characteristic of a thermistor, at "zero power," is expressed by

$$\frac{R_T}{R_{\text{ref}}} = e^{\beta(1/T - 1/T_{\text{ref}})}$$

where R_T = zero-power resistance at measured absolute temperature T

R_{ref} = zero-power resistance at known absolute temperature T_{ref}, usually at 298.15 K (25 °C)

β = material constant, K

(e = 2.718; base of natural logarithm)

Typical values of β (beta) are between 3000 and 4500 K, as determined from resistance measurements at the ice point and at a temperature somewhat above room temperature, usually 50 °C. The values of zero-power resistance (sometimes called "cold resistance") at 25 °C can be between 500 Ω and over 10 MΩ.

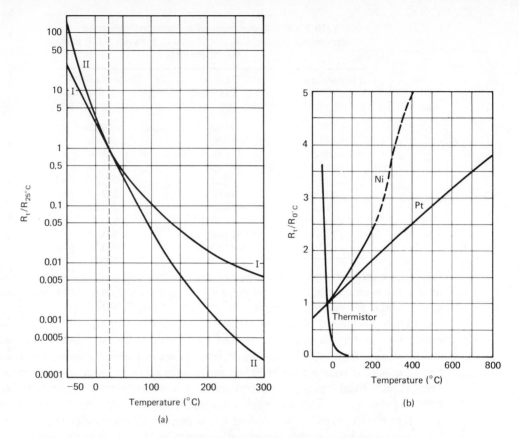

Figure 4-7. R versus T characteristics of thermistors, nickel and platinum: (a) typical thermistor curves; (b) comparison with conductors.

Germanium temperature-sensing elements were developed primarily for the very low cryogenic region, between about 1 and 35 K. The element is single-crystal doped germanium; various controlled impurities are used as dopants. Their R vs. T characteristics exhibit a nonlinearity similar to that of thermistors. Temperature sensors using germanium elements have been favored when measurements with close repeatability are required from below the helium boiling point to around the hydrogen boiling point; repeatabilities within 0.001 K have been reported for the former and within 0.05 K for the latter.

Gallium arsenide (GaAs) diode elements are also used primarily for cryogenic temperature measurements, although their usable range is generally between 1 and 300 K. The forward voltage of a GaAs diode, at a constant current (of about 100 μA), increases fairly linearly (compared to curves for thermistors or germanium elements) with decreasing temperatures. The excitation current must be controlled within small tolerances and the associated load resistance must be quite high since the output impedance of a GaAs diode is relatively high (typically around 15 kΩ at 20 K).

Thermal Quantities

Carbon resistors of commercially available types have been used for cryogenic temperature measurement but are now largely replaced by other devices. At temperatures below 60 K their R vs. T characteristics are somewhat similar to those of thermistors and germanium elements. Although carbon resistors exhibit good sensitivity at very low temperatures, they tend to be deficient in long-term stability and can be affected by variations in ambient pressure, such as encountered in pressurized vessels or ducts.

Silicon crystals, doped typically with phosphorous impurities, were developed for use in the medium-temperature range as well as for the low cryogenic range. Electrical conduction takes place in the diffused surface layer. The R vs. T characteristic is unique in that it exhibits a positive and fairly linear slope above -50 °C, whereas below this temperature the slope becomes sharply negative. Different doping techniques can alter these characteristics. Use of silicon elements for liquid-hydrogen temperature measurements has been reported.

4.2.1.4 Other temperature-sensing methods.

Quartz crystals, used as the frequency-controlling element in oscillator circuits, can be used for temperature sensing. The sensitivity of such crystals to temperature changes has long been accepted in the field of communications engineering. This phenomenon is utilized for temperature measurements in the -50 to $+250$ °C range, using quartz crystals specially designed and cut from synthetic single-crystal quartz at an orientation that optimizes the linearity of the frequency vs. temperature relationship. When connected into an oscillator circuit and excited at its third overtone resonance (typically around 30 MHz) such a crystal can provide a sensitivity of about 1 kHz/°C. The oscillator output is usually mixed (heterodyned) with the output of a reference oscillator so that a beat frequency is obtained. This difference frequency can then be displayed on a frequency counter.

Thermal-noise temperature sensors *(noise thermometers)* have been developed for experimental use. The operating principle here is the temperature dependence of (thermal) noise generated in a resistor. The resistor is connected to a high-gain amplifier which is so designed that it will amplify the thermal noise in the resistor without contributing any significant amount of noise of its own. When used for low-temperature measurements between about 10 and 90 K, some means of obtaining a reference temperature is required to minimize calibration uncertainties such as those due to amplifier gain and bandwidth uncertainties. However, at temperatures sufficiently low to make superconducting devices operable (below 10 K), absolute temperature measurements have been obtained using a Josephson junction as preamplifier, typically with this junction connected into an oscillator circuit so that a frequency output proportional to temperature is obtained with variations in thermal noise in a shunt resistor. Absolute temperature measurements well below 1 K have been obtained with Josephson-junction noise thermometers.

Acoustical temperature sensing has been employed in experimental measurements of not only low cryogenic temperatures (below 20 K) but also of high and very high temperatures up to about 17 000 K (e.g., for plasma temperature measurements). Various techniques have been used to obtain temperature measurements on the basis of temperature effects on the propagation velocity of sound through a hot (or cold) solid, liquid, or gas. This velocity tends to decrease with increasing temperature for solids and liquids, and to increase with temperature for gases. Either changes in frequency or changes in pulse transit time are used for temperature determinations.

Capacitive temperature sensors depend on temperature-induced changes in the characteristics of the dielectric for their operation. Such sensors have been used primarily for measurements in the cryogenic and low cryonic regions. The material of the dielectric is selected for optimized temperature dependence in the intended measuring range. The effect is multiplied in multilayer capacitors. Developments have included small thin-film capacitive sensors with fast response times (below 1 ms). The relative absence of errors due to magnetic fields is a reported advantage of capacitance thermometers.

Nuclear magnetic resonance *(NMR)* and nuclear quadrupole resonance *(NQR)* techniques have also been applied experimentally to temperature sensing.

4.2.2 Design and Operation

4.2.2.1 Thermocouple thermometers. The simplest type of thermocouple is made from two insulated wires of the "positive" and "negative" materials, by stripping the insulation from the wires where they are to be joined and then forming a good electrical junction between the two bare wire tips. More commonly, *wire thermocouples* are made from two-conductor *(duplex)* insulated, shielded or unshielded, thermocouple cable, with solid or stranded conductors (depending on mechanical flexibility required) or from metal-sheathed, swaged, ceramic-insulated thermocouple cable which exists in a large variety of diameters and with various conductor, sheath, and insulator materials. For a given type of junction, response time decreases with wire size *(wire gage)* used.

Junctions (see Figure 4-8) can be made by a number of different techniques of wire joining. The junction is usually welded, sometimes silver-sol-

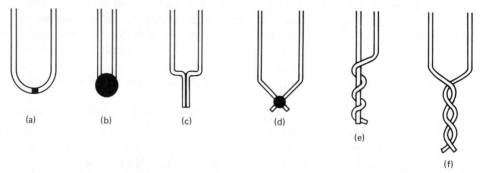

Figure 4-8. Thermocouple wire junctions: (a) butt-welded; (b) beaded; (c) lap-welded; (d) cross-wire; (e) coiled-wire; (f) twisted-wire.

Thermal Quantities

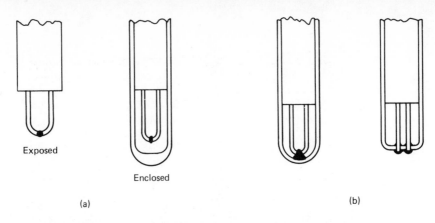

Exposed

Enclosed

(a)

(b)

Figure 4-9. Examples of ungrounded and grounded thermocouple junctions: (a) ungrounded; (b) grounded.

dered or brazed. *Butt-welded junctions* are made by pressing the two sanded-flat wire ends together (using spring loading) and joining the ends by resistance welding. *Beaded junctions* are usually formed by heating the joined wire ends to their melting points, then rotating the weld until a bead is formed at the tip. For *lap-welded junctions* the wire ends are formed so that they are in contact with each other, over a length of about 3 mm, and then resistance-welded. *Cross-wire junctions* are made by bending the two wire ends at an angle of less than 90°, laying one wire over the other, welding them together at this crossing, and then cutting excess wire material off the ends. In *coiled-wire junctions* one wire is kept straight, and the other is wound tightly over the straight wire end. This type, as well as *twisted-wire junctions,* are usually gas-welded or arc-welded but can also be brazed or silver-soldered.

Thermocouple junctions can be grounded or ungrounded, exposed or enclosed (see Figure 4-9). The shortest time constants (fastest response time) are obtained with butt-welded *exposed* junctions (for a given wire diameter). In many applications, however, the junction must be protected from the measured fluid. *Enclosed* ("protected") junctions are then used, and they can be grounded or ungrounded. *Ungrounded* enclosed junctions (again for a given wire diameter) have the longest time constants. *Grounded* enclosed junctions can be used when such grounding is compatible with the associated circuitry, when noise pickup in the wiring from the junction is not a significant problem, and when conduction error (error due to heat conducted away from the sensing tip) can be minimized or is acceptable. Grounded junctions can be made by joining and welding the wire ends together and to the inside of the sheath (probe) tip, or by welding the two wire ends separately, but in close proximity to each other, to the probe tip. Wire thermocouple junctions become grounded junctions when they are welded to a measured surface which is conducting and which is at system ground potential.

Thermocouple elements are designed primarily for use in thermocouple thermometer assemblies. Typical elements are shown in Figure 4-10. Bare elements are those which are not equipped with insulators; however, the individual wires may be insulated. Insulated elements are used most frequently.

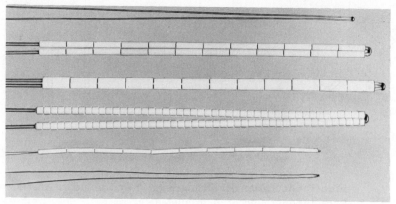

Figure 4-10. Bare and insulated thermocouple elements. (Courtesy of Omega Engineering, Inc., an Omega Group Co.)

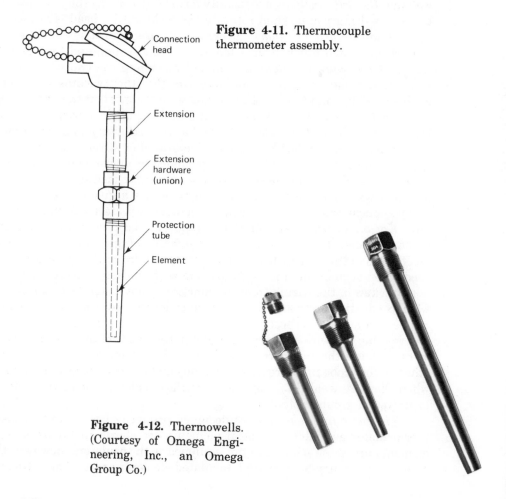

Connection
head

Extension

Extension
hardware
(union)

Protection
tube

Element

Figure 4-11. Thermocouple
thermometer assembly.

Figure 4-12. Thermowells.
(Courtesy of Omega Engineering, Inc., an Omega
Group Co.)

Continuous asbestos insulation can be used, but ceramic insulators are more common. Such insulators have the form of short segments and can be intended for a single conductor (single-hole insulators) or two conductors (double-hole or double-bore insulators), they can be round or oval in cross section, and they can be square-edged or fish-spine-shaped.

Thermocouple thermometer assemblies, as typically used in industrial (as opposed to aerospace, research, or specialized) applications, are composed of a number of piece parts that are usually assembled nonpermanently, that is, by threading rather than by methods such as welding. A typical assembly (see Figure 4-11) consists of a *connection head,* an optional extension (connection head extension) with any required extension hardware (a union is shown in the illustration as an example), and a protection tube, which may be open or closed at its end. Other mountings and pressure-seal fittings are available. In many applications, especially those in which the measured fluid is pressurized, a *thermowell* (see Figure 4-12) is used, a hollow fitting, closed at its tip, with provisions for its pressure-tight installation to a vessel, and with additional provisions (such as an internal thread) to receive a thermocouple (or other) thermometer. Use of a thermowell enables removal of a thermometer without breaking a pressure seal. Thermometers used in thermowells normally provide some form of mechanical protection, such as a sheath, for the thermocouple element. A terminal block is almost invariably included in the connection head to facilitate making (and changing) external electrical connections to the thermometer assembly. Some electrical circuitry (e.g., signal-conditioning circuitry) may also be included in the connection head.

Thermocouple probes used in aerospace and some other nonindustrial (e.g., nuclear) applications are typically assembled permanently, with as much as possible of the probe integrally machined and any additional pieces welded, with external electrical connections made to a cable that is not removable from the probe assembly, and usually equipped with mounting threads which are precision-machined to provide a pressure seal (when this is a requirement) in conjunction with a compression seal (e.g., metal O-ring). Alternatively, such probes can be designed for mounting by welding.

Among the many other varieties of thermocouple probes are those with very thin, diagonally cut tips of the same size and shape as a hypodermic needle; implantable flexible probes; externally threaded probes that can be mounted directly into plastic extruder heads or die adaptors of injection molding machines; spring-loaded probes; and probes for surface temperature measurements intended either for fixed installations or for hand-held operation (see Figure 4-13).

There are thermocouple assemblies other than probe types. *Clamp-on* thermocouples are configured as pipe clamps with integral sensing junction and connecting cable. Similarly, *washer-type* thermocouples (see Figure 4-14), intended for mounting under a bolt head or a nut, contain a sensing junction at the washer and are equipped with an integral cable.

Foil thermocouples (Figure 4-15) are designed for surface temperature measurements where very thin, flat sensing junctions are required. Each half

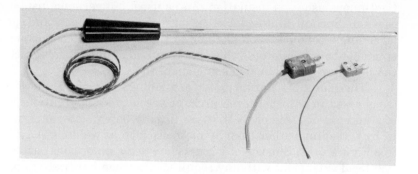

Figure 4-13. Hand-held thermocouple probe. (Courtesy of Omega Engineering, Inc., an Omega Group Co.)

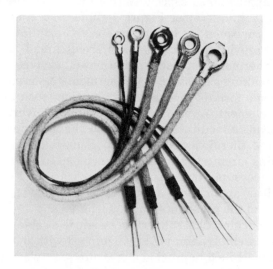

Figure 4-14. Washer thermocouple assemblies. (Courtesy of Omega Engineering, Inc., an Omega Group Co.)

of the symmetrical foil pattern is made of a different thermocouple material and the junction is usually of the butt type. Among the design versions are a free-foil style with removable carrier base and a matrix type with the foil embedded in very thin plastic material. Either type can be bonded to flat or curved, conducting or nonconducting, surfaces. The foil construction method has also been applied to miniature thermopiles for surface temperature and heat-flow measurements. Related to foil gages are micro-miniature thin-film (e.g., evaporated-film) thermocouples and thermopiles used in specialized applications (e.g., as sensing elements in infrared radiometers).

4.2.2.2 Platinum-wire resistance thermometers. Although some nickel-wire, nickel-alloy-wire, copper-wire, and some other wire resistance elements are

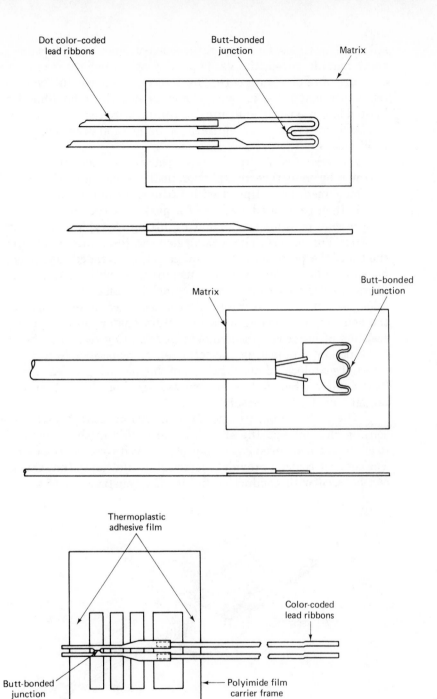

Figure 4-15. Foil thermocouples. (Courtesy of RdF Corp.)

still used, at times, for temperature measurement and, in some instances, still being manufactured, the vast majority of wire-element resistance thermometers use pure platinum wire. The descriptions of conductive-element resistive temperature sensors, for wire elements as well as for film elements, will be limited to those using platinum. Platinum-wire resistance thermometers exist in two major types of configurations: immersion probes and surface-temperature sensors.

Immersion probes (probe-type resistive temperature sensors) are usually mounted by their threaded portion near the housing. The threaded section is also machined, or equipped with fittings, for obtaining a pressure seal. The seal is then completed by use of a gasket, a rubber or metal O-ring, or by compression of tubing or a mating fitting. A typical probe configuration is shown in Figure 4-16. The *sensing element* (resistance winding) is located near the tip of the probe *sheath* (or shield). The threaded mount is just below the housing, or *head*. The housing is usually filled with packing such as insulating fibers. An electrical connector (receptacle), or an end plate provided either with solder terminals or an integrally connected cable (or individual leads), caps the housing. The head may also contain one or more trimming or adjusting resistors or other circuit elements. A *trimming resistor,* when used, provides the function of adjusting the total sensor resistance to a specified value. An internal seal, located near the root of the mounting threads, enables the probe (particularly when it has an exposed sensing element) to be mounted into pressurized ducts or vessels.

The probe illustrated contains a ceramic-*coated* (ceramic-encapsulated) sensing element and the sheath is perforated in the sensing-element region to admit the measured gas or liquid so that it contacts the element thermally. The ceramic coating provides electrical insulation so that this type of element can be used with conductive fluids. The construction of such an element is

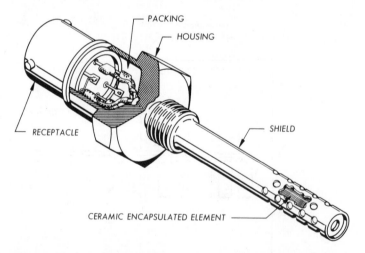

Figure 4-16. Platinum-wire immersion-probe temperature sensor. (Courtesy of Rosemount Inc.)

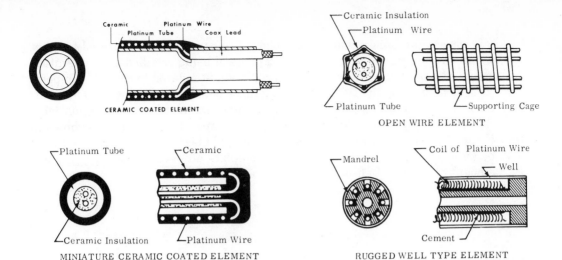

Figure 4-17. Typical forms of platinum-wire element construction: (a) ceramic-coated element; (b) miniature ceramic-coated element; (c) open-wire element; (d) rugged well type element. (Courtesy of Rosemount Inc.)

shown in Figure 4-17. A thin-walled platinum tube, coated with ceramic, is used as the mandrel for the platinum winding, which is then coated with the same type of ceramic. The thermal coefficient of expansion of tube, ceramic, and wire are closely matched to assure strain-free performance of the element under wide temperature variations. The same illustration shows a miniature version of the coated element; the connecting leads of this design are carried through the platinum tube and they are insulated by ceramic within the tube. When such an element is intended to be exposed to fluids with significant conductivity, an additional coating of organic composition or of Teflon can be applied over the element.

Two other types of element construction are also shown in Figure 4-17. In the *exposed* or open-wire element the platinum wire is wound loosely over a supporting cage of thin platinum rods which are coated with ceramic at the points of wire contact to provide fixing of the element as well as electrical insulation between wire and cage. This type of element has the shortest time constants but cannot be used with very rapidly moving or conductive fluids. Time constants of coated elements are about 5 to 10 times as long as those of the exposed elements. For applications requiring full enclosure of the element a "well-type" element can be used. Such elements can be used with highly corrosive and very rapidly moving fluids. However, the time constants of *enclosed* elements are in the order of 50 times as long for the type of construction shown as compared to the exposed element. In many applications such relatively long time constants are acceptable, and the "rugged-well-type" element does offer the necessary strain-free characteristics by employing a number of coiled windings fixed in the mandrel by ceramic only over a fraction of each wire turn. In all such elements using ceramic for fixing the winding the wire becomes annealed when the ceramic is brought to its firing temperature.

Special and more complex methods of construction are required for platinum-wire resistance thermometers capable of being certified as temperature standards, that is, acceptable as interpolation standards to convert temperature, as defined by the IPTS 68, to resistance over the range 13.81 to 903.9 K. Such thermometers are also used as reference standards in calibration laboratories. One type of construction of such a temperature standard is shown in Figure 4-18. The platinum wire is run through holes in ceramic tubing without being fixed at any point to assure the complete absence of even the smallest amount of strain. High-purity alumina are used as insulators.

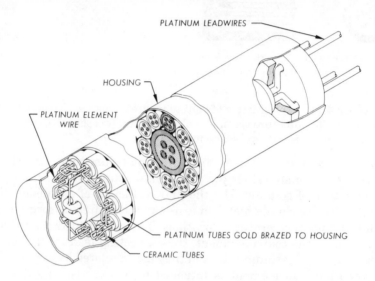

PLATINUM LEADWIRES

HOUSING

PLATINUM ELEMENT WIRE

PLATINUM TUBES GOLD BRAZED TO HOUSING

CERAMIC TUBES

Figure 4-18. Construction of a calibration-standard platinum resistance thermometer. (Courtesy of Rosemount Inc.)

Platinum-wire resistance thermometers intended for industrial applications (notably those in process measurement and control) are configured similarly to the thermocouple assembly shown in Figure 4-11. Enclosed elements are most frequently used and thermometer assemblies with waterproof connection heads are frequently designed for installation into a thermowell (see Figure 4-19). The connection head may contain circuitry to convert the resistance changes into current changes (e.g., the range 4 to 20 mA commonly used in process measurement systems).

Surface-temperature sensors, using platinum-wire elements, in most designs and nickel or iron–nickel alloys in some designs, exist in many sizes and configurations and are intended for installation by various methods. The sensor type illustrated in Figure 4-20 consists of a wire grid in an insulating carrier material. The sensors, which are bondable (i.e., intended to be cemented in place), have a thickness of 0.2 to 0.3 mm; a few models are up to 1 mm thick. The resistance winding is of platinum, nickel, or nickel–iron alloys. Carrier materials include polyimide, mica, phenolic-impregnated paper, and silicone-

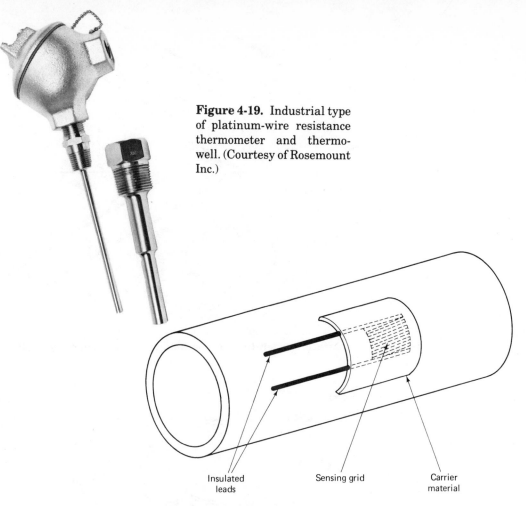

Figure 4-19. Industrial type of platinum-wire resistance thermometer and thermo-well. (Courtesy of Rosemount Inc.)

Insulated leads   Sensing grid   Carrier material

Figure 4-20. Flexible surface-temperature sensor bonded to pipe. (Courtesy of RdF Corp.)

impregnated glass cloth. For high-temperature measurements an alumina-insulated element with a weldable stainless-steel support plate can be used. The connecting leads can be made of nickel-plated copper or nickel wire, or they can be nickel or platinum ribbons. Related to these designs is an element overmolded with silicone rubber intended for clamp-on installation. The wire grids resemble those of wire-type strain gages (see Section 1.8.2.1); hence care must be exercised not to introduce strain error in the temperature measurement.

Many surface temperature sensor designs use coiled platinum-wire elements. Such elements tend to be essentially free of strain effects. A (patented) coiled-wire element, in which the coil is fixed to the bottom plate of a sensor over only a small fraction of a turn, is used in the sensors shown in Figure 4-21. An air gap between the element and the top plate insulates the element from ambient temperatures. Depending partly on the configuration, the sensors

Thermometry   **349**

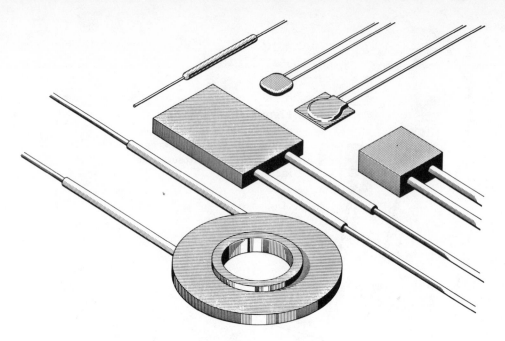

Figure 4-21. Typical surface temperature sensor configurations. (Courtesy of Rosemount Inc.)

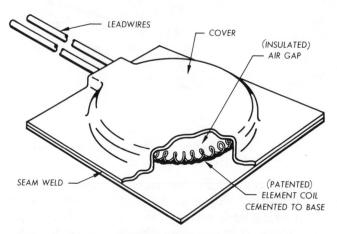

Figure 4-22. Construction of surface temperature sensor using minimally anchored platinum-wire coil element. (Courtesy of Rosemount Inc.)

are mounted by cementing or by clamping (in the case of the rectangular sensors). Washer-type sensors are intended to be fastened under a screw head or nut. The thinnest of the sensors illustrated (0.75 mm thick), which is either cemented or spot-welded to the measured surface, is shown in more detail in Figure 4-22. The connecting leads are Teflon-insulated copper or (bare) platinum leads.

When choosing an installation method for a surface temperature sensor it is important to match the sensor configuration (including the nature of the connecting leads) to the installation so that heat conduction from the measured surface is maximized and so that the sensor sees a minimum of heating or cooling due to convection or radiation to or from other sources. When cementing a sensor to a surface the amount of adhesive must be kept to a minimum. Insulation can be applied over the installed sensor to insulate it from ambient conditions. In some installations it is necessary to make the sensor an integral part of the measured surface, which can be provided with a cutout or spot-faced portion into which the sensor is cemented, potted, or welded. Care must also be taken to prevent conduction errors that may be introduced by the connecting leads and temperature gradients existing along these leads.

4.2.2.3 Platinum-film resistance thermometers. Various design approaches have been tried in the development of resistive temperature transducers uti-

(a)

(b)

Figure 4-23. Platinum-film temperature sensors: (a) cylindrical configuration; (b) flat configurations. (Courtesy of Matthey Bishop, Inc.)

lizing a metal film deposited on an insulating substrate. Some designs, using platinum, have been successful and have resulted in practical, producible sensors with predictable behavior. The main advantage of such film-type sensors is their relatively low cost. Two platinum-film sensor configurations are shown in Figure 4-23. The sensors contain a composite platinum and glass film deposited, typically by screen printing, onto a ceramic substrate and then fired. The cylindrical sensors have dimensions of 3 mm diameter by 28 mm long and are equipped with 0.37-mm-diameter platinum leads. The dimensions of the flat configurations are $25.4 \times 25.4 \times 1.0$ mm thick for the square wafer, and $4.7 \times 32.0 \times 0.76$ mm thick for the rectangular wafer. An alpha on the order of 0.00392, typical for platinum-wire sensors, is not obtainable for film-type sensors; however, an alpha of 0.00385 is characteristic of the sensors shown in the illustrations. The sensors are, therefore, capable of exhibiting an R vs. T characteristic corresponding to the "European curve" and of complying to such standards as B.S. 1904 (U.K.) and DIN 43760 (F.R.G.), including accuracy and stability tolerances. The sensors usually have a base resistance, $R_{0°C}$, of 100 Ω, and they are usable over a measuring range of -70 to $+600$ °C within their specified tolerances.

Thin-film platinum sensors are being developed further since their relatively low cost (due to modern production technology), together with a high base resistance, good stability, and R vs. T relationship per the "European curve," together with small size (units $1.25 \times 2.5 \times 0.5$ mm are now in production) makes them attractive to manufacturers as well as to users.

4.2.2.4 Thermistor thermometers. Thermistors are characterized by their small size, high negative temperature coefficient, fast time constant (obtainable with small bead types), and wide range of available base resistances (usually given at 25 °C rather than at the ice point), ranging from hundreds of ohms to about 1 MΩ. When used for temperature measurement the current flowing through thermistors must be kept very low (typically less than 100 μA) to assure near-zero power dissipation and near-zero self-heating.

Thermistors exist in many configurations and sizes (typically ranging from small to very small); they can be used in their basic form or as installed in a probe assembly (see Figure 4-24). Not all of the thermistor configurations are normally used for temperature measurement. They are also used for such electronics functions as switching, current-surge suppression, and time delay, for temperature control, for ac power measurement, for liquid-level measurement and, in combination with other elements, for dew-point measurement. Their use for such other measurements is covered in applicable sections of this handbook. The bead thermistor is the most common configuration for temperature measurements; it is also most frequently used in probe assemblies.

The fabrication of bead thermistors involves mixing metal oxide powders and a binder material in prescribed proportions, shaping, sintering, and encapsulation (bare beads are rarely used). Lead attachment is typically performed during the shaping process. Other thermistor types, such as disks, are pressed into their shape, sintered, metallized, trimmed to adjust their resist-

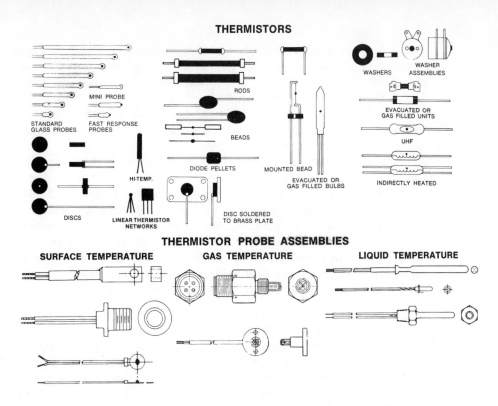

Figure 4-24. Thermistor and thermistor-probe configurations. (Courtesy of Fenwal Electronics.)

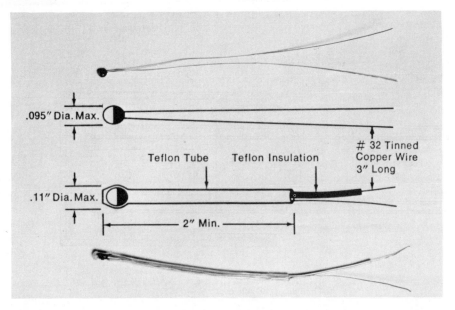

Figure 4-25. "High-reliability" (USA space-qualified) thermistors. (Courtesy of Yellow Springs Instrument Co., Inc.)

ance value, provided with leads, and then encapsulated (e.g., in epoxy). Beads can then be glass-coated, made part of a small glass probe, or fixed within a glass tube or envelope (glass-coated beads need not have been encapsulated). The sintering temperature is quite high, in the order of 1300 °C.

Small epoxy- or glass-coated bead and small-disk thermistors have been designed and fabricated for many applications. Figure 4-25 shows designs suitable for critical research work and for prolonged use in a space environment. The now commonly used medical "electronic thermometer" employs similar thermistors. When bonded to a metal plate they can be used as a surface-temperature probe. They can be embedded in threaded metal inserts for in situ temperature measurement. Beads or small glass probes (depending on ruggedness and flow rate requirements) are used in gas-temperature (including air-temperature) probes. When fully encapsulated or enclosed in a metal sheath they are used in immersion probes for liquid temperature measurements; such probes are available with a variety of thread mounts, pressure-sealing provisions, and sheath or housing configurations.

4.2.2.5 Germanium resistance thermometers. Thin slices of specially grown germanium crystals, typical doped with such materials as arsenic, gallium, and (in very slight amounts) antimony, are used in germanium resistance thermometers. The crystal, in a typical thermometer of this type (see Figure 4-26) is provided with two pairs of gold wires, 25 μm in diameter, using techniques to assure good ohmic contacts with the crystal. The crystal is mounted strain-free to a header, a glass/platinum hermetic seal through which four 0.13-mm-diameter platinum wires pass. The four-wire connection is necessary

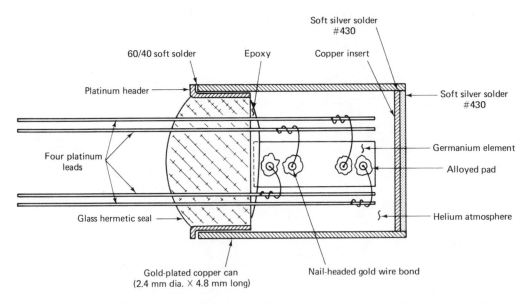

Figure 4-26. Internal construction of germanium resistance thermometer. (Courtesy of Scientific Instruments, Inc.)

since, to provide precise measurements, one of each pair of contacts is used as current contact (to be connected to a current source) whereas the other contact in each pair is used as voltage contact (from which the output signal is taken). The thin gold wires are attached to the platinum leads. A gold-plated copper case is placed over the assembly and then evacuated, back-filled with helium, and sealed to the header. Later, color-coded, Teflon-insulated, stranded-copper leads are attached to the outside ends of the platinum wires and the region in which the connections are made is encapsulated with epoxy, filling this region up to the outside edge of the hermetic seal. To stabilize the thermometer's characteristics, each unit is temperature-cycled repeatedly from room temperature to 4.2 K. Specification limits call for a repeatability within ± 0.0005 K at 4.2 K as the acceptance criterion.

The completed thermometer can be used in its basic configuration. It can also be equipped with a bolt-down flange surface, or installed in the head of a small screw for mounting in a tapped hole, or mounted in the tip of the stainless-steel sheath of an immersion probe. The measuring range of germanium resistance thermometers is usually the full cryogenic range, 1.5 to 100 K; however, some models are available for portions of this range, including for very small portions near absolute zero (0.5 to 3.2 K) and for the ^{3}He range (0.3 to 3.2 K). Over the range 2 to 20 K such thermometers are used as primary and reference standards. The R vs. T relationship is nonlinear and, over the range 1.5 to 100 K, exhibits slope changes. It is important to use the individual calibration curve for each thermometer; repeatability, as referenced to this curve, can then be expected to be very close.

4.2.2.6 Other types of thermometers. Electronic temperature-sensing devices other than those described in more detail above, and notably those whose sensing principles were explained in Section 4.2.1.4, are in considerably less general use and are intended mainly for specialized applications, primarily for cryogenic temperature measurements. Certain types of thermometers appear to have decreased in popularity due to evolving technologies. For example, the quartz-crystal thermometer, whose frequency-output lent itself to a digital display of temperature, may well have become less marketable in an era where low-cost single-chip analog-to-digital converters are available for use with virtually all types of temperature sensors.

Gallium-arsenide-diode thermometers offer the advantage of being usable over a temperature range from 1 to 400 K. They exist in configurations based on standard transistor cans as well as in other configurations, such as small probes and threaded inserts. The slope of their R vs. T curve and their sensitivity are quite different below about 70 K (and especially below about 10 K) than for the higher portion of their overall measuring range. A well-regulated constant-current source is required for their excitation, with fixed polarity, and a sensitive voltmeter with a high input impedance (or a preamplifier with equivalent characteristics) is needed for their output. Their relatively small size (typically less than 5 mm) and mass (0.5 g or less, except for threaded-insert types) makes fast time constants not difficult to achieve.

Silicon-diode thermometers have characteristics somewhat similar to those of the GaAs diodes in that their output (voltage) vs. temperature curve also exhibits a radical slope change for very low temperatures (below about 30 K). The average sensitivity at low temperatures is approximately 20 times as great as at temperatures about 40 K. A small-probe configuration is usual for these devices.

Capacitance thermometers have a usable range from near 0.01 K to about 60 K; they are also usable for temperatures between 70 and 400 K but have different characteristics over this higher range and are rarely used there. The multilayer glass/ceramic-metallized electrode devices offer the advantage that they are essentially unaffected by even very strong magnetic fields. Small (about 10 mm long) configurations, flat as well as cylindrical, have been produced.

Acoustical thermometers, which are usable to extremely high temperatures, and *noise thermometers,* which have been applied in the very low cryogenic region, belong in the categories of developmental and research devices. Both types have been applied experimentally to temperature measurements near absolute zero. For experiments involving the measurement of plasma temperatures in the tens of thousand degrees, acoustical thermometry offers a viable means of temperature determination.

4.2.2.7 Temperature switches.

Temperature switches, which can be considered discrete-output thermometers, are frequently used in control applications, rarely in measurement systems. They can be grouped in two categories: direct-actuating types and analog thermometers with gating circuitry. Another type is the sealed metal bulb, liquid-or gas-filled, which provides a pressure change as temperature sensed by the bulb varies. Although such devices can be used in conjunction with a pressure switch, they are usually designed for directly operating a control element or providing a pneumatic output (e.g., 3 to 15 psi) rather than an electrical output.

The most commonly used directly actuating temperature switches employ a bimetallic element (two mechanically joined strips or disks having different thermal coefficients of expansion) which effects a switch closure when it deflects to a preset position, due to heating or cooling. Thermostats used in home heating and airconditioning systems typically use such elements; however, bimetallic temperature switches are employed in numerous other applications as well.

More flexibility, improved accuracy, and (when required) faster response time is provided by analog thermometric sensors whose output is converted into one or more discrete levels by appropriate signal-conditioning circuitry. This circuitry can be designed for on/off control outputs or for two-position control (e.g., high and low limit) and set points cannot only be changed by a simple manual adjustment, they can also be programmable. Additionally, the circuitry can be designed for proportional control in one, two, or three modes. The temperature-sensing devices used with such switch-output circuitry can be thermocouples, resistive sensors (conductive or thermistors), or radiation pyrometers.

Essential characteristics of temperature switches include span (the range over which the switching point or points can be set), set-point repeatability ("accuracy"), threshold (often incorrectly called "sensitivity"), hysteresis (dead band), response time (or time constant), and any delay effected by circuitry to prevent rapid cycling around the set point.

Temperature switches find their applications wherever temperature has to be controlled within more or less narrow limits; they are also used to provide alarm indications (e.g., overheating alarms). Associated circuitry and devices can provide control, alarm indication (visible or audible or both), and numerical display.

4.2.3 Design and Performance Characteristics

The number and types of design and performance characteristics that should be considered for the specification or the selection of temperature sensors (temperature transducers—the terms are used interchangeably here) for sensor designs of different complexity. A limited number of characteristics apply to "basic" sensors, that is, sensing elements which are either installed or used as such, or are assembled into a sensor package by the user. A larger number of characteristics apply to such relatively simple "packaged" sensors as surface-temperature transducers. A far larger number of characteristics need to be considered for devices such as completely packaged immersion probes. The most prevalent "basic" temperature sensors are thermocouple wire and bead thermistors.

Wire thermocouples—with sensing junction, connecting hardware, and associated circuits completed by the user—are specified by their wire material, wire gauge or diameter, number of conductors in a cable, insulation and coverings, and "limits of error" (accuracy, usually just stated as either "standard" or "special"). For most commonly used thermocouple wire and extension wire types there are standard designations for these characteristics, established in readily available national, technical society, or governmental standards. Such standards are frequently reprinted in manufacturers' bulletins and should be adhered to and used to the greatest extent possible. Manufacturers' standards exist for numerous types of metal-sheathed, ceramic-insulated thermocouple cable, and cable characteristics can be selected from such tabulated data.

Bead thermistors can be specified by their bead dimensions and covering, the materials, dimensions, insulation (if any) and configuration of the leads, base resistance ("cold resistance," normally the zero-power resistance at 25 °C), usable or intended temperature range, and either the material constant β or, more simply, a *characteristic curve,* a curve or table of R vs. T and the expectable deviation of actual values from this curve. Specifications for time constant and dissipation constant, together with applicable conditions, are usually also included.

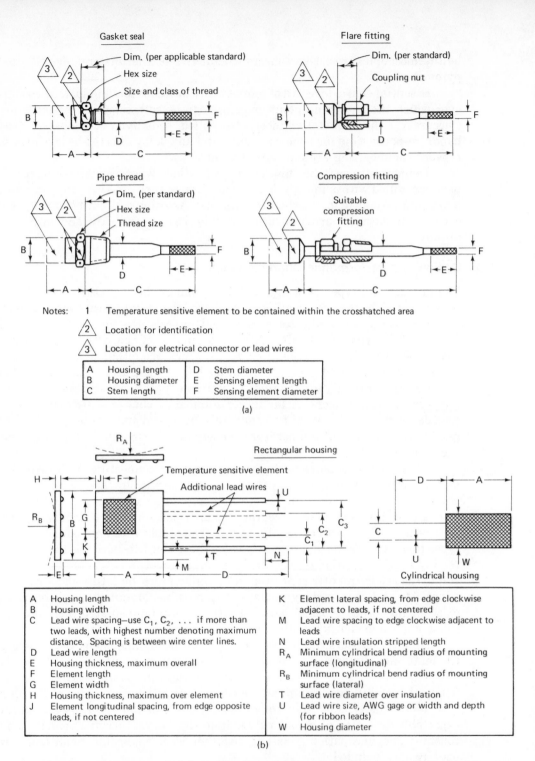

Notes: 1   Temperature sensitive element to be contained within the crosshatched area

2   Location for identification

3   Location for electrical connector or lead wires

A	Housing length	D	Stem diameter
B	Housing diameter	E	Sensing element length
C	Stem length	F	Sensing element diameter

(a)

A	Housing length	K	Element lateral spacing, from edge clockwise adjacent to leads, if not centered
B	Housing width		
C	Lead wire spacing—use C_1, C_2, ... if more than two leads, with highest number denoting maximum distance. Spacing is between wire center lines.	M	Lead wire spacing to edge clockwise adjacent to leads
		N	Lead wire insulation stripped length
D	Lead wire length	R_A	Minimum cylindrical bend radius of mounting surface (longitudinal)
E	Housing thickness, maximum overall		
F	Element length	R_B	Minimum cylindrical bend radius of mounting surface (lateral)
G	Element width		
H	Housing thickness, maximum over element	T	Lead wire diameter over insulation
J	Element longitudinal spacing, from edge opposite leads, if not centered	U	Lead wire size, AWG gage or width and depth (for ribbon leads)
		W	Housing diameter

(b)

Figure 4-27. Dimensional specifications for temperature sensors: (a) typical immersion-probe configurations; (b) typical surface-temperature transducer configurations.

358

Mechanical design characteristics for immersion probes and surface-temperature sensors include several important considerations. Characteristics for hand-held and ambient-air probes are somewhat similar to those of immersion probes, and surface-temperature sensors include not only bondable (cementable) designs but also such configurations as threaded-insert types and washer types. Configuration and dimensions have to be chosen with extreme care. Typical examples are shown in Figure 4-27 for integrally assembled immersion probes and for bondable, weldable, or potted-in-place surface-temperature sensors. Mounting provisions and methods, and their effect on configuration, should be determined; they are critical factors for having the sensor respond only to the temperature to be measured (to the best extent possible).

The stem length of an immersion probe intended for installation in a pipe or duct should, as a "rule of thumb," be so chosen as to place the center of a resistive sensing element, or the junction of a thermocouple, at a radial position located $0.72r$ (for turbulent flow) or $0.58r$ (for laminar flow) from the centerline of the pipe, where r is the radius of the pipe (or duct).

For "industrial"-type immersion probes, which are usually disassemblable and may be assembled either by the user or the manufacturer, the individual piece parts that make up the assembly are selected, usually from a catalog. The parts include the connection head assembly, any required extension hardware (which, in effect, extends the head assembly from the mounting boss), the type and length of thermocouple element, any required protection tube or sheath, and the associated thermowell, if used.

Configurational considerations include the protection of the sensing element, which may be exposed (bare) or enclosed, or, for certain types of platinum-wire sensors, coated (but without a metal enclosure). For some applications a "stagnation fitting" may be required around the sensing element, a cage designed to minimize impact pressure, due to flow velocity, acting on the element. Another provision that may have to be specified or considered is the nature of any spring-loading arrangement.

The physical and chemical properties of all measured fluids that will come in contact with the sensor (or a thermowell) have to be known and sensor compatibility with the fluids must be established. The maximum flow velocity of measured liquids and gases should be stated for immersion probes, and the operating pressure range, proof pressure, and burst pressure rating of the probe must be specified. If necessary, appropriate leak-test requirements can be imposed.

Mechanical characteristics to be considered for surface temperature sensors should include carrier or matrix material, lead pull-out strength, and any limitations on mounting procedures, including maximum torque for washer types and maximum clamping force for clamp-on types.

Electrical design characteristics pertain to the sensing element as well as to any additional electrical components that may be packaged integrally with the sensor (e.g., contained within the connection head). Some examples of internal schematics of thermoelectric and resistive temperature transducers are shown in Figure 4-28. Thermocouple junctions must be specified as either

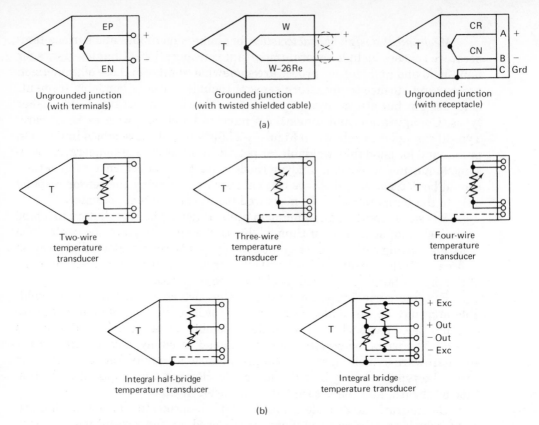

Figure 4-28. Typical internal schematic diagrams of temperature transducers: (a) thermoelectric transducers; (b) resistive transducers.

grounded or ungrounded. Insulation resistance (or breakdown voltage rating, or both) should be specified for all sensors having an ungrounded element; this is of particular importance for surface-temperature sensors. Additional characteristics for sensors with passive elements (all except thermocouples) include nominal and maximum excitation current, or voltage and power, type and power requirements, if any, of integrally packaged signal conditioning circuitry, and, sometimes, the nominal resistance across the transducer's terminals, at room temperature (for continuity checks). When ac excitation or pulsed dc excitation is to be applied to a sensor with a wirewound element, the inductive reactance of the element at the specified form of excitation should be considered; it may cause errors or pulse-shape distortion in the sensor's output.

Performance characteristics comprise primarily range, output, dynamic response, and accuracy characteristics. These characteristics can be influenced significantly by their intended use. *Range* is usually shown as the lower and upper limits of temperature over which accuracy and other performance characteristics and their tolerances apply. In most cases this is the overall "usable" or "recommended" range of a sensor. In some cases, however, the user may have standardized on certain output spans that match the signal-conditioning equipment and data system. This is sometimes advisable when a significant number of temperature measurements must be made in a given installation. If the user has, for example, selected an amplifier that requires 50 mV for a full-scale deflection of his telemetry or display equipment, the range of a thermocouple used will be dictated by the temperature at which 50 mV is produced by the thermocouple. The range could be shifted up or down by biasing the input to the amplifier or, for a thermocouple, by appropriate selection of the reference-junction temperature. Similarly, in the case of resistive sensors, the user may have selected a resistance bridge standardized so that a resistance change of 100 Ω in the leg represented by the sensor (which may be in series with a trimming resistor) provides his required full-scale deflection. The range of the resistive sensor is then given by the limits between which the 100-Ω resistance change occurs.

Output is governed by similar considerations. For most applications the output of the sensor is given, for thermocouples, by applicable emf vs. temperature tables and, for resistive sensors, by a table or curve (*theoretical curve* or *reference curve*) of the nominal R vs. T relationship (or that obtained by an individual calibration); equivalent reference curves (tabulated or in graphical form) define the output of frequency-output, voltage-output, or current-output sensors. However, the use of standardized signal-conditioning equipment may force the output to be shown by specific end points or by a specific change over a stated temperature range.

Maximum and minimum temperature are often shown as overrange conditions beyond specified range limits. When so specified, the accuracy characteristics do not apply over these extended portions of the range; however, the sensor is expected not to be damaged and, usually, not lose its normal performance by exposure to such temperatures over stated periods of time.

Repeatability is the most essential accuracy characteristic of temperature sensors. It can be stated in terms of temperature indicated by the output of the sensor (e.g., "within 0.05 °C) or in terms of output (e.g., "within 0.5 Ω" or "within 0.03 mV"), sometimes in terms of percent of (output) reading. *Stability* is sometimes specified additionally, as repeatability (with larger tolerances) applicable over either a long period of time or over a large number of temperature cycles. *Linearity* is rarely specified for temperature sensors, since all types are inherently nonlinear to some extent; it is sometimes shown for sensors permanently connected into some sort of linearization network. *Hysteresis* is normally negligible in temperature sensors.

Error (or an *error band*) refers to the maximum deviation, over the specified temperature range, of output values from a reference curve (which is usually shown in tabular form). For thermocouples the same is accomplished by "limits of error"; the standardized emf vs. temperature tables (or equivalent tables furnished by a manufacturer for nonstandardized thermocouples) serve as the reference curve. When the same error tolerances are specified for a number of sensors to all of which a given reference curve applies (as is the case for thermocouples), these tolerances are also indicative of *calibration interchangeability*. When error, limits of error, or an error band is specified, the tolerances apply to deviations due to causes attributable to the sensor in its intended use, regardless of the source of the error. A number of specific sources of error in temperature sensors are explained below.

Thermoelectric potentials can be generated within a resistive temperature sensor, at internal connections between wires of different metals such that a temperature gradient exists along one or more of the wires. This error is best avoided by using internal connecting leads of the same metal as used for the sensing element, if it is conductive, and assuring isothermal connection points when more than one lead material is used in a sensor containing a semiconductive element.

Self-heating (I²R heating) can cause errors in resistive sensors, particularly in semiconductor sensors. Self-heating is dependent on the power dissipation of the element as established by element resistance, current through the element, and heat transfer to the measured fluid or surface. Self-heating will be more severe, for example, when the same sensor, using the same excitation current, is used in still air than when it is immersed in a rapidly flowing liquid. One way of determining self-heating error is to take a measurement with the sensor using the nominal excitation current and then, without changing any other measurement condition, repeating the measurement using a fraction (e.g., 20%) of the nominal current. The difference in output readings, if any, is the self-heating error. The conditions under which the measurement is made must, of course, correspond closely to the intended use of the sensor.

Conduction error is caused by heat conduction between the sensing element and the mounting of a temperature sensor. This occurs primarily in immersion probes and can be quite severe when the element is enclosed and the enclosing sheath is short. Conduction error can also occur in surface sensors, due to heat conduction along the connecting leads to the nearest terminal; it can be minimized by making the leads as thin as possible and mounting the nearest electrical terminals close to the point of measurement. The conduction error of an immersion probe can be roughly determined by a test during which the probe is first immersed into an agitated temperature bath (a liquid whose temperature is known and controlled within close limits) only a little above the sensing-element region while the head of the sensor is artificially cooled or heated to a temperature that differs from the bath temperature by the same amount that it would differ in the probe's intended application. Next, the sensor is immersed in the bath up to nearly the outermost edge of the head (so as to avoid immersing the electrical terminals or connector pins into the bath). The two readings are then compared and their difference is due to conduction error.

Mounting error ("strain error") can occur in surface-temperature sensors after they are bonded to the measured surface, due to strain in the measured region. It can be determined by measuring the output of the sensor, at the same temperature, before and after mounting. Mounting error can also be introduced by using an improper mounting procedure.

Time constant is the most essential dynamic characteristic of a temperature sensor. Its specification is meaningful only when the value is accompanied by a statement of the two temperatures that constitute the step change as well as by statements of the type of fluid used at each of the two temperatures and the flow rate of both fluids. An example of a correct specification would read: "Time constant: 50 ms, max., from still air at 25 ± 2 °C to distilled water at 80 ± 2 °C moving at 1 m/s." When only the second fluid and its flow rate are specified, still air at 25 ± 5 °C can usually be assumed as the first fluid. *Response time* is sometimes specified as 98% or 99% response time under the same test conditions applicable to time constant.

Recovery error is sometimes stated for temperature sensors intended to be used at measured-fluid flow velocities in excess of Mach 0.2, especially when the flow is transverse to a probe-type sensor. Recovery error, then, is the error in total temperature (the temperature indicated by the output of the sensor) caused by the assumption of a unity *recovery factor*. The recovery factor is the proportion of kinetic energy converted into heat, expressed as the ratio of the difference between recovery temperature and absolute temperature to the difference between total temperature and absolute temperature. The recovery error can be determined by appropriate calculations.

Environmental characteristics are frequently not specified for temperature sensors; however, environmental conditions of the type generally applicable to transducers should be considered. Vibration acting on long-immersion probes may cause noise or discontinuities in the output; if sufficiently severe, it may even cause physical damage. Many sensors are not suitable in a nuclear radiation environment because of materials used in them. Portions of sensors exposed to the ambient atmosphere must withstand any contamination or corrosion that could be caused by its constituents.

4.2.4 Considerations for Selection

The selection of a temperature sensor can involve a relatively larger matrix of considerations than is necessary for selection of other generic types of sensors. Primarily, it is necessary to select a sensor design whose sensing element will attain the temperature of the measured fluid or surface, and to attain it within the time available for making the measurement. The output of a temperature sensor at any time is merely a measure of the temperature of its sensing element. It is often difficult to assure that this temperature is, indeed, the same as the temperature that is required to be measured.

For most applications the following selection criteria are of primary importance: the nature and characteristics of the measured fluid or solid; the measuring range (and possible overrange limits); the time constant; and the type of the associated signal conditioning, data system, and display equipment available or intended to be used.

Measured fluids, whose temperature is sensed with immersion probes, can be liquids or gases; they can be corrosive or noncorrosive, oxidizing or reducing; they can be stagnant or moving at low, medium, high, or very high velocities; and they can be free or contained in a pipe, a duct, a tank, a vessel, or a cavity.

The temperature of a contained fluid can usually be measured with an immersion-probe-type sensor. A thermowell can be permanently installed in an opening in the wall of the container when the operating life of the installation is much greater than the expected useful life of the sensor, or when it is expected that the sensor must be removed fairly frequently for calibration or maintenance, and when it is impractical or undesirable to have an "open hole in the container" for probe replacements. Thermowells lengthen the time constant of a measurement substantially; hence, when temperature fluctuations are slow, and when conduction error can be minimized, thermowells would not compromise measurement accuracy; when such fluctuations are rapid, the loss in measurement accuracy due to a relative inability of the sensing element to follow such fluctuations, and due to a probable increase in conduction error, must be traded off against the maintainability considerations described above.

All materials of an immersion probe must be compatible with the fluids that can come in contact with them. When an enclosed-element probe is used, it is usually only the sheath material and the material of a portion of the mounting that needs to be considered. When an exposed-element probe is used, the design must be analyzed carefully to determine all the various sensor materials (sensing element, connecting leads, supports, cage, partial sheath) that may come in contact with the measured fluid; compatibility of each of the materials must then be assured. When a thermowell is used, only the thermowell material needs to be considered. For considerations of material compatibility and structural/mechanical integrity of a probe, the term "measured fluid" must be extended to encompass all fluids that may come in contact with the probe in its installation; besides the measured fluid, these may include test fluids and purge fluids. Table 4-6 shows probe sheath and thermowell materials recommended for immersion in various fluids. The table is based on such considerations as catalytic reactions, contamination, and electrolysis. It should be noted that additional factors will often have to be considered that may void these recommendations, which are largely based on economy. It can also be seen that many of the recommended metals are proprietary alloys of types available mainly in the United States and that equivalent alloys available in other countries may have to be found.

Resistive elements are normally enclosed or, at least, coated when immersed in liquids and most gases. Exposed resistive elements cannot be immersed in conductive or contaminating fluids. They can, however, be used in dry air and in a limited number of other gases and some liquids when their fast time constant is required. For such applications in stagnant or slowly moving fluids, some sort of cage usually surrounds the element for mechanical protection. Somewhat more attention needs to be paid to the design of such a cage when it is also intended to shield the element from radiated heat, or when stagnation temperatures must be considered. For exposed-junction thermocouples, general material-compatibility considerations point to the use of Type J for reducing fluids; Types K, E, R, and S for oxidizing fluids; and Type T for oxidizing as well as reducing fluids or atmospheres. Exposed tungsten—

rhenium junctions are limited to use in vacuum or clean inert gases; such junctions also tend to be brittle and require careful handling. Thermistors are usually coated and can be used in most fluids; however, material-compatibility considerations still apply to other elements that are part of a thermistor probe. The elements of specialized types of cryogenic sensors (e.g., Ge, GaAs) are usually enclosed, primarily for structural/mechanical protection, and to prevent contamination. The choice of ungrounded vs. grounded thermocouple junctions is primarily given by a trade-off between the faster time constant of a grounded junction against the potential increase in electrical noise in the associated measurement circuitry; many data systems require single-point grounding, which dictates the use of ungrounded junctions.

A number of other considerations can affect immersion-probe design. The probe must be rated for the specified operating, proof, and burst pressure. It must withstand the maximum specified transverse-flow velocity. It should have an immersion length appropriate to obtaining a measurement of the mean temperature in a pipe or duct; yet the probe should also be long enough to minimize conduction error, and these two requirements may be in conflict and require a trade-off.

When an opening in a pipe, duct, or vessel is impractical or prohibited, so that an immersion probe or thermowell cannot be used, a temperature measurement, whose accuracy is often adequate, can still be obtained by clamping or bonding a surface-temperature sensor to the outside of the wall. To assure a reasonable amount of measurement accuracy, the sensor must be thermally insulated from the ambient atmosphere and from sources of heat radiation and the heat conduction from the wall, to which it is mounted, to its sensing element must be optimized by sensor design and installation.

Measured solid materials can be metallic or nonmetallic, of different thickness and cross-sectional configuration, and exposed to various ambient environmental conditions. Any type of surface-temperature sensor will modify the characteristics of the surface or subsurface of the material and configuration to some extent. The sensor, and its installation method, must, therefore, be chosen so that such disturbances are minimized. An ideal sensor would be made entirely of the same material as the solid and would become an integral part of it so that the characteristics of the configuration at and around the point of measurement are not altered in any manner. A good practical sensor, and its installation, introduce as little foreign material into the solid as possible and affect the configuration as little as possible. This rule applies also to associated electrical connections, housing, and mounting materials.

Most temperature measurements of solids are made at the surface, by cementing or welding a thin resistive or thermoelectric sensor to the surface. Any envelope or housing of such a sensor should match the surface material as closely as possible. A variety of such sensors are available with a thickness of 1 mm or less, including resistive (wire, film, and thermistor) as well as thermoelectric (foil, thin-wire, and thin-film) types. Metal-sheathed ceramic-insulated thermocouple cable (two-conductor) has been made with overall diameters down to 0.3 mm. Very small weldable clips are available for such

Table 4-6   Recommendations for Sensor Materials in Contact with Measured Fluids

Substance	Conditions	Recommended Metal
Acetate solvents	Crude or pure	Monel or nickel
Acetic acid	10%, 70 °F	304 stainless steel
	50%, 70 °F	304 stainless steel
	50%, 212 °F	316 stainless steel
	99%, 70 °F	430 stainless steel
	99%, 212 °F	430 stainless steel
Acetic anhydride		Monel
Acetone	212 °F	304 stainless steel
Acetylene		304, Monel, nickel
Alcohol ethyl	70 °F	304 stainless steel
	212 °F	304 stainless steel
Alcohol methyl	70 °F	304 stainless steel
	212 °F	304 stainless steel
Aluminum	Molten	Cast iron
Aluminum acetate	Saturated	304 stainless steel
Aluminum sulfate	10%, 70 °F	304 stainless steel
	Saturated 70 °F	304 stainless steel
	10%, 212 °F	316 stainless steel
	Saturated, 212 °F	316 stainless steel
Ammonia	All concentrations, 70 °F	304 stainless steel
Ammonium chloride	All concentrations, 212 °F	316 stainless steel
Ammonium nitrate	All concentrations, 70 °F	304 stainless steel
	All concentrations, 212 °F	304 stainless steel
Ammonium sulfate	5%, 70 °F	304 stainless steel
	10%, 212 °F	316 stainless steel
	Saturated, 212 °F	316 stainless steel
Aniline	All concentrations, 70 °F	304 stainless steel
Amylacetate		Monel
Asphalt		Steel (C1018), phosphor bronze, Monel, nickel
Barium carbonate	70 °F	304 stainless steel
Barium chloride	5%, 70 °F	Monel
	Saturated, 70 °F	Monel
	Aqueous, hot	316 stainless steel
Barium hydroxide		Steel (C1018)
Barium sulfite		Nichrome
Benzaldehyde		Steel (C1018).
Benzene	70 °F	304 stainless steel
Benzine		Steel (C1018), Monel, Inconel
Benzol	Hot	304 stainless steel
Boracic acid	5%, hot or cold	304 stainless steel
Bromine	70 °F	Tantalum
Butadiene		Brass, 304 stainless steel
Butane	70 °F	304 stainless steel
Butylacetate		Monel
Butyl alcohol		Copper
Butylenes		Steel (C1018), phosphor bronze

Table 4-6 (continued)

Substance	Conditions	Recommended Metal
Butyric acid	5%, 70 °F	304 stainless steel
	5%, 150 °F	304 stainless steel
Calcium bisulfite	70 °F	316 stainless steel
Calcium chlorate	Dilute, 70 °F	304 stainless steel
	Dilute, 150 °F	304 stainless steel
Calcium hydroxide	10%, 212 °F	304 stainless steel
	20%, 212 °F	304 stainless steel
	50%, 212 °F	317 stainless steel
Carbolic acid	All, 212 °F	316 stainless steel
Carbon dioxide	Dry	Steel (C1018), Monel
Carbon dioxide	Wet	Aluminum, Monel, nickel
Carbon tetrachloride	10%, 70 °F	Monel
Chlorex caustic		316, 317 stainless steel
Chlorine gas	Dry, 70 °F	317 stainless steel
	Moist, 70 °F	Hastelloy C
	Moist, 212 °F	Hastelloy C
Chromic acid	5%, 70 °F	304 stainless steel
	10%, 212 °F	316 stainless steel
	50%, 212 °F	316 stainless steel
Citric acid	15%, 70 °F	304 stainless steel
	15%, 212 °F	316 stainless steel
	Concentrated, 212 °F	317 stainless steel
Coal tar	Hot	304 stainless steel
Coke oven gas		Aluminum
Copper nitrate		304, 316 stainless steel
Copper sulfate		304, 316 stainless steel
Core oils		316 stainless steel
Cottonseed oil		Steel (C1018), Monel, nickel
Creosols		304 stainless steel
Creosote crude		Steel (C1018), Monel, nickel
Cyanogen gas		304 stainless steel
Dowtherm		Steel (C1018)
Epsom salt	Hot and cold	304 stainless steel
Ether	70 °F	304 stainless steel
Ethyl acetate		Monel
Ethyl chloride	70 °F	304 stainless steel
Ethylene glycol		Steel (C1018)
Ethyl sulfate	70 °F	Monel
Ferric chloride	1%, 70 °F	316 stainless steel
	5%, 70 °F	Tantalum
	5%, boiling	Tantalum
Ferric sulfate	5%, 70 °F	304 stainless steel
Ferrous sulfate	Dilute, 70 °F	304 stainless steel
Formaldehyde		304 stainless steel
Freon		Steel (C1018)
Formic acid	5%, 70 °F	316 stainless steel
	5%, 150 °F	316 stainless steel

Table 4-6 (continued)

Substance	Conditions	Recommended Metal
Gallic acid	5%, 70 °F	Monel
	5%, 150 °F	Monel
Gasoline	70 °F	304 stainless steel
Glucose	70 °F	304 stainless steel
Glycerine	70 °F	304 stainless steel
Glycerol		304 stainless steel
Heat treating		446 stainless steel
Hydrobromic acid	48%, 212 °F	Hastelloy B
Hydrochloric acid	1%, 70 °F	Hastelloy C
	1%, 212 °F	Hastelloy B
	5%, 70 °F	Hastelloy C
	5%, 212 °F	Hastelloy B
	25%, 70 °F	Hastelloy B
	25%, 212 °F	Hastelloy B
Hydrocyanic acid		316 stainless steel
Hydrofluoric acid		Hastelloy C
Hydrogen peroxide	70 °F	316 stainless steel
	212 °F	316 stainless steel
Hydrogen sulfide	Wet and dry	316 stainless steel
Iodine	70 °F	Tantalum
Kerosene	70 °F	304 stainless steel
Lactic acid	5%, 70 °F	304 stainless steel
	5%, 150 °F	316 stainless steel
	10%, 212 °F	Tantalum
Lacquer	70 °F	316 stainless steel
Latex		Steel (C1018)
Lime sulfur		Steel (C1018), 304 stainless steel Monel
Linseed oil	70 °F	304 stainless steel
Magnesium chloride	5%, 70 °F	Monel
	5%, 212 °F	Nickel
Magnesium sulfate	Cold and hot	Monel
Malic acid	Cold and hot	316 stainless steel
Mercury		Steel (C1018), 304 stainless steel, Monel
Methane	70 °F	Steel (1020)
Milk		304 stainless steel, Nickel
Mixed acids (sulfuric and nitric —all temp. and %)		Carpenter 20
Molasses		Steel (C1018), 304 stainless steel, Monel, nickel
Muriatic acid	70 °F	Tantalum
Naptha	70 °F	304 stainless steel
Natural gas	70 °F	304 stainless steel
Neon	70 °F	304 stainless steel
Nickel chloride	70 °F	304 stainless steel
Nickel sulfate	Hot and cold	304 stainless steel

Table 4-6 (continued)

Substance	Conditions	Recommended Metal
Nitric acid	5%, 70 °F	304 stainless steel
	20%, 70 °F	304 stainless steel
	50%, 70 °F	304 stainless steel
	50%, 212 °F	304 stainless steel
	65%, 212 °F	316 stainless steel
	Concentrated, 70 °F	304 stainless steel
	Concentrated, 212 °F	Tantalum
Nitrobenzene	70 °F	304 stainless steel
Nitrous acid		304 stainless steel
Oleic acid	70 °F	316 stainless steel
Oleum	70 °F	316 stainless steel
Oxolic acid	5%, Hot and cold	304 stainless steel
	10%, 212 °F	Monel
Oxygen	70 °F	Steel (C1018)
Oxygen	Liquid	304 stainless steel
Palmitic acid		316 stainless steel
Petroleum ether		304 stainless steel
Phenol		304 stainless steel
Pentane		304 stainless steel
Phosphoric acid	1%, 70 °F	304 stainless steel
	5%, 70 °F	304 stainless steel
	10%, 70 °F	316 stainless steel
	10%, 212 °F	Hastelloy C
	30%, 70 °F	Hastelloy B
	30%, 212 °F	Hastelloy B
	85%, 70 °F	Hastelloy B
	85%, 212 °F	Hastelloy B
Picric acid	70 °F	304 stainless steel
Potassium bromide	70 °F	316 stainless steel
Potassium carbonate	1%, 70 °F	304 stainless steel
Potassium chlorate	70 °F	304 stainless steel
Potassium chloride	5%, 70 °F	304 stainless steel
	5%, 212 °F	304 stainless steel
Potassium hydroxide	5%, 70 °F	304 stainless steel
	25%, 212 °F	304 stainless steel
	50%, 212 °F	316 stainless steel
Potassium nitrate	5%, 70 °F	304 stainless steel
	5%, 212 °F	304 stainless steel
Potassium Permanganate	5%, 70 °F	304 stainless steel
Potassium sulfate	5%, 70 °F	304 stainless steel
	5%, 212 °F	304 stainless steel
Potassium sulfide	70 °F	304 stainless steel
Propane		304 stainless steel
Pyrogallic acid		304 stainless steel
Quinine bisulfate	Dry	316 stainless steel
Quinine sulfate	Dry	304 stainless steel
Resin		304 stainless steel

Table 4-6 (continued)

Substance	Conditions	Recommended Metal
Rosin	Molten	304 stainless steel
Seawater		Monel
Salammoniac		Monel
Salicylic acid		Nickel
Shellac		304 stainless steel
Soap	70 °F	304 stainless steel
Sodium bicarbonate	All concentrations, 70 °F	304 stainless steel
	5%, 150 °F	304 stainless steel
Sodium bisulfate		Monel
Sodium carbonate	5%, 70 °F	304 stainless steel
	5%, 150 °F	304 stainless steel
Sodium chloride	5%, 70°F	316 stainless steel
	5%, 150 °F	316 stainless steel
	Saturated, 70 °F	316 stainless steel
	Saturated, 212 °F	316 stainless steel
Sodium fluoride	5%, 70 °F	Monel
Sodium hydroxide		304 stainless steel
Sodium hypochlorite	5% still	316 stainless steel
Sodium nitrate	Fused	317 stainless steel
Sodium peroxide		304 stainless steel
Sodium phosphate		Steel (C1018)
Sodium silicate		Steel (C1018)
Sodium sulfate	70 °F	304 stainless steel
Sodium sulfide	70 °F	316 stainless steel
Sodium sulfite	150 °F	304 stainless steel
Steam		304 stainless steel
Stearic acid		304 stainless steel
Sulphur dioxide	Moist gas, 70 °F	316 stainless steel
	Gas, 575 °F	304 stainless steel
Sulphur	Dry, molten	304 stainless steel
	Wet	316 stainless steel
Sulphuric acid	5%, 70 °F	Carp. 20, Hastelloy B
	5%, 212 °F	Carp. 20, Hastelloy B
	10%, 70 °F	Carp. 20, Hastelloy B
	10%, 212 °F	Carp. 20, Hastelloy B
	50%, 70 °F	Carp. 20, Hastelloy B
	50%, 212 °F	Carp. 20, Hastelloy B
	90%, 70 °F	Carp. 20, Hastelloy B
	90%, 212 °F	Hastelloy D
Tannic acid	70 °F	304 stainless steel
Tar		Steel (C1018), 304 stainless steel Monel, nickel
Tartaric acid	70 °F	304 stainless steel
	150 °F	316 stainless steel
Tin	Molten	Cast iron
Toluene		Aluminum, phosphor bronze, Monel
Trichloro ethylene		Steel (C1018)
Turpentine		304 stainless steel

Table 4-6 (continued)

Substance	Conditions	Recommended Metal
Varnish		304 stainless steel
Vegetable oils		Steel (C1018), 304 stainless steel Monel
Vinegar		304 stainless steel
Water	Fresh	Copper, steel (C1018) Monel
Water	Salt	Aluminum, brass, Monel
Whiskey, wine		304 stainless steel, nickel
Xylene		Copper
Zinc	Molten	Cast iron
Zinc chloride		Monel
Zinc sulfate	5%, 70 °F	304 stainless steel
	Saturated, 70 °F	304 stainless steel
	25%, 212 °F	304 stainless steel

Courtesy of Omega Engineering, Inc., an Omega Group Co.

cables; their connection to larger-diameter extension cable should be made sufficiently far away not to affect the surface configuration near the point of measurement.

Subsurface-temperature measurements are made with small embeddable sensors or threaded inserts. They are typically installed so that their outer edge, in the as-installed configuration, is flush with the outside surface of the measured material. The material of the threaded insert should be the same as, or at least very similar to, the measured material. When washer-type sensors are used, care must be taken to assure that the temperature attained by the washer will be as nearly as possible the temperature to be measured.

Measuring range strongly influences the selection of a temperature sensor. Platinum-wire sensors can be used when the range is any reasonably sized portion of their overall useful range. Relatively narrow ranges often require the base resistance of such a sensor to be fairly high so that a sufficiently large resistance change can be obtained. The large resistance changes provided by thermistors make these sensors very suitable for narrow measuring ranges (e.g., those of medical thermometers). Thermocouples tend to be more useful when a fairly large portion of their usable range is to be measured. The ice point should preferably be included in the range since thermocouple emf tables are referenced to that temperature (and reference junctions are normally kept at that temperature or adjusted to simulate it). The reason for using thermocouples for larger temperature ranges is given by their output and associated requirements imposed on signal-conditioning equipment. For example, even the most sensitive material combination, Type E, provides an output of only 3 mV at 50 °C (referred to 0 °C) and data systems usually require larger input signals than that. This means that the signal has to be amplified and amplifier cost, complexity, instability, and noise are inversely proportional to input signal level, as a general rule. For the same thermocouple type, the output signal would be 53 mV for the range 0 to 700 °C, and it would be 76.4 mV for the range 0 to 1000 °C, and such larger signal levels are easier to work with. Sensor linearity over a given range may be an additional factor in sensor selection. Specialized cryogenic-temperature sensors such as germanium resistance thermometers are particularly useful when narrow portions of temperature ranges in the low cryogenic region must be measured.

Response time, usually expressed in terms of *time constant*, is another essential criterion for sensor selection. When, for example, the temperature of a liquid in a storage tank is being monitored, the time constant of the temperature sensor is of no great importance. However, when temperature must be measured in a shock tube during an experiment, the time constant becomes the governing criterion for sensor selection. The time constant of a temperature sensing element is proportional to the ratio of its heat capacity to the heat transfer between measured material and element. Relatively short time constants can be obtained using bead thermistors and exposed-junction fine-wire thermocouples, whereas ungrounded, enclosed-junction thermocouple immersion probes, particularly when inserted into a thermowell, will have relatively long time constants.

Time constants are usually stated for a condition where the step change in temperature terminates in a well-controlled, steady-state temperature of a moving liquid, primarily because properly controlled tests for such a condition are convenient. Such statements of time constant are useful for comparing different sensor designs since they can be tested under the same conditions. However, the knowledge of a sensor's time constant, established on such a basis, provides little useful information about temperature measurements obtained from the sensor when it is exposed to rapidly fluctuating temperatures such as would be experienced in turbulent gas flows. *Dynamic temperature measurement* is really a specialized field of study involving considerable expertise and complex calculations. Reasonable approximations of the dynamic behavior of a sensor can often be obtained by tests in which the conditions that will prevail in the sensor's intended use are simulated as closely as possible.

Associated circuits, primarily signal-conditioning circuits, will affect sensor selection, mainly when more than one temperature measurement is handled by a common data system, particularly when the design of the signal-conditioning circuitry was frozen prior to the time the sensor is selected. When reference junctions and thermocouple-signal amplifiers are readily available, a preference for thermoelectric sensors would be quite understandable and insistence on using a resistive sensor may well meet with objections. For installations in which all signal levels are standardized (e.g., 4 to 20 mA, or 0 to 5 V dc), either resistive or thermoelectric sensors can be used since both types can be equipped with the required integrally packaged signal conditioning circuitry (at additional cost). Typical circuits associated with temperature sensors are described in the following section.

4.2.5 Measurement Circuits

Thermocouples require a reference junction in their circuit; this reference junction must assure that both terminals (the terminals for the positive and the negative wire) are at the identical temperature and that this temperature is known; further, for most applications this temperature is chosen as exactly zero degrees Celsius, primarily because thermocouple reference tables (T vs. emf tables) are based on this being the reference-junction temperature. The classic ice-point reference junction (Figure 4-29) is one that is immersed in an *ice bath,* a mixture of ice and water contained in a well-insulated container (e.g., dewar flask). Since the duration of the effectiveness of such ice baths is limited, alternatives to this technique have been developed. One method employs a refrigerator, such as one based on the (thermoelectric) Peltier effect, with good closed-loop control so that an ice/water equilibrium is maintained in the ice bath. Closely controlled ovens have also been used for maintaining a known reference-junction temperature. One reference-junction block may be used for two or more reference junctions. When the reference-junction temperature cannot be maintained at exactly the same value, a temperature sensor can be embedded in the reference-junction block so that the temperature can be monitored and appropriate corrections to the output readings be made.

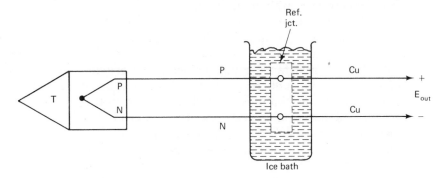

Figure 4-29. Ice-point reference-junction control.

A resistive temperature sensor embedded in, or in very close thermal contact with a reference-junction block is used in one arm of a bridge circuit for *reference-junction compensation.* In such *reference-junction compensators* a specified temperature is simulated rather than maintained by direct means. The compensation circuit (Figure 4-30) is initially adjusted so that the specified reference temperature (e.g., 0 °C) is simulated. When the temperature of the reference junction changes from these initial conditions, usually because of changes in the ambient temperature, the resulting resistance change of the embedded temperature sensor is used to create an error signal which causes a compensating voltage to be inserted in series with the thermocouple circuit. The polarity and magnitude of the compensating voltage is such that the output voltage, E_{out}, equals that voltage that would have been obtained had the ref-

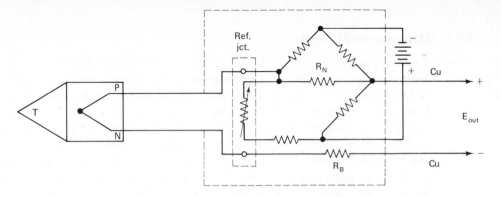

Figure 4-30. Reference-junction compensation.

erence-junction temperature remained at its specified value. In the typical circuit illustrated, resistance R_N is related to the nonlinearity of the temperature sensor and resistance R_B balances its leg of the thermocouple circuit for the equivalent resistance of the compensation network (including the power supply) in the other leg. The power supply can be external, or it can be a small battery (typically a mercury battery) integrally packaged with the compensator ("self-powered" compensator), in which provisions for verifying that the battery voltage is correct are usually included.

Resistive sensors usually require circuitry that converts their resistance changes into voltage changes. This voltage can then be fed to a display device or into a telemetry system or other data system. The sensor can also be connected into a resistance bridge (Wheatstone bridge or more precise versions of it) in which variable resistors in the adjacent bridge arm are adjusted manually until bridge balance is indicated by a null indicator. The resistance settings of the variable resistors are then read. This technique, however, is usually employed only for bench tests and calibrations of such sensors.

The simplest resistance-to-voltage conversion circuit is the *voltage divider* (Figure 4-31a). The fixed resistor, R, is usually chosen larger in value than the base resistance of the temperature sensor. The output voltage, E_{out}, varies as the ratio between the variable (sensor) resistance and the fixed resistance changes. This circuit is often used with thermistors but has also been used with conductive wire- and film-element sensors, with best results obtained when the excitation source is a constant-current supply. Such a supply is also used in the *voltage-drop* circuit (Figure 4-31b) in conjunction with a load (e.g., voltmeter) having a high input impedance; lead-resistance effects on the output voltage are minimized in this circuit, which is often used with germanium resistance thermometers but can be used with any resistive sensor; the current must always be kept within appropriate limits. A simple means of monitoring the current is the insertion of a resistor between one supply terminal and the sensor terminal normally connected to it and then monitoring the voltage drop across this fixed resistor.

The *unbalanced-bridge* circuit shown in Figure 4-31c is typical for circuits used in many telemetry systems. The trimming resistor, R_T, connected in

Thermal Quantities

series with the sensor, R_X, can be adjusted to balance the bridge at a sensor resistance corresponding to the lower end point of the temperature range to be measured. This circuit, as well as the one shown in Figure 4-31d, is typically used with platinum-wire sensors. The output voltage of the bridge, E_{out}, can be calculated for any combination of resistance values and any excitation voltage, E_{exc}, by

$$E_{out} = E_{exc}\left(\frac{R_1}{R_1 + R_X + R_T} - \frac{R_2}{R_2 + R_3}\right)$$

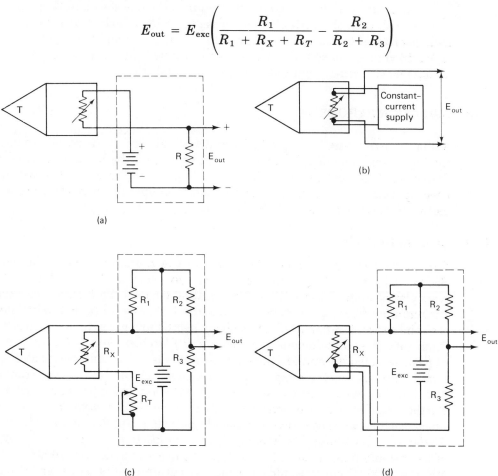

Figure 4-31. Typical resistive-sensor circuits providing a voltage output: (a) voltage divider; (b) voltage drop; (c) basic unbalanced bridge with trimming resistor; (d) unbalanced bridge for three-wire transducer.

Three-wire sensors can be connected into an unbalanced bridge circuit (Figure 4-31d) so that changes in long sensor connecting leads are compensated. All three sensor connecting leads have the same length (and resistance). Two of these leads are connected to the same sensor terminal, but one of them is placed in the excitation branch, the other in the opposite leg of the bridge. The lead from the other sensor terminal is, of course, in the same leg as the sensor.

Hence, lead-resistance changes in the sensor leg of the bridge are compensated by equal changes in the R_3 leg when the resistance R_3 is approximately equal to the resistance of the sensor. More complex bridge circuits have been designed to compensate further for lead-resistance changes, to provide adjustments for zero and slope of the output, to linearize the output when sensor characteristics are nonlinear, and for differential-temperature measurements.

For diode-type sensors a circuit similar to the one shown in Figure 4-31b can be used, with the variable resistor replaced by a diode (GaAs diode). Circuits additional to those shown have been devised to amplify output voltages to specified levels or to convert them into specified current changes (e.g., 4 to 20 mA) when data-system requirements demand this.

4.3   RADIATION PYROMETRY

Radiation pyrometry, as explained and described here, is the remote (noncontacting) measurement of temperatures of objects on the basis of thermal radiation emanating from them. The term "pyrometry" has, in the past, also been applied to thermometry, notably thermocouple thermometry, but such use of the term is considered obsolescent.

4.3.1   Sensing Methods

Pyrometric sensing methods are based on the radiation laws explained in Section 4.1.2.3 (see also Section 5.1.1). The five curves shown in Figure 4-32 were plotted on the basis of Planck's radiation formula. Each curve represents the *radiation intensity,* or *radiant exitance,* per $\Delta\lambda$, as a function of wavelength (i.e., the *spectral radiance*) of a blackbody heated to a given temperature. This family of curves also demonstrates *Wien's displacement law:* since the product of peak wavelength and absolute temperature is a constant, the peak wavelength decreases as the temperature increases; this can be observed from the fact that the peaks of the curve shift toward the left as temperature increases. Further, the curves also demonstrate the *Stefan–Boltzmann law:* the area under each curve (not shown completely on this graph) equals the total radiation emitted from a blackbody, which is proportional to the fourth power of its absolute temperature. Integration of the areas under the 1600 °C curve and the 2000 °C curve would give more accurate results; however, a coarse approximation can be obtained by calculating the ratio of the fourth power of the two temperatures (27×10^{12} and 12.25×10^{12}, ratio = 2.2) and noting the radiation intensity at the peak of the two curves (111 and 51, respectively, ratio = 2.18).

The pyrometric sensing principles are also illustrated in Figure 4-32. The output of a *wide-band* ("total radiation") *pyrometer* is proportional to most of (only theoretically "all" of) the energy under a curve. The output of a *narrow-band pyrometer* ("brightness pyrometer," "monochromatic radiation pyrometer") is proportional to the energy at a specific wavelength (in practice: in a very narrow band of wavelengths); the dashed line marked "$W_{0.8}$ "indicates the radiation intensity, for each of three temperatures, that would be observed at 0.8 μm. The output of a *ratio pyrometer* ("two-color pyrometer," "color-ratio pyrometer") is proportional to the ratio of two energies emitted at two different wavelengths; in the example illustrated, energy x would be observed at 2.5 μm and energy y would be observed at 2.2. μm; the pyrometer output would be indicative of the ratio x/y.

It can also be noted that the dashed "$W_{0.8}$" line intersects only the three

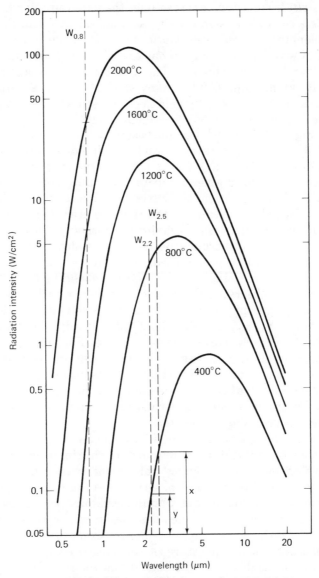

Figure 4-32. Radiation intensity as function of wavelength for different source temperatures (assuming that $\varepsilon = 1.0$).

upper curves. Because of the effect of Wien's displacement law in shifting the peaks of lower temperatures toward longer wavelengths, different wavelengths are used in narrow-band and ratio pyrometers for different temperature ranges.

The curves in Figure 4-32 are based on the *emissivity* of the source being 1.0 (i.e., that of an ideal blackbody). The emissivities of real materials, however, are generally significantly less than unity; additionally, for a given material and surface finish they vary with temperature and with wavelength. *Total emissivity* is emissivity expressed for the total radiation (at "all" wavelengths); *spectral emissivity* is emissivity at a stated wavelength (or as a function of wavelength); and *monochromatic emissivity* is the emissivity in a very narrow band of wavelengths. Carbon has one of the highest emissivities, around 0.81 (total) and 0.85 (at 0.65 μm). The total emissivities of metals are much lower: 0.08 for aluminum, 0.09 for many steels, 0.25 for cast iron, and only 0.02 for gold; the latter shows why gold is often used when a good thermal reflector is needed: its reflectivity is $1.0 - 0.02 = 0.98$.

Figure 4-33, which was purposely plotted somewhat differently than Figure 4-32 (using linear rather than logarithmic coordinates to obtain a different form of graphic display), shows how a curve of spectral radiance as function of wavelength, for a given temperature, changes for different emissivities. To simplify the illustration, the curves assume that the emissivity is not wavelength-dependent. It can be seen that the area under each of the curves gets significantly reduced with decreasing emissivity. Further, the ascending slope of each curve is different (the descending slopes are also different but the difference is not as pronounced.) The curves illustrate an advantage of the ratio pyrometer. Using the same two wavelengths as in Figure 4-32 (2.2. and 2.5 μm) and observing the energies at both wavelengths, x and y, it can be seen (with appropriate scaling) that the ratio $x_{1.0}/y_{1.0}$ is the same as the ratios $x_{0.7}/y_{0.7}$ and $x_{0.4}/y_{0.4}$, namely about 1.33. Ideally, then, a ratio pyrometer can be used to obtain accurate temperature readings regardless of emissivity (i.e., they can be used with varying or unknown emissivities). In practice, some errors could still be introduced by not accounting for differences in monochromatic emissivity at the two wavelengths; they can also be introduced by such other factors as unequal absorbtivity of smoke or fumes in the optical path between source and radiometer.

The "disappearing filament" pyrometer is one of the earliest versions of a narrow-band (brightness) pyrometer. This instrument cannot be considered as an electronic sensing device, at least not in its original form, since it requires the eye of an observer. The observer sees the measured object as well as the tungsten ribbon filament of a "standard lamp." He varies the current through the filament until it matches the measured object in brightness. When the filament "disappears" (i.e., provides an exact brightness match), the current is read and the temperature of the measured object is determined from a calibration chart. It should be noted that the IPTS68, above the freezing point of gold (1064.43 °C, 1337.58 K), is defined on the basis of thermal radiation and instruments based on the "disappearing filament" principle are used as calibration devices. Automatic versions of this type of pyrometer alternately

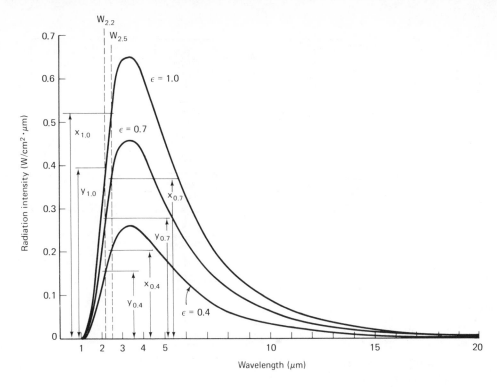

Figure 4-33. Radiation intensity of a 600 °C source as function of wavelength for different values of source emissivity (assuming that ε is not wavelength-dependent).

image the measured surface and standard-lamp filament on a photoelectric sensor (e.g., by use of a rotating sector disk or by an oscillating mirror). The output due to unequal brightness is used as error signal in the filament control loop. The current through the filament is thus varied automatically until a null condition is reached with a brightness match. The temperature of the measured object (which may be a "standard blackbody") is then determined from the filament-current reading, using a calibration chart.

The detectors in pyrometers (i.e., the devices that convert the radiation incident on them into an electrical signal) are of the types described in Section 5.2. Wide-band pyrometers typically use bolometric or thermopile detectors, whereas narrow-band and ratio pyrometers usually employ photovoltaic or photoconductive detectors, especially those having sharply peaking spectral response, in conjunction with spectrum-limiting windows and filters. The former are classified as *thermal detectors* (or energy detectors), whereas the latter are classified as *quantum detectors* (or photon detectors).

4.3.2 Design and Operation

Radiation pyrometers are remote-temperature-sensing systems consisting of three subsystems: the optical subsystem, the detector subsystem, and the electronics subsystem. These subsystems as well as typical pyrometer configurations are described below. It should be noted that additional information about

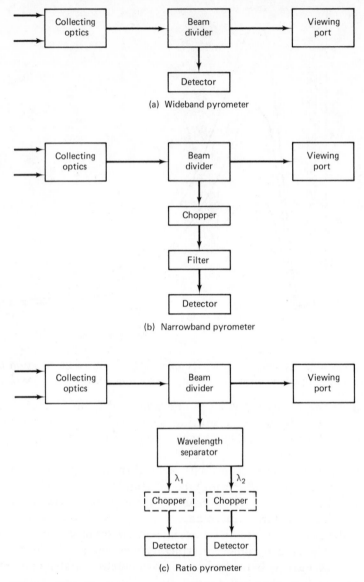

Figure 4-34. Typical pyrometer optical path block diagrams: (a) wide-band pyrometer; (b) narrow-band pyrometer; (c) ratio pyrometer.

detector characteristics and requirements, window characteristics, monochromators, and choppers is included in Chapter 5.

4.3.2.1 Optics. The primary function of pyrometer optics is to focus the incoming radiation onto the detector in the form required for proper operation of the pyrometer system. A secondary function of the optics is to make the target (portion of measured surface to be viewed by the pyrometer) visible to a human operator, so that the pyrometer can be pointed appropriately. This secondary function is sometimes performed by a separate sighting tube attached to the pyrometer housing; it is more frequently performed by a beam divider in the optics, which focuses a portion of the incoming energy onto a viewing port or eyepiece. The optics subsystem is the primary determinant of whether a pyrometer is of the wide-band, narrow-band, or ratio type.

Wide-band pyrometer optics are the simplest since such devices as filters are generally excluded in order to sense as wide a band of wavelengths as possible (Figure 4-34a). Also, the detectors tend to be of the more slowly responding thermistor bolometer or thermopile types and choppers are usually omitted. The wide-band requirements apply to any window in front of the entrance aperture as well as the surface of the beam divider that focuses the energy onto the detector.

Narrow-band pyrometer optics are designed to focus only energy in the required narrow band of wavelengths on the detector. The detector itself is also chosen to respond best in that wavelength region. Any window used reflects this requirement. At least one narrow-band filter is placed into the optical path between beam divider and detector. The IR photon detectors used in such pyrometers are characterized by short time constants; hence, a chopper can be used to modulate the energy beam so that the detector output is quasi-ac, which is easier to amplify stably than is dc. A block diagram for this optical path is shown in Figure 4-34b.

Ratio pyrometer optics are not only designed to pass a relatively narrow band of wavelengths; they must additionally separate energy in two extremely

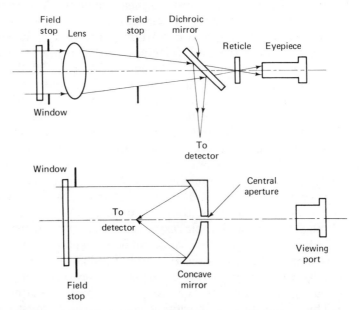

Figure 4-35. Examples of collecting optics and beam divider configurations.

narrow wavelength bands, which are very close to each other. The energy in each of these quasi-monochromatic bands is then focused onto a separate detector (Figure 4-34c). Choppers are often used in conjunction with the fast-response IR detectors.

Examples of the constituent elements of pyrometer optics are shown in Figure 4-35. The beam divider can be a *concave mirror* with a central aperture (sighting hole); in this case the detector is located between the mirror and the entrance aperture. More frequently the beam-dividing function is performed by a *beamsplitter,* typically by a *dichroic mirror,* which reflects energy primarily in the IR region toward the detector but transmits energy primarily in the visible region toward an eyepiece. Most of the focusing functions are then performed by a *lens. Field stops* are used to delineate the beam and prevent any unwanted energy (e.g., scattering products) from being included in the beam. A window is usually placed in front of the collecting lens. Its material must be able to withstand ambient temperatures, which can be fairly high; it must especially be selected for spectral response characteristics (see Figure 5-26). Most pyrometer optics are fixed in configuration, hence their focus is fixed. Some designs, however, provide for adjustable focusing.

4.3.2.2 Detectors. The wavelengths sensed by radiation pyrometers are generally in the infrared *(IR)* region of the electromagnetic spectrum. This region includes *near IR* (0.7 to 2 µm) and *far IR* (2 to 1000 µm). This breakdown is sometimes shown as near IR (0.7 to 1.2 µm), *middle IR* (1.2 to 7 µm), and far IR (7 to 1000 µm). However, even wide-band pyrometers usually do not respond to wavelengths significantly in excess of 20 µm, and this limit is adequate for essentially all remote temperature measurements. The choice of detector is governed primarily by spectral response requirements, secondarily by time constant (response time) and detectivity (sensitivity). Wideband response is obtained from such thermal detectors as thermopiles (Sections 4.2.1.1 and 5.2.2.6), thermistor bolometers (Sections 4.2.1.3 and 5.2.2.7), and pyroelectric sensors (Section 5.2.2.8). When narrow-band response is required (including for ratio pyrometers), photovoltaic (Section 5.2.2.1) or, more commonly, photoconductive (Section 5.2.2.2) sensors are used. Among these, silicon, germanium, lead sulfide (PbS), and indium antimonide (InSb) detectors are probably most common in pyrometers. The response of silicon detectors extends only to about 1.1 µm; hence such detectors are used mainly in narrow-band pyrometers when high temperatures must be sensed. The spectral response of germanium detectors extends to about 1.9 µm. PbS detectors are very often used in narrow-band and ratio pyrometers; they are usable at wavelengths up to about 2.8 µm. InSb detectors, with their response extending up to about 6.5 µm, are very useful when the temperature range to be measured is medium or low.

Semiconductor IR detectors, notably InSb, improve significantly in their sensitivity when they operate at lower temperatures. Such operation can be attained by use of a cooler; thermoelectric coolers are often used for this purpose. The mounting of a detector is very critical. It must not only be dimensionally stable over a range of temperatures but must also provide good thermal isolation for the detector so that a minimum of the incident heat energy is lost by conduction to adjacent parts. A detector subsystem, then, includes the detector, its mounting, and any cooler that may be used.

4.3.2.3 Electronics. Pyrometer electronics can range from very simple to quite complex, depending on type of detector used and functions required. Very simple circuitry, consisting essentially of a reference-junction compensator (see Section 4.2.3.3), has been used in conjunction with thermopile detectors. The pyrometer output is then in millivolts; it can be displayed directly on the type of millivoltmeter typically used for thermocouples; it can also be amplified for other display or data system uses. Thermistor bolometers require the signal-conditioning circuitry needed to convert the resistance change of the thermistor into a voltage change. The output from this circuitry is usually low enough to require amplification.

Electronics associated with IR detectors (radiation pyrometers using such detectors are often called "IR radiation pyrometers" or "noncontact IR thermometers") are somewhat more complex (see Figure 4-36). A *preamplifier* is

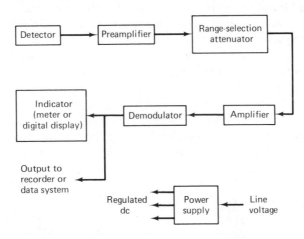

Figure 4-36. Typical pyrometer electronics block diagram (simplified).

usually located physically very close to the detector, which is characterized by a relatively high output impedance. When a chopper is used it can also provide a synchronization *(sync)* signal, for example, by having the same slotted disk also interrupt a beam between a lamp and a light sensor whose output is then the sync signal. The chopper produces an ac (or pulsed dc) signal from the detector. After preamplification the signal is fed to an *amplifier*. Besides further amplifying the signal, this unit can also perform linearization and it provides for such adjustments as *emissivity control* (gain adjustment to allow for known values of the target's emissivity) and *calibration setting* (adjustment of the output indication to a value obtained in a calibration mode). Many pyrometers include a *calibration source* in their optics, a lamp or heated blackbody that emits a known amount of heat energy toward the detector, which is blocked from seeing the target's radiation at that time.

The output of the amplifier is fed to a *demodulator,* which converts the ac or pulsed signal into dc suitable for display or as an input to a strip-chart recorder or a multifunction data system. Synchronous demodulation is desirable and such demodulation can be obtained by using the sync signal derived from the chopper. A power supply converts the ac line voltage into one or more regulated dc voltages required by the electronics. Some pyrometers are battery-operated rather than line-voltage-supplied. Special functions such as "peak hold" are usually optional.

4.3.2.4 Pyrometer configurations The most frequently encountered configuration of a radiation pyrometer consists of a sensing head and an electronics unit connected to the sensing head by a cable. The electronics unit provides a meter for temperature display and all adjustments (calibrate, emissivity control, etc.). Additional outputs are usually available at the rear panel. Some designs have integrally packaged electronics. A meter may also be provided at the rear of the pyrometer housing, or a connector is provided to furnish one or more outputs (one output is usually intended for a meter designed to match the characteristics of the pyrometer).

A pyrometer with integral electronics is illustrated in Figure 4-37. This unit is basically a wideband pyrometer (1 to 20 μm); however, among many optional accessories are narrow-band optical filters. The unit is shown on its adjustable mount. Among mounting options (and these are typical for many pyrometers) are a tripod, a wall bracket with swivel mount, and a flange mount. The unit can be provided sealed and with air-purge provisions for use in a hazardous environment. It can also be furnished with a water-cooled jacket

Figure 4-37. Radiation pyrometer with integral electronics. (Courtesy of Mikron Instrument Co., Inc.)

for operation in high ambient temperatures. Sighting provisions (using a 45° mirror as beam divider and a second 45° mirror to reflect the image backward to a sighting aperture) are also optional for this instrument, although such provisions are often included as "standard" in other designs. Sighting is not critical when target areas are large. The plastic (polyethylene) window (wideband, long wavelengths) can be replaced by a quartz window for operation at high ambient temperatures and when the measured temperatures are high (short wavelengths). All adjustments (emissivity control, zero, span, and optional "peak picker" or "valley picker" rate) are located at the rear of the unit, as is the electrical (12-pin) connector. This design uses a concave mirror to focus the radiant energy onto the detector, which is located between this mirror and the window.

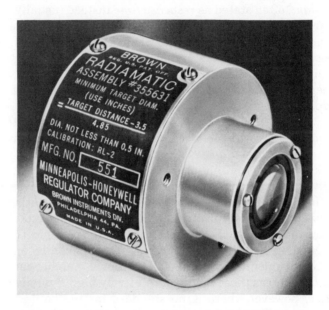

Figure 4-38. Miniature radiation pyrometer with thermopile sensor (6 cm in diameter × 7 cm long). (Courtesy of Honeywell Process Control Div.)

Another design is shown in Figure 4-38. This unit is basically a wideband radiation pyrometer which employs a thermopile detector and provides a thermocouple-type output in millivolts to a meter or strip-chart recorder. The wavelengths band and, hence, the usable temperature range (0.3 to 10 μm, approximately 250 to 1750 °C) are established primarily by the calcium fluoride window. Related designs use fused silica and optical crown glass windows for lower wavelengths and high temperature ranges. This design has a 98% response time of 2 s. Related designs can be equipped with many of the optional provisions described above (e.g., water cooling, various mounts). The design illustrated is intended for applications where installation space is limited. Besides the fixed-mounted configurations, including a (movable) tripod mount, pyrometer configurations include a hand-held type, typically with pistol grip.

4.3.3 Performance Characteristics

A relatively small number of essential characteristics establish the primary criteria for selection and use of a radiation pyrometer. The *temperature (measuring) range* usually shows the upper and lower limits of temperature that will be sensed and displayed by a pyrometer. Ranges extend up to about 4000 °C (in a few instances even higher) but, for most available designs, tend to be under 2800 °C. The lower temperature limit is never zero; it is typically between 5 and 20% of the upper limit. Many units have range selector switches and can provide full-scale displays of portions of the full range. The *time constant,* often stated as *response time* instead (usually meaning 98% response time), is dependent primarily on the type of detector used; typical values range from a fraction of a second to about 2 s. The type of detector used and the spectral response of the pyrometer (including optics) are very often stated in manufacturers' literature. Unless "wide-band" or "narrow-band" is stated elsewhere, this categorization can be obtained by looking at the callout for spectral response.

Since the proper operation of radiation pyrometers, particularly wide-band and narrow-band types, requires that the target fill the field of view, the *minimum target diameter* (minimum diameter of the measured object) must be known. This minimum diameter is, of course, a function of the distance between the pyrometer lens and the object and is given by the characteristics of the optics used in the pyrometer. This characteristic is stated in various ways. In many specifications it is shown as the *resolution factor, F,* which is equal to the ratio of the separation distance, D, to the minimum acceptable target diameter, d, or $F = D/d$. F numbers can be anywhere between 3 and 500. Instruments having a relatively low F number can be referred to as *wide-angle,* whereas those having a relatively high F number can be called *narrow-angle;* however, there is no standard for the borderline between those two categories. The resolution factor can also be shown as *distance-to-size ratio* and is then expressed as, for example, "60:1" instead of the (equivalent) "$F = 60$." This ratio can also be expressed as an angle. If so, the corresponding resolution factor is equal to 60 divided by the angle (in degrees); for example, an angle of 4° corresponds to a resolution factor of 15. Some specifications simply show a table of separation distance (distance between lens and target) vs. minimum target diameter for a given pyrometer design. A statement of (minimum) *operating distance* is sometimes added.

Accuracy is shown in percent of full-scale output (usually meaning full-scale indication on an associated meter), or in percent of reading, or in units of (indicated) temperature; such tolerances are applicable when the instrument has been properly calibrated. Additionally, *repeatability* is often specified. When one or more outputs are provided (besides the usually provided meter) the characteristics and ranges of these outputs are stated. When special output holding features are included or optionally available, they are described. They may include "peak hold" (the peak reading over the period a button is depressed will be displayed), "valley hold" (same mechanization but for the lowest reading), and "meter hold" or "reading hold" (any reading is held while a button is depressed). Other important characteristics include the *ambient temperature range* (sometimes accompanied by statements of window material used); the range of available *emissivity compensation* ("emissivity control range"); mass, size, and power consumption (sometimes type of power source); available options as described in Section 4.3.2.4; and all "standard" as well as "optional" provisions for control functions.

4.4   HEAT FLUX

Heat flux is measured as heat flow to a surface. For the purpose of the measurement, the surface is the active surface (or one of two surfaces) of the sensor. Basic concepts and units of measurement are described in Section 4.1.3, but they are expanded here so that a better understanding of this group of sensors can be obtained.

Heat flux is the time rate of transfer of heat energy. Energy is expressed in joules *(J)* and time in seconds *(s);* hence, heat flux is expressed in *J/s* or watts *(W),* since the watt, the unit of power, is equal to J/s. Other units (non-SI units) have been used to express heat power, and their conversion factors are: $1\ W = 1\ J/s = 9.498 \times 10^{-4}\ Btu/s = 10^7\ ergs/s = 0.2389\ g\cdot cal/s$. Conversion factors for the *Btu (British thermal unit)* are: $1\ Btu = 8.139 \times 10^{-5}\ W\cdot s = 1055\ J = 252\ g\cdot cal = 1.055 \times 10^{10}\ ergs$.

Because heat flux is measured as heat flow to a surface it is also expressed in units of (radiant, conductive, or convective) *heat flux per unit area,* that is, in W/m^2. Other (non-SI) units are still in popular use in the United States, and the most commonly used unit has been the $Btu/ft^2\cdot s$ (Btu per square foot per second). Conversion factors for this unit are: $1\ Btu/ft^2\cdot s = 3600\ Btu/ft^2\cdot h = 0.00695\ Btu/in^2\cdot s = 0.271\ cal/cm^2\cdot s = 975\ cal/cm^2\cdot h = 1050\ W/ft^2 = 7.3\ W/in^2 = 1.136\ W/cm^2 = 1.136 \times 10^4\ W/m^2$.

Since radiant heat flux measurements include measurements of the heat energy received from the sun (and such measurements have emerged from the theoretical to the practical in the many new solar energy applications) another unit needs to be introduced: the *solar constant,* defined as the energy per unit time (power) received from the sun per unit area, at the average sun–earth distance, and in the absence of the earth's atmosphere. The solar constant had been given the value of 1398 W/m^2 (frequently rounded off to 1400); however, more precise measurements were able to be made during the past decade and the currently accepted value (as formally reported by M. P. Thekaekara, NASA/ Goddard Space Flight Center, United States) is *1353 W/m^2.* Hence, *1 solar constant = 1353 W/m^2 = 0.1353 W/cm^2 = 0.119 Btu/ft^2·s = 428.5 Btu/ft^2·h = 1.945 cal/cm^2·min = 125.66 W/ft^2.*

It should be noted that this value is based on energy distribution with wavelengths ranging from 0.115 to 1000 μm, and the value for the average sun–earth distance (1353 W/m²) is based on the values obtained at the earth's perihelion (closest distance to the sun), 1399 W/m², and at aphelion (farthest distance from the sun), 1309 W/m². When measured on the earth's surface, this value is modified by the effects of the earth's atmosphere.

Heat flux sensors can be grouped into three categories: *radiometers* sense radiant heat flux (and related instruments such as the *pyrheliometer* sense specific types of radiant heat flux, as explained in Section 4.4.2), *calorimeters* sense the combined radiant and convective heat flux, and *surface heat-flow sensors* sense conducted, convected, or radiated heat flux, or a combination of these, to or from a specific surface.

4.4.1   Calorimeters

A calorimeter measures the heat flow into a system from the surroundings. (*Note:* This definition applies specifically to the sensing devices described here.) Design variations of three basic types of calorimeter are available: the foil calorimeter, the slug calorimeter, and the thermopile calorimeter.

A *foil calorimeter* ("membrane calorimeter," "Gardon gauge") consists of a thin disk of one type of metal, bonded around its rim to a heat sink of a different type of metal. The two metals are so chosen that their junction, around the rim of the foil disk, forms a thermocouple junction. Since copper makes a good heat sink, and since Constantan with copper forms a Type T thermocouple, Constantan is commonly used for the foil disk and copper is used for the heat sink, which forms the body of the sensor. A thin copper wire is then welded to the exact center of the Constantan foil, forming a second thermocouple junction (Figure 4-39). The two junctions act as differential thermocouples

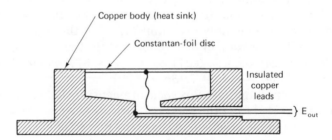

Figure 4-39. Foil calorimeter.

since the foil disk, when exposed to heat flux, is always hotter at the center than at the rim, where it is joined to the heat sink. The exterior surface of the foil disk is blackened, using a high-absorptivity coating, so that the calorimeter responds well to radiant heat flux as well as to convective heat flux. Heat absorbed by the foil disk is transferred radially to the heat sink. The millivolt output of the sensor is proportional to incident heat flux. At constant heating rates the output provides a steady-state indication of the heat flux.

The *slug calorimeter* ("slope calorimeter") employs a circular metallic body ("slug") as thermal mass whose exterior surface is covered with a high-absorptivity (high-emissivity) coating (black). The mass is thermally insulated from its support in the housing of the sensor (Figure 4-40). A thin-wire thermocouple (or other very small temperature sensor) is attached to the center of the interior surface of the mass. Most of the incident heat flux will be retained as heat in the thermal mass, causing the temperature of the mass to

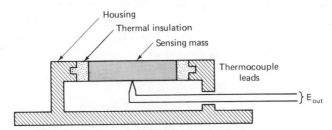

Figure 4-40. Slug calorimeter.

rise. At a constant heating rate the slope of output voltage vs. time is indicative of heat flux; that is, the heat flux can be determined from the temperature history of the "slug." A second sensing junction can be placed at the inside of the housing, near the thermal barrier that insulates the thermal mass. The two junctions can then be connected as differential thermocouple so that the output is independent of the heat rise in the housing.

A disadvantage of the slug calorimeter is that it cannot be used for continuous measurements and that it tends to lose accuracy, during a measurement, due to heat losses as the temperature rises.

The *thermopile calorimeter* consists basically of an insulating wafer around which are wound a series of thermocouples in such a manner that consecutive thermoelectric junctions fall on opposite sides of the wafer. Hence, the junctions on the upper surface of the wafer can all be considered "sensing junctions," whereas the junctions on the bottom side of the wafer can all be considered "reference junctions." This assembly is bonded to a heat sink to assure heat flow through the wafer/thermopile assembly. Heat is received on the exposed (upper) surface of the wafer and conducted through it to the heat sink. A temperature drop across the wafer is thus developed and is sensed by each of the junctions of the differential thermopile. As is typical for such thermopiles, the voltages produced by each of the junctions are additive, thereby amplifying the signal from one junction proportionally to the total number of junctions. The temperature drop across the wafer, and thus the output signal of the differential thermopile, is directly proportional to the heating rate. The appearance of the wafer with its thermopiles is somewhat similar to the thermopile shown in Figure 4-42 except that only one set of junctions would be visible; the other set of junctions would be on the underside of the element; additionally, the junctions would be no bigger in size than the leads, since wire, rather than deposited metal, is used in the thermopile calorimeter.

Foil and thermopile calorimeters are used primarily for the measurement of transient heating rates or of sustained heating rates. Slug calorimeters are used mainly for the measurement of total heat quantity over a short period of time. A variety of calorimeter designs have been developed for different applications and different mounting methods; some of these are illustrated in Figure 4-41. Foil and thermopile calorimeters are often provided with means for water cooling (e.g., the sensor at the left of Figure 4-41a). In some applications it is necessary to obtain a measure of the pure radiant constituent of heat flux; two calorimeters can then be used, one with the usual black high-absorptivity surface, the second with a polished gold (low-absorptivity) surface.

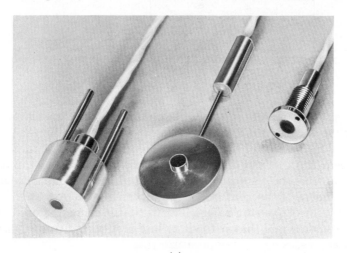

(a)

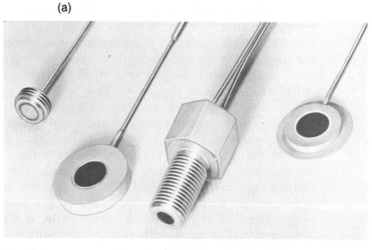

(b)

Figure 4-41. Typical calorimeter designs: (a) foil calorimeters; (b) slug calorimeters. (Courtesy of Hy-Cal Engineering, a Subsidiary of Leeds & Northrup.)

Thermal Quantities

Two sensors are used simultaneously and are placed close together. The "gold" calorimeter will then provide an output of just the convective (and conductive, if any) heat flux, and the output of the "black" calorimeter can be corrected by subtracting this amount from its output. A number of different calorimeter designs have also been developed for special applications, and some designs have been tailored to utilize the advantages offered by miniature thermopiles in providing a higher output for lower values of heat flux.

4.4.2 Radiometers

Radiometers are related to radiation pyrometers in that they respond to incident radiant heat flux; they differ from radiation pyrometers not only by being calibrated in terms of heat flux (in W/cm² or equivalent units) but mainly by having a generally much wider viewing angle, typically 45 to 90° (although designs with other viewing angles exist) as compared to the angles ranging between a fraction of one degree to a few degrees typical for radiation pyrometers. This wider angle simplifies their design since collimating optics are not needed and viewing ports (requiring a beamsplitter) are rarely used.

The simplest form of radiometer is a calorimeter with a window sealed over the sensing surface so as to isolate it from convective heat flux. Only when used in a vacuum (where there is no heat convection) can a windowless radiometer be used. The window tends to limit the spectral response; the thermal sensors used in radiometers, typically thermopiles, sometimes resistive sensors, have an inherently wide-band spectral response. Differential thermopiles, with their sensing junctions exposed to the incident heat radiation and the reference junctions shielded from it, have been used in radiometers. The example shown in Figure 4-42 provides a sensing area, along the center of its mount, which is 1.5 mm wide and 15 mm high for the 12-junction thermopile illustrated. Circular differential thermopiles are used similarly, when the (small) aperture is circular. The radiation–sensitive area is blackened with

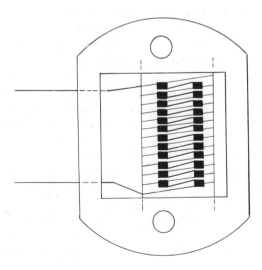

Figure 4-42. Thermopile sensing element for radiometer use. (Courtesy of The Eppley Laboratory, Inc.)

a high-absorptivity (low-reflectance) coating. Other thermal detectors include wirewound thermopiles, pyroelectric detectors, and bolometers. Wide-band window materials used for radiometers include (with usable upper limit of transmittance shown in parentheses) quartz (4.5 μm), synthetic sapphire (6.5 μm), calcium fluoride (10 μm), silicon (about 200 μm but nonuniform above 10 μm), and cesium iodide (over 50 μm); the latter is quite hygroscopic and should not be exposed to humidity above 45% RH.

Radiometers are often equipped with gas purge provisions, used to prevent window contamination, and water-cooling provisions for use in high-temperature environments. The unit shown in Figure 4-43 has such provisions; its recessed aperture has antireflection serrations; the diameter of the housing is 3.8 cm; it uses a synthetic sapphire window and a thermoelectric detector.

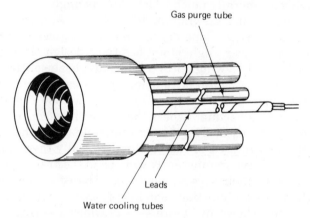

Figure 4-43. Compact radiometer with air-purge and watercooling provisions. (Courtesy of Hy-Cal Engineering, a Subsidiary of Leeds & Northrup.)

Radiometers are used wherever radiant or radiated energy is to be measured as such, and read out in terms of energy received, or received per unit time. Applications range from measuring the radiant energy from heating lamps, engine performance analyses, and rocket exhaust plume studies to high-temperature research and airborne radiometric measurements. An important application of radiometers has evolved with the increasing use of lasers. Laser radiometers are used to measure laser power and provide a direct readout in terms of energy, in joules. A wavelength band of about 0.3 to 1.1 μm handles most types of lasers and allows the use of fused-quartz windows in such radiometers (see laser wavelengths, Table 5-1); other windows can often be supplied when far-IR laser power (e.g., Co_2, 10 μm) needs to be measured.

Specialized types of radiometers are used to measure the energy due to, or related to, solar thermal radiation received on earth. A *pyrheliometer* measures direct solar radiation intensity at the surface of the earth and typically provides an output in solar constants. Pyrheliometers can be mounted on a servo-controlled solar tracker to measure radiation at normal incidence continuously. The *Angstrom pyrheliometer* has a detector composed of two blackened magnesium strips, one of which is shaded from the sun and heated by an electrical current while the other is exposed to the direct solar beam. The current through the heater is adjusted until the temperatures of the two strips are balanced. The solar intensity can then be determined at the null condition, using the instrument constant. This type of instrument is usable in good weather with steady sky conditions. The *absolute cavity pyrheliometer* absorbs radiation on a high-absorptance (0.997 or greater) conical receiver, uses a wirewound toroidal thermopile detector, and determines heat flux by electrical substitution; this type of instrument can be self-calibrating.

A *pyranometer* measures the "global radiation," the combination of direct solar radiation and diffuse sky radiation incident on a horizontal surface. An important application of the pyranometer is in the evaluation of solar panels. Two designs of a pyranometer have been developed, the blackened-surface and the black-and-white receiver. The blackened-surface type has two domes (hemispheres); the inner one blocks the infrared radiation from the outer one. The hemispheres can be of clear optical glass or fused quartz, depending on spectral response requirements. A thermopile detector is used, with the hot junctions under the black receiver responding to the incident radiation and the cold junctions facing downward toward the interior of the instrument. In the black-and-white type (see Figure 4-44) the output signal is produced by a differential thermopile with the hot-junction receivers blackened and the cold-junction receivers whitened. A single optical-glass hemisphere is used; it provides uniform transmittance from 0.285 to 2.80 μm and protects the instrument from the weather. The instrument base is provided with a circular spirit level and adjustable leveling screws.

Figure 4-44. Pyranometer (black-and-white type). (Courtesy of The Eppley Laboratory, Inc.)

A *pyrgeometer* is a wide-band, far-IR radiometer used to measure (separately) incoming or outgoing unidirectional terrestrial radiation (measurements needed, e.g., for thermal balance studies). A typical design uses a silicon window with an interference filter vacuum-deposited on its inside surface to make the instrument solar blind and provide a spectral response from about 4 to 50 μm in daylight as well as darkness. Radiation emitted by the thermopile detector is automatically compensated.

4.4.3 Surface Heat-Flow Sensors

This category comprises thin surface-mounted sensors, typically employing a differential thermocouple or thermopile to sense the difference in temperature between their two surfaces due to heat conduction through the sensor. The heat flow measured by such sensors can be the flow through a wall across which a temperature gradient exists, or it can be the heat flow to or from any type of surface (e.g., walls, pipes, tanks). The heat flow sensed can be due to conduction, radiation, or convection or combinations of these. The outside (when mounted) surface is blackened to provide good emittance when heat flow from a surface is measured, and to provide good absorptance when heat flow into a surface is measured (see Figure 4-45). The units can be mounted with adhesive or pressure-sensitive tape; some models are provided with mounting holes. Thickness of the sensors ranges between 0.7 and 1.5 mm, and up to 3 mm for some designs. Most units are thin enough to be able to be attached to a curved surface; precurved designs are also available.

Figure 4-45. Surface heat-flow sensors. (Courtesy of Hy-Cal Engineering, a Subsidiary of Leeds & Northrup.)

Bibliography

1. *Temperature—Its Measurement and Control in Science and Industry,* Vol. 3, Pts. 1, 2, and 3. New York: Reinhold Publishing Corp., 1962.

2. **Hsu, S. T.,** *Engineering Heat Transfer.* Princeton, NJ: D. Van Nostrand, Inc., 1963.

3. "Thermistor Definitions and Test Methods," *EIA Standard RC8* (2nd ed.). Washington, DC: Electronic Industries Association, 1963.

4. "Industrial Platinum Resistance Thermometer Elements," *British Standard BS 1904:1964*. London: British Standards Institute, 1964.

5. **Svet, D. Y.,** *Thermal Radiation*. New York: Consultants Bureau, 1965.

6. **Moeller, C. E.,** et al., "NASA Contributions to Development of Special Purpose Thermocouples," *NASA SP-5050*. Washington, DC: U.S. Government Printing Office, 1968.

7. **Roots, W. K.,** *Fundamentals of Temperature Control*. New York: Academic Press, 1969.

8. Comité International des Poids et Mesures, "The International Practical Temperature Scale of 1968," *Metrologia,* Vol. 5, No. 2, Apr. 1969.

9. **Sinclair, D. H., Terbeck, H. G., and Malone, J. H.,** "Cryogenic Temperature Measurement," *NASA TM X-52825*. Washington, DC: U.S. Government Printing Office, 1970.

10. **Pollock, D. D.,** *The Theory and Properties of Thermocouple Elements*. Stamford, CT: Omega Press, 1971.

11. **Plumb, H. H.** (Ed.), *Temperature, Its Measurement and Control in Science and Industry,* Vol. IV, Pts. 1, 2, and 3. Research Triangle Park, NC: Instrument Society of America, 1972.

12. **Schooley, J. F., Soulen, R. J., Jr., and Evans, G. A., Jr.,** "Preparation and Use of Superconductive Fixed Point Devices, SRM 767," *NBS Special Publication 260-44*. Washington, DC: National Bureau of Standards, Dec. 1972.

13. **Swartz, J. M., and Swartz, D. L.,** "Cryogenic Temperature Measuring Devices and Their Applications," *Paper No. 73–550*. Research Triangle Park, NC: Instrument Society of America, 1973.

14. "Platinum Resistance Thermometry," *NBS Monograph 126*. Washington DC: U.S. Government Printing Office, April 1973.

15. **Cataland, G.,** et al., "NBS Cryogenic Thermometry and the Proposed Cryogenic Extension of the IPTS," *NBS Technical Note 830*. Washington, DC: National Bureau of Standards, May 1974.

16. *Manual on the Use of Thermocouples in Temperature Measurement* (orig. publ. as ASTM Special Technical Publication 470). Stamford, CT: Omega Press, 1974.

17. "Thermocouple Reference Tables Based on the IPTS-68," *NBS Monograph 125*. Washington, DC: U.S. Government Printing Office, 1974. (*Note:* also available from Omega Press, Stamford, CT, published 1975, and incorporated in *Standard E 230-72* by American Society for Testing and Materials, Philadelphia, PA).

18. **Baker, H. D., Ryder, E. A. and Baker, N. H.,** *Temperature Measurement in Engineering,* Vol 1 (1953) and Vol 2 (1961). Stamford, CT: Omega Press, reprinted 1975.

19. **Hofmann, D.,** *Dynamische Temperaturmessung* (Dynamic Temperature Measurement). Berlin, GDR: VEB Verlag Technik, 1976.

20. "Instrumentation in the Cryogenic Industry," *Proceedings of the First Biennial Symposium on Cryogenic Instrumentation*. Research Triangle Park, NC: Instrument Society of America, 1976.

21. "Temperature Measurement Thermocouples," *ANSI Standard MC96.1-1975*. Research Triangle Park, NC: Instrument Society of America, 1976.

22. **Benedict, R. P.,** *Fundamentals of Temperature, Pressure and Flow Measurement.* New York: John Wiley & Sons, Inc., 1977.

23. **Kevern, J. C., Waghorne, R. M., Hatt, B. A., and Page, J. K. R.,** "Thermo-couples and Thermocouple Attachment Methods," *Report No. ESA-CR P-1130.* Stokes Poges, England: Fulmer Research Institute, 1978.

24. "The Nicrosil-vs-Nisil Thermocouple," *NBS Monograph 161.* Washington, DC: U.S. Government Printing Office, April 1978.

chapter five

Optical Quantities

5.1 BASIC CONCEPTS

5.1.1 Light Intensity

Light is a form of radiant energy, an electromagnetic radiation propagated in wave form. It is usually defined as that portion of the electromagnetic spectrum between 10 and 1×10^6 nanometers (nm) in wavelength (the long-wavelength limit has been placed between 100 and 1000 μm and has never been defined authoritatively). By strict definition, however, only *visible radiation* (380 to 780 nm) can be considered as "light." The band of wavelengths between 10 and 380 nm is better termed *ultraviolet (UV) radiation* and the band between 780 and 10^6 nm *infrared (IR) radiation*. Within the IR band, the portion between 780 and 3000 nm (3 μm) is sometimes called *near IR*, whereas the longer wavelengths (above 3 μm) are considered as *far IR*.

Most of the IR band overlaps the *heat radiation* band of electromagnetic radiation. Optical quantities can be stated in terms of *visual* as well as *nonvisual* (radiative) magnitudes, and sensors for optical quantities can be divided into two major groups, photon sensors and radiation sensors.

Spectral characteristics of light are most commonly shown in terms of wavelength. However, they can also be shown in terms of frequency, wavenumber, or photon energy. The interrelationship of these parameters, which also include blackbody temperature, are graphically illustrated in Figure 5-1.

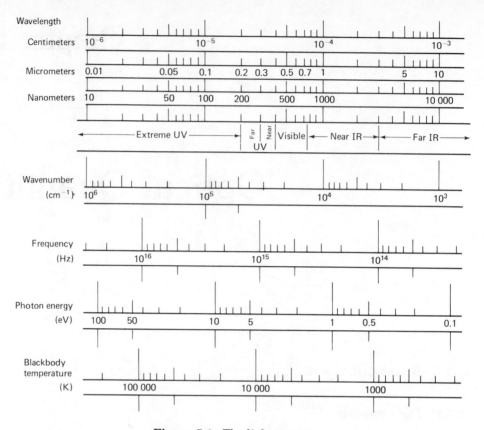

Figure 5-1. The light spectrum.

Frequency of light is related to wavelength by the speed of light (2.997 93 $\times$ 10^{10} cm/s, normally rounded off to 3×10^{10} cm/s) in vacuum:

$$\nu = \frac{3 \times 10^{10}}{\lambda}$$

where ν = frequency of light, Hz

λ = wavelength of light, cm

Wavenumber is the reciprocal of wavelength (in cm); hence, wavenumber is expressed in cm^{-1}.

Photon energy is related to the frequency of light by *Planck's constant:*

$$\mathscr{E}_p = h\nu$$

where $\mathscr{E}_p$ = photon energy, J (*Note:* 1 electron volt = 1.6022 $\times$ 10^{-19} joule)

h = Planck's constant, 6.626 196 $\times$ 10^{-34} J $\cdot$ s

ν = frequency, Hz

398

Blackbody temperature, the temperature at which a blackbody radiates energy such that the radiation has greatest intensity at a certain wavelength, is related to wavelength by *Wien's displacement law:*

$$\lambda_m T = 0.2897 \text{ cm·K (a constant)}$$

where λ_m = wavelength at which radiant energy density is maximum, cm

  T = absolute temperature of blackbody radiator, K

Luminous flux is the time rate of flow of light; the equivalent nonvisual quantity is *radiant flux.*

Luminous intensity is the luminous flux (emitted by a point source) per unit solid angle; the equivalent nonvisual quantity is *radiant intensity,* the radiant flux per unit solid angle.

Illuminance (illumination) is the luminous flux per unit area (of a uniformly illuminated surface on which this flux is incident); the equivalent nonvisual quantity is *radiant flux per unit area.*

Luminance ("brightness") is the luminous intensity of a (light-emitting) surface, in a given direction, per unit of (projected) area of the surface, as viewed from the given direction; the equivalent nonvisual quantity is *radiance,* the radiant flux per unit area, per unit solid angle.

Luminosity is the ratio of the luminous flux to the corresponding radiant flux.

5.1.2 Color

Color is a characteristic of visible light associated with its wavelength (see Figure 5.2), especially its dominant wavelength, also with purity and with luminance (see definition in Section 5.1.1; visually perceived brightness is approximately proportional to the cube root of luminance).

Purity (colorimetric purity) is the degree to which a primary color is pure (not mixed with the other two primary colors); for any color, it is the ratio of a spectrally homogeneous component to the luminance of the achromatic light with which it must be mixed to match the chromaticity of a sample of light.

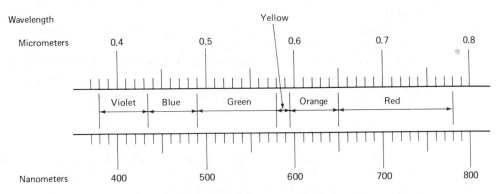

Figure 5-2. The color spectrum.

Chromaticity is the color quality of light that can be defined by its *chromaticity coordinates,* the ratios of each of the three tristimulus values of a sample to the sum of these values; chromaticity depends on the hue and saturation of a color, not on its luminance; it is also definable by dominant wavelength and purity, taken together.

Hue is the subjectively perceived spectral characteristic of color which determines whether the color is called red, green, greenish blue, reddish purple, and so on; it corresponds to the perceived (psychophysiological) dominant wavelength.

Dominant wavelength is the (single) wavelength of light that matches a color of a sample when combined in suitable proportions with a reference standard light.

Saturation (color saturation) is the degree to which a color differs from a near-gray color of the same perceived hue; it can also be described as the degree to which a color is mixed with white; the more it is mixed with white, the lower is the saturation; for example, low saturation characterizes a "vivid red," whereas high saturation characterizes a "dull red" or "weak red"; saturation has also been equated with and referred to as *chroma.*

Monochromatic light is light in a narrow band of wavelengths (ideally at a single wavelength).

Achromatic color is devoid of any hue; "gray" is achromatic color.

Color temperature is the blackbody temperature required to produce the same chromaticity as the light being examined.

Tristimulus values are the magnitudes of three different standard stimuli needed to match a given sample of light; the most commonly used standard stimuli are the CIE (International Commission on Illumination or Commission Internationale d'Éclairage) color mixture functions known as X, Y, and Z, where Y is the *luminosity function* ("light-dark"), Y-Z corresponds to yellow-blue, and X-Y to red-green; X, Y, and Z can be computed for a sample of light by a color match produced by adjusting the mixture of "red," "green," and "blue" lights (the *working primaries*).

Complementary chromaticity is the property of two light samples by which they produce achromatic color (as visually perceived) when combined in suitable proportions.

Chrominance is the difference between any color and a reference color of specified chromaticity and of equal luminance.

Primary colors are colors of constant chromaticity and variable luminance which can produce (or can be used to specify) other colors when mixed in suitable proportions.

5.1.3 Light Interaction with Substances

Absorption is the process by which (a portion of) the incident (light) energy is transferred to the substance receiving that energy; this phenomenon is related to characteristic molecular structures of substances.

Absorptance is the ratio of the (luminous or radiant) flux absorbed in a substance to the flux incident on the substance.

Absorbance is the logarithm to the base 10 of the reciprocal of the *transmittance*.

Transmittance is the ratio of the radiant power transmitted by a substance to the radiant power incident on the substance.

Reflectance (radiant) is the ratio of the radiant flux reflected by the surface of a substance to the radiant flux incident on that surface.

Refraction is the change in direction of a light beam (or ray of radiation) as it passes from one medium to another medium having a different *refractive index*.

Diffraction is the interference pattern resulting from the uniting, at each point, of rays from different points around an opaque object, or of rays through different parts of an opening.

Interference is the variation, due to the superposition of two or more waves, in wave amplitude, with distance and time.

Scattering is the change in the direction of photons caused by their collisions with other particles.

Fluorescence is the reemission of radiant energy (light) from a substance as a result of electromagnetic radiation or a stream of charged particles incident on the substance and being absorbed in it; when, upon removal of the incident energy, the emission of light takes longer than 10^{-8} s to decay, the phenomenon is known as *phosphorescence* rather than fluorescence, and the light-emitting substance is called a *phosphor*.

Opacity is the reciprocal of transmittance.

Turbidity is the cloudiness in a fluid due to the presence of suspended powdered or granular solids.

The *nephelos* of a substance is its ability to reflect light from within itself due to optical discontinuities in the substance, such as may be caused by a relatively weak suspension of particles in it.

5.1.4 Units of Measurement

Luminous Intensity (of a Point Source). The unit of luminous intensity is the *candela (cd)*, one of the base units of the SI. It is defined as the luminous intensity, in the perpendicular direction, of a surface of 1/600 000 m^2 (1/60 cm^2) of a blackbody at the temperature of solidifying (freezing) platinum under a pressure of 101 325 Pa. A proposed redefinition of the candela is the luminous intensity in a given direction of a source emitting a monochromatic radiation of frequency 540 $\times$ 10^{12} Hz and whose radiant intensity in that direction is 1/683 W/sr.

An older unit, still popular, was the *candlepower (cp)*, defined as the luminous flux of one *candle* (see luminous flux, below) when viewed in the horizontal plane. There is a one-to-one relationship between the old and new units (1 cp = 1 cd).

Basic Concepts   **401**

Luminous Flux. The unit of luminous flux is the *lumen (lm)*, defined as the flux emitted within a solid angle of one steradian by a point source having a uniform intensity of 1 candela *(lm = cd · sr)*. An older unit was the *candle*, the luminous flux from a spermaceti candle burning at the rate of 120 grains per hour.

Illumination (of an area). The unit of illuminance is the *lux (lx)*, the illumination of one lumen per square meter *(1 lx = 1 lm/m²)*. An older unit was the *footcandle (fc)*, the illumination at a spherical distance of 1 foot from a 1-candle source *(1 fc = 10.76 lx)*.

Brightness (Luminance). The unit of luminance is the *candela per square meter (cd/m²)* (of light-emitting area). An older unit is the *footlambert (fL)*, the luminance equal to $1/(4\pi)$ candle per square foot *(1 fL = 3.426 cd/m²)*. Among other units that have been used are the *lambert (L)*, the luminance equal to $1/\pi$ candle per square centimeter *(1 L = 3183 cd/m²)* and the *stilb (sb)*, the brightness equal to 1 candle per cm² *(1 sb = 10 000 cd/m²)*.

Wavelength. Wavelength in the UV and visible portions of the spectrum is expressed in *nanometers (nm)*, whereas it is usually expressed in *micrometers (μm)* in the IR region. The micrometer has previously been often referred to as a "micron (μ)." Another older unit, whose use is now discouraged, was the ångstrom (Å, or just A) which is equal to 0.1 nm *(10 Å = 1 nm)*.

Other Quantities. Luminosity is expressed in *lumens per watt (lm/W)*.
Blackbody temperature is expressed in *kelvins (K)*.
Photon energy is usually expressed in *electron volts (eV)* or *ergs;* the SI unit is the *joule (J)* *(1 eV = 1.602 × 10⁻¹⁹ J; 1 erg = 10⁻⁷ J)*.
Wavenumber is expressed in *cm⁻¹*.
Nonvisual magnitudes: Radiant flux is expressed in *watts*, radiant intensity in *watts per steradian*, radiant flux per unit area in *watts per square meter*, and radiance in *watts per square meter per steradian (W m⁻² sr⁻¹)*.

5.1.5 Performance Characteristics of Light Sensors

Since many of the essential performance characteristics of light sensors are substantially different from those normally specified for most other types of sensing devices, these characteristics are grouped separately here.
Sensitivity is generally defined as the ratio of the change in output (of a sensing device) to a change in the measurand. This characteristic is often specified for photoemissive light sensors, primarily photomultiplier tubes, as cathode (or anode) luminous (or radiant) sensitivity. *Cathode luminous sensitivity* is the ratio of photoelectric emission current (from the photocathode) to the incident luminous flux (under specified conditions), expressed in *A/lm*. *Cathode radiant sensitivity* is the ratio of the photoelectric emission current to the incident radiant flux (at a given wavelength and under specified conditions of irradiation), expressed in *A/W. Anode luminous (or radiant) sensi-*

tivity is defined similarly except that the sensitivity is referred to the anode instead of the cathode.

Quantum efficiency is the average number of photoelectrons (or similar electronic charges) emitted from the light-sensitive portion of a light sensor (e.g., a photocathode) per incident photon, expressed in *percent (%);* it is either shown for a given wavelength or, as *peak quantum efficiency,* for the wavelength of peak radiant sensitivity of the light-sensitive surface.

Responsivity is the ratio of the sensor's output amplitude to the incident radiant flux (at a stated wavelength), expressed in *V/W* or *A/W,* depending on type of sensor.

The following three characteristics are specified primarily for radiant-energy (IR) sensors; they relate incident radiant power to signal-to-noise ratio, the ratio of the signal voltage to the noise voltage produced across the output terminals of the sensing device.

Noise equivalent irradiance is the minimum radiant flux density necessary to provide a signal-to-noise ratio of 1, when the noise is normalized to unit bandwidth; it is expressed in $W/Hz^{1/2} \cdot cm^2$.

Noise equivalent power (NEP), at a given wavelength, is the minimum radiant flux necessary to provide a signal-to-noise ratio of 1 when the noise is normalized to unit bandwidth; it is usually expressed in $W/Hz^{1/2}$, but can also be expressed in *W* at a specified bandwidth (greater than 1 Hz).

Detectivity is usually shown as D^* *(D-star),* a "figure of merit" originally introduced to remove the dependence of NEP on the radiation-sensitive area of the sensing device; it is the actual detectivity normalized to unit bandwidth and unit area and is a measure of the signal-to-noise ratio. Detectivity (D^*) is given by

$$D^* = \frac{S/N(A \cdot \Delta f)^{1/2}}{W}$$

where S/N = signal-to-noise ratio (ratio of signal voltage to noise voltage)

$\quad A \quad$ = sensitive area of sensing device, cm^2

$\quad \Delta f \quad$ = noise equivalent bandwidth of amplifier in test setup, Hz

$\quad W \quad$ = rms value of radiant power incident on sensitive area, W

It is usually expressed as: "$D^*(\lambda, f_c, \Delta f)$ = _____ cm $\cdot$ Hz$^{1/2} \cdot$ W^{-1}"; that is, the value of D^* is given at a specified wavelength (λ), chopper frequency of the test setup (f_c), and noise equivalent bandwidth (Δf); in some specifications the absolute temperature of a blackbody source (e.g., 500 K) is substituted for λ. D^* is related to NEP by: NEP = $A^{1/2}/D^*$.

Wavelength cutoff is that value of wavelength, reached with increasing wavelengths, at which the responsivity is reduced to 30% of the peak spectral responsivity; it is usually expressed in μm.

Dark current is the current flowing in a light sensor in the complete absence of any incident luminous or other radiant flux. An equivalent term, sometimes applied to photoconductive sensors, is *dark resistance.*

Field of view is the solid angle, or the angle in a specified plane, over which radiant energy incident on the sensitive area is measured within specified tolerances.

Spectral response is the band of wavelengths over which the sensor performs within specified tolerances under stated conditions. It is frequently shown as a graph of percent relative response (with peak response = 100%) vs. wavelength, or some other measure of sensor response (e.g., cathode radiant sensitivity, quantum efficiency, D^*, etc.) vs. wavelength. It can also be shown as the two wavelength values bracketing the peak response and at which the sensor response is reduced to a stated fraction or percentage of peak response; sometimes the wavelength of peak response is additionally shown.

Other light-sensor performance characteristics are of the type frequently specified for many other types of sensing devices and are, therefore, not discussed here in detail.They include response time (time constant, rise time, decay time), power dissipation, and various electrical, mechanical, and environmental characteristics (e.g., electrical connections, dimensions, mounting provisions, operating temperature range, etc.). It should be noted that certain light-sensor designs exhibit a marked temperature sensitivity and some types (notably some IR sensor designs) are intended to operate at very low temperatures.

5.2 VISIBLE, ULTRAVIOLET, AND INFRARED LIGHT INTENSITY

Sensors that provide a usable electrical output in response to incident electromagnetic radiation in the UV–visible–IR portion of the spectrum are referred to as light sensors, light detectors (or, specifically, UV detectors or IR detectors), photosensors, photodetectors, "photocells," or light (or UV or IR) transducers. Their transduction element usually acts also as their sensing element.

5.2.1 Sensing Methods

Light sensors can be classified into two general categories: quantum detectors (or photon detectors) and thermal detectors. *Photon detectors* depend on effects produced when quanta of incident radiation (photons) react with electrons in a sensor material. *Thermal detectors* respond to total incident radiant energy; they are used primarily for IR sensing. Photon detectors employ photovoltaic, photoconductive, photoconductive-junction, photoemissive, or photoelectromagnetic transduction. Thermal detectors use thermoelectric, bolometric, or pyroelectric transduction methods. These transduction methods are illustrated in Figures 5-3 and 5-4 (where shown, e = electrons, $h\nu$ = *photons or radiant energy*).

5.2.1.1 Photovoltaic transduction. Photovoltaic sensors are self-generating; that is, they require no external excitation power. Their output voltage is a

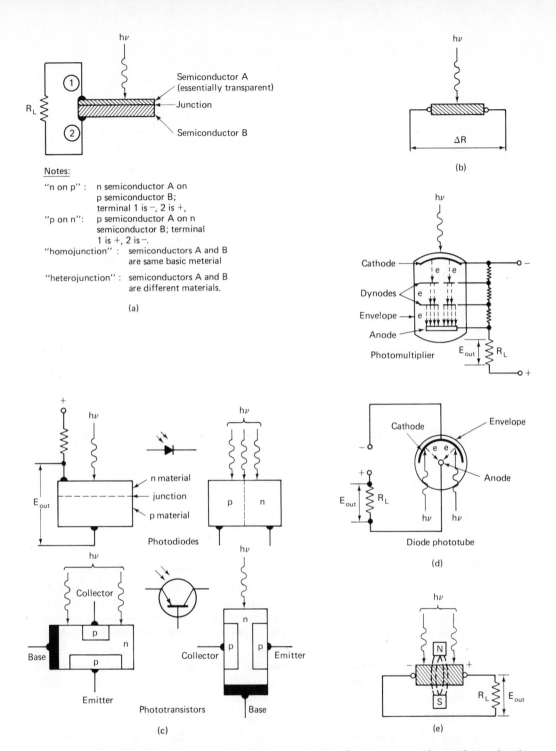

Figure 5-3. Basic light-sensing methods (photon detection): (a) photovoltaic; (b) photoconductive; (c) photoconductive-junction; (d) photoemissive; (e) photoelectromagnetic.

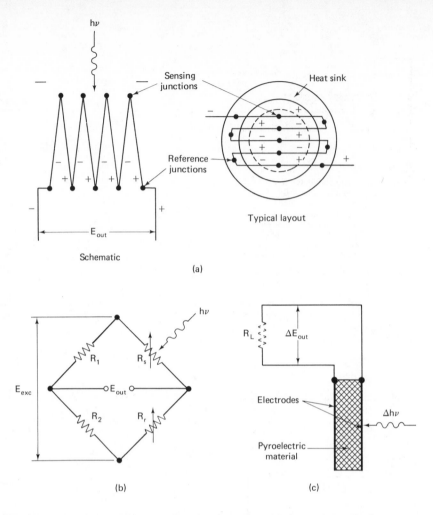

Sensing junctions

Reference junctions

E_{out}

Schematic

Heat sink

Typical layout

(a)

E_{exc}

R_1

R_s

E_{out}

R_2

R_r

hν

(b)

R_L

ΔE_{out}

Electrodes

Pyroelectric material

Δhν

(c)

Figure 5-4. Basic light-sensing methods (thermal detection): (a) thermo-electric (thermopile); (b) bolometric; (c) pyroelectric.

function of the illumination of a junction between two dissimilar materials (Figure 5-3a). The junction acts as potential barrier across which electron flow is excited by incident photons. Several types of material pairs exhibit the photovoltaic effect, such as iron/selenium (used in the relatively popular selenium cell) and copper/copper oxide. Semiconductor photovoltaic sensors, employing materials such as silicon, germanium, or indium antimonide, use a "p-n" junction as their potential barrier. The junction is formed by introducing different types of impurities (dopants) into opposite ends of the semiconductor material. In a variant of the semiconductor photovoltaic sensor the junction is formed by "n"-type glass deposited on "p"-type single-crystal silicon.

5.2.1.2 Photoconductive transduction. Photoconductive sensors (Figure 5-3b) are made of semiconducting materials which reduce their resistance in response to increasing illumination. The material is contained between two con-

406

ductive electrodes to which connecting wires can be attached. The change in conductance results from a change in the number of charge carriers created by the absorption of the energy of incident photons. Polycrystalline films (e.g., lead salts and indium antimonide) as well as bulk single-crystal materials (doped germanium or silicon) are used as photoconductors. A popular example of a photoconductive sensor is the cadmium sulfide (CdS) "cell," used in many cameras for automatic exposure control.

5.2.1.3 Photoconductive-junction transduction. In these versions of the photoconductive sensor the resistance across a junction between n and p semiconductor material changes as a function of incident light. The junction photocurrent increases with increasing incident photon flux. This principle is employed in photodiodes as well as in phototransistors (Figure 5-3c).

5.2.1.4 Photoemissive transduction. Photoemissive sensors emit electrons from a cathode when photons impinge on it (Figure 5-3d). The electrons are ejected from the cathode surface when the energy of the radiation quanta is greater than the work function of the cathode material. This effect is utilized in the diode phototube (either evacuated or gas-filled) as well as in the photomultiplier tube. In the diode phototube some of the electrons are collected by an anode which is at a positive potential with respect to the cathode. This causes current flow which can be used to produce an output voltage across a load resistor in series with the anode. In the photomultiplier tube additional electrodes (dynodes), at sequentially higher positive potential, are located between cathode and anode so as to amplify the electron current by means of secondary emission from the dynodes.

5.2.1.5 Photoelectromagnetic transduction. This specialized transduction method is effected in a semiconductor (typically made from indium–antimonide crystals) acted upon by an external magnetic field. When photons are absorbed near the front surface of the semiconductor, the resulting excess of carriers at that surface and their absence at the rear surface cause a diffusion of carriers toward the rear. The force due to the application of a transverse magnetic field then deflects the holes toward one end of the semiconductor and the electrons toward the other end, thus causing an emf to be developed between the two end terminals (Figure 5-3e). The advantage of this method is a reduction of internally generated thermal noise.

5.2.1.6 Thermoelectric transduction. The thermoelectric (Seebeck) effect is explained in more detail in Chapter 4, as are the thermocouple and the thermopile whose operation is based on this effect. Theromopiles produce an output voltage when the temperature of their sensing junctions is higher than the temperature of their reference junctions; they consist of a number of thermocouples connected in series. Thermopiles used for radiant-flux sensing have their reference junctions in thermal contact with a heat sink, whereas their sensing junctions are blackened (to absorb heat radiation) and thermally isolated from the heat sink (Figure 5-4a). The reference ("cold") junctions remain relatively stable in temperature; they are also shielded so as not to receive any of the incident radiant flux. The sensing junctions are heated by the radiant flux. If the heat-sink temperature is known, the temperature difference between the reference and sensing ("hot") junctions, as indicated by the thermopile output voltage, is a measure of the incident radiant flux.

5.2.1.7 Bolometric transduction. Bolometers used for radiant-flux sensing consist of a pair of matched thermistors (or other temperature-sensing resistive devices; see Chapter 4), connected in a half-bridge or full-bridge circuit, one of which is blackened and mounted in such a manner that it senses radiant flux, the second one being isolated from radiant flux and responding only to the temperature of the heat sink. A typical bolometer circuit is shown in Figure 5-4b, where R_s is the radiation-sensing thermistor, R_r the reference thermistor shielded from radiation, and R_1 and R_2 are a pair of matched, stable resistors, usually located some distance away from where thermal radiation is being sensed. When an excitation voltage (E_{exc}) is applied to the circuit, the output voltage will be proportional to the difference in resistance between R_s and R_e, which, in turn, is a measure of incident radiant flux. If this were a half-bridge circuit, E_{exc}, R_1, and R_2 would be replaced by two excitation voltages of exactly the same amplitude but opposite polarity, inserted in the place of R_1 and R_2. An example of a sensing element employed in lieu of the thermistor, for R_s and R_r in a bolometer circuit, is single-crystal gallium-doped germanium.

5.2.1.8 Pyroelectric transduction. Pyroelectric sensors are composed of a ferroelectric crystal material (e.g., triglycene sulfate) between two electrodes. The crystal exhibits a spontaneous polarization (electric charge concentration) which is temperature-dependent. Changes in incident radiant flux, absorbed by the crystal, cause a change in the crystal temperature, resulting in a change of the potential difference (voltage) across the electrodes. This voltage is later neutralized by current flow through the internal leakage resistance and the external load resistance. Figure 5-4c illustrates the pyroelectric sensing method. It should be noted that pyroelectric sensors are basically capacitive in nature.

5.2.1.9 Pressure-actuated photoelectric transduction. This transduction method is employed in the *Golay-type IR detector (Golay cell)*. A gas of low thermal conductivity (e.g., xenon) is enclosed in a cylinder capped by a blackened membrane on one end and a mirror-coated diaphragm at the other end. IR radiation incident upon the blackened membrane causes the gas to expand and the mirror-surfaced diaphragm to deform. The diaphragm is positioned in the optical path between a light source and a light sensor in such a manner that deformation of the diaphragm causes the light reflected by the mirrored surface toward the light sensor to increase with increasing pressure. The output of the light sensor is then proportional to incident IR radiation.

5.2.2 Design and Operation

5.2.2.1 Photovoltaic light sensors. Selenium and silicon sensors are the most popular light sensors employing the photovoltaic transduction principle. Their spectral response is in the visible and near-IR region. Photovoltaic sensors of other materials were developed primarily for far-IR sensing.

The *selenium photovoltaic sensor* (selenium cell) uses a junction between selenium, which is *p*-type semiconductor material (contains an excess of holes), and cadmium oxide (*n*-type, contains an excess of electrons) for its operation (Figure 5-5). A polycrystalline layer of selenium, about 75 μm thick, is de-

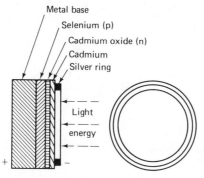

Figure 5-5. Selenium photovoltaic sensor.

posited on a metal (e.g., iron) base plate. A film of cadmium is then vacuum-deposited over the selenium in such a manner that the cadmium in contact with the selenium is oxidized. The junction region, consisting of a gradient layer of cadmium selenide and cadmium oxide, is then grown. The cadmium film as well as the junction are of molecular thickness so that they are quasi-transparent to light. A low-temperature, high-conductivity alloy (e.g., silver alloy) is then deposited in a line or ring on the active surface for lead-attachment purposes. The same alloy can also be deposited on the rear surface (metal base).

When an external electrical load is connected across the terminals, incident light is converted into an electron flow from the *p*-type selenium to the *n*-type active surface whose lead-connecting alloy then becomes the negative terminal of the sensor. The output current depends on the load resistance as well as on the illumination, although the load-resistance dependency is not as great for some designs as it is for most others. Typical output-current vs. illumination curves show an approximately linear relationship for load resistances up to 100 Ω, which becomes increasingly nonlinear as saturation occurs with higher load impedances. The spectral response (Figure 5-6) peaks at about 570 nm. In some special designs the ratio of blue to red response is increased, at a cost of overall efficiency, by evaporating a transparent gold electrode over the junction.

The *silicon photovoltaic sensor* (silicon cell) uses a junction between *p*-type silicon and *n*-type silicon to produce an output current proportional to incident illumination (Figure 5-7). Most such sensors have a *p*-on-*n* junction as shown in the illustration. A typical design consists of an arsenic-doped, thin (about 0.5 mm) slice of silicon (*n*-type), with boron diffused into its upper surface to create a light-transparent layer of *p*-type silicon there. The *p-n* junction acts as a permanent electric field. When the active surface (*p*-type

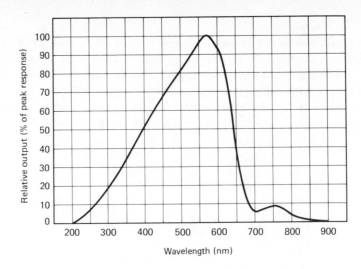

Figure 5-6. Spectral response of selenium cell. (Courtesy of Vactec, Inc.)

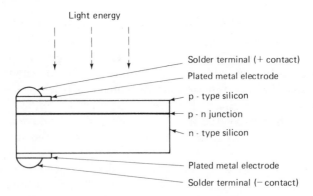

Figure 5-7. Silicon (*p*-on-*n*) photovoltaic sensor.

layer) is illuminated, the incident photons cause a flow of "holes" (positive charges) and electrons. The electric field at the junction directs the flow of holes toward the *p*-type silicon and the flow of electrons toward the *n*-type silicon. The resulting unbalance of charge carriers within the sensor causes an emf to be developed between the two surfaces. When a load resistance is connected across the surfaces, on which solder terminals have been formed on metallized (e.g., nickel-plated) areas, the hole and electron carriers flow through the circuit until a balance condition is achieved. This current flow is then a function of the incident photon flux (illumination).

Some silicon cells use an *n*-on-*p* junction instead of the more common *p*-on-*n* junction. In a typical design this is accomplished by diffusing a molecular layer of phosphorus (*n*-type layer) into the surface of a boron-doped silicon slice (*p*-type). This tends to shift the spectral response curve of the sensor slightly toward the blue. The response peak of an *n*-on-*p* silicon cell is near 800 nm, whereas the response of *p*-on-*n* silicon cells (see Figure 5-8) has its

Optical Quantities

peak around 900 nm. Some special silicon cell designs ("blue-enhanced," "blue-sensitive," "blue cell") have spectral response peaks as low as 560 nm, the peak of the human eye's response. The response time of silicon cells depends on load resistance, illumination level, and junction capacitance. Rise times and decay times are substantially equal for low illumination levels and are around 20 μs in typical circuits. At high illumination levels the rise time tends to be considerably shorter than the decay time. Special low-capacitance designs have rise and decay times as low as 2 μs.

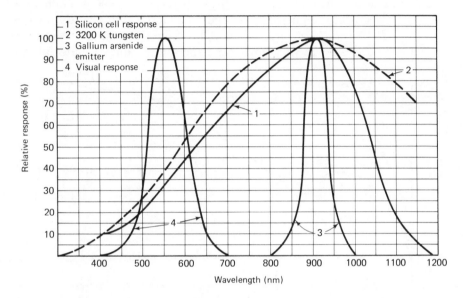

Figure 5-8. Relative spectral response of silicon cell, compared with spectral characteristics of human eye, tungsten emitter, and GaAs (LED) emitter. (Courtesy of Vactec, Inc.)

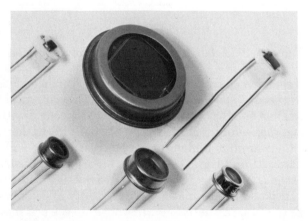

Figure 5-9. Typical silicon photovoltaic sensors. (Courtesy of Vactec, Inc.)

Visible, Ultraviolet, and Infrared Light Intensity

Typical silicon photovoltaic sensor configurations are illustrated in Figure 5-9. These are typical for silicon cells used for light-sensing purposes. Silicon ("solar") cells are also widely used for conversion of solar energy into electrical power. For such applications a large number of typically square, thin cells are mounted in close proximity to each other in the form of large "solar arrays." The cells are connected in series, to provide the required output voltage, and series strings are connected in parallel to provide the required output current.

Germanium photovoltaic sensors are similar to silicon types in construction and operation. Their spectral response, however, peaks near 1.5 µm and their operating temperature range tends to be significantly narrower.

Photovoltaic infrared sensors, used for IR sensing in the spectral region 1 to 15 µm, exist in various designs and semiconductor material combinations.

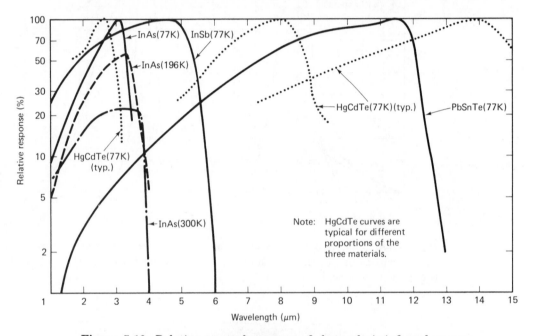

Figure 5-10. Relative spectral response of photovoltaic infrared sensors.

A common characteristic is their performance (detectivity) improvement with decreasing operating temperatures. They are most frequently used while mounted in a small cryogenic dewar, usually cooled with liquid nitrogen to 77 K, sometimes while mounted on a Peltier-effect (thermoelectric) cooler and cooled to somewhat higher temperatures. Included in this group are InAs, InSb, PbSnTe, and HgCdTe sensors. Figure 5-10 illustrates the relative spectral response of each of these types of sensors, which are described briefly below. It should be noted that the detectivity at peak response differs for each of these sensors; the individual response curves are shown on the same graph only for the purpose of showing relative spectral characteristics.

Photovoltaic indium arsenide sensors consist of a small wafer of single-crystal indium arsenide (InAs) into which a relatively broad-area *p-n* junction is diffused. If they are intended to operate at room temperature (300 K) they are typically packaged in a "TO-18" (transistor-type) case, about 5 mm in diameter by 5 mm high, evacuated and sealed with a sapphire or quartz window. For operation (with improved detectivity) at dry ice (196 K) or liquid nitrogen (77 K) temperatures they are integrally packaged within a small dewar whose liquid-nitrogen holding time is between 8 and 12 hours. For operation at relatively low temperatures without use of liquid cooling they are integrally packaged with a thermoelectric cooler. As detectivity is improved with decreasing operating temperature, the output impedance of the sensor increases (from about 15 Ω at 300 K to about 0.5 MΩ at 77 K). InAs photovoltaic sensors have a time constant of about 1 μs.

Photovoltaic indium antimonide (InSb) sensors employ single-crystal InSb with a broad-area diffused *p-n* junction. Since they are intended to operate at 77 K they are integrally packaged in a cooling assembly (coolant well) which is either used as dewar for liquid nitrogen or provides a volume sufficient for incorporation of nonliquid (e.g., thermoelectric) coolers. The sensing surface is always maintained within an evacuated area, sealed by a window typically made from 0.5-mm-thick sapphire. Complete sensor assemblies with provisions for flow-through cryogenic cooling are as small as 2 cm in diameter by 4 cm long. The sensing element itself can be circular or rectangular and range in size from 0.2 to 10 mm in diameter, with comparative dimensions for rectangular units. At 77 K, InAs sensors provide a detectivity D^* (5 μm, 900, 1) of approximately 40 to 75 $\times$ 10^9 cm $\cdot$ Hz$^{1/2}$/W and a time constant around 1 μs, at an output impedance of 20 to 50 kΩ.

Photovoltaic lead–tin–telluride (PbSnTe) sensors are trimetal photovoltaic sensors which utilize intrinsic photoconductivity in single-crystal PbSnTe material but are operated in the photovoltaic mode. They are intended for operation at 77 K and are typically packaged integrally in a small dewar filled with liquid nitrogen. They are capable of providing a very short response time (down to 50 ns). Their spectral response is in the region 8 to 12 μm.

Photovoltaic mercury–cadmium–telluride (HgCdTe) sensors are made from very thin (10 to 15 μm) slabs of this ternary alloy material and provide time constants down to about 10 ns. They are intended for operation at 77 K but can operate at slightly higher temperatures (around 120 K) without a severe degradation of performance. One of their outstanding characteristics is that their spectral response curve can be adjusted to any desired relatively narrow band within the overall wavelength band of 2 to 14 μm by varying the proportions of the three materials in the alloy. Examples are shown by the three dashed curves in Figure 5-10. Photographic techniques have been successfully applied to the production of single-element sensors as well as multielement arrays.

Heterojunction photovoltaic sensors have been developed with a variety of semiconductor material combinations. *Heterojunctions* are junctions between two different semiconductor materials, whereas *homojunctions* are junctions between differently doped portions of the same material (e.g., *p*Si–*n*Si

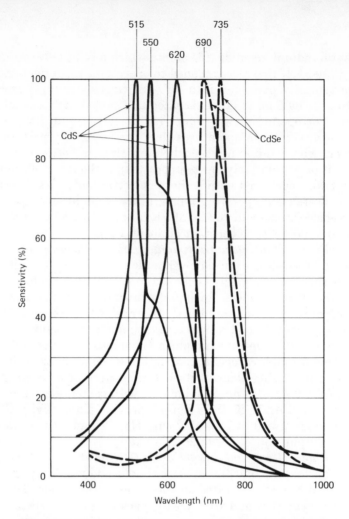

Figure 5-11. Spectral response of typical CdS and CdSe photoconductive sensors. (Curves courtesy of Clairex Electronics.)

as in the silicon photovoltaic sensors described above). Although most of the research in the heterojunction area has been aimed at developing cheaper, lighter, and more efficient solar-energy converters, some of the results have shown the feasibility of producing light-sensing devices having certain desirable characteristics, such as sensitivity within certain broad spectral regions and, for special applications, a wavelength-dependent polarity change. The latter is peculiar to isotype heterojunctions (e.g., nGe–nSi). Anisotype heterojunctions have been utilized in a photovoltaic sensor containing n-type special transparent material on p-type single-crystal material resulting in a significantly improved blue response as compared to homojunction nSi–pSi sensors. Thin-film solar cells with a pCu$_2$-S–nCdS heterojunction were developed primarily for aerospace solar-power-generation purposes. Spectral response from about 0.5 to 2 μm has been reported for pSi–nCdS and pGe–nGaP heterojunction sensors. Many other material combinations have been examined and some of them show promising characteristics for different areas of applications, including as infrared sensors.

5.2.2.2 Photoconductive light sensors.

5.2.2.2 Photoconductive light sensors. Light sensors employing bulk-effect photoconductors are resistive devices whose resistance decreases with increasing illumination. They have also been referred to as "photoresistors." The absolute resistance value of a photoconductive sensor, at any instant, depends on the photoconductive material chosen, the thickness, surface area and geometry of the material, the geometry of its electrodes, the spectral composition of the incident light, the illumination level, the operating temperature, and the difference between present and previous light levels as well as the exposure times at those levels *(light history effect).*

Cadmium sulfide (CdS) and cadmium selenide (CdSe) photoconductive sensors are the most popular types because their spectral response is close to the visible-light region and because of their relatively high sensitivity to changes in illumination level. Their sharply pronounced spectral response peak also enhances their usefulness in colorimetry. Typical spectral response curves for several types of CdS and CdSe photoconductors are shown in Figure 5-11. The ratio of dark-to-light resistance of these sensors is between 100 : 1 and 10^4 : 1, depending on the specific material used. The measurand-to-output (illumination-to-resistance) relationship is generally nonlinear. The nonlinearity becomes more pronounced with increasing illumination. Temperature coefficients of resistance are higher for CdSe than for CdS and the polarity of the coefficients is usually negative for CdS, positive for CdSe. The coefficients also vary as an inverse function of light level. Response time is normally shorter for CdSe than for CdS and decreases with increasing illumination levels. Rise times are longer than decay times. At an illumination of 10 lx, typical rise times are 35 to 150 ms for CdS and 25 to 90 ms for CdSe on a time-constant basis (63% of final output). The active area geometry is sometimes simply rectangular, more often of a special "wavy" shape (see Figure 5-12), obtained by evaporation techniques, which achieves a much larger active area

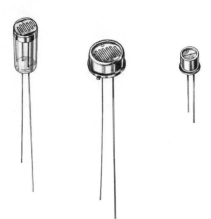

Figure 5-12. CdS and CdSe photoconductive light sensors. (Courtesy of Clairex Electronics.)

for a given sensor size. Development efforts are directed mainly at improving linearity, expanding the usable spectral region, and reducing the light history effect. Research for this has been reported in the areas of combining CdS and CdSe, in varying proportions, in one photoconductive element, in treating the light-sensitive surface by the admixture of various chemical elements, and in studies of the interface between the (conductive) electrodes and the photoconductor.

Lead sulfide (PbS) and lead selenide (PbSe) photoconductive sensors are used for light sensing in the near-infrared region of the spectrum. The PbS spectral response is between 1 and 3 μm (at room temperature) and 1 and 4.5 μm (at 77 K). The PbSe spectral response is between 1 to 4.5 μm (at room temperature) and 1 to 5.5 μm (at 77 K). PbS sensors have a somewhat better detectivity than PbSe sensors; however, time constants are substantially shorter for PbSe than for PbS material (between 1 and 5 μs for PbSe, between 40 and 1000 μs for PbS, at room temperature). Time constants increase with decreasing sensing element temperatures. Typical time constants, at 77 K, are 5000 μs for PbS and 80 μs for PbSe. Sensor configurations include the plate type (see Figure 5-13), the hermetically sealed type (e.g., TO-5 transistor package) with or without an integrally packaged thermoelectric cooler, and the dewar type (side or end-on viewing) with the photoconductive material mounted within glass vacuum containers. The sensitive area of the plate-type sensors is typically between 1 × 1 and 4 × 4 mm in size, but can be between 0.25 × 0.25 and 10 × 10 mm for some PbS sensors.

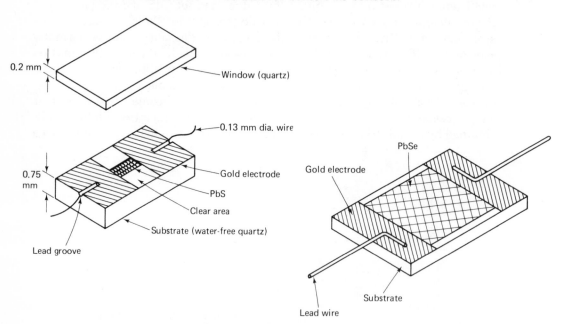

Figure 5-13. Construction of PbS and PbSe (plate type) photoconductive sensors. (Courtesy of Infrared Industries, Inc.)

Gold-doped germanium [*Ge(Au)*] and *mercury-doped germanium* [*Ge(Hg)*] *photoconductive sensors* are used for far-infrared sensing, with a spectral response from 1 to 9 μm for Ge(Au) and from about 4 to 14 μm for Ge(Hg). Developments in this area have included other dopants for germanium, such as cadmium, copper, and zinc, and spectral response up to 40 μm has been reported. Developments in doped silicon sensors have also been carried on. All such *extrinsic-semiconductor* sensors require cryogenic cooling (below about 40 K).

Mercury cadmium telluride (HgCdTe) sensors, described in Section 5.2.2.1 have also been designed to operate in the photoconductive mode. Their overall characteristics, including the unique capability of adjusting the wavelength of peak response at any point between about 3 and 14 μm by varying the ratio of the amounts of HgTe and CdTe in the material, are similar to those of the photovoltaic HgCdTe sensors. Although the photoconductive HgCdTe sensors are capable of operation at room temperature, their detectivity improves by about 1½ orders of magnitude when cooled to 77 K.

Some research has been carried on in developing photoconductive sensors whose spectral response extends into the ultraviolet. Solid-solution *ZnCdS photoconductors* are reported to have the capability of providing spectral response peaks of 400 nm or below.

5.2.2.3 Photoconductive-junction light sensors.

This category encompasses phototransistors, avalanche photodiodes, and those types of solid-state photodiodes not operable, or not usually operated, in the photovoltaic mode.

P-n junction photodiodes have a built-in field enabling them to operate in the photovoltaic mode but have better performance in the photoconductive (reverse-biased) mode. A typical design is illustrated in Figure 5-14. The rel-

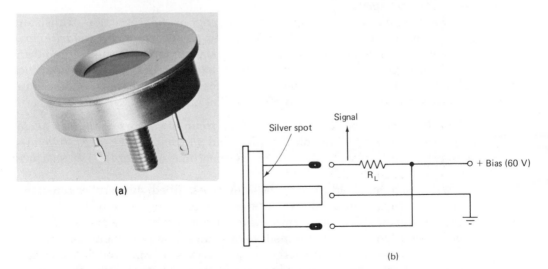

Figure 5-14. Silicon *p-n* photodiode operated in photoconductive (reverse-biased) mode: (a) photodiode; (b) basic circuit diagram. (Courtesy of EMI Electronics Ltd.)

ative response, at the peak wavelength of about 950 nm, is only 60% in the photovoltaic mode with the response in the photoconductive mode taken as 100%. The light-sensitive portion of a *p-n* junction photodiode can be in the *p* region, in the *n* region, or in the depletion region at the junction. Typical spectral response is 400 to 1100 nm and rise times are in the vicinity of 10 ns, typical for most types of photodiodes (rise times of 100 ps are reported for some special designs).

P-n photodiodes are characterized by an intrinsic layer (which defines the depletion layer) between the *p* and *n* regions. They can operate in the photoconductive or photovoltaic mode. Their operation is based on the excitation of electron–hole pairs in the intrinsic layer by photons received at the surface of the *p* region and passing through this region. Spectral response and rise-time characteristics are essentially the same as for *p-n* junction photodiodes. "UV-enhanced photodiodes" have somewhat better response below 400 nm.

Avalanche photodiodes are depletion-layer photodiodes whose bias voltage, across the diode, is increased to the point where hole–electron pair multiplication by collision (avalanche effect) takes place in the depletion region. The avalanche effect produces significant amplification of the photocurrent with negligible noise. The operation of avalanche photodiodes is similar to that of photomultiplier tubes and they have sometimes been referred to as "silicon avalanche photomultipliers." Amplification factors of 200 times, or more, have been achieved without difficulties. Avalanche photodiodes are usually packaged integrally with their amplifier and control modules (see Figure 5-15).

Amplifying photodiodes are photodiodes integrally packaged, in a small can, with an amplifier. A related sensor is the photosensitive field-effect transistor *(photofet)* which consists of a photodiode and high-impedance amplifier, integrally packaged.

Phototransistors are light-sensitive *pnp* or *npn* junction transistors which provide inherent amplification of the photocurrent. *Photodarlingtons* are planar epitaxial phototransistors with a Darlington-connected second transistor in a single device (see Figure 5-16) for additional gain. Typical rise times are between 1.5 and 10 µs (about 100 µs for photodarlingtons) and spectral responses usually peak between 800 and 850 nm.

5.2.2.4 Photoemissive light sensors.

This group of sensors comprises *phototubes* (vacuum or gas-filled photodiodes) and *photomultiplier tubes*. A related sensor, the electron multiplier, which is sometimes used for far-UV measurements, is described in Chapter 6.

Phototubes are cold-cathode vacuum (or gas-filled) diode tubes consisting of a photocathode, an anode, sometimes a guard ring, an envelope, and an entrance window. When a potential is applied across cathode and anode, electrons are emitted by the photosensitive cathode and some of them are attracted toward the anode so that a current (photocurrent) flows through the circuit. Phototube characteristics depend primarily on the photocathode material and the window material. Spectral response can extend into the near-IR region

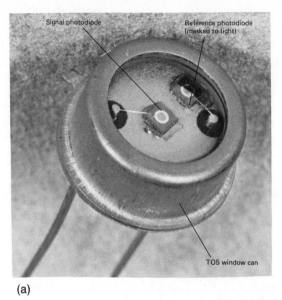

(a)

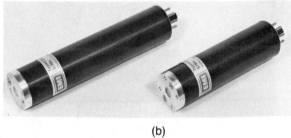

(b)

Figure 5-15. Avalanche photodiode: (a) avalanche photodiode (double-chip type); (b) complete photodiode packages (including control and amplification circuitry). (Courtesy of EMI Electronics Ltd.)

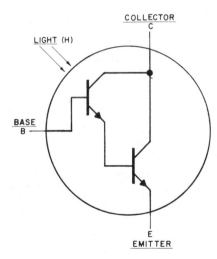

Figure 5-16. Photodarlington circuit. (Courtesy of Clairex Electronics.)

419

(to about 1100 nm). Some designs are particularly intended for UV measurements and have a spectral response to below 150 nm. Rise times are between about 1 µs and less than 1 ns. Gas-filled photodiodes provide greater sensitivity since the gas ion plasma flow releases more electrons than in a vacuum photodiode of equivalent design; however, the photocurrent vs. luminous flux characteristics of the gas-filled types are less linear. Phototubes exist in a variety of configurations. The tube illustrated in Figure 5-17 has 13 pin connections

Figure 5-17. Vacuum photodiode. (Courtesy of ITT Electro-Optical Products Div.)

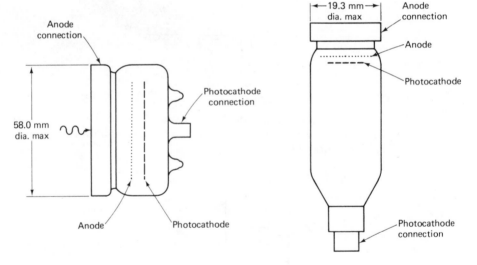

Figure 5-18. Vacuum photodiode configurations. (Coutesy of ITT Electro-Optical Products Div.)

of which only two are external connections. Its photocathode is deposited on the inner surface of the entrance window. Two biplanar vacuum phototube configurations are shown in Figure 5-18. Among many other designs are those having sturdy plug-in sockets and those containing a curved cathode with a central, very slim anode.

   Photomultiplier tubes (PMT) are photoemissive devices differing from photodiode tubes in that additional electrodes *(dynodes)* are placed between

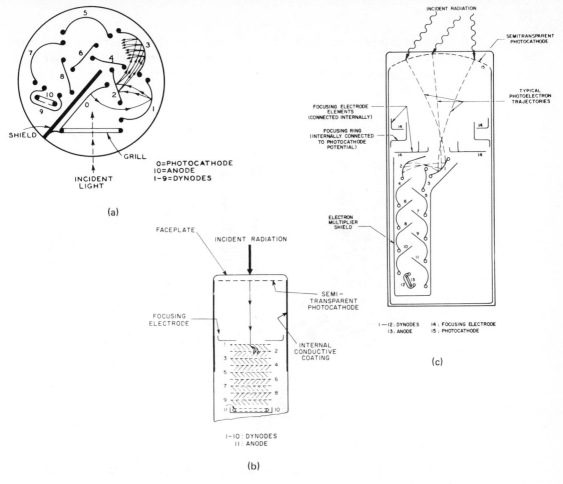

Figure 5-19. Schematic arrangements of photomultiplier tube internal structures: (a) circular cage; (b) venetian-blind cage; (c) in-line cage. (Courtesy of RCA Corporation.)

photocathode and anode. The dynodes are connected into a voltage-divider network in such a manner that, starting with the dynode nearest the photocathode, each successive dynode has a higher potential applied to it. The dynode nearest the anode is at a potential close to the high voltage applied to the anode itself. When photons strike the cathode, free electrons are liberated and drawn to the first (lowest-voltage) dynode because its potential is positive with respect to the cathode. Several electrons are liberated at the first dynode for each electron emitted by the cathode. These secondary-emission electrons are drawn to the next dynode because its potential is positive with respect to the previous dynode. Several electrons are liberated from the second dynode for each electron emitted by the first dynode. This process is multiplied by each successive dynode (hence the term "photomultiplier"). All electrons resulting from this multiplication process are collected by the anode. The amplification of the cathode photocurrent, due to the multiplication process, is typically between 10^5 and 10^8 *(current gain),* depending primarily on the number of dynodes in the photomultiplier tube. Three basic dynode structural arrangements are used: the circular cage, venetian-blind cage, and in-line cage structure (see Figure 5-19). Typical photomultiplier configurations are shown in Figure 5-20.

Figure 5-20. Typical photomultiplier tubes. (Courtesy of EMI Electronics Ltd.)

Spectral response characteristics of photomultiplier tubes depend on the material of the photocathode surface as well as on the *window* material (the portion of the tube's envelope directly in front of the photocathode). Many different types of photocathode materials have been developed to meet a variety of application requirements. The spectral response characteristics of some of these materials are illustrated in Figure 5-21. Some of the materials are identified by a "spectral response" (S-) number, such as AgO–Cs (S-1), or BiO–Ag–Cs, semiopaque (S-10). Others are identified by the material mixture (e.g., GaAs, GaInAs, GaAsP) or by a generalized material term such as bialkali (Sb–Na–K) or multialkali (Na–K–Cs–Sb), including the "ERBA" (extended-range bialkali) and "ERMA" (extended-range multialkali) photocathode materials. Additional materials are often designated just by a manufacturer-assigned number or name. Among window materials, lime glass and fused silica are most frequently used. Other materials are used for obtaining specific overall spectral characteristics, such as LiF or MgF for response in the UV portion of the spectrum. Certain photocathode-window material combinations have

Optical Quantities

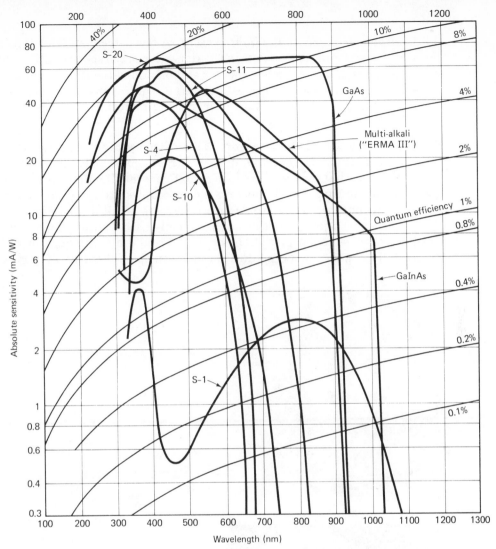

Figure 5-21. Typical photocathode spectral-response characteristics. (Courtesy of RCA Corporation.)

resulted in the development of "solar blind" photomultipliers, those having a spectral response only in the UV, with a cutoff below 350 nm. Multialkali, GaAs, GaInAs, or GaAsP photocathodes are used when response in the IR region of the spectrum is required. Photomultipliers have very short response times, in many cases less than 10 ns, but they require the provision of a very stable high-voltage (600 to 1500 V) supply. A 1% change in this voltage can produce a 10% variation in current gain. Some photomultiplier tubes are available in an integral package with their voltage-divider network.

Crossed-field detectors are a special version of a photomultiplier in which very fast response time is obtained by the addition of a magnet such that the electric and magnetic fields cross each other.

5.2.2.5 Photoelectromagnetic light sensors. A few detectors of this type have been developed for measurements in the IR portion of the spectrum. This device can measure radiation between about 2 and 6.5 μm without artificial cooling. A permanent magnet is used to establish the required magnetic field for the indium antimonide (InSb) photovoltaic sensing material. The time constant is less than 1 μs.

5.2.2.6 Thermoelectric light sensors. This category of thermal detectors for light sensing comprises thermocouples and thermopiles which are so designed and configured that they will produce a (self-generated) output in response to incident radiant flux. Single-junction thermocouples are no longer commonly used for this purpose. They are described in more detail in Chapter 4.

Thermopile sensors are the only commonly used devices employing thermoelectric transduction of radiant energy. Thin-film techniques have been successfully applied to the production of thermopile elements of very small

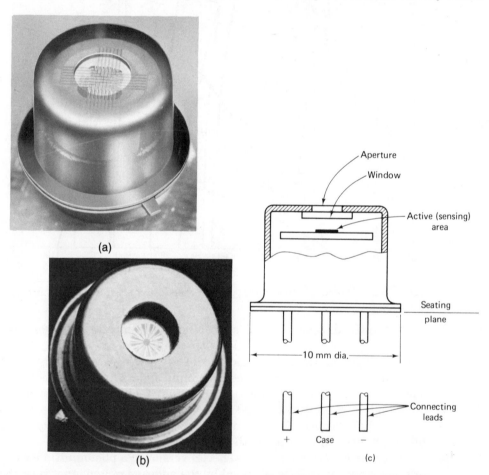

(a)

(b)

(c)

Figure 5-22. Thermopile sensors: (a) with rectangular sensing-junction pattern; (b) with radial sensing-junction pattern; (c) typical construction. (Courtesy of Sensors, Inc.)

size, so that a large number of blackened sensing junctions can be located within an extremely compact area (active area). Figure 5-22 illustrates two thermopile sensor designs, both within a standard TO-5 case. The radial pattern permits the sensing junctions to be located within an area of minimum size but limits the number of junctions (and thermocouple pairs) that can be incorporated in the design.

The sensor shown in Figure 5-22b contains 12 sensing junctions in an area 1 mm in diameter. A rectangular sensing-junction pattern permits a greater number of junctions to be located within a slightly larger area. Figure 5-22a shows a sensor with 28 junctions within an active area of 1.5 × 1.5 mm. Other typical configurations include rectangular patterns of 1 × 8 mm, with 8 junctions, 6 × 6 mm with 120 junctions, and 4.7 × 5.6 mm with over 300 (very small) junctions. The thin-film patterns are so designed as to optimize the utilization of the active area, such as by suitable staggering or interleaving of sensing junctions together with their respective (thermocouple) leads. As the amount of thermocouple material is reduced, however, the overall resistance of the thermopile (thermocouples connected in series) is increased. This reduction in sensor source impedance results in increased noise pickup and, hence, poses a significant design trade-off.

The reference ("cold") junctions of the thermopile are in good thermal contact with a heat sink, usually annular in shape, but electrically isolated from it. By appropriate thermal coupling the heat sink is stabilized at the temperature of the surface to which the sensor is mounted. The aperture in the case (see Figure 5-22c) is sufficiently small to admit radiant energy only to the active area but not to the heat sink.

Although some thermopile sensors are used in a windowless configuration, most of them are provided with a window of a material chosen so as to establish the spectral response of the sensor, which can range from ultraviolet to far infrared unless limited by the window material to serve a specific application. The window also acts as a seal. Most thermopile sensors are evacuated and then back-filled with an inert gas such as argon or xenon. Although this preserves sensor characteristics for long periods of time, it reduces the sensitivity. Thermopile sensors intended for operation in vacuum (e.g., beyond the earth's atmosphere) are normally vented of their inert gas shortly before the start of their intended use, to optimize their sensitivity.

The external configuration of thermopile sensors is by no means limited to the TO-5 case shown in the illustration. A variety of configurations have been developed, some smaller, some larger than the 8-mm-diameter case. Some sensors are designed as integral parts of instrument systems, which can include lenses, two or more filters, and field stops for limiting the radiant-energy beam width.

Thermopile sensors produce a dc output voltage in reponse to incident radiant energy. Since their element resistance (source impedance) is typically between 1 and 25 kΩ they can be connected to relatively simple amplifiers. Representative values of dc responsivity are between 1 and 12 V/W. Time constants are around 20 to 40 ms. Typical values of D^* (500 K, dc) are between

0.4×10^8 and 2.0×10^8 cm $\cdot$ Hz$^{1/2}$/W but can exceed 2×10^9 cm $\cdot$ Hz$^{1/2}$/W for some special designs, usually with the compromise of longer time constants.

5.2.2.7 Bolometer light sensors. Although certain photoconductive sensors are sometimes used in the bolometric mode (in a bolometer circuit), bolometer sensors usually employ a matched pair of thermistors (see Chapter 4) for their operation. An active (radiation-sensing) thermistor flake and a compensating flake, shielded from radiation, are typically cemented to a block of solid material (e.g., sapphire) which acts as heat sink. In an "immersed" design the active flake is attached to the inside surface of a lens and the compensating flake is mounted in the base of the sensor. The two thermistors are electrically connected as two arms of a bridge circuit. Two voltage sources providing equal voltage, but of opposite polarity, form the other two arms of the bridge circuit. A difference in resistance of the closely matched thermistors, due to incident radiant flux on the active flake, then causes an output voltage of the bridge circuit.

Thermistor bolometer sensors (detectors) are intended for operation at room temperature and normally require no cooling. They can provide a usable spectral response from about 0.25 to over 35 µm but are more frequently equipped with a window, sealed to the case, which limits the response to a particular band of wavelengths in the IR portion of the spectrum, for example, a germanium window for a reponse in the 2- to 20-µm band or a silicon window for a response in the 1- to 16-µm band. Bolometer time constants are about 1 to 5 ms. Bolometers with special high-resistance thermistors, in small configurations, have been used where rapid response to fluctuations in weak radiation signals (e.g., IR interferometers) was required.

A recent development in the area of thermistor bolometers is a design employing thermistors made of semiconducting chalcogenide glass by casting, hot-pressing, vacuum deposition, or photolithographic processes which lend themselves to mass-production methods.

5.2.2.8 Pyroelectric light sensors. Pyroelectric sensors are thermal detectors utilizing the pyroelectric effect provided by certain materials whereby an output is generated by the rate of change of the temperature of the sensor due to the rate of change of incident radiant flux. Their performance characteristics depend primarily on the sensing material, the preparation and geometry of the electrodes, the use of absorbing coatings, the thermal design of the structure of the sensor, and the nature of the electronic interface. Since the output is rate-of-change-dependent, the radiant flux incident upon the sensor must be chopped, pulsed, or otherwise modulated. The sensors are normally operated at room temperature or other ambient temperatures, without artificial cooling.

The spectral response of pyroelectric sensors extends from below the far (vacuum) UV to beyond the far IR but is often limited to a band of wavelengths in the IR region by means of a window. Rise times are between less than 1 ns to about 200 ns. Detectivites are in the vicinity of 10^8 cm $\cdot$ Hz$^{1/2}$/W.

Figure 5-23 illustrates a pyroelectric sensor, including details of the sensing head. Other available configurations include small TO-5 cans and similar

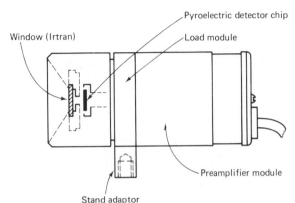

Window (Irtran)

Pyroelectric detector chip

Load module

Preamplifier module

Stand adaptor

Figure 5-23. Pyroelectric sensor. (Courtesy of Laser Precision Corp.)

plug-in or lead-mounted sensors with pyroelectric elements varying from about 1 to 8 mm in diameter (or similar square shapes).

Developments in pyroelectric sensors have been primarily in the area of the pyroelectric materials. These are, in general, single crystals, ceramics, or plastics. Triglycine sulfate (TGS) was the orginally most widely used material. Although it is characterized by a very good responsivity, it was found difficult to manufacture, it is hygroscopic, and it has a very low Curie point (49°C), the temperature at which depolarization occurs and pyroelectric properties are lost. Lithium tantalate ($LiTaO_3$) was found to have comparable pyroelectric properties but with a much higher Curie point (610°C). Research in plastic pyroelectric materials has led to the production of polyvinylidene fluoride and PVF_2 (polyvinyl fluoride) detectors which, in some cases, could provide detectivities as high as 10^9 cm $\cdot$ Hz$^{1/2}$/W, although detectivities of plastic pyroelectrics generally tend to be lower than this. A significant advantage of plastic pyroelectric material is their producibility and relatively low cost.

5.2.2.9 Golay-type sensors. Pressure-actuated photoelectric transduction of radiant energy, primarily in the IR portion of the spectrum, is employed by the Golay-type sensor (*Golay detector, Golay cell*). The basic sensor was invented by M. J. E. Golay in 1947 to satisfy a requirement for a relatively sensitive detector having a flat spectral response curve over a wide portion of the infrared spectrum.

Figure 5-24 illustrates a Golay-type sensor and its operating principles. The sensing system consists of a chamber filled with a gas of low thermal conductivity and a flexible mirror. Incident radiation passes through a window made from a material chosen for a specific reponse in the IR region of the spectrum (A) and reaches a thin energy-absorbing film (B) which warms the

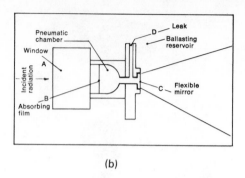

(b)

(a)

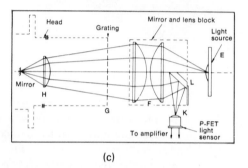

(c)

Figure 5-24. Golay-type IR detector: (a) complete sensor package; (b) sensing system (pneumatic chamber); (c) transduction system (photoelectric). (Courtesy of Cathodeon Ltd. and Oriel Corporation of America.)

gas in the chamber. The resulting gas expansion causes a deflection of the mirror membrane (C) which seals the other end of the chamber. A fine leak (D) compensates for changes in ambient temperatures. The incident radiation is periodically interrupted by an external chopper (not shown) so that radiation pulses at a repetition rate of between 5 and 25 Hz (selectable) are incident on the absorbing film, which causes the deflections of the flexible mirror to occur at the same rate. However, the amplitude of each deflection is given by the amount of radiation in each pulse. The flexible mirror receives a light beam originating at the light source (E) via a condenser lens (F), a grating (G), and a meniscus lens (H). This lens focuses the beam so that an image of one part of the grating is superimposed on another part of the same grating when the flexible mirror is not deflecting. When the flexible mirror deflects, a corresponding change in the relations of line image and grid occurs. This varies the intensity of light reflected from the flexible mirror through lenses H and F (and grating, G) toward stationary mirror (L) and light sensor (K). In the case of the design illustrated, the light source is a light-emitting diode and the light sensor is a photo-FET whose output is fed to a solid-state amplifier contained in the same sensor package.

428 *Optical Quantities*

The spectral response of the sensor is essentially flat from 0.5 to 1000 μm. The choice of windows determines the specific spectral response of a sensor within this broad band of wavelengths. It also affects the sensitivity since different windows have different values of transmittance. Typical detector-package sensitivities are 3×10^6 V/W with KBr, KRS-5, or CsI windows (spectral response below about 50 μm) and 1.5×10^6 V/W with diamond, quartz, or Si windows (spectral response above 50 μm, to between 350 and 900 μm). The 90% response time is around 20 ms, followed by a longer recovery time.

5.2.3 Specification Characteristics

The design, performance, and environmental characteristics that should be specified for light sensors are listed and described below. Since some fundamental differences exist between sensor types, not all characteristics are specified for all sensor types. For purposes of brevity, the following abbreviations will be used: PV, photovoltaic; PC, photoconductive; PCJ, photoconductive-junction; PED, photoemissive diodes; PMT, photomultiplier tubes; TP, thermopiles; BOL, bolometers; PYR, pyroelectric.

Design characteristics always include the overall configuration with all necessary dimensions, mounting means and mounting dimensions, type and dimensions of external electrical connections, location and dimensions of any integrally packaged components, such as windows, lenses, coolers, or preamplifiers; degree of sealing, if any; and the nature of the internal atmosphere (vacuum or a specific gas) if the sensor is sealed. The viewing configuration (side viewing or end viewing) is usually specified for PMT and for some other sensor types if they are contained within a cooling jacket. The light-sensitive material and the dimensions of the light-sensitive area (active area) are shown for all types except for most BOL; in the case of PED and PMT the size and type of photocathode are stated. When the sensor employs a combination of two or more sensing materials, all materials are stated. The location of the sensitive surface is frequently defined (e.g., by its distance from a lens or window). The material and thickness of an integrally packaged window is always specified. The number of dynodes, the dynode structure, and, sometimes, the dynode material are shown for PMT. For TP the number of junctions is stated. The field of view is normally shown only for sensors with integrally packaged optics. Many light sensors are purchased "bare" and then connected with other components by the user.

Electrical design characteristics include the (element or output) impedance (or resistance) for most types of sensors; the resistance at a specified illumination for PC; the dark resistance for PC; the capacitance (between electrodes) for PV, PCJ, PED, and PYR; the maximum supply voltage for PC, PED, and PMT; a typical, nominal, or recommended supply (or bias) voltage for PC and PMT; and the maximum electrical-power dissipation for PCJ and PMT. For phototransistors, the breakdown voltage rating (collector-to-emitter and emitter-to-collector) and the collector–emitter saturation voltage are

Visible, Ultraviolet, and Infrared Light Intensity

stated. Sensors having a high output impedance require a very closely coupled preamplifier to avoid noise and interference pickup in the interconnecting leads.

Performance characteristics always include the spectral response of the sensor, usually shown in graphical form, sometimes stated in numerical form together with the wavelength of peak spectral response. For thermal sensors (TP, BOL, PYR) the spectral response is dictated primarily by the material of any integrally packaged window.

"Sensitivity" is specified in one or more ways for the various sensor types. Responsivity (usually in terms of current, sometimes in terms of voltage) is specified for all sensors except PMT. For BOL, a graph of responsivity vs bias voltage is typical. Detectivity (D^*) and noise equivalent power (NEP) are stated for all except photoemissive devices. For PMT it is customary to show the anode and/or cathode radiant and/or luminous sensitivity. Current or voltage sensitivity is specified for PV and PCJ sensors. Specifications for PV sensors usually show the open-circuit output voltage as well as the short-circuit current, at a specified illumiation, and the dark reverse current. Quantum efficiency is sometimes stated, particularly for PCJ and PED. For some applications it is important that the sensitivity is uniform over the entire active surface. In such cases a tolerance for variations of sensitivity is specified and special techniques are used to map the active area in order to establish any nonuniformities in sensitivity.

Response time (sensor reponse to a step input in luminous or radiant flux) is shown, in various ways, for all sensors. It is sometimes shown in graphical form, in other cases as 90% (or some other percentage) response time, as rise time (and fall time), or as time constant. Additionally, frequency response is stated for some types of sensors. PMT specifications usually show time-response characteristics as anode pulse rise time, anode pulse FWHM (full width at half magnitude), and transit time.

Additional performance characteristics, shown only for certain types of light sensors, include linearity (PV and PCJ), dark current (PCJ and PMT), current amplification (PMT), gas amplification (gas-filled PED), maximum anode current (PED, PMT), and maximum as well as minimum-detectable radiant-power density for some thermal detectors.

Environmental characteristics normally include the operating temperature range (or one or more recommended operating temperatures) and thermal effects on sensitivity, reponsivity, or detectivity. For some applications, requiring ruggedized sensors, the shock and vibration environments to be withstood by the sensor are also specified, either as operating or as nonoperating conditions.

5.2.4 Sensing Systems

Light sensors are almost invariably used in conjunction with components which modify the incident light as well as components and subsystems which modify the output of the sensor. Additionally, many types of light sensors require a

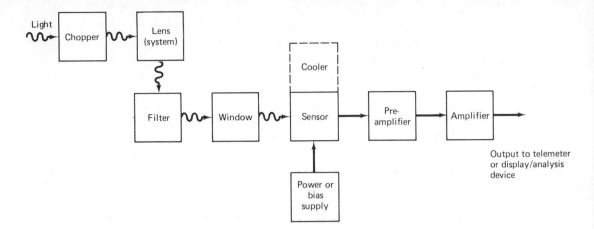

Figure 5-25. Functional block diagram of typical light-sensing system.

power (or bias) supply and a means for cooling the sensor to a temperature lower than room temperature. Figure 5-25 illustrates a typical sensing system. Not all of the components are used in all light-sensing systems. On the other hand, more sophisticated sensing systems can include a number of additional components, especially those modifying the incident light. Some of those components are briefly mentioned below; however, since such more complex sensing systems are used primarily for chemical analysis (e.g., spectrometry), they are described in Chapter 8.

Choppers are used to periodically interrupt the light beam to be detected by the sensor. This causes the sensor output to be ac rather than dc, and ac is easier to amplify. Furthermore, some sensors perform better with chopped light (pyroelectric sensors require chopping in all applications). Finally, chopping provides brief periods during which the sensor is "dark," which facilitates the correction of sensor output signals for any shifts or drifts not related to the light being sensed (e.g., thermally caused shifts, random drifts, aging).

Most choppers are rotary electromechanical devices in which a rotating blade alternatingly covers and uncovers a hole through which the light beam passes. Various blade shapes are used, such as a butterfly-shaped blade (which interrupts the light beam twice per revolution) or a disk with a hole in the same position as the hole through which the light beam passes. Some sensing systems employ a chopping mirror, electromechanically driven so that it moves back and forth through a small angle and reflects the incident light beam either to the sensor or away from the sensor. Variable-speed controls are used to select the angular speed of the blade or mirror and, hence, the *chopping frequency,* which is typically between 5 and 400 Hz but can be 4 kHz or higher. The blades, or mirror drives, are so designed that the chopped light beam has a specific waveshape (e.g., square wave, sinusoidal). An angular-speed sensor (e.g., reed switch, optoelectronic) is usually built into the chopper to provide an output usable for synchronization of the sensor-output electronics.

Lenses are used to focus the light beam onto the active area of the sensor. The characteristics of lenses of various shapes (e.g., convex, biconvex, concave, biconcave, meniscus, etc.) can be found in any basic optics text and will not be described here in detail. Various glasses are used as lens materials. Some lenses are made from materials described below as window materials (e.g., Ge, Si, KRS-5, BaF_2) and can then perform the additional spectral-response controlling function otherwise provided by windows. Lens systems, consisting of two or more lenses, are employed in some light-sensing systems.

Filters are used to limit the spectral response of the sensor (often in combination with a window) to a desired band of wavelengths. They are square or circular in shape, with parallel surfaces, and usually less than 1 cm thick. Two or more filters can be used in combination. The filter is either made from one of a large variety of carefully selected materials or material mixtures, or from a glass or quartz substrate coated with a thin film of such materials or mixtures.

A variety of spectral-response characteristics can be obtained by proper selection of a filter. *Band-pass filters* have a high transmittance over a selected band of wavelengths and a transmittance asymptotic to zero for wavelengths above and below this band. *Narrow-band filters* are a version of band-pass filters having a very narrow passband and a very sharp peak. *Short-pass filters* transmit wavelengths below a specified wavelength. *Long-pass* filters transmit wavelengths longer than a specified value. Filters are often classified by the portion of the spectrum in which they transmit light (i.e., UV, visible, or IR filters). *Interference filters* (usually used as narrow-band filters) consist of several parallel and partially reflecting surfaces, each such surface being the interface between two thin layers of transparent dielectric materials having different refractive indices. The principle of interference is used so that some transmitted wavelengths are reinforced, whereas other wavelengths are weakened. *Neutral density filters* are used to attenuate the incident light by specified amounts. They are designed either for the visible portion of the spectrum or for a broader range (UV to near IR). The different levels of attenuation are attained by different thicknesses of one or two metallic coatings on either glass or quartz. Standard densities range from "0.1" (79.5% transmission) to "4.0" (0.01% transmission) in eight standardized steps. Continuously variable band-pass as well as neutral-density filters are used for some applications, as are filter wheels which place one of several selectable filters into the optical path.

Among other optical components sometimes used in light-sensing systems are *right-angle prisms* (which reflect a light beam 90°); *dispersing prisms; beam splitters* (prisms or "pellicle" membranes), which reflect a portion of the light beam 90° while permitting the remaining portion of that beam to travel straight through; and *coatings* (usually for antireflection purposes, sometimes to provide reflection). *Monochromators* are continuously variable very narrow band-pass devices. *Field stops* are opaque disks with a small hole; they can be placed in front of a light sensor to assure that only an appropriately narrow beam of the light to be measured will reach the sensor and that all other light (or radiation) will be excluded.

Windows are those optical components of a light-sensing system that are placed closest to the sensitive area of the sensor. In photomultiplier tubes they

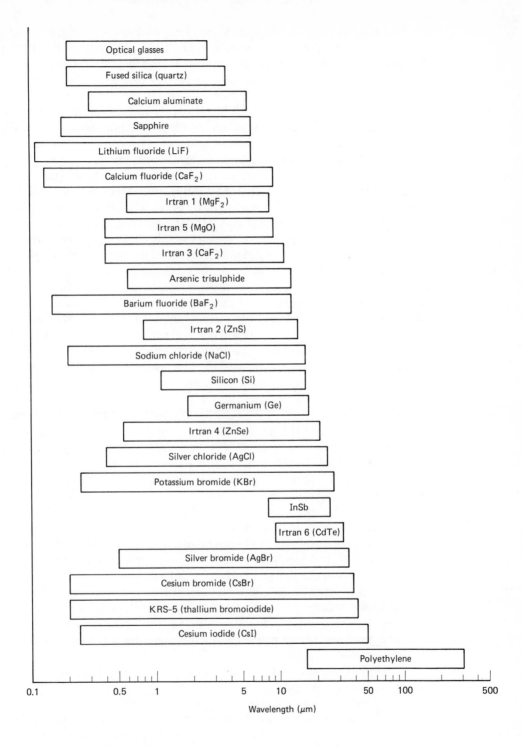

Figure 5-26. Transmission ranges of window materials.

Visible, Ultraviolet, and Infrared Light Intensity

are an integral part of the tube's envelope and are directly in front of the photocathode. In many other sensor types they are used as the transparent seal which protects the sensing material from the ambient atmosphere. The light-transmission range of window materials (see Figure 5-26) is the most essential window characteristic. Some materials are usable for UV (e.g., LiF, sapphire); others are most useful in relatively narrow or relatively wide portions of IR. Many sensor designs are available with a choice of materials for their window to provide the desired spectral response. The spectral-response characteristics of the light-sensing material itself must, of course, be compatible with the window transmission range. Other important characteristics of window materials, which influence design and selection, are the refractive index (specified at a stated wavelength or wavenumber), the thickness, reflection losses, solubility (NaCl and KBr are water soluble), the hardness, and any tendency to cold flow. Some sensors employ more than one window.

Coolers (detector cooling devices) are used for sensors whose performance improves significantly as their operating temperature is reduced below room temperature. They are necessary accessories, in particular, for many types of IR sensors, some of which are commonly operated at cryogenic temperatures (between 4 and 77 K). Very low sensor temperatures are attained by means of a dewar, a cryostat, or a Joule–Thomson cooler. A *dewar* (dewar flask) is a double-walled "vacuum bottle," a vessel in which the region between the two walls has been evacuated and sealed. The wall surfaces in contact with the evacuated space are metallized (e.g., silvered) for heat-rejection (reflection) purposes. A liquefied gas stored in a dewar can maintain its temperature for varying periods of time. A *cryostat* is a vessel holding liquefied gas whose temperature is maintained over relatively long periods of time by externally controlling the pressure in the vessel. The sensor is mounted within the dewar (or cryostat), which is provided with a window. Detector temperatures down to 4 K have been obtained by means of dewars and cryostats. Temperatures below 4 K have been achieved by the use of superfluid helium in a dewar.

A *Joule–Thomson cooler* relies on the adiabatic expansion of a pressurized gas through a small orifice at which the temperature of the escaping gas becomes much colder than the temperature upstream of the orifice. The sensor is mounted so that it remains in good thermal contact with the point at which the gas flows from the orifice. Such coolers have been used to provide temperatures down to about 23 K, with temperatures considerably below that considered achievable.

Refrigerators *(cryorefrigerators)*, using the expansion-engine principle to expand a gas from a high pressure to a low pressure, in closed-cycle operation, provide another alternative for detector cooling. Such mechanical refrigerators have cooled IR detectors to about 13 K in some applications. Development efforts on absorption (thermal) refrigeration systems and on magnetic refrigeration systems promise potential temperature reductions of detectors to below 1 K. Mechanical refrigerators tend to consume fairly large amounts of power (between tens of watts to over a kilowatt), a disadvantage in power-constrained applications.

Thermoelectric coolers employ the Peltier effect, by which heat is absorbed by a thermocouple junction when current of the correct polarity is passed through the junction. These devices are quite popular for applications where sensors must be cooled to 273 K (0°C) or slightly below this point, since they are small in size and consume little electrical power (15 to 25 W). Multistage thermoelectric coolers can provide lower temperatures, down to about 170 K, at a somewhat higher power consumption (around 50 W).

When optical-quantity sensors, especially IR sensors, are flown on satellites, spacecraft, or even high-altitude research balloons, passive cooling can be applied, using techniques by which heat from the detector region is radiated out toward space. In some applications of this type, detector temperatures down to 90 K have been achieved by using passive cooling techniques (usually by means of *radiator plates* or otherwise configured radiators).

Optical components used in conjunction with cooled sensors frequently require cooling as well, so as to reduce local background radiation effects and increase the contrast between target and background.

Power supply or bias supply circuitry is needed for all except the self-generating (photovoltaic, thermoelectric, pyroelectric) sensors. Resistive (photoconductive, bolometric) sensors require a well-regulated bias supply. Photoconductive-junction diodes require a bias supply. Phototransistors require a power supply of a type typical for transistors in general. Photoemissive diodes require a power supply to provide the potential difference between anode and cathode. A basic circuit is shown in Figure 5-27; the picoammeter in this circuit can be replaced by a load resistance across which a variation in output voltage can be detected and fed to a preamplifier and amplifier. Photomultiplier tubes

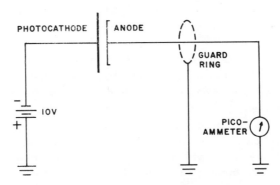

Figure 5-27. Typical photodiode operating circuit. (Courtesy of ITT Electro-Optical Products Div.)

require a well-regulated high-voltage supply. Either the positive or the negative terminal of the power supply is grounded, depending on the application, and a carefully designed voltage-divider network is connected between anode and cathode to provide the proper voltage to each of the dynodes (see Figure 5-28).

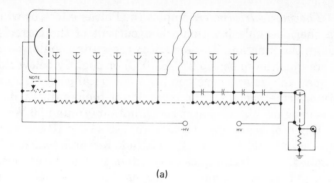

(a)

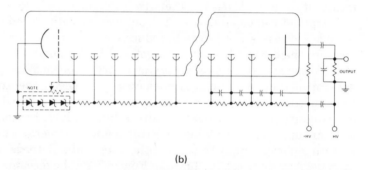

(b)

Figure 5-28. Typical voltage-divider arrangements for photo-multiplier tubes: (a) anode return at ground potential (for fast-pulse-response and high-peak-current systems); (b) photocathode at ground potential (for scintillation counting systems). (Courtesy of RCA Corporation.)

Preamplifiers are used with most types of light sensors which typically provide relatively small output signals and sometimes have a very high output impedance. The preamplifier is located physically very close to the sensor to keep the length of the interconnecting leads as short as possible. In some designs the preamplifier is packaged integrally with the sensor in a single "sensing head" ("optical head"). Preamplifiers must be matched to the sensor output impedance (which can be between less than 100 and more than $10^6 \Omega$) and should provide a high and stable gain while minimizing electrical noise. Their output impedance should be low; this helps to minimize noise pickup in the cable connecting the preamplifier to an amplifier or other electronics.

Amplifiers are often required to further amplify the sensor output signal and to present a signal of the appropriate level and characteristics to the display, analysis, or telemetry equipment. When the light detected by the sensor is chopped, a demodulator is used to remove the chopper-induced modulation from the signal. The demodulator is synchronized with the chopper by means of synchronization pulses generated by the chopper.

Optical Quantities

5.3 COLOR

5.3.1 Sensing Methods

Two different methods are used to measure color: the *direct method* and the *comparison method*. Both methods are employed to measure the color characteristics of either reflected light *(reflectance mode)* or transmitted light *(transmittance mode)*. In the direct method, the sample of light, whose color characteristics are to be determined, is collected by suitable optics, passed through either a continuously adjustable or discrete-step adjustable monochromator, and is then converted into electrical output signals by one or more light sensors. In the indirect method, color is determined by means of the visual equivalence of the sample to a synthesized stimulus. Both methods require a source of illumination of known characteristics.

5.3.2 Design and Operation

Two categories of instruments are used for color measurement: spectrophotometers and colorimeters. *Spectrophotometers* measure the spectral distribution of radiant energy (luminance) over the visible spectrum of light. Two basic types of this instrument are in use: (1) the *full* (or *dispersive*) *spectrophotometer* employs a continuously adjustable monochromator, such as a variable interference filter; *dispersion* refers to the (rotary) dispersion of polarized light (e.g., by varying the adjustments of Nicol prisms); and (2) the *abridged spectrophotometer*, or abridged narrow-band filter-type spectrophotometer, uses a number of separate filters, typically also interference filters, to divide the spectrum into discrete bands of wavelengths; typical filter intervals range between 20 nm (16 filters, 380 to 700 nm) and 10 nm (37 filters, 380 to 750 nm). The spectrophotometer output signals are visually displayed, most frequently graphically recorded *(recording spectrophotometer)*, and can be processed by a minicomputer to provide corrections for zero and 100% line errors as well as calculations of color coordinates. Spectrophotometric measurements are usually referenced to "100% white," using a very white material such as barium sulfate to provide the reference color. To allow for fluorescence in the measured sample, however, spectrophotometers are often designed to provide readings up to "200% white." Spectrophotometers are widely used for chemical analysis (see Section 8.8.1).

Colorimeters are light source–filter–light sensor combinations which simulate the tristimulus functions of visual color perception *(tristimulus colorimeters)*. Three filters and either one or three light sensors are employed to provide three separate outputs for X, Y, and Z. In their simplest form, one output is obtained for the amount of "red," one for the amount of "green," and one for the amount of "blue" in the sample. In the so-called three-color method of colorimetry the sample is matched with a mixture of variable amounts of three components of light with different (but known) chromaticities. Three broad-band filters are incorporated in colorimeters for spectral separation.

Colorimeters are used mainly for comparisons between similarly colored specimens; hence, most designs also provide outputs in terms of color difference. To further simulate human visual response the outputs are often made proportional to the cube root of luminance.

5.3.3 Performance Criteria

Spectrophotometric color characterization is generally more accurate than colorimetric determinations; however, interpretation of colorimetric data is considerably simpler than that of spectrophotometric data. Important performance characteristics for spectrophotometers include the spectral resolution given by either the design of the continuously variable monochromator or by the number of separate filters used and their band-pass characteristics; photometric linearity is another important characteristic, together with photometric resolution and the time required to scan the complete spectrum *(scan speed)*. Scan speeds of between 30 and 45 s are common, as are spectral resolution between ± 0.2 and 0.5 nm and photometric resolution to 0.01%. Photometric resolution below about 5% reflectance is generally poorer than that at higher reflectance values. It should be noted that instruments designed for transmittance cannot readily be used for operation in the reflectance mode; however, many instruments are designed to operate equally well in both modes.

For colorimeters, the linearities and sensitivities inherent in the various readouts are essential performance characteristics. Lighting and viewing geometries must be selected to fit the application; the viewing geometry is most commonly zero degrees; lighting geometries include 45°, 360° (circumferential), and spherical chambers for diffuse hemispherical viewing. In the transmittance mode the light seen by the light sensor should include scattered as well as transmitted light to provide correct color characterization. The spectral quality of the light source (or other illumination) must be accurately known for all color measurements, and calibration stability as well as ease of calibration are important characteristics of all color measurement devices.

5.4 LIGHT INTERACTION WITH SUBSTANCES

5.4.1 Sensing Methods

A number of important material-characterization methods are based on the interaction of light with substances, other than color determinations. These include measurements of transmittance and opacity, of absorption and scatter, of reflection, of turbidity, of nephelos, and of index of refraction. The most common objective of such measurements is to detect the content and concentration of particulates in liquids and gases; however, some other physical and chemical properties of materials can also be determined by such methods.

The four basic sensing methods are illustrated in Figure 5-32. The elements common to all these methods are: a light source which emits a collimated light beam into the sample fluid, and a light sensor which responds to the results or products, in the form of light or its modification, of the interaction between the light beam and the sample fluid. It should be noted that the basic methods illustrated are those considered most widely used by industry; several additional methods have also been used and some of these will be mentioned briefly.

The principles of *turbidimetry* (Figure 5-29a) are also applied to the measurement of opacity and transmittance. The light beam passes from the light source, through the sample, and to a light sensor. If the fluid is perfectly clear, the light sensor will detect the maximum light intensity. When the sample is not perfectly clear, especially when it contains solid particles, the light beam will be attenuated while passing through the sample and the light intensity seen by the sensor will be reduced. The two main causes for this attenuation are *absorption* and *scattering* of light. Absorption occurs in accordance with *Beer's law*, which states that the absorption of light by a solution changes exponentially with the concentration (all else remaining the same). When the

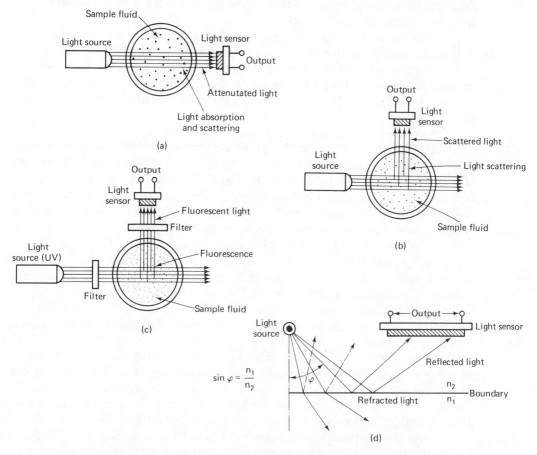

Figure 5-29. Sensing methods—interaction of light with substances: (a) turbidimetry; (b) nephelometry; (c) fluorimetry; (d) refractometry.

attenuation of the light beam is solely due to absorption, this sensing method is known as *absorptometry*. Additional attenuation will occur when the particles in the sample fluid are large enough to scatter light. The ratio of the intensities of scattered to incident light, at a specified distance, is known as the *Rayleigh ratio*. The scattered energy is maximum when the radius of the (assumed to be spherical) particle equals the wavelength of the light beam. When this radius is much larger than the wavelength, the scattered energy is nearly independent of wavelength. When this radius is much smaller than the wavelength *(Rayleigh scattering)*, the scattered energy decreases with the inverse of the fourth power of wavelength. Another characteristic of Rayleigh scattering is that the intensity of scattered light, as scattered in any direction of angle θ with the incident-light direction, will be directly proportional to $1 + \cos^2 \theta$. A further characteristic of Rayleigh scattering is that the light will also be plane-polarized. The amount of polarization (of a light beam through a colloidal solution of high dispersity) depends on the size of the particles; polarization is complete when the size of the particles is much smaller than the wavelength *(Tyndall effect)*.

For some applications it has been found advantageous to base turbidity sensing on scattering (from relatively large particles) only. Such turbidimeters employ optics, between the sample cell and the light sensor, which block the transmitted light and admit only *forward-scattered* light to the sensor; this blocking is not required in another type of turbidimeter in which *back-scattered* light is sensed.

Three special units of measurement are often used in turbidity measurement. One of these is the *JTU* (Jackson Turbidity Unit), derived from an early version of a turbidimeter, the *Jackson Candle Turbidimeter*. It consists of a flat-bottomed glass tube, graduated in JTU, below which a special candle is mounted. The sample liquid is slowly poured into the tube while visually observing the image of the candle flame from the top of the tube. A reading is then taken when the image disappears in a uniform glow, (i.e., when the intensity of scattered light equals that of transmitted light). The scale is based on turbidity caused by a suspension of diatomaceous earth in distilled water. Another unit is the *FTU* (Formazin Turbidity Unit), which is based on a solution of a chemical mixture called Formazin in distilled water. For nephelometric turbidimeters (see below) a unit known as the *NTU* (Nephelometric Turbidity Unit) was developed and standardized by a U.S. governmental agency.

Nephelometry (see Figure 5-29b) is based on the sensing of light scattered at 90° from the incident light beam, or, in some cases, at 90° from the surface of a liquid illuminated by a light beam at a relatively shallow angle with the surface (a variant of this method has been used when the sample fluid is air). In some designs a second light sensor, placed at 180° with the first, is employed to increase the scattered-light detection capability. The transmitted light is either absorbed by a hood or sensed by a light sensor for reference purposes. Since light is scattered only when turbidity exists, nephelometers provide increasing signal amplitudes with increasing turbidity. A relatively short light path tends to increase the upper end of the turbidity measuring range.

In *fluorimetry* (see Figure 5-29c) the light source emits a beam of light at wavelengths extending downward to about 200 nm (ultraviolet light). A filter (primary filter) is placed between light source and sample cell to enable the selection of the appropriate wavelengths. The fluorescent light from the sample is filtered (to exclude nonfluorescent products) and sensed at right angles to the incident beam. Fluorescence occurs when light is first absorbed, then reemitted from a substance after a very short time (about 10^{-8} s); when the elapsed time is between about 10^{-4} and over 5 s, the reemitted light is known as *phosphorescence*. It has been found that the fluorescence intensity from very weak solutions (around 1 ppm) is proportional to concentration.

Refractometry (see Figure 5-29d) is a measurement of the *index of refraction* of a substance. *Snell's law* states that as a light beam enters a more dense medium it will deflect (it *refracts*) toward the normal (with the direction of transmission). The index of refraction, n, is the ratio of the velocity of light in empty space to the velocity of light in a given material; it is a function of wavelength as well. Refractometry is usually based on sensing light reflected at the *critical angle*. When light through a more dense medium (whose index of refraction is n_2) meets the boundary with a less dense medium (whose index of refraction is n_1), the critical angle (ϕ) is the smallest angle with the normal (to the boundary) at which the light is totally reflected back into the more dense medium. The sine of the critical angle is equal to the ratio n_1/n_2. There are other methods of refractometry, such as the comparison of refraction loss through a sample, compared to transmittance through a reference sample, by interferometric means in the *Rayleigh refractometer*.

5.4.2 Design and Operation

5.4.2.1 Smoke density and other opacity monitors. Opacity sensing devices (sometimes called "transmissometers") employ the sensing method shown in Figure 5-29a. They measure the attenuation of light in the sample fluid due to absorption and scattering (% opacity = 100% − % transmittance). The light incident upon the light sensor decreases with increasing opacity in the sample.

The measurement of smoke density in exhaust ducts and smoke stacks is probably the most common application of opacity monitors. A typical device is illustrated schematically in Figure 5-30. The mounting tubes, which provide a protected transmittance path as well as filtered purging air for the transmission and reception optics, are attached to precisely aligned openings, 180° apart, in the duct or stack. Some opacity monitors, such as this design, have removable light-source and light-sensor assemblies. All designs provide lens-cleaning air. A field stop (aperture plate) is sometimes mounted between the light sensor optics and the sensor to reduce the viewing angle. Instead of placing the light source and light sensor at opposite ends of the transmission

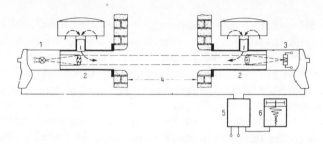

Figure 5-30. Smoke density monitor: 1, light source; 2, mounting tube with oil-filtered lens-purging air inlets; 3, light sensor; 4, test gap in stack or flue-gas duct; 5, control and signal-handling electronics; 6, strip-chart recorder. (Courtesy of Siemens A.G.)

path, they can alternatively both be placed at the same end, with a suitable reflector placed at the opposite end; this increases the effective transmission path length.

Readout devices display the output of opacity monitors in various terms. Included in these is % transmittance, % opacity, and optical density. The latter is equal to the $\log_{10}$ of $1/(1-\text{opacity})$. Percent opacity can also be shown in terms of the "Ringelman scale," four rasters representing four discrete "shapes of gray" in steps of 20% opacity ("2" = 20% ..., "4" = 80%) printed at 90° spacing around a hole, of the same dimension as each of the rasters, through which smoke venting from a stack is viewed (with the sun behind the observer) and its opacity compared with the opacity represented by the rasters. Opacity monitors can be calibrated by inserting standard neutral density filters into the transmission path.

Lasers have found increasing use as light sources in stack monitors as well as in other opacity-based "air quality monitors" in which the light sensor is placed a sufficient distance away to allow an appropriate volume of air to be sampled (or packaged together with the laser light source for nephelometric determinations). Lasers lend themselves to such applications because they provide a well-collimated beam of linearly polarized light at a single wavelength.

5.4.2.2 Turbidimeters. This category, as described here, does not include nephelometric turbidemeters; those are described in section 5.4.2.3. It does include primarily transmittance turbidimeters, secondarily forward-scatter and back-scatter turbidimeters. Figure 5-31 illustrates the operating principle of a transmittance-type design. The sample liquid fills the glass tube, which also provides the optical surface for the windows at the light source and light sensor ("photocell") necessary to complete the transmission path. Attenuation of the light beam, due to scatter and absorption in the sample, is indicative of the suspended solids concentration of the sample, and the conditioned output signal is displayed in ppm. This particular design includes a motor-driven reciprocating piston within the glass tube; it draws in and later expels the

442

sample while simultaneously wiping the optical surface of the sampling chamber. Similar turbidimeters are designed for in-line installation, some of them including provisions for making the flow laminar in the measuring region.

Back-scatter turbidimeters typically contain light source, light sensor, and optics for both in a single sensing head that is mounted so that it is in contact with the sampled fluid. The light sensor detects scattered and reflected light from the suspended solid particles in the sample fluid. In forward-scatter turbidimeters the light-sensor optics are so designed that the transmitted light is blocked and only forward-scattered light is detected. Alternatively, two light sources and two sensors can be employed in a pulsed mode; scattered and unscattered light is detected, and the ratios of those two light intensities can be computed by appropriate circuitry. An important design characteristic is freedom from error-causing effects of contaminating deposits on the walls of the sampling chamber when such deposits would be within the transmission path.

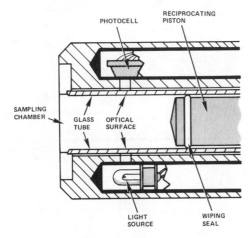

Figure 5-31. Transmittance turbidimeter. (Courtesy of Biospherics Inc.)

5.4.2.3 Nephelometers and nephelometric turbidimeters. Most of these instruments measure turbidity by measuring the light scattered by the sample fluid at 90° to the incident light beam. As shown in Figure 5-32, the beam from a lamp, collimated by lenses, enters the sample cell (from the bottom, in this design) and passes through the sample fluid to a light shield. Light scattered from the sample at 90° is detected by the light sensor (a photomultiplier type in this unit) after passing through a window in the side of the cell holder assembly. In the laboratory-model nephelometric turbidimeter illustrated, one of several (Formazin dilution) sealed turbidity standards, or a focusing template, can be substituted for the sample cell. The turbidity standards are used to calibrate the instrument and the focusing template is used to adjust the position of the lamp. Circuitry is used to condition the photomultiplier output signal so that the readout on the indicating meter is in NTU (in five ranges, from 0 to 0.2 to 0 to 1000 NTU).

Sensing of light scattered at 90° is also used in many in-line turbidimeters.

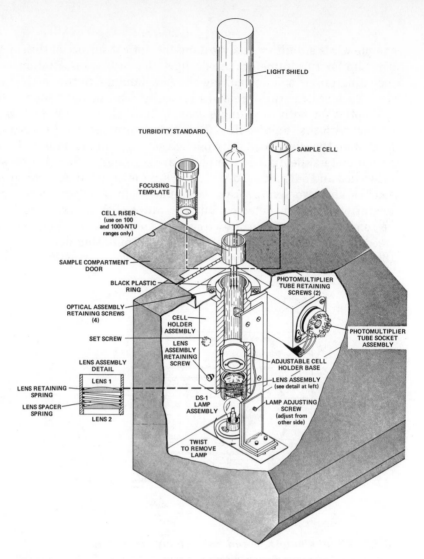

Figure 5-32. Optical assembly of laboratory-style nephelometric turbidimeter. (Courtesy of Hach Chemical Co.)

In the instruments illustrated schematically in Figure 5-33 the flow of the
sample liquid is upward toward the measuring region. The light from the lamp
in the design shown in Figure 5-33a passes through a sealed quartz window
through a series of aperture disks which serve to collimate the light and remove
any stray light from the beam. The light beam passes the photomultiplier tube
window through which light scattered at 90° is sensed by the photomultiplier.
The light beam then passes into a light trap in which it is absorbed. The design
illustrated in Figure 5-33b uses two light sensors to detect the light scattered
at 90° in both directions and thereby improve the sensitivity of the instrument
and allow the determination of trace amounts of turbidity. Both light sensors
are submerged in the sample liquid. Stray light effects are minimized by virtue

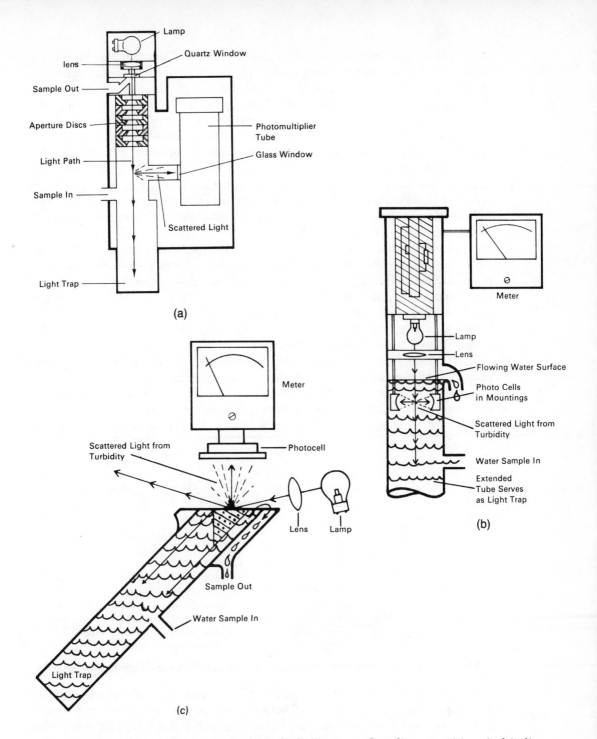

Figure 5-33. In-line nephelometric turbidimeters—flow diagrams: (a) typical in-line design; (b) dual-light-sensor design for extended low range; (c) surface scatter turbidimeter. (Courtesy of Hach Chemical Co.)

of admitting the light through the upper surface of the sample. Similarily, light scattering at the surface of the sample liquid where the light beam enters it in the instrument illustrated in Figure 5-33c is negligible. In this instrument, however, the sealed window is eliminated (and so is periodic cleaning of a window) and the light beam strikes the surface at an angle of about 15°. Light scattered at 90° to the surface is detected by the light sensor ("photocell"). As shown in Figure 5-33c, the cross section of the sample which is illuminated and from which light is scattered is a solid triangle, about 4 cm deep at its apex. As the turbidity reaches high values, the strength of the light beam reaching this depth is reduced; hence, the response of the instrument to turbidities above about 1000 FTU becomes nonlinear but still provides repeatable measurements to about 5000 FTU.

The instruments described above are used for liquid samples, notably for water and wastewater analyses. Nephelometric sensors are also used for gaseous samples, primarily for the detection of particles suspended in air. A popular example is one type of *smoke detector* used in homes. A light beam is directed at a sample volume of air, and light reflected and scattered at 90° by smoke entering this volume is detected by a light sensor. The output of this sensor is used to activate an alarm.

An example of a nephelometer used mainly for air pollution determinations is the *integrating nephelometer* shown in Figure 5-34. An air sample is drawn through a chamber in which it is illuminated by a flash lamp. The scattered light is detected by a photomultiplier tube shielded from the light source, but viewing the sample air volume. The photomultiplier output is

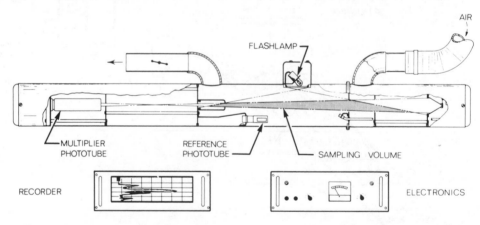

Figure 5-34. Integrating nephelometer. (Courtesy of Meteorology Research, Inc.)

averaged and compared with the output of a reference light sensor which senses the light from the light source. The geometry of the light beam and sample volume are such that light scattered at angles covering close to 180° is detected, which is equivalent to integrating the scattering over this range of angles. The reduction in scattered light intensity due to distance from the point of detection is compensated for by the geometry of the sensing volume which is greater at

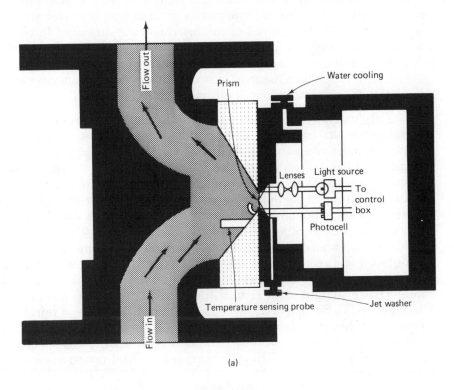

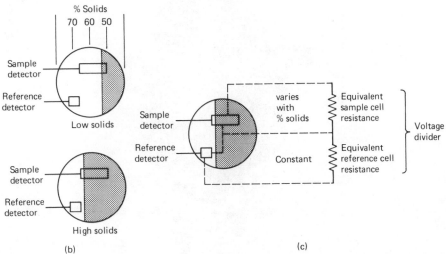

Figure 5-35. Operating principle of a process refractometer: (a) schematic layout of instrument assembly; (b) refractometer image; (c) simplified measuring circuit. (Courtesy of Anacon Inc.)

those greater distances. The amount of light scattering is proportional to the mass concentration of particulate matter in air as long as the relative humidity is less than 70%. The output of the instrument is displayed in terms of the *scattering coefficient*, defined as the reciprocal of the distance in which 63% of the light is lost from a light beam. A derived measurement of visibility, "local visual distance," which assumes that the sample is representative of the total local atmosphere, is additionally displayed.

5.4.2.4 Refractometers. Sensing devices which measure the index of refraction of substances are frequently used in process measurement to obtain not only refractive index measurements but determinations of solids concentration in liquids that can be correlated with index of refraction. A typical instrument is shown schematically in Figure 5-35a. It contains a light source, optics for beam collimation, a dual-element (photoconductive-junction) light sensor, and a prism which is brought in contact with the measured liquid. The prism in this design is made of spinel (synthetic diamond) since this material is very hard, resists abrasion and contamination, and has a long operating life. The light beam is directed at the boundary between prism and liquid. The light incident at this boundary changes sharply from mostly transmitted light to totally reflected light at the critical angle (see Figure 5-29d). The critical angle, as explained in Section 5.4.1, is dependent upon the index of refraction of the liquid and, hence, on the dissolved solids concentration in the liquid. The reflected-light image as seen by the dual-light-sensor (photodetector) is illustrated in Figure 5-35b. With increasing index of refraction (increasing solids

Figure 5-36. Insertion-probe-type refractometer. (Courtesy of Anacon Inc.)

concentration) the upper light sensor (sample detector) receives decreasing light, due to the change in critical angle, while the lower light sensor (reference detector) receives a constant amount of light. The two detectors are connected as a voltage divider with one leg of fixed resistance and the other leg of variable resistance so that an output voltage proportional to index of refraction is obtained (Figure 5-35c).

The instrument shown in Figure 5-35 is of the valve-body type, provided with flanges for mounting in a pipeline. An instrument of similar design but of the immersion-probe type, is shown in Figure 5-36; it is installed by threading it into a standard threaded fitting on a pipeline, tank, or other vessel. Both designs incorporate a temperature sensor and associated circuitry to compensate the refractometer readings for temperature as well as to provide a separate readout of temperature. Some of the other refractometer designs include, instead, a thermostatically controlled constant-temperature bath surrounding the sample line or cell (the index of refraction varies with temperature). The readout can be in terms of refractive index, of percent solids (in a specified liquid), or for sugar solutions, in "Brix degrees," which are units of the hydrometric "Brix scale."

5.4.3 Performance Characteristics

Performance characteristics considered essential for opacity sensors, turbidimeters, nephelometers, and refractometers are given partly by general measuring-instrument considerations, partly by their applications, and partly by their nature as optical-quantity sensors. Characteristics in common to these instruments are such accuracy functions as zero stability, sensitivity shift and drift, repeatability, threshold and resolution (sometimes erroneously called "sensitivity" in specifications), and response time (which should be defined more specifically, such as "95% response time"); the amount of stray light, if any, is sometimes specified, as is dark current of the light sensor (in terms of instrument output signal). Outputs available from the instrument are always specified; typical outputs are 1 to 10 V dc (or 0 to 10 or 0 to 5 V dc); 1 to 5, 4 to 20, 10 to 50 mA dc; and optional contact closures, at specified outputs, for the activation of alarms (or controls, in some instances). For in-line instruments, the allowable temperature and pressure ranges, as well as some other important characteristics such as corrosiveness, of the measured fluid are specified, as are those materials of the instrument that will come in contact with the measured fluids. Permissible ambient environmental characteristics are shown for instruments installed either outdoors or, in severe or contaminating environments, indoors.

Except for opacity sensors, whose range is usually 0 to 100% opacity (or the equivalent), the range (or ranges, when selectable) of the instrument is shown in one or more units such as parts per million (ppm), sometimes in "ppm D.E.," where "D.E." refers to diatomaceous earth used as reference material, in JTU, FTU, or NTU, in "% suspended solids," and sometimes (for nephelometry of air) in micrograms per cubic meter; refractometers show readouts in index of refraction, sometimes additionally in solids concentration (for a specified liquid).

Opacity monitors used as smoke density sensors are often governed by specifications developed by governmental agencies such as, in the United States, the Environmental Protection Agency (EPA). These typically include requirements for *photopic* response of the light sensor (human-eye equivalent), for an angle of view (of the light sensor) and an angle of projection (of the light source) of less than 5° ($\pm 2.5°$) and for specific limits on performance characteristics such as 95% response time and repeatability. Air purge of light source and sensor are a requirement, and it is desirable to assure air flow by monitoring it. For turbidimeters an additional requirement is insensitivity of the instrument to measured-fluid color. Input voltage and other power supply characteristics are specified for all instruments.

Bibliography

1. **Fink, D. G.** (Ed.), *Television Engineering Handbook.* New York: McGraw-Hill Book Company, 1957.

2. **Fishman, M.,** *Light Scattering by Colloidal Systems: An Annotated Bibliography.* River Edge, NJ: Technical Services Laboratories, 1957.

3. **van de Hulst, H. C.,** *Light Scattering by Small Particles.* New York: John Wiley & Sons, Inc., 1957.

4. **Walsh, J. W. T.,** *Photometry* (3rd ed., rev.). London: Constable & Co. Ltd., 1958.

5. **Boutry, G. A.,** *Instrumental Optics.* New York: Interscience Publishers, 1962.

6. **Summer, W.,** *Ultra-Violet and Infra-Red Engineering.* New York: Interscience Publishers, 1962.

7. **Wright, W. D.,** *The Measurement of Colour.* London: Hilger & Watts, 1963.

8. **Wolfe, W. L.** (Ed.), *Handbook of Military Infrared Technology.* Washington, DC: U.S. Government Printing Office, 1965.

9. **Wyszecki, G., and Stiles, W. S.,** *Color Science: Concepts and Methods, Quantitative Data and Formulas.* New York: John Wiley & Sons, Inc., 1967.

10. **Calder, A. B.,** *Photometric Methods of Analysis.* New York: American Elsevier Publishing Co., Inc., 1969.

11. **Kerker, M.,** *The Scattering of Light.* New York: Academic Press, Inc., 1969.

12. **Yariv, A.,** *Introduction to Optical Electronics.* New York: Holt, Rinehart and Winston, 1971.

13. **Nimeroff, I.** (Ed.), "Precision Measurement and Calibration Colorimetry," *NBS Special Publication 300,* Vol. 2. Washington, DC: National Bureau of Standards, 1972.

14. **Moss, T. S., Burrell, G. J., and Ellis, B.,** *Semiconductor Opto-electronics.* New York: Halstead Press, 1973.

15. **Wright, H. C.,** *Infrared Techniques.* Oxford: Clarendon Press, 1973.

16. **Hecht, E., and Zajac, A.,** *Optics.* Reading, MA: Addison-Wesley Publishing Co., 1974.

17. **Kaminow, I. P.,** *An Introduction to Electrooptic Devices.* New York: Academic Press, 1974.

18. **Perkins, W. D.,** "An Infrared Bibliography," *Infrared Bulletin No. 42.* Norwalk, CT: Perkin-Elmer, Instrument Div., 1974.

19. **Stimson, A.,** *Photometry and Radiometry for Engineers.* New York: John Wiley & Sons, Inc., 1974.

20. **Dainty, J. C., and Shaw, R.,** *Image Science.* New York: Academic Press, Inc., 1975.

21. **Hudson, R. D., Jr., and Hudson, J. W.** (ed.), *Infrared Detectors.* Stroudsburg, PA: Dowden, Hutchinson & Ross, Inc., 1975.

22. **Padgham, C. A., and Saunders, J. E.,** *The Perception of Light and Colour.* New York: Academic Press, 1975.

23. **Tanaka, S.,** *Optical Methods in Scientific and Industrial Measurements.* Tokyo: Japanese Journal of Applied Physics, 1975.

24. **Beesley, M. J.,** *Lasers and Their Applications.* New York: Halstead Press, 1976.

25. **Gloge, D.** (Ed.), *Optical Fiber Technology.* New York: IEEE Press, 1976.

26. **Hinkley, E. D.** (Ed.), *Laser Monitoring of the Atmosphere.* New York: Springer-Verlag, New York, Inc., 1976.

27. **Kallard, T.,** *Exploring Laser Light.* New York: Optosonic Press, 1976.

28. **Okoshi, T.,** *Three-Dimensional Imaging Techniques.* New York: Academic Press, Inc., 1976.

29. **Sahm, W. H.,** *General Electric Optoelectronics Manual.* Syracuse, NY: General Electric Co., 1976.

30. **Yu, F. T. S.,** *Optics and Information Theory.* New York: Wiley-Interscience, 1976.

31. **Fox, R. W.,** *Optoelectronics Guidebook.* Blue Ridge Summit, PA: TAB Books, 1977.

32. **Gonzalez, R. C.,** *Digital Image Processing.* Reading, MA: Addison-Wesley Publishing Co., Inc., 1977.

33. **Melen, R., and Buss, D.** (Ed.), *Charge-Coupled Devices: Technology and Applications.* New York: IEEE Press, 1977.

34. **Wolfe, W. L., and Zissis, G. J.** (Ed.), *The Infrared Handbook.* Ann Arbor, MI: Infrared Information and Analysis Center, 1978.

chapter six

Nuclear Radiation

6.1   BASIC CONCEPTS

Nuclear radiation is the emission of charged and uncharged particles and of electromagnetic radiation from atomic nuclei. *Charged particles* include alpha and beta particles and protons. *Uncharged particles* are typified by the neutron. Gamma rays and X-rays are forms of (nuclear) *electromagnetic radiation* (see Figure 6-1).

Elementary particles comprise electrons, positrons, neutrons, protons, various mesons, and hyperons, neutrinos, and photons.

Alpha particles (α-particles) are nuclei of helium atoms; an alpha particle consists of two protons and two neutrons and has a double positive charge.

Beta particles (β-particles) are negative electrons or positive electrons (positrons); they are emitted when *beta decay* occurs in a nucleus, a radioactive transformation by which the atomic number is changed by +1 or −1 while the mass number remains unchanged.

Gamma rays (γ-rays) are electromagnetic radiation quanta resulting from quantum transitions between two energy levels of a nucleus.

X-rays are quanta of electromagnetic radiation originating in the extranuclear part of the atom. It can be noted from Figure 6-1 that *hard X-rays* are more energetic than *soft X-rays* and, therefore, have a greater penetrating power. Also see *Bremsstrahlung,* below.

Cosmic rays are high-energy charged particles from outer space. *Primary cosmic rays* are almost entirely composed of positively charged atomic nuclei and about 92% of these are protons. *Secondary cosmic rays* are formed by collisions of primary cosmic rays with air nuclei in the earth's upper atmosphere and contain mostly gamma rays, electrons, mesons, and neutrinos.

Protons are positively charged elementary particles of mass number 1.

Neutrons are uncharged elementary particles of mass number 1. They can exist only briefly in a free state. The energy ranges are up to 10^3 eV for *slow neutrons*, 10^3 to 10^5 eV for *intermediate neutrons*, and above 10^5 (to about 5×10^7) eV for *fast neutrons*. *Thermal neutrons* are slow neutrons having velocities in equilibrium with the velocities of thermal agitation of the molecules in the medium in which they are situated; the energy of thermal neutrons is in the lowest portion of the slow neutron energy range (0.03 eV or less).

Ionization is the process of formation of atoms with a positive or negative charge *(ions)*.

Scintillation is the emission of light energy *(photons)* by a photoluminescent material *(phosphor)* due to the incidence of ionizing radiation upon the material.

Bremsstrahlung is a continuous spectrum of X-radiation produced by the acceleration or deceleration applied to a high-velocity charged particle when it is deflected by another charged particle. The literal translation of this German word is "braking radiation," from *Bremse* (brake).

Cerenkov radiation is the radiation emitted by a high-energy charged particle when it passes through a medium in which its speed is greater than the speed of light. The index of refraction of such a medium must be greater than unity.

Compton scattering is the elastic scattering of photons by electrons. A *Compton electron* is one set in motion by interaction with a photon.

Neutron density is the number of neutrons per unit volume.

Neutron flux is the product of neutron density and speed (for neutrons of a given energy).

Half-life is the time required for the disintegration of half the atoms of a radioactive substance. *Biological half-life* is the time required for a living biological organism to eliminate one-half of a radioactive substance, that was introduced to it, by means of biological processes. The *effective half-life* is the half-life of a radioactive isotope in a biological organism, expressed as the product of radioactive and biological half-life divided by the sum of radioactive and biological half-life.

Dose is a quantity of ionizing radiation to which a biological sample is exposed, or which it absorbs *(exposure dose, absorbed dose)*.

6.1.1 Related Fundamental Constants

Speed of light in vacuum, c = 2.997 925 $\times$ 10^8 m/s (round off to 3×10^8)

(Unified) atomic mass unit (amu), u = 1.660 565 $\times$ 10^{-27} kg (round off to 1.66×10^{-27})

Electron rest mass, m_e = 9.109 534 $\times$ 10^{-31} kg (round off to 9.11 $\times$ 10^{-31})

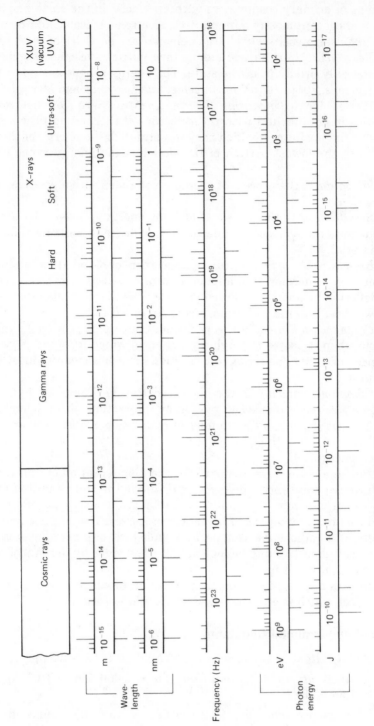

Figure 6-1. Electromagnetic spectrum below 10 nm.

Proton rest mass, m_p = 1.672 648 × 10^{-27} kg (round off to 1.673 × 10^{-27})

Neutron rest mass, m_n = 1.674 954 × 10^{-27} kg (round off to 1.675 × 10^{-27})

Electron charge, e = 1.602 189 × 10^{-19} C (round off to 1.602 × 10^{-19})

Planck constant, h = 6.626 176 × 10^{-34} J·s (round off to 6.626 × 10^{-34})
= 4.135 673 × 10^{-15} eV·s (round off to 4.136 × 10^{-15})

6.1.2 Related Laws

Special Theory of Relativity

$$E = mc^2 \qquad m = \frac{m_0}{\sqrt{(1 - v^2/c^2)}}$$

where E = energy
m = mass (in motion)
m_0 = mass (at rest) *(rest mass)*
c = velocity of light
v = velocity of mass

Planck's Law

$$\mathscr{E} = h\nu$$

where $\mathscr{E}$ = photon energy, J   or $\mathscr{E}$ = photon energy, eV
ν = frequency, Hz ν = frequency, Hz
h = Planck constant, J·s h = Planck's constant, eV·s

Radioactive Decay Law

$$N = N_0 e^{-\lambda t}$$

where N = number of atoms (of a radioactive species) at time t
N_0 = number of atoms present at $t = 0$
t = elapsed time
e = base of natural logarithm (2.71828)
λ = *decay constant*

6.1.3 Units of Measurement

Radioactivity (activity of a radionuclide) is expressed in becquerels. The *becquerel (Bq)* is the activity of a radionuclide decaying at the rate of one spontaneous transition per second (Bq = s^{-1}). The becquerel is the SI unit that replaces the curie. The *curie (Ci)* equals the quantity of any radioactive material in which the number of disintegrations per second is 3.7×10^{10}. *Conversion: 1 Ci = 3.7 $\times$ 10^{10} Bq.*

Absorbed dose is expressed in grays. The *gray (Gy)* is the absorbed dose when the energy per unit mass imparted to matter by ionizing radiation is 1 joule per kilogram (Gy = J/kg). The gray is the SI unit that replaces the rad. The *rad (rad)* is the absorbed dose when the energy per unit mass imparted to matter by ionizing radiation is 100 ergs per gram. *Conversion: 1 rad = 10^{-2} Gy.*

Exposure dose (X-ray and gamma-ray exposure) is expressed in coulombs per kilogram. *The coulomb per kilogram (C/kg)* is the exposure when X rays or gamma rays produce in free air 1 coulomb of electrical charge per kilogram of dry air. The C/kg is the SI unit that replaces the roentgen. The *roentgen (R)* equals the quantity of X-ray or gamma-ray radiation whose associated secondary ionizing particles produce ions, in air, carrying one electrostatic unit of charge (of either sign) per 0.001293 g of air. *Conversion: 1 R = 2.58 $\times$ 10^{-4} C/kg.*

Dose equivalent (in radiobiology) is expressed in sieverts. The *sievert (Sv)* is the dose equivalent when the absorbed dose of ionizing radiation multiplied by the dimensionless factors Q (quality factor) and N (product of any other multiplying factors) stipulated by the International Commission on Radiological Protection is 1 joule per kilogram (Sv = J/kg). The sievert is the SI unit that replaces the rem. The *rem (rem),* a unit whose name was derived from "roentgen equivalent, man," is the unit of *relative biological effectiveness dose (RBE dose).* It equals the absorbed dose (in rads) times an agreed conventional value of the RBE. It was originally defined as the absorbed dose that will produce the same effect in human tissue as that produced by one roentgen. *Conversion: 1 rem = 10^{-2} Sv.*

Energy (electromagnetic energy, or *photon energy* since the photon is a quantum of electromagnetic energy) is expressed in joules. The *joule (J)* is the SI unit that replaces the *electron volt (eV). Conversion: 1 eV = 1.602 $\times$ 10^{-12} erg = 1.602 $\times$ 10^{-19} J (1 erg = 10^{-7} J).*

Neutron flux is expressed in *neutrons per square meter-seconds (n/m²·s);* the use of the centimeter instead of the meter is fairly common (n/cm²·s).

The *window thickness* of a radiation detector is commonly expressed in *milligrams per square centimeter (mg/cm²).*

6.2 SENSING METHODS

The sensing and transduction of nuclear radiation is commonly referred to as *radiation detection,* and nuclear-radiation transducers are known as *radiation detectors.* In virtually all radiation detectors the detection process is based on the interaction of the radiation with a substance contained in the detector.

6.2.1 Radiation Detection Using Ionization

This method of detection relies upon the production of an ion pair in a gaseous or solid material and the separation of the positive and negative charges by an electric field to produce an output signal.

Charged particles, such as alpha and beta particles and protons, can exert sufficient electromagnetic forces on the outer electrons of atoms which they pass at high velocity to separate one of the electrons. When this occurs, an ion pair is formed. The ions move to the electrodes of opposite sign, and an ion current is created. One particle can cause such ionization to take place several

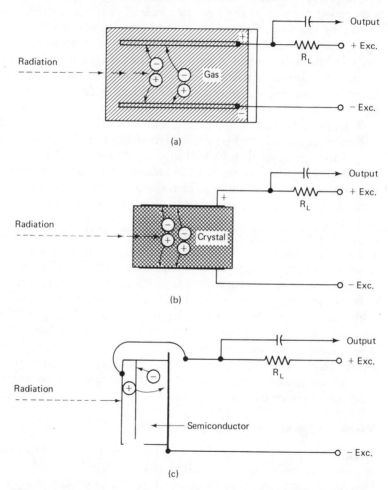

Figure 6-2. Radiation detection using ionization (shown for output in pulse mode; output is taken directly across R_L in current mode): (a) ionization in gas; (b) ionization in solid crystal; (c) ionization in solid semiconductor.

times before its energy is expended. Electrons that are released in the ionization process can be accelerated sufficiently to produce additional ions.

Neutrons and other uncharged particles can produce ionizing particles by transferring some of their energy to nuclei with which they collide. X-rays and gamma rays can remove secondary electrons from atoms with which they interact and these electrons then produce ion pairs.

Radiation detection by ionization in different substances is illustrated in Figure 6-2. The separation of positive and negative ions is due to the electric field between two electrodes (cathode and anode), or between the positively and negatively charged material of a semiconductor, by connecting them across a dc power supply. In the *current mode* of operation, the increase in current caused by the flow of charges to the electrodes of opposite polarities (the *ionization current*) can be monitored as the average IR drop across the load resistor (R_L). In the *pulse mode* of operation, the ionization is measured as a single event. The output is a train of voltage pulses, each pulse generated by the ionization due to one particle. The output pulses are conveniently taken through a coupling capacitor.

Different particles cause different amounts of ionization; hence, the output pulse amplitude can be indicative of the types of incident particles.

The ionization current will also be greater when some of the same type of particles have higher energy than others. The pulse amplitude then becomes a measure of particle energy. The average ionization current resulting from a steady radiation flux can be used as a measure of the average magnitude of this flux.

Ionization due to nuclear radiation occurs in certain gases and solids to various extents. Figure 6-2a shows ion pairs formed in a gas such as argon or krypton. Ionization in solid crystals, such as diamond or silver chloride, has also been used for radiation detection. Charge separation and flow of ionization current are effected by two electrodes of opposite polarity, on opposite crystal surfaces, connected to a dc power supply, as shown in Figure 6-2b. Solid-crystal detectors have been largely replaced by semiconductor detectors. Semiconductor materials, such as germanium and silicon, can produce positive/negative charge pairs (electron–hole pairs) as a result of incident radiation in the presence of an electric field established by the junction between p- and n-type material when dc excitation is applied, as illustrated in Figure 6-2c.

6.2.2 Radiation Detection Using Scintillation

Certain materials have been found to convert nuclear radiation into light with a relatively high conversion efficiency. Such *scintillator* materials are used, in conjunction with a photon detector, in radiation detectors. Photomultipliers are used for the detection of the photons produced in the scintillator (see Figure 6-3). The scintillator is optically coupled very closely with the photocathode of the multiplier. Due to their light emitting action, scintillator materials act as *phosphors*. These materials can be organic or inorganic, solid, liquid, or gaseous.

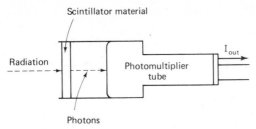

Figure 6-3. Radiation detection using scintillation.

A different effect, unrelated to scintillation, also produces light in response to nuclear radiation. The *Cerenkov effect* (first observed by Cerenkov, in 1934, in the USSR) occurs in pure, transparent, nonluminescent material (e.g., certain glasses) whose refractive index is such that the velocity of the radiation through the material is greater than the velocity of light through the material. Cerenkov radiators are used, in conjunction with photon detectors, in detectors known as *Cerenkov counters,* for the detection of very high energy radiation.

6.2.3 Electron Detection

The detection of electrons, as such, can be performed by a very high input-impedance *electrometer tube* or by other electrometers such as the quartz-fiber and vibrating-reed type. The most commonly used devices, however, are *electron multipliers,* in which the incoming electron releases secondary electrons in increasing numbers *(avalanche effect)* from a number of dynodes or one continuous dynode. The dynodes are placed ahead of the anode, and the output signal is a change in anode current due to total electron flow toward the anode.

6.3 DESIGN AND OPERATION

Emphasis in this section is placed on those types of radiation detectors that are most commonly available commercially. Some additional types are described briefly. Categorized by transduction principle, ionization chambers, proportional counters, and Geiger counters are gas-filled ionizing transducers, semiconductor detectors are solid-material ionizing transducers, and scintillation counters are photoelectric transducers.

6.3.1 Ionization Chambers

The usual configuration of an ionization chamber ("ion chamber") is cylindrical (Figure 6-4). The outer metallic cylinder is the cathode. An internal rod or wire running along the axis of the cylinder is the anode. The outer surface of the cathode is usually uninsulated since it is normally kept at ground potential. Electrical connections are simple and are not necessarily peculiar to the configurations illustrated. The *end-window* ionization chamber (Figure 6-4a) mates with a socket that provides spring contacts for the cathode and an insulated female socket for the anode pin. The *side-window ionization chamber*

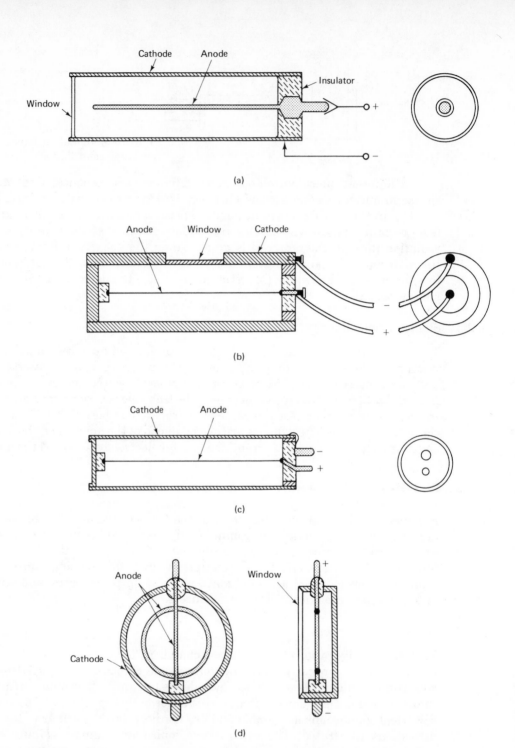

Figure 6-4. Typical configurations of ionization chambers: (a) with end window; (b) with side window; (c) without window; (d) pancake style, with window.

(Figure 6-4b) has leads attached to cathode and anode terminals. The *windowless ionization chamber* (Figure 6-4c) is shown with two connector pins of different diameters. The "pancake" style (Figure 6-4d) is a special configuration of compact design. Cathodes are usually made from a corrosion-resistant metal such as stainless steel. Earlier designs have a glass envelope surrounding cathode and anode.

Although all gases will produce some ionization, those used in ionization chambers are selected for optimum ionization potential and energy per ion pair. Typical fill gases are argon, krypton, neon, xenon, helium, hydrogen, nitrogen, and certain compounds such as barium trifluoride (BF_3) and methane (CH_4). Favorable operation can be obtained by admixing a small amount of a different gas, for example, neon with a small amount of argon, xenon or argon with a small amount of nitrogen. The pressure of the gas within the chamber can be below, at, or above atmospheric pressure. When very thin windows are used it must be close to atmospheric pressure to minimize any pressure differential across the window.

Window material and thickness are governing factors of the response of an ionization chamber to different types and energy levels of radiation to be measured. If the mean range of a heavy particle or a particle of very low energy is exceeded by the window thickness, the particle will be stopped by the window and will not be detected. Hence, very thin windows are required for alpha-particle detection. Mica windows having a thickness of less than 4 mg/cm^3 are typically used to meet this requirement. Thin metal windows are used for beta, gamma, and X-rays when no alpha radiation needs to be measured. Windowless thin-wall chambers have a nearly spherical field of view. Their cylindrical case, typically 30 to 50 mg/cm^3 thick, acts as window as well as cathode. When narrow fields of view are required, the chamber can be placed in a thick-walled enclosure *(shield)* having a small aperture. For gamma-ray detection, windows should be made of a metal having a large gamma-ray absorption coefficient (e.g., tantalum or tungsten). Stainless steel has been used as a compromise material for windows and thin-wall-chamber cathodes when both beta and gamma rays are to be detected. Anodes are typically made of thin tungsten wire.

6.3.2 Proportional Counters

When the excitation voltage across the electrodes of a gas-filled chamber is close to zero, most ion pairs will be lost due to recombination. As the voltage is increased the recombination loss is negligible and ionization-chamber operation is achieved. As the voltage is further increased, the chamber operates in the *proportional region* where *gas amplification* occurs: electrons released in the primary ionization are accelerated sufficiently to produce additional ionization and thus add to the collected charge. The output pulse is proportional to the total collected charge, which is proportional to the energy of the incident particle that causes the primary ionization. As the voltage is increased still further, the output pulse size becomes increasingly independent of the primary ionization, until a region called the *Geiger plateau* is reached (see Section 6.3.3) in which the collected charge is entirely independent of the amount of initial ionization.

In gas amplification (gas multiplication) the additional ions multiply themselves by an avalanche effect. Each secondary electron ionizes additional gas molecules, producing more secondary electrons, and so on. The avalanche effect starts at a threshold value of anode-to-cathode potential and increases when the potential is raised above that value. Threshold values and gas amplification factor (which can vary between 1 and 10^6) depend on excitation voltage, on detector geometry, and on the fill gas. Gas mixtures such as xenon/nitrogen, argon/CO_2, or hydrogen/CH_4 are often used in detectors which operate in the proportional region and are, therefore, called *proportional counters*. The admixture of gases such as CO_2 and CH_4 (methane) greatly reduces the ionization caused by ultraviolet radiation created during the avalanche process; the absorption of this UV radiation by the gas additives allows higher anode voltages to be used and larger gas amplification factors to be realized (see Figure 6-5) while maintaining stable counter operation.

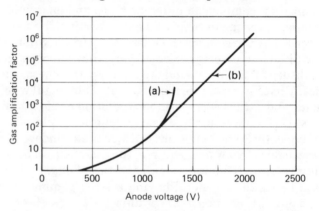

Figure 6-5. Gas amplification factor as a function of anode voltage for (a) pure argon and (b) 95% argon/5% CO_2.

Since a proportional counter produces a pulse for each ionizing event, and since the amplitude of the output pulse is proportional to the energy of the incident radiation (as long as the counter operates within the truly proportional region), this type of detector can be used to differentiate between various particles (e.g., to measure alpha particles in the presence of beta and gamma radiation). This is accomplished by pulse-height discrimination in the output conditioning circuitry.

The windowless *gas-flow counter* is a special version of the proportional counter (it can also be a special version of the Geiger counter). It is very usable for the detection of alpha radiation and weak beta radiation such as emitted by certain commonly used radioisotopes (e.g., C^{14}, S^{35}, Ca^{45}, and H^3). It consists of an ionization chamber hood, equipped with inlet and outlet hose connections, that is slipped over and sealed against a sample holder (see Figure 6-6). A gas (-mixture) supply is connected to the counter, and the required voltage is applied to it while the gas flows through the counter. The quick make-and-break seal allows the rapid insertion and removal of radiation emitting samples. Continuous replacement of the gas also extends the life of the counter substantially. Very thin replaceable windows (about 0.25 mg/cm³) are sometimes used in gas-flow counters to reduce possible effects of static charges, accidental contamination from a loosely packed sample, and vapor effects from moist samples.

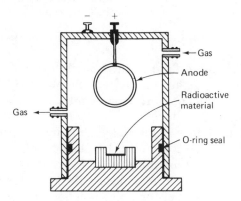

Figure 6-6. Gas-flow counter.

6.3.3 Geiger Counters

As explained at the outset of Section 6.3.2, increasing the anode-to-cathode potential of a proportional counter above the proportional region causes it to operate in a different region, called the *Geiger–Mueller (G-M)* region, in which the total collected charge, greatly increased by gas amplification, is independent of the energy that initiated the primary ionization. If the anode potential is increased still further, the discharge region is reached. Discharge can, however, be kept from becoming continuous *(quenched)* by admixture to the gas, in the chamber, of a *quenching agent*. The quenching vapor, typically alcohol or a *halogen* such as bromine or chlorine, quenches the discharge by preventing the production of secondary electrons by positive ions at the cathode. A counter that operates in this region and contains a quenching agent is called a *Geiger–Mueller tube,* or *G-M tube,* or *Geiger counter.*

There is, of course, a limit to the anode potential that can be applied before discharge becomes continuous, even in the presence of a quenching agent. The anode-to-cathode potential must be kept within a *plateau* bounded by minimum and maximum voltage limits (see Figure 6-7). The quenching action begins to fail when the voltage exceeds that maximum, and operation reverts to the proportional mode when the voltage decreases below the minimum. Hence, the anode voltage is set, and regulated about, a value equivalent to the center of the plateau. It should be noted that the absence of such a plateau characteristic in proportional counters (and some ionization chambers)

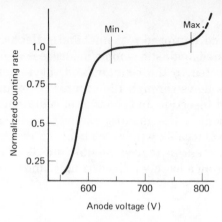

Figure 6-7. Plateau of typical Geiger counter.

poses a much more severe requirement for the regulation of their power supplies.

Since some of the quenching fluid is dissociated during each discharge, alcohol-quenched Geiger counters have a limited life (about 10^8 counts). Halogen quenching gas, however, tends to recombine after dissociation and does not impose a constraint on the life of the counter. Gas-flow proportional counters can be operated as Geiger counters by admixing a quenching agent to the gas and raising its anode voltage into the Geiger region.

The output pulse of a Geiger counter is characterized by a fast rise time (less than 1 μs) and a duration of several μs before its decay due to quenching following the discharge. The decay of the pulse is followed by a *dead time* of 50 to 150 μs. During a subsequent *recovery time,* usually shorter than the decay time, the counter gradually becomes capable of producing a full-height output pulse again. The counter is inoperative during the dead time, and any particle that could produce an ionizing event would not be detected during this time. A particle causing an ionizing event during the recovery time would create an output pulse of less than full height.

Dead time can be reduced by pulsing the anode voltage rather than applying it steadily. The pulses extend from a quiescent voltage at which no ionization occurs, or even from a slightly negative bias level, to the voltage required for operation in the Geiger region. The counter is then operative only while the Geiger-region voltage pulse is applied. The pulse on and off times are selected as much shorter than the normal dead time and recovery time. As a result, the counter will respond to a larger number of particles per unit time.

6.3.4   Semiconductor Detectors

Semiconductor detectors tend to be significantly more efficient than gas-filled ionization detectors: the material is about 10^3 times denser; its average threshold energy, for electron–hole pair production, is roughly 10 times lower; its carrier mobilities are higher; and the difference between the mobilities of positive and negative charges is less.

Intrinsic semiconductors are pure crystals; the concentration of charge carriers is characteristic of the material itself rather than of impurity content or imperfections within the crystal. Intrinsic semiconductor detectors have been used for gamma-ray and X-ray measurements as well as light measurement. Charge carriers (electron–hole pairs) are produced in intrinsic semiconductor material (typically Si or Ge) by the interaction between incident photons and the atoms of the material as a result of (1) the elastic scattering of photons by electrons, which sets other electrons into motion *(Compton effect);* (2) the ejection of a bound electron from an atom with absorption of all of the photon's energy *(photoelectric effect);* and (3) the conversion of a photon, traversing a strong nuclear electric field, into an electron and a positron *(pair production).* When an excitation potential is applied across the two electrodes on the crystal, incident radiation will create electron–hole pairs, with the electrons and holes flowing toward their corresponding electrodes; the resulting current can then be detected as an *IR* drop across the load resistor *(R_L)* and becomes the detector's output voltage (see Figure 6-8).

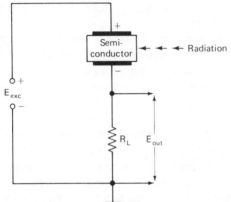

Figure 6-8. Intrinsic-semiconductor radiation detector.

The output pulse produced by each event is characterized by a short rise time and a somewhat slower decay time because the electrons have a mobility typically three times that of the holes. Although noise current is reduced by using materials with high bulk resistivity, the thermal noise level of intrinsic semiconductor detectors at room temperature tends to be very high; far more efficient operation is obtained by cryogenic cooling of the detector. *High-purity (HP)* detectors are intrinsic semiconductors.

Extrinsic semiconductors are those whose properties are dependent on controlled impurities added to the crystal. They exist in two major types. The *surface-barrier* type (Figure 6-9a) usually consists of *n*-type single-crystal silicon on one surface of which a *p*-type layer of silicon dioxide is formed. This thin (often monomolecular) layer is typically covered with an evaporated gold film which serves as contact (electrical ground). The back electrode, to which the bias voltage is applied, is also formed by evaporation; gold or aluminum are typically used. A few designs use *p*-type silicon with an *n*-type layer; here, the ground contact (entrance contact) is at positive potential and a negative

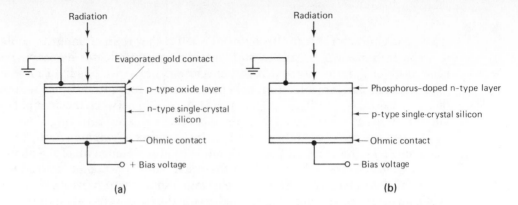

Figure 6-9. Basic types of extrinsic-semiconductor radiation detectors: (a) surface barrier type; (b) diffused junction type.

bias voltage is applied to the back electrode. The *diffused-junction* type (Figure 6-9b) is commonly made by a shallow diffusion of phosphorus to form an *n*-type layer in *p*-type single-crystal material; *p*-type diffusion in *n*-type material has also been used in a few designs.

N-type silicon has an excess of electrons (negative charges) and *p*-type silicon has an excess of holes (positive charges). An electric field (potential gradient) exists in the space-charge region *(depletion layer)* close to the junction, where the net charge density of donors and acceptors is not neutralized by the mobile-carrier density and is, hence, substantially different from zero. It is in this *depletion region* that electron–hole pairs are produced by incident radiation. The depth of the depletion region (the *depletion depth*) is governed by the resistivity (bulk resistivity) of the silicon wafer and by the externally applied bias voltage (voltage applied across the two electrodes). The depletion depth must be chosen on the basis of the maximum energy of the particle to be detected. The *range in silicon* (determined from particle type and energy) required to stop that particle then equals the required depletion depth. Once this depth has been established the appropriate combination of bulk resistivity and bias voltage can be calculated (or read off a nomogram). In *partially depleted* detectors the depletion depth is some fraction of the silicon wafer thickness. In *totally depleted* detectors the depletion depth is equal to the wafer thickness.

Between the sensing surface of the detector and the active region there exists a layer in which some of the incident energy is dissipated without producing electron–hole pairs collectable by the electrodes *(dead layer)*. The dead layer of surface-barrier detectors is usually smaller than that of diffused-junction detectors. This advantage is somewhat offset by the location of the barrier right at the surface, which makes surface-barrier detectors more subject to mechanical damage. The schematic representation, construction, and two configurational examples of a typical silicon surface barrier detector are shown in Figure 6-10.

In the *p-i-n junction* radiation detector the *n*- and *p*-regions are separated by an intrinsic region to increase depletion depth. The best known detectors

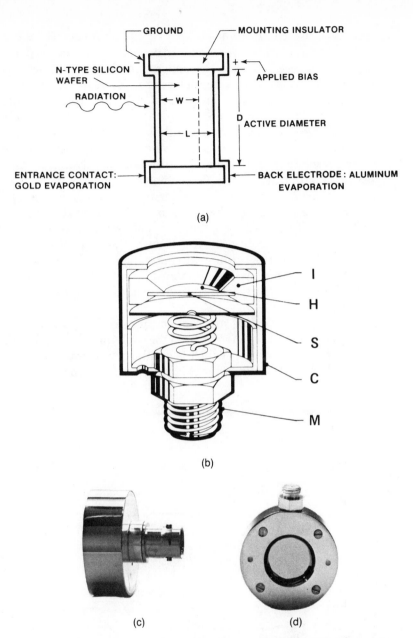

(a)

(b)

(c)   (d)

Figure 6-10. Typical silicon surface-barrier radiation detector. (a) Schematic representation: D, effective diameter (active area); W, depletion depth; L, Si-wafer thickness. (b) Sectional view: I, insulating ring; H, sensitive surface (20-nm-thick gold layer); S, circular silicon wafer; C, metal case (to which front surface of insulating ring is grounded); M, coaxial minature electrical connector. (c) Detector in standard mount. (d) Detector in demountable transmission mount. (Courtesy of EG&G ORTEC.)

of this type are the *lithium-ion drifted silicon* detectors, abbreviated *Si(Li),* and the *lithium-drifted germanium* detectors, abbreviated *Ge(Li).* Lithium ions, which act as high-mobility donors, are drifted (diffused) into *p*-type material, in the presence of a high electric field, at elevated temperatures. This process causes the lithium ions to drift deeply into the *p*-region, where they migrate to and electrically compensate acceptor sites, thus forming an intrinsic region (of high resistivity) at a small distance below the sensing surface. The thickness of this intrinsic region governs the depletion depth of this type of detector. Depletion depths are typically significantly larger than in most other types of radiation detectors. The completed detector must, however, be kept at a cryogenic temperature, even during storage. It is, therefore, assembled to a cryostat or dewar, which maintains the detector at a temperature of about 77 K [(for Ge(Li); Si(Li) detectors can operate at 150 to 200 K)], and is not removed from this cooling device. If such a sensor is mistakenly exposed to room temperature, the lithium will start to precipitate, since the lithium drift process is not stable at this temperature, and the detector will cease to be usable. Ge(Li) detectors operate in a vacuum of the type provided for HPGe detectors (see below).

The Ge(Li) detectors are commonly used for gamma-ray detection and spectrometry. Another detector used for such purposes is the *high-purity germanium (HP Ge)* detector, which is similarly maintained at a cryogenic temperature; however, the cryostat (Figure 6-11) or dewar also performs the func-

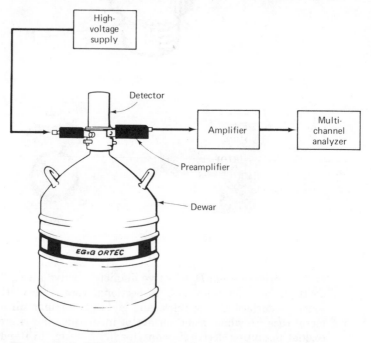

Figure 6-11. HP Ge detector and preamplifier with cryostat in typical detector system. (Courtesy of EG&G ORTEC.)

tion of providing a vacuum environment for the HP Ge detector, by cryosorption pumping. The detector, which may have a center contact formed by ion-implantation techniques rather than conventional methods, is kept closely coupled to a preamplifier (typically of the field-effect-transistor, or FET, type) which also operates at the cryogenic temperature the detector is cooled to. An advantage of the HP Ge detector over the Ge(Li) type is that it can be exposed (nonoperating) to room temperature, including for storage.

Besides Si and Ge, a few other semiconductor materials are used in radiation detectors. Although some of these are still in various stages of development, *cadmium telluride (CdTe)* detectors have been in production for some time. They can be used, at room temperature, for beta, X-ray, and gamma detection. CdTe surface-barrier-type detectors are characterized by the nearly intrinsic resistivities of their large single crystals.

The implementation of recent technology developments in semiconductor manufacture can be expected to show increasing use of ion-implantation and epitaxy techniques.

6.3.5 Scintillation Counters

In a scintillation counter the scintillator (phosphor material in its enclosure) acts as the sensing element of a transducer in that it produces a burst of light quanta (photons) in response to an incident radiation particle; the light sensor, usually a photomultiplier tube (see Section 5.2.2.4), acts as the transduction element, converting light into an output current (or, as IR drop across a load resistor, an output voltage). The term "counter" should really be applied to the entire detection system, but is commonly applied to the detector itself. Figure 6-12 illustrates a scintillation-counter system. There are two basic groups of scintillators: Cerenkov scintillators, which are used in specialized high-energy-particle detection and are made of transparent solids such as glasses, and fluorescent scintillators, which are made of organic or inorganic crystals or plastic or liquid phosphors (solution scintillators).

Inorganic crystals are impurity-activated; the impurity content is less than 0.1%. In scintillator nomenclature the symbol of the activator is placed in parentheses behind the symbol of the compound of the crystal. Thallium-activated sodium iodide, *NaI(Tl),* is the most frequently used material; it produces the highest light output and its wavelength of maximum emission is 410 nm, well within the spectral response of many photomultipliers. Other thallium-activated alkali halides used as scintillators are CsI(Tl), CsBr(Tl), and KI(Tl), with additional such materials used less frequently. CsI(Tl) has a wavelength of maximum emission between 420 and 570 nm, but its light output (relative pulse height) is only about 25% of that of NaI(Tl). There are other activators besides thallium. CsI(Na) provides a relative pulse height about 60% that of NaI(Tl), and LiI(Eu) provides a relative pulse height about 30% that of NaI(Tl). The decay constant is shortest for NaI(Tl), about 0.25 μs. The decay constants of other inorganic crystals, including CaF_2(Eu), are between 0.9 and 1.4 μs.

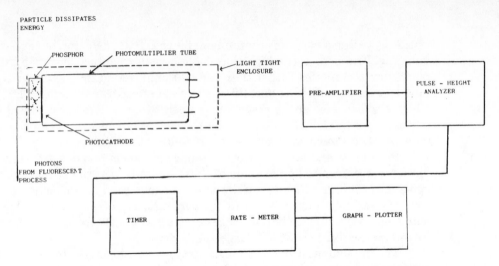

Figure 6-12. Scintillation counter system. (Courtesy of EMI, Ltd.)

Organic crystals are typically grown from coal-tar derivatives such as naphthalene ($C_{10}H_8$) and anthracene ($C_{14}H_{10}$), which have conjugate double bonds in their benzene-ring structures. Other organic scintillator materials include naphthacene, pentacene, and trans-stilbene. The relative pulse height of these materials is 50% or less compared to NaI(Tl); however, their decay constants tend to be in the nanosecond region.

Solution scintillators are usually either solid plastics (plastic phosphors) or solid materials dissolved in a liquid such as toluene. An example of a plastic scintillator is a polymerized solution of *p*-terphenyl and tetraphenylbutadiene in styrene. These scintillator materials are characterized by very short decay constants, on the order of a few nanoseconds; their relative pulse height tends to be between 10 and 20% compared to NaI(Tl). Gaseous scintillators (e.g., xenon) are infrequently used.

Photomultiplier tubes, normally used in conjunction with scintillators, are discussed in Section 5.2.2.4. The optical coupling between scintillator and photocathode must be very close. It can be a thin layer of silicone oil, or a glass or plastic "light pipe" which may be relatively long. The assembly comprising scintillator, optical coupling, and photomultiplier tube (and, often, its dynode voltage-divider resistors) is covered by an enclosure that is lightproof (except at the scintillator sensing surface) and frequently acts also as a magnetic shield. The emission spectra of scintillator and photocathode should be closely matched. Scintillator peak-emission wavelengths tend to be in the blue region. Certain compounds *(wavelength shifters)* can be added to some scintillator materials to shift their spectral response toward the red, if required by photocathode characteristics.

6.3.6 Electron Multipliers

Conventional electron detectors include the electrometer tube, and some design modifications of it, and the electron multiplier of the multiple-dynode type.

The latter is used more widely than nonmultiplying sensitive devices such as the electrometer, for the detection of electrons, as such, or as the primary detection element in such devices as mass spectrometers. Many electron multiplier designs are available; they contain typically between 10 and 14 dynodes and are all very similar in design to photomultiplier tubes (see Section 5.2.2.4) except that they lack the photocathode and usually also the (glass or metal) envelope because they are intended to be operated in vacuum. A typical design is shown in Figure 6-13. The operating principle is the avalanche effect due to secondary electron emission. The anode is operated at a high potential (typically between 2000 and 4500 V dc) referred to electrical ground. A resistance network is connected between each of the dynodes and the anode so that voltage increments are equal between successive dynodes. Incoming electrons impact the first dynode, where they release secondary electrons; because of the higher potential on the second dynode, these electrons are all accelerated toward it; upon impact with the second dynode additional secondary electrons are released by the already multiple electron stream, and this process continues until a vastly multiplied electron stream reaches the anode. By use of this avalanche effect, current amplifications between 10^5 and 10^6 can be attained.

Figure 6-13. Fourteen-dynode electron multiplier, with in-line cage structure. (Courtesy of Radio Corporation of America.)

However, it must be noted that the current of the electrons entering the entrance aperture of the electron multiplier (the "radiation opening") is in the order of some picoamperes; hence, the total anode current is usually in the order of one or a few microamperes. It is, therefore, important that the preamplifier to which the electron multiplier *(EM)* is connected is coupled to it as closely as possible. Copper–beryllium is most commonly used as dynode material, and many designs use only high-temperature metal and ceramic materials in their construction; this permits bake-out at temperatures between 450 and 600 °C, as required for use in ultra-high-vacuum systems. Besides the in-line cage structure illustrated, the other cage structures used in photomultipliers (venetian blind, circular cage, etc.) are also employed in electron multipliers.

Electron multipliers of the multiple-dynode type as well as those of the continuous-dynode type described below are generally usable for the detection of positive and negative electrons, ions (positive and negative), protons, and electromagnetic radiation in the soft X-ray and vacuum ultraviolet (XUV) regions.

The continuous-dynode *channel electron multiplier (CEM)* is a hollow glass cylinder with a resistive secondary-emission coating on its inside surface. The electron multiplication (typically around 10^7 to 10^8) is a result of cascade action in which incoming (primary) electrons collide with the secondary-emission-coated inner wall and cause several secondary electrons to be emitted. These secondary electrons become primary electrons for the next collision with the wall surface farther along the cylinder *(channel)* wall. A high-voltage potential is applied across the two ends of the channel; it sets up the axial electric field that accelerates the continuously multiplying electrons from the entrance-aperture end to the exit end of the channel. The cascade and multiplication process continues down the channel length (see Figure 6-14a) until the end is reached or gain saturation occurs. For CEMs having an *l/d* ratio between 60 and 100, gain saturation results from the device having a net secondary-emission gain of unity in the last portion of the channel length. This gain saturation results in output pulses which are all of nearly constant amplitude.

CEMs exist in a number of curved configurations. The most common configuration is shown in Figure 6-14b. Cones of various sizes can be used to expand the input aperture diameter but are not used on all designs. The anode (collector) can be user-furnished, spaced about 1 mm away from the channel exit, and supplied with a voltage of about $+250$ V dc, referenced to the high-voltage (2 to 3 kV) supply's positive terminal, which is then connected directly to a contact at the exit end of the channel. The collector can also be furnished in the form of a thin metallic cap, bonded to the exit end with conductive epoxy, and electrically connected as shown in Figure 6-14b; however, this reduces the gain significantly and reduces the bake-out temperature from 300 °C to about 100 °C. The configuration shown has a subtended arc of 270°. Other configurations include helical channels subtending arcs of 840°. Electron gain varies with excitation voltage (high voltage across channel ends), with this relationship becoming nonlinear above a gain of about 10^6 and then becoming asymptotic to a gain of around 10^8. The diameter of the circular-arc configuration illustrated is 4.6 cm.

The Spiraltron® CEM is used where configurational constraints impose

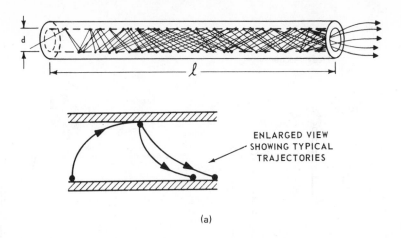

ENLARGED VIEW
SHOWING TYPICAL
TRAJECTORIES

(a)

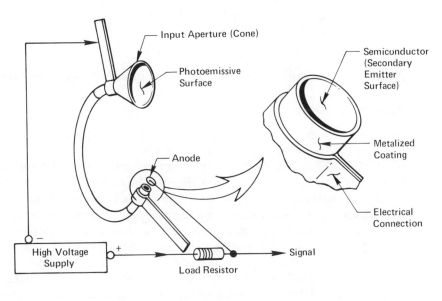

Input Aperture (Cone)

Photoemissive
Surface

Semiconductor
(Secondary
Emitter
Surface)

Metalized
Coating

Anode

Electrical
Connection

High Voltage
Supply

Signal

Load Resistor

(b)

Figure 6-14. Continuous-dynode channel electron multiplier (CEM): (a) principle of CEM operation; (b) Channeltron® electron multiplier. (Courtesy of Galileo Electro-Optics Corp.)

a preference for a straight-line, rather than a curved, design. This detector has a conical entrance aperture, a straight channel "preamplifier" section, and a section containing six thin channels which have been twisted together. Spiraltron® electron multipliers (SEMs) can be connected (with a collector bias of around +200 V, referenced to the "+ H.V." terminal) either in a two-terminal mode, with "+ H.V." at the exit end and "− H.V." at the (grounded) aperture end, or in a three-terminal mode, with an intermediate terminal located at the junction of the preamplifier and twisted-channel sections. A typical SEM is 5.3 cm long, and is illustrated in Figure 6-15.

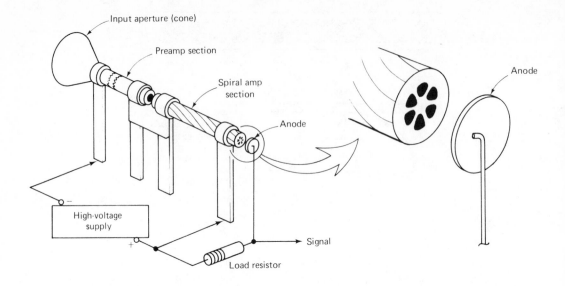

Figure 6-15. Spiraltron® electron multiplier. (Courtesy of Galileo Electro-Optics Corp.)

6.3.7 Neutron Detectors

Neutrons, which are uncharged particles, are detected by detecting charged particles emitted from a material in which a nuclear reaction is caused by the incident neutrons. The reaction can be caused by the interaction of the neutrons with atomic nuclei, or by recoils of charged particles from collisions with neutrons. The materials *(conversion materials)* used for this purpose are usually stable isotopes of elements having a high absorption cross section in the energy range of interest. They can be employed either as a fill gas or as internal coating, or both, in an ionization chamber or proportional counter; they can be used as a constituent of a scintillator material; or they can be the material of a film, or on a foil, placed in front of the sensitive area of a charged-particle or gamma-ray detector (depending on the reaction used and its products).

Lithium and boron isotopes are often used as conversion materials for *slow neutron* detection. In the $Li^6(n,\alpha)T$ reaction the most penetrating particle (besides the neutron) is the triton (T); alphas and tritons are produced in this reaction of neutrons with Li^6. In the $B^{10}(n,\alpha)Li^7$ reaction, in which alphas and Li^7 nuclei are produced as charged particles, the α particle has the greater range. B^{10} is commonly used in ionization chambers and proportional counters in the form of B^{10}-enriched BF_3 (boron trifluoride) gas. In semiconductor detectors (see Figure 6-16) the conversion material is deposited on thin (0.5-mm-thick) metal (typically aluminum or stainless steel) foil, with a plastic light-tight cap providing the retainer for the foil as well as a cover for the detector. In another design, the conversion material is vacuum-evaporated onto the active surface of a semiconductor detector, which is then mounted face to face with another such detector. The resulting "sandwich" geometry allows simultaneous counting of the two reaction products in the two detectors.

Fast neutron detection requires different conversion materials. He^3, used as fill gas in proportional counters, and pressurized at between 1 and 10 atm, is usable from the thermal through the fast neutron range. Li^6F (solid) can also be used for neutron energy ranges from slow to fast. H^1 has been used, as polyethylene film, for fast-neutron conversion. Semiconductor detectors can be provided with a layer of hydrogenous material for fast-neutron detection; recoil protons, resulting from *(n,p)* scattering, are then the detected particles. An alternative is to use a Li^6F or B^{10} layer and surround the entire detector in paraffin; fast neutrons are moderated in the paraffin and detected as slow neutrons. Heavy charged particles can also be produced, as *fission fragments*, by neutron reactions with materials such as Pu^{239}, U^{235}, Np^{237}, and Th^{232}.

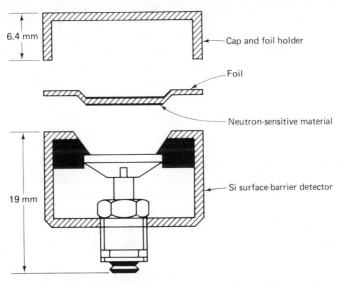

Figure 6-16. Surface-barrier detector adapted for neutron detection. (Courtesy of EG&G ORTEC.)

6.3.8 Signal-Conditioning and Display Equipment

A number of special design considerations apply to signal-conditioning circuitry and to display equipment for nuclear radiation detectors.

Low-level output signals are typical for many detectors. Ionization chambers, for example, produce output currents as low as 10^{-15} A which must be conditioned and displayed. To obtain a measurable IR drop across the load resistor, such resistors can have values up to 10^{13} Ω, and special design and manufacturing precautions must be taken with such resistors. Electrometer tubes characterized by low grid current, or quartz-fiber electrometers have been used to match the high output impedances of many types of detectors and avoid loading errors. Integration of the instantaneous ionization currents over long time periods, during which the weak current charges a capacitor, has provided another means for measuring currents below 1 pA. FET preamplifiers are now often used for a high-output-impedance match and weak-signal amplification.

Since detector outputs are typically in pulse form, the associated amplifiers are specifically designed as *pulse amplifiers,* with large gain adjustment ranges (e.g., 50 to 50,000) and the ability to amplify pulses with a variety of rise times and decay times. Except for spectrometry, the usual output indication is either in terms of total counts (over a given time interval) or count rate (e.g., counts per minute). Electronic counters can display total counts at fairly high rates; when the rates are too high to be handled by such a counter, a *scaler* is used; it produces and displays one output pulse for a specified number of input pulses. Counting-rate meters *(rate meters)* indicate the time rate of occurrence of pulses averaged over a specified time interval. Selection of this interval can be accomplished by changing circuit constants of an integrating network, thus changing its time constant, in known discrete increments. Analog indications of counting rate can be displayed on a panel meter.

The *pulse-height analyzer* furnishes displays of radiation energy spectra. It can indicate either the number of pulses falling within one or more specified amplitude ranges, or the rate of occurrence of such pulses. Each channel of such an analyzer is adjusted to pass only those pulses whose amplitude is between a threshold voltage V and an upper limit $V + V_W$, where V_W is the energy *window width,* and the range of energies passed by such a *single-channel amplifier (SCA)* is called the *energy window.* Both the threshold voltage and the window width are usually adjustable. A spectral plot can be obtained by adjusting the window width to a fixed value and then *sweeping* the threshold voltage at a known rate to provide a time correlation for each energy level analyzed. SCAs and multichannel analyzers (MCAs) are described further in Section 8.8.4.

Coincidence circuits are used to assure that a given indication is due only to a specific particle (or several genetically related particles). The circuit obtains separate inputs from at least two detectors and uses logic electronics to produce an output pulse only when a specified number or a specified combination of input terminals receive pulses within a specified short time interval. A *delayed coincidence circuit* is actuated by two input pulses (from genetically related events), one of which is delayed by a specified time interval with respect to the other. An *anticoincidence circuit,* on the other hand, produces an output pulse only when one of two input terminals receives a pulse and the other receives no pulse. Such a circuit is useful in reducing unwanted *background counts* (counts caused by ionizing events other than those that are to be detected).

Some semiconductor detector designs are available with integrally packaged hybrid-electronics circuitry including not only a preamplifier but also a shaping amplifier and single-channel amplifier (SCA) with provisions for window selection.

6.4 DESIGN AND PERFORMANCE CHARACTERISTICS

Mechanical characteristics such as outline dimensions, dimensions and location of mountings and electrical connections, and of gas connections (for gas-flow counters), case material and sealing, identification markings, and mass ("weight") are described for radiation detectors in the same manner as for other types of sensing devices. Additionally, the following are shown: window material and thickness; for gas-filled ionization-type counters, the cathode material is described (if different from the case, or envelope, material), also anode thickness and material, effective cathode dimensions, and type and composition of the fill gas and its pressure (and type of quenching agent for Geiger counters). For scintillation counters, descriptions are included of the scintillator dimensions and material, type of optical coupling, and either the model number of a commercial photomultiplier (or CEM with photocathode) or the complete characteristics of an integrally packaged scintillation detector. For semiconductor detectors, the material, sensitive area and wafer thickness (or volume, for some types of detectors), and depletion depth are stated.

Electrical characteristics include the range of operating excitation voltages (anode voltages or equivalent), maximum allowable voltage, and separate bias voltage, if any. For gas-filled detectors, sufficient details must be given to establish output impedance and load characteristics, for example, recommended range of external series resistances, internal capacitance, and conductor and insulator materials of electrical connections. Maximum anode current is shown for scintillation counters and electron multipliers. Plateau characteristics are shown for Geiger counters. For semiconductor detectors, bulk resistivity, internal capacitance, bias voltage, and depletion depth are shown.

Performance characteristics list the types of radiation to be measured by the detector as well as the characteristics of wanted outputs and those of unwanted outputs. The latter comprise the maximum *background counts,* or *dark counts,* per second or per minute, maximum leakage current (for semiconductors), and maximum *dark current* (for photomultiplier scintillation counters) at a nominal operating voltage. For Ge(Li) detectors, the unwanted output is established by the Compton edge. The peak-to-Compton ratio (photoelectric events vs. Compton events) is one of the most critical characteristics of such detectors (various versions of coincidence circuits have been developed to improve this ratio for a detector system). Output pulses are described by rise time and decay time.

Transfer characteristics are shown as detection efficiency for given types of radiation (in percent), as charge collection efficiency for some types of semiconductor detectors, or as counting efficiency. Timing characteristics are often shown, mainly to facilitate coincidence-circuit design. Energy resolution is shown as *full width at half maximum (FWHM)* for semiconductor detectors; this is the width, expressed in energy units, of a monoenergetic peak, as measured at an amplitude corresponding to 50% of the peak height. For some detectors the *full width at one-tenth maximum (FWTM)* is additionally specified. When FWHM is shown for scintillation and proportional counters, this term refers to the width of an energy distribution curve (which somewhat resembles a Gaussian distribution curve) measured at one-half the height of the peak of this curve. Energy resolution is the smallest difference in energy, between two particles (or photons), that can be discerned by the detector.

Geiger-counter specifications should show dead time as well as recovery time. The effects of photosensitivity and the hysteresis, if any, should also be stated. For scintillation counters, the wavelength of maximum scintillator emission (or a curve descriptive of the complete emission spectrum) is usually shown in specifications. Where detector life is limited (e.g., by radiation damage, or by use of an organic quenching fluid in a Geiger counter), the detector life is shown, as maximum obtainable counts.

Environmental characteristics are normally limited to thermal characteristics; only in some cases are capabilities of withstanding shock, vibration, and acceleration specified. The operating temperature range, and effects of temperature variations within this range on detector output, should be stated. More complete temperature characteristics must be specified for those types of semiconductor detectors that are intended to be operated at cryogenic temperatures; in this case the effects on the detector of exposure to room temperature should also be stated. Special considerations are also necessary for detectors that are intended for operation in a vacuum.

6.5 SELECTION CRITERIA

The selection of a specific detector design can often be based on known radiation-emission characteristics of materials used in a given process or procedure. The alpha, beta, and gamma energies of radioactive isotopes as well as their half-life are generally well established. The detector design should be optimized for the required interaction of the radiation with the sensitive material of the detector. When two or more types of radiation can be incident simultaneously on a detector, response to only one selected type of radiation can sometimes be accomplished by appropriate detector design; it can also be accomplished by the design of the associated counting circuitry, including use of coincidence or anticoincidence circuits.

Heavy charged particles such as alphas and protons of low or medium energy lose energy rapidly in passing through matter, without appreciable scattering. Their mean range decreases with increasing absorber density. Alpha particles can be detected with scintillation counters using silver-activated zinc as scintillator material, with proportional and Geiger counters, with windowless or thin-window semiconductor detectors, and with windowless gas-flow counters.

Very high energy charged particles are usually measured with fluorescent or Cerenkov scintillation counters.

Beta and gamma radiation can be detected with virtually all basic types of radiation detectors, although gamma rays are not charged particles and must first interact with matter to produce ions. Weak beta radiation detection requires a very sensitive detector such as a windowless or ultra-thin-window gas-flow counter. Thin beryllium windows have been found usable in low-energy X-ray and gamma-ray spectrometry. Window material and thickness can often be selected to exclude beta particles and provide an output only for gamma radiation when both are present. Since gamma rays and X-rays differ only in their energy level, those types of detectors that are suitable for gamma-ray measurements are often usable for X-ray measurements as well. Where particularly high performance, including fine energy resolution, is required from gamma-ray detectors, especially in spectrometry, the cryogenically cooled Ge(Li) and HP Ge detectors have been found most suitable. CdTe gamma-ray detectors have found applications, primarily in nuclear medicine, health physics, and general radiation monitoring, where compact detectors, capable of operating at room temperature, are required.

Bibliography

1. **Sharpe, J.,** *Nuclear Radiation Measurement*. London: Temple Press Ltd., 1960.

2. **Chase, R. L.,** *Nuclear Pulse Spectrometry*. New York: McGraw-Hill Book Company, 1961.

3. **Clark, G. L.,** *The Encyclopedia of X-Rays and Gamma Rays*. New York: Van Nostrand Reinhold Company, 1963.

4. **Price, W. J.,** *Nuclear Radiation Detection*. New York: McGraw-Hill Book Company, 1964.

5. **Broda, E., and Schonfield, T.,** *Technical Applications of Radioactivity*. Elmsford, N.Y.: Pergamon Press, Inc., 1966.

6. **Dearnaley, G., and Northrop, D. C.,** *Semiconductor Counters for Nuclear Radiation* (2nd ed.). New York: Barnes & Noble, Inc., 1966.

7. **Polishuk, P.** (Ed.), *Nucleonics in Aerospace*. New York: Plenum Press, 1968.

8. **Kaelble, E. F.,** *Handbook of X-Rays*. New York: McGraw-Hill Book Company, 1974.

9. *Nuclear IEEE Standards,* Vols. 1 and 2. New York: John Wiley & Sons, Inc., 1979.

10. "A Handbook of Radioactivity Measurement Procedures," *NCRP Report No. 58*. Washington, DC: National Council on Radiation Protection and Measurements, 1979.

Selected Periodicals

1. *Nucleonics*. New York: McGraw-Hill Book Company.

2. *Nuclear Instruments and Methods*. Amsterdam and New York: Elsevier/North-Holland.

3. *IEEE Transactions on Nuclear Science*. New York: Institute of Electrical and Electronics Engineers.

chapter seven

Electrical and Magnetic Quantities

Measuring instruments for electrical and magnetic quantities, with the emphasis on the former, are represented adequately in available technical literature. The purpose of this chapter is not to describe such devices as voltmeters, ammeters, wattmeters, and gaussmeters but to provide a very brief guide to those types of sensing devices that provide an output signal to a remote display device, telemetry system, or data system in response to an electrical or magnetic measurand.

7.1 BASIC CONCEPTS AND UNITS

The units of electrical and magnetic quantities, and, hence, the quantities themselves are well defined in the International System of Units (SI). The basic quantities involved in the interrelating definitions are force, quantity of electricity, and electric current. Force is given by the basic units for mass, length, and time; the unit of force is the *newton (N)* [$N = kg \cdot m/s^2$]. Energy is based on force; the unit for energy is the *joule (J)* [$J = N \cdot m$]. Power is the time rate of change of energy; the unit of power is the *watt (W)* [$W = J/s$]. [*Note:* Relationships shown in brackets show derivations of the *units.*] The only one of the six base units of the SI that pertains to electrical quantities is the unit of *electric current,* the *ampere (A).* The ampere is that constant current which, if maintained in two straight parallel conductors of infinite length, of negligible cross section, and placed 1 meter apart in a vacuum, would produce between those conductors a force equal to 2×10^{-7} newton per meter of length.

Derived units (derived from the six base units) are used to express other electrical as well as magnetic quantities, as explained below.

Charge (electric charge) is a quantity of electricity, and current is the flow of charge per unit time. The unit of charge is the coulomb (*C*), defined as the quantity of electricity transported in 1 second by a current of 1 ampere, hence $[C = A \cdot s]$.

Voltage refers to either *electric potential difference* or *electromotive force (emf)*; the unit for both is the *volt (V)*, defined as the difference of electric potential between two points of a conductor carrying a constant current of 1 ampere, when the power dissipated between these points is equal to 1 watt; $[V = W/A]$.

Resistance (electric resistance) is expressed in *ohms* (Ω). The ohm is the electric resistance between two points of a conductor (which is not the source of any electromotive force) when the constant difference of potential of 1 volt, applied between these two points, produces in this conductor a current of 1 ampere; $[\Omega = V/A]$.

Conductance is the reciprocal of resistance (1/*R*); it was formerly expressed in reciprocal ohms ("mho"); the SI unit for conductance is the *siemens (S)*; $[S = 1/\Omega = A/V]$.

Capacitance (electric capacitance) is expressed in *farads (F)*; the farad is the capacitance of a capacitor between the plates of which there appears a potential difference of 1 volt when it is charged by a quantity of electricity equal to 1 coulomb; $[F = C/V = A \cdot s/V]$.

Inductance (electric inductance) is expressed in *henrys (H)*; the henry is the inductance of a closed circuit in which an emf of 1 volt is produced when the electric current in the circuit varies uniformly at a rate of 1 ampere per second; $[H = V \cdot s/A]$.

The *impedance (Z)* of an ac circuit is comprised of a *real* part, *resistance (R)*, and an imaginary part, *reactance (X)*; $Z = R + jX$; the reactance can be *capacitive* (X_C) or *inductive* (X_L); where both exist in a circuit, $Z = \sqrt{R^2 + (X_L - X_C)^2}$; impedance as well as reactance are expressed in *ohms*.

Similarly, the *admittance (Y)* of an ac circuit is the reciprocal of its impedance, $Y = 1/Z$; admittance consists of a *real* part, *conductance (G)*, and an *imaginary* part, *susceptance (B)*; $Y = G + jB$; admittance as well as susceptance are expressed in *siemens* (they were formerly expressed in reciprocal ohms, "mho").

Frequency is expressed in *hertz (Hz)*; the hertz is a frequency of 1 cycle per second.

Resistivity (ρ), also called *specific resistance*, is the resistance offered by a unit cube of a substance to the flow of current; $\rho = R \cdot A/l$, where *R* is the resistance of a uniform conductor, *A* its cross-sectional area, and *l* its length; resistivity is expressed in *ohm-meters* ($\Omega \cdot m$) or its submultiple, ohm-centimeters.

Conductivity (σ) is the ratio of the current density to the electric field in a material; *current density* is the current per unit cross-sectional area of a conductor (or conductive substance); *electric field intensity* or *electric field strength* is the electric force (vector) per unit positive (test) charge, expressed in volts per meter; electrical conductivity is expressed in *siemens per meter (S/m)* or per centimeter.

Magnetic flux is expressed in *webers (Wb);* the weber is the magnetic flux, which, linking a circuit of one turn, produces in it an emf of 1 volt as it reduced to zero at a uniform rate in 1 second; $[Wb = V{\cdot}s]$.

Magnetic flux density is expressed in *teslas (T);* the tesla is the magnetic flux density given by a magnetic flux of 1 weber per square meter; $[T = Wb/m^2]$.

The unit of *magnetomotive force* is, strictly speaking, the *ampere (A)*, but the *ampere turn* is more commonly used; a magnetomotive force of one ampere turn may be the result of a current of 1 ampere flowing in 1 turn of wire, or the result of a current of 0.01 ampere flowing in 100 turns of wire.

The unit of *magnetic field strength* is the *ampere per meter (A/m)*.

Non-SI units for electrical and magnetic quantities, and their conversion factors, are listed below in alphabetical order.

$$1 \text{ abampere} = 10 \text{ A}$$
$$1 \text{ abcoulomb} = 10 \text{ C}$$
$$1 \text{ abfarad} = 10^9 \text{ F}$$
$$1 \text{ abhenry} = 10^{-9} \text{ H}$$
$$1 \text{ abmho} = 10^9 \text{ S}$$
$$1 \text{ abohm} = 10^{-9} \text{ }\Omega$$
$$1 \text{ abvolt} = 10^{-8} \text{ V}$$
$$1 \text{ electron volt (eV)} = 1.6 \times 10^{-19} \text{ J}$$
$$1 \text{ faraday (physical)} = 9.6522 \times 10^4 \text{ C}$$
$$1 \text{ gamma} = 10^{-9} \text{ T } (= 1 \text{ nT})$$
$$1 \text{ gauss} = 10^{-4} \text{ T}$$
$$1 \text{ gilbert} = 0.7958 \text{ ampere-turn}$$
$$1 \text{ horsepower (electric)} = 746 \text{ W}$$
$$1 \text{ maxwell} = 10^{-8} \text{ Wb}$$
$$1 \text{ oersted} = 79.58 \text{ A/m}$$
$$1 \text{ unit pole} = 1.25664 \times 10^{-7} \text{ Wb}$$

7.2 SENSING METHODS AND DEVICES

7.2.1 Voltage Sensors

The most commonly used device for sensing ac voltages, particularly in electrical power distribution, is the *voltage transformer (potential* transformer), which steps down the high voltage into a low-voltage, low-current signal suitable for information display or processing. When the data system requires a dc input signal, the output of the potential transformer is rectified for this purpose.

In such applications as power supplies handling relatively low ac and dc voltages a magnetic amplifier (amplifier using saturable reactors) can be used, with one of the saturable-reactor windings connected across the voltage to be measured and acting as control winding. When an ac voltage is to be measured it is first rectified into dc before being applied to the *voltage-controlled magnetic amplifier.*

Voltage dividers are also used for sensing (usually low-power) voltages. A voltage divider consists of two resistors connected in series, with their end terminal connected across the voltage source and the signal taken between the center connection and the ground line of the source. Unlike the two sensors described above, a basic voltage divider does not provide electrical isolation between voltage source and data system. Isolation can be provided by connecting a differential amplifier across the signal terminals. The resistor across which the signal is taken should always have a lower resistance than the other resistor, low enough so that a short circuit across it does not affect the voltage source. AC voltages sensed by a voltage divider are usually rectified as part of the signal-conditioning process.

A *root-mean-square (rms)* value is equal to the square root of the time average of the square of the quantity; in practice, for an ac voltage, it is the effective value equivalent to a similar dc voltage in ability to do work in a resistive load. When ac voltages are measured as rms values, the corresponding peak and average voltages can be calculated as $V_{peak} = 1.414 V_{rms}$ and $V_{avg} = 0.901 V_{rms}$. These relationships assume a sinusoidal waveshape. Very small dc voltages can be sensed by devices described for the measurement of very small currents, below.

Discrete (switch-type) outputs can be obtained from a *voltage comparator,* which compares the voltage sensed to a set-point voltage and actuates a relay when the voltage increases above, or decreases below the set point. The set point can be adjustable over a fairly wide range and the switch-point accuracy can be maintained within very close tolerances. *Hall-effect* devices similar to those explained for current sensing, below, are also used as voltage transducers. *Modified D'Arsonval meters,* as explained for current sensing, below, are used for voltage sensing as well.

7.2.2 Current Sensors

Basic current sensors are the shunt for dc currents and the current transformer for ac currents. A *shunt* is a section of conductor having a low resistance (typically in the form of a short bus bar) inserted in series with the conductor in which the current is to be measured. The resistance of the shunt is so selected that a specified current will produce a known amount of *IR* drop across it. The potential difference across the shunt is then measured as a voltage. A *current transformer* is a transformer which has a primary winding, consisting of a relatively small number of turns of heavy-gage wire, which is connected in series with the current-carrying conductor, and a secondary winding, consisting of a relatively large number of turns of small-gage wire, from which the signal voltage is taken. The turns ratio is so selected that a specified current through the primary winding will produce a known voltage in the secondary winding.

When isolation is required between power supply and data system and relatively low dc currents are to be measured, a *current-controlled magnetic amplifier* can be used. One of the saturable-reactor windings is the control winding, which is connected in series with the current-carrying conductor. A single-turn control winding is usually sufficient.

Clamp-on current sensors are used for current measurements on a sampling basis (as opposed to a fixed sensor installation). They do not need to be connected to the current-carrying conductor. Instead, they contain a circular ferromagnetic (usually ferrite) core that is cut in half but provides a continuous core when the two halves are clamped together. The sensor is opened, slipped around the wire, then clamped together. It then acts as a current transformer, with the current-carrying conductor itself acting as the primary and a multiturn winding around the core acting as the secondary which produces an output voltage proportional to ac current.

Hall-effect current sensors can be used for dc as well as ac measurements. The current is caused to change the magnetic field in which a *Hall device* is located. This device is a semiconductor of a type specifically selected for this usage (one having a high Hall constant, or Hall coefficient). It produces an electric field which is both transverse to an excitation current passing through it and transverse to the magnetic field. The output voltage created by the electric field is proportional to the magnetic field, at constant excitation current. The magnetic field is usually generated by a ferromagnetic, gapped, toroidal core through which the current-carrying conductor runs. Most sensors of this type provide a circular opening through which the conductor must run. The opening is in the sensor housing which is made from an insulating material. The core is placed immediately inside of this opening. Four terminals are usually provided, two for the dc excitation of the Hall device, and two for the output signal. Split-core, clamp-on versions are also available. The output voltage is of the same form as the input current. A dc input current produces a dc output voltage, and an ac input current produces an ac output voltage of the same waveshape. Depending on the frequency response of the sensor (which can extend from dc to over 1 MHz), transients in the measured current will be reproduced in the output signal. The excitation current must be closely controlled. When a dc output is required for ac current measurement, the output signal can be rectified (circuitry for this can be located within the sensor housing). Other forms of signal conditioning can also be provided within the sensor housing and additional terminals may then be provided to supply external power to such circuitry. Some designs include a relay and control circuitry so that a switch output is provided at a set current level.

Very small currents (down to 10^{-12} A) can be measured by an *electrometer tube* (a high-vacuum, high-input-impedance electron tube), a vibrating-reed capacitor, or by amplifiers using varactor diodes, metal–oxide–semiconductor field-effect transistors (MOSFET), or junction FETs. In some low-power applications (e.g., scientific instruments) the current drawn from a high-voltage secondary can be derived from a calibration that provides correlation with a conventional measurement of the current through the low-voltage primary winding of a transformer.

Modified D'Arsonval meters are also used for current sensing. Such meters contain an axially pivoted coil, of rectangular configuration, through which the measured current flows. A pointer is integral with the coil assembly. The coil rotates between the pole pieces of a permanent magnet. The angle of rotation is proportional to current through the coil. The meter is modified by having a transduction element (e.g., capacitive) attached to the pointer so that an output signal proportional to the angular displacement of the pointer is produced. The meter can also be modified by attaching a contact to the pointer and one or more contacts to the meter face so that one or more discrete outputs are produced as the pointer rotates.

7.2.3 Power Sensors

DC power can be derived from simultaneous current and voltage measurements; the power is the product of voltage and current; in data systems incorporating some computational capability very simple software can be employed for an essentially real-time display of power when voltage and current data are fed into the data system.

DC and, much more frequently, ac power can be sensed by *Hall effect power transducers* that are similar in operating principle to the Hall-device current transducer described in Section 7.2.2. Hall devices in such power transducers are used as *Hall multipliers*. The output voltage of a Hall device is dependent on the excitation current through the device as well as on the magnetic field to which the device is exposed. In current sensors the excitation current is held constant and the measured current is made to vary the magnetic field. In power transducers, which have to respond to both voltage and current, the voltage is typically connected to a potential transformer in the transducer; the output of the transformer is conditioned into a proportionally varying excitation current through the Hall device. At the same time the current is sensed by passing the conductor through a gapped toroidal core and the magnetic field produced by this electromagnet is applied to the Hall device; the field varies proportionally to current sensed. The Hall device thus multiplies the voltage and the current sensed. AC power is the vectorial sum of *real* power ($V_{rms}I_{rms} \cos \phi$) and *imaginary* power ($V_{rms}I_{rms} \sin \phi$), where ϕ is the *phase angle* (and $\cos \phi$ is the *power factor*). Real power is expressed in watts, whereas imaginary power is expressed in *vars; var* is a contraction of "volt-ampere reactive." AC power transducers are, therefore, known as either *watt transducers* or *var transducers,* depending on whether they are designed to measure real or reactive (imaginary) power. Such Hall-effect transducers are available for use on single-phase, three-phase/three-wire or three-phase/four-wire lines.

They can be used for power ranges having an upper limit between 50 W and 800 kW (single-phase) or 1.5 MW (three-phase) and with power-line frequencies of 50 or 60 Hz as well as with power supply frequencies extending to about 10 kHz (for the lower power ranges).

The ranges of var transducers are typically between 500 and 1500 var, but can be made to cover the same ranges as watt transducers if required. Similar devices are specifically designed as *power factor transducers;* they typically provide a bidirectional voltage output for power factor ranges between unity and 0.3 lead and lag to unity and 0.7 lead and lag (the phase angle for a power factor of 0.3 is 70°, and it is 45° for a power factor of 0.7). *Phase-angle transducers* provide an output calibrated in terms of (and sometimes linearized for) phase angle.

At very high frequencies (e.g., microwave range) electrical power is typically measured by using a portion of the power to heat a temperature sensor; the temperature rise is measured and correlated to power by a calibration curve.

7.2.4   Electrostatic-Charge Sensors

Electrostatic charge accumulation on surfaces and electrostatic fields can be measured by several types of potential gradient sensors. Most designs are capable of measuring electrostatic voltage (typically in kV) or electrostatic field (in V/m or V/cm) without physical contact between sensor and measured surface. The measuring range is given not only by a range selector switch on the instrument but also by the distance between sensor and surface, which is typically between 5 and 30 cm.

One design uses an electromagnetically driven oscillating electrode located behind a small circular aperture in a metallic plate. The electrode is in a feedback loop which neutralizes the net field at the electrode by feeding a dc signal back to the aperture plate. The oscillation of the electrode provides an ac error signal proportional to the electrostatic field sensed. The output of the device is a dc signal given by the amplitude of the feedback voltage. Another design uses a small radioisotope source in conjunction with a high-resistance voltage sensor for transduction of the electrostatic charge or voltage measured. Typical configurations include a hand-held instrument, with a pistol grip, that is pointed at the measured surface from a known distance, and small probes connected by a cable to a control/display unit. A related design uses a dissipation array, in fixed or mobile installations, to detect charge buildup in the atmosphere, and can provide lightning warning.

7.2.5   Frequency- and Time-Sensing Devices

Time as well as frequency, which is the inverse of time, are measured by referencing them to a periodic phenomenon, one whose periodicity is known within an amount of error (uncertainty) adequate for a given measurement. The earliest periodic phenomenon used for time determinations was the pendulum, which is still in use in some clocks, which, when properly designed and adjusted, can provide time displays with very low error. More recently the quartz-crystal oscillator was developed and refined; it is widely used in electronic equipment as a reference for frequency and time. The use of countdown circuitry allows obtaining exact submultiples of the frequency at which the crystal oscillates. The most recently developed frequency standards are atomic in nature. The resonance of the cesium atom has been used to define the unit of time, the second (as adopted by the CGPM in 1967): "The second is the duration of 9 192 631 770 periods of the radiation corresponding to the transition between the two hyperfine levels of the ground state of the cesium-133 atom."

Other atomic frequency standards include the hydrogen-atom maser and the rubidium gas cell; however, the primary frequency standard is the cesium beam standard, and continuing improvements in equipment design have enhanced the usability and stability of this device.

An unknown frequency is measured by comparing it with a known frequency. Within a limit on very high frequencies, this can be done by using a reference frequency to establish a known time interval (e.g., exactly 1 second), converting the waveshape of the unknown signal into pulses, and then digitally counting the number of pulses over the time interval.

A method also usable at extremely high frequencies is to mix the unknown frequency with a standard frequency (*beat* one against the other) and then measure the frequency difference (*beat frequency*) by a device such as a frequency counter. Various types of circuits are used in *frequency-to-dc converters* which convert a specified range of frequencies into a dc voltage. The simplest of these is the FM discriminator, which produces zero output voltage at a preset center frequency and produces increasing dc voltage, at frequency deviations from this center frequency, that is linear within a certain band of such frequency deviations; the polarity of the output voltage depends on whether the measured frequency is above or below the center frequency. *Frequency-to-digital converters* convert the count of an absolute or beat frequency into coded form (e.g., binary, binary-coded decimal). Frequency-to-voltage conversion techniques also include resistive–capacitive *(RC)* networks in feedback loops of operational amplifiers in conjunction with diodes or with a saturable-transformer/rectifier.

7.2.6 Magnetic-Flux-Density Sensors

This category of sensors includes devices known as gaussmeters, magnetic field probes, and magnetometers. Since the SI unit for the quantity measured is the *tesla (T)*, the term "gaussmeter" is now obsolescent *(1 gauss = 0.1 mT)*. The weak magnetic fields sensed by magnetometers have been measured in *gammas* and are now measured in *nanoteslas (1 gamma = 1 nT)*.

The most commonly used magnetic-flux-density sensors are those using Hall devices. As explained for Hall-device current and power sensors, these devices (Figure 7-1) produce an output voltage proportional to the flux density of a transverse magnetic field when a constant excitation current is passed

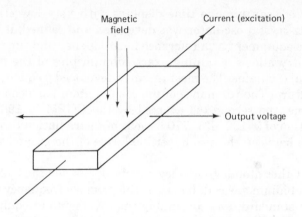

Magnetic field

Current (excitation)

Output voltage

Figure 7-1. Hall-effect device—operating principle.

through them. The Hall-effect device is usually contained near the tip of a probe; the probe is connected to an excitation- and signal-conditioning and display unit by a cable. Such probes *(Hall probes)* are designed for responding to either an axial or a transverse magnetic field. *Axial probes* are generally circular in cross section, whereas *transverse probes* are blade-shaped in most designs. Some probe designs include a flexible stem between handle and probe tip. Probes are also available for simultaneous measurements of an axial and a transverse magnetic field *(two-axis probe)* or an axial and two mutually orthogonal transverse fields (Z, X, and Y axes, *three-axis probe*). The excitation current can be dc or ac; the latter effects chopping of the sensed field and provides an ac output voltage which can then be amplified and synchronously demodulated. Two-axis probes contain two (and three-axis probes contain three) mutually orthogonally placed Hall devices in their tip.

Inductor probes consist of an air-core inductor in a nonmagnetic (e.g., brass) housing. This type of probe responds to the rate of change of an ambient magnetic field or, generally, to varying (not steady-state) magnetic fields. It is quite usable for ac fields. The flux changes induce a voltage in the coil. This device is the sensor in a *search-coil magnetometer*. It is also used as the sensing coil in a *fluxmeter,* which can be used to measure steady-state magnetic fields by spinning the coil through the field so that an ac voltage, given by the spin rate, is induced in the coil.

The *nuclear magnetic resonance (NMR) magnetometer* (or magnetic field sensor) is based on proton precession *(proton-precession magnetometer)*. The resonance frequency (in the RF range) of certain substances varies exactly and linearly with magnetic flux density. The resonance frequency manifests itself by a sharp dip in applied RF power due to absorption, as the frequency of an RF generator is swept through a given range of frequencies. The resonance frequency shift of a proton (H^1) is 42.5776 MHz/T (4257.76 Hz/gauss). The resonance frequency shift for lithium (Li^7) is 16.5461 MHz/T, and for deuterium (H^2 or D) it is 6.54 MHz/T. The sensing probe contains the substance in a small enclosed sample chamber which includes the RF coil system. The probe is connected to an oscillator and frequency counter in an excitation/display unit.

The *fluxgate magnetometer* operates on the basis of permeability changes. It employs a core saturated in both directions (or two saturated cores whose windings are mutually opposed in polarity). The saturable reactor(s) are connected into an ac impedance bridge circuit which is balanced in the absence of any magnetic field. A second-harmonic signal is generated when a magnetic field changes core saturation. In a *vector fluxgate magnetometer* three such fluxgates are mounted so that they are mutually orthogonal; the combined sensor can then provide information as to strength as well as direction of a magnetic field. Closed-loop servo control has been applied to this type of device, where the amount of current needed to restore balance is a measure of the magnetic field. Sensitive magnetometers exemplified by the fluxgate magnetometer can detect fields of 1 or a few nT (gammas). Other very sensitive magnetometers include the *helium magnetometer* and the *rubidium vapor magnetometer,* whose operation is based on optical pumping of monochromatic light and transition changes in resonance levels due to changes in the magnetic field.

Bibliography

1. **Lenk, J. D.,** *Handbook of Practical Electronic Tests and Measurements.* Englewood Cliffs, NJ: Prentice-Hall, Inc., 1969.

2. **Thomas, H. E., and Clarke, C. A.,** *Handbook of Electronic Instruments and Measurement Techniques.* Englewood Cliffs, NJ: Prentice-Hall, Inc., 1967.

3. **Blair, B. E.** (Ed.), "Time and Frequency: Theory and Fundamentals," *NBS Monograph 140.* Washington, DC: U.S. Government Printing Office, 1974.

4. **Fink, D. G.** (Ed.), *Electronics Engineers' Handbook.* New York: McGraw-Hill Book Company, 1975.

5. **Besançon, R. M.** (Ed.), *The Encyclopedia of Physics.* New York: Van Nostrand Reinhold Company, 1974.

chapter eight

Chemical Properties and Composition

Whereas the other chapters of this book discuss sensing methods in depth and describe typical sensing devices in detail, the field of chemical-properties sensing and chemical-composition analysis is so vast that this chapter can only be introductory in nature. Numerous valuable reference books and textbooks exist for each of the many areas that are covered briefly in this chapter, far more than exist for most of the quantities covered in all the other chapters of this book. It is the intent of this chapter, then, to provide the reader with a cursory understanding of the basic principles of instruments and methods used for many (but not all) measurements and analyses of chemical properties and chemical composition.

8.1 BASIC CONCEPTS

Chemical properties, as opposed to physical properties such as viscosity and density (see Chapter 2), include primarily solution concentration and alkalinity and acidity (pH). Most of the instruments described in this chapter are used for determinations of chemical composition. Compositional analyses can be *qualitative* ("What elements are contained in a sample?") or *quantitative* ("How much of one or more given element is contained in a sample?"). Either type can be a *single-component analysis* or a *multicomponent analysis*. An example of the purpose of a single-component qualitative analysis could be: "Is there any cadmium in the sample?", whereas if this sample would be applied to a quantitative analysis, the purpose would be "How much cadmium is in this sample?" or "What percentage of the sample is cadmium?" Similarly, multi-component analyses can be qualitative or quantitative, and they can be directed at finding two or more elements in a sample (or the quantity of those elements) or at finding all elements that compose a sample (or finding the quantities of all those elements). When a sample of a process stream (or other fluid) is to be analyzed, one of two sampling methods can be employed: *in situ sampling* (the analyzer is located in, or immediately at, the process stream), or *extractive sampling* (a sample is extracted from the process stream and transported to an analyzer located elsewhere). Recent technological developments have led to another method: analysis by *remote sensing* (from ground-based equipment or from satellites). The types of substances that can be found as a result of a compositional analysis can be elements in their *atomic* form (e.g., O, N) or *molecular* form (e.g., O_2, N_2); they can be more or less abundant *isotopes* of an element (with the same *atomic number* but a different *mass number*); they can be *inorganic compounds* or *organic compounds* (compounds based on carbon chains or rings, also containing hydrogen with or without oxygen, nitrogen, or other elements); and they can be solids, liquids, or gases, or *two-phase* liquids (e.g., oil + water), or mixtures, slurries, suspensions, or solutions.

The development of many types of analysis instruments received a new impetus when water- and air-pollution controls went into effect. Some of the *acronyms* which became popular due to such extended use of such instruments are the following:

BOD: biochemical oxygen demand

COD: chemical oxygen demand

ORP: oxidation–reduction potential, "redox potential," "redox"

TC: total carbon

TOC: total organic carbon

NO_x: nitrogen oxides (NO, NO_2, NO_3)

Refer to Tables 8-1 and 8-2 for a listing of the elements and some of their characteristics.

8.1.1 Units of Measurement and Underlying Concepts

The SI unit of substance is the *mole (mol)*, the amount of substance of a system which contains as many elementary entities as there are carbon atoms in 0.012 kg of carbon-12 *(C^{12})*; the elementary entities must be specified and may be atoms, molecules, ions, electrons, other particles, or specified groups of such particles.

Atomic weight (at wt.) is the relative mass of an atom based on a scale on which a specific carbon atom, C^{12}, is assigned the mass value 12.

Molecular weight is the sum of the atomic weights of all the atoms in a molecule.

Mole fraction is the ratio of the moles of a given substance, in a mixture

Table 8-1   The Elements: Alphabetical Listing

Element	Symbol	At. No.	Element	Symbol	At. No.
Actinium	Ac	89	Molybdenum	Mo	42
Aluminum	Al	13	Neodymium	Nd	60
Americium	Am	95	Neon	Ne	10
Antimony	Sb	51	Neptunium	Np	93
Argon	A	18	Nickel	Ni	28
Arsenic	As	33	Niobium	Nb	41
Astatine	At	85	Niton (see *Radon*)	—	—
Barium	Ba	56	Nitrogen	N	7
Berkelium	Bk	97	Osmium	Os	76
Beryllium	Be	4	Oxygen	O	8
Bismuth	Bi	83	Palladium	Pd	46
Boron	B	5	Phosphorus	P	15
Bromine	Br	35	Platinum	Pt	78
Cadmium	Cd	48	Plutonium	Pu	94
Calcium	Ca	20	Polonium	Po	84
Californium	Cf	98	Potassium	K	19
Carbon	C	6	Praseodymium	Pr	59
Cassiopeium (see *Lutetium*)	—	—	Promethium	Pm	61
			Protactinium	Pa	91
Cerium	Ce	58	Radium	Ra	88
Cesium	Cs	55	Radon	Rn	86
Chlorine	Cl	17	Rhenium	Re	75
Chromium	Cr	24	Rhodium	Rh	45
Cobalt	Co	27	Rubidium	Rb	37
Columbium (see *Niobium*)	—	—	Ruthenium	Ru	44
			Samarium	Sm	62
Copper	Cu	29	Scandium	Sc	21
Curium	Cm	96	Selenium	Se	34
Dysprosium	Dy	66	Silicon	Si	14
Erbium	Er	68	Silver	Ag	47
Europium	Eu	63	Sodium	Na	11
Fluorine	F	9	Strontium	Sr	38
Francium	Fr	87	Sulfur	S	16
Gadolinium	Gd	64	Tantalum	Ta	73
Gallium	Ga	31	Technetium	Tc	43
Germanium	Ge	32	Tellurium	Te	52
Gold	Au	79	Terbium	Tb	65
Hafnium	Hf	72	Thallium	Tl	81
Helium	He	2	Thorium	Th	90
Holmium	Ho	67	Thulium	Tm	69
Hydrogen	H	1	Tin	Sn	50
Indium	In	49	Titanium	Ti	22
Iodine	I	53	Tungsten	W	74
Iridium	Ir	77	Uranium	U	92
Iron	Fe	26	Vanadium	V	23
Krypton	Kr	36	Wolfram (see *Tungsten*)	—	—
Lanthanum	La	57			
Lead	Pb	82	Xenon	Xe	54
Lithium	Li	3	Ytterbium	Yb	70
Lutetium	Lu	71	Yttrium	Y	39
Magnesium	Mg	12	Zinc	Zn	30
Manganese	Mn	25	Zirconium	Zr	40
Mercury	Hg	80			

Table 8-2   Properties of the Elements: In Order of Atomic Number[a]

At. No.	Element	Symbol	Valence	Atomic Weight	Mass Number (in Order of Abundance)[b]
1	Hydrogen	H	1	1.00797	1, 2
2	Helium[c]	He	0	4.0026	4, 3
3	Lithium	Li	1	6.939	7, 6
4	Beryllium	Be	2	9.0122	9
5	Boron	B	3	10.811	11, 10
6	Carbon	C	±4, 2	12.01115	12, 13
7	Nitrogen	N	−3, 5, 2	14.0067	14, 15
8	Oxygen	O	−2	15.9994	16, 18, 17
9	Fluorine	F	−1	18.9984	19
10	Neon[c]	Ne	0	20.183	20, 22, 21
11	Sodium	Na	1	22.9898	23
12	Magnesium	Mg	2	24.312	24, 26, 25
13	Aluminum	Al	3	26.9815	27
14	Silicon	Si	4	28.086	28, 29, 30
15	Phosphorus	P	5, ±3	30.9738	31
16	Sulfur	S	6, 4, −2	32.064	32, 34, 33, 36
17	Chlorine	Cl	±1, 7, 5	35.453	35, 37
18	Argon	A	0	39.948	40, 36, 38
19	Potassium	K	1	39.102	39, 41, (RA)40
20	Calcium	Ca	2	40.08	40, 44, 42, 48, 43, 46
21	Scandium	Sc	3	44.956	45
22	Titanium	Ti	4, 3	47.90	48, 46, 47, 49, 50
23	Vanadium	V	5, 4, 2	50.942	51, (RA)50
24	Chromium	Cr	6, 3, 2	51.996	52, 53, 50, 54
25	Manganese	Mn	7, 4, 2, 6, 3	54.9380	55
26	Iron	Fe	3, 2	55.847	56, 54, 57, 58
27	Cobalt	Co	3, 2	58.9332	59
28	Nickel	Ni	2, 3	58.71	58, 60, 62, 61, 64
29	Copper	Cu	2, 1	63.54	63, 65
30	Zinc	Zn	2	65.37	64, 66, 68, 67, 70
31	Gallium	Ga	3	69.72	69, 71
32	Germanium	Ge	4	72.59	74, 72, 70, 76, 73
33	Arsenic	As	5, ±3	74.9216	75
34	Selenium	Se	6, 4, −2	78.96	80, 78, 82, 76, 77, 74
35	Bromine	Br	±1, 5	79.909	79, 81
36	Krypton[c]	Kr	0	83.80	84, 86, 82, 76, 77, 74
37	Rubidium	Rb	1	85.47	85, (RA)87
38	Strontium	Sr	2	87.62	88, 86, 87, 84
39	Yttrium	Y	3	88.905	89
40	Zirconium	Zr	4	91.22	90, 94, 92, 91, 96
41	Niobium	Nb	5, 3	92.906	93
42	Molybdenum	Mo	6, 3, 5	95.94	98, 96, 92, 95, 100, 97, 94
43	Technetium	Te	7	98.9062	(RA:97, 98, 99)
44	Ruthenium	Ru	3, 4, 6, 8	101.07	102, 104, 101, 99, 100, 96, 98
45	Rhodium	Rh	3, 4	102.905	103

Table 8-2   (continued)

At. No.	Element	Symbol	Valence	Atomic Weight	Mass Number (in Order of Abundance)[b]
46	Palladium	Pd	2, 4	106.4	106, 109, 105, 110, 104, 102
47	Silver	Ag	1	107.868	107, 109
48	Cadmium	Cd	2	112.40	114, 112, 111, 110, 113, 116, 106, 108
49	Indium	In	3	114.82	115, 113
50	Tin	Sn	4, 2	118.69	120, 118, 116, 119, 117, 124, 122, 112, 114, 115
51	Antimony	Sb	3, 5	121.75	121, 123
52	Tellurium	Te	4, 6, −2	127.60	130, 128, 126, 125, 124, 122, 123, 120
53	Iodine	I	−1, 5, 7	126.9045	127
54	Xenon[c]	Xe	0	131.30	132, 129, 131, 134, 136, 130, 128, 124, 126
55	Cesium	Cs	1	132.9054	133
56	Barium	Ba	2	137.34	138, 137, 136, 135, 134, 130, 132
57	Lanthanum	La	3	138.9055	139, 138
58	Cerium[d]	Ce	3, 4	140.12	140, 142, 138, 136
59	Praseodymium[d]	Pr	3	140.9077	141
60	Neodymium[d]	Nd	3	144.24	142, 144, 146, 143, 145, 148, 150
61	Promethium[d]	Pm	3	(145)	(RA:145, 146, 147)
62	Samarium[d]	Sm	3	150.35	152, 154, 147, 149, 148, 150, 144
63	Europium[d]	Eu	3, 2	151.96	153, 151
64	Gadolinium[d]	Gd	3	157.25	158, 160, 156, 157, 155, 154, 152
65	Terbium[d]	Tb	3	158.9254	159
66	Dysprosium[d]	Dy	3	162.50	164, 162, 163, 161, 160, 158, 156
67	Holmium[d]	Ho	3	164.9304	165
68	Erbium[d]	Er	3	167.26	166, 168, 167, 170, 164, 162
69	Thulium[d]	Tm	3	168.9342	169
70	Ytterbium[d]	Yb	3, 2	173.04	174, 172, 173, 171, 176, 170, 168
71	Lutetium[d]	Lu	3	174.97	175, 176
72	Hafnium	Hf	4	178.49	180, 178, 177, 179, 176, 174
73	Tantalum	Ta	5	180.9479	181
74	Tungsten	W	6	183.85	184, 186, 182, 183, 180
75	Rhenium	Re	7, 4, −1	186.2	187, 185

Table 8-2   (continued)

At. No.	Element	Symbol	Valence	Atomic Weight	Mass Number (in Order of Abundance)[b]
76	Osmium	Os	4, 6, 8	190.2	192, 190, 189, 188, 187, 186, 184
77	Iridium	Ir	3, 4, 6	192.22	193, 191
78	Platinum	Pt	4, 2	195.09	195, 194, 196, 198, 192, 190
79	Gold	Au	3, 1	196.9665	197
80	Mercury	Hg	2, 1	200.59	202, 200, 199, 201, 198, 204, 196
81	Thallium	Tl	1, 3	204.37	205, 203
82	Lead	Pb	2, 4	207.19	208, 206, 207, 204
83	Bismuth	Bi	3, 5	208.9804	209
84	Polonium	Po	2, 4	209	(RA:209)
85	Astatine	At	—	(210)	(RA:210, 211)
86	Radon[c]	Rn	0	(222)	(RA:222)
87	Francium	Fr	1	(223)	(RA:223, 212)
88	Radium	Ra	2	226.0254	(RA:226)
89	Actinium	Ac	3	(227)	(RA:228)
90	Thorium[e]	Th	4	232.0381	(RA)232
91	Protactinium[e]	Pa	5	321.0359	(RA:231)
92	Uranium[e]	U	6, 5, 4, 3	238.029	(RA)238, (RA)235, (RA)234
93	Neptunium[e]	Np	6, 5, 4, 3	237.0482	(RA:237)
94	Plutonium[e]	Pu	6, 5, 4, 3	(242)	(RA:244, 242, 239, 240)
95	Americium[e]	Am	3	(243)	(RA:243, 241)
96	Curium[e]	Cm	3	(247)	(RA:247)
97	Berkelium[e]	Bk	4, 3	(249)	(RA:247, 248, 249)
98	Californium[e]	Cf	3	(251)	(RA:251, 249)
99	Einsteinium[e]	Es	—	(254)	(RA:254, 252)
100	Fermium[e]	Fm	—	(257)	(RA:257)
101	Mendelevium[e]	Md	—	(258)	(RA:257)
102	Nobelium[e]	No	—	(255)	(RA:255, 253)
103	Lawrencium[e]	Lw	—	(256)	(RA:256, 258, 259)
104	Kurchatovium[f]	Ku	—	(261)	(RA:257, 259, 260)
105	Hahnium[f]	Ha	—	(262)	(RA:262, 261, 260)
106[f]		—	(263)	(RA:263)	
107[f]		—	(264)		

[a]Selected and compiled from various sources; atomic weights are based on carbon-12.

[b]Stable or long-lived isotopes; "(RA: . . .)" = radioactive isotope(s) having longest half-life, or reasonably close half-life, in that order, where more than one is shown; "(RA)" = radioactive element or isotope whose abundance has been established.

[c]"Inert gas" ("noble gas").

[d]Lanthanide (series).

[e]Actinide (series).

[f]Tentatively identified; names not yet formally adopted.

or solution, to the total number of moles of all components in that mixture or solution.

Gram-equivalent weight (gram-molecular weight) is the equivalent weight of an element or compound expressed in grams on a scale in which carbon-12 has an equivalent weight of 3 grams in those compounds in which its formal valence is 4.

An *atomic mass unit (amu)* is an arbitrarily defined unit in terms of which the masses of individual atoms are expressed; the standard is the unit of mass equal to $1/12$ the mass of the carbon-12 atom (the carbon atom having as nucleus the isotope with mass number 12).

The quantity of a single component in a mixture or solution is commonly expressed in *percent (%)*, or in *parts per million (ppm)* or *parts per billion (ppb)*, where a billion is 10^9; in order to be more consistent with the SI, the latter two units could be expressed as "$\ldots/10^6$" and "$\ldots/10^9$", respectively.

The ratio of unit mass to unit volume is often used in compositional analyses, typically expressed in *micrograms per milliliter ($\mu g/ml$)*, or in $\mu g/m^3$.

The frequency of spectral lines or bands, in optical and quasi-optical spectrometry, is usually expressed as *wavenumber*, in cm^{-1}; the wavenumber is the reciprocal of the wavelength, with the wavelength expressed in centimeters.

The *atomic number* of an element is the number of protons in its nucleus.

The *mass number* of an element is the sum of the numbers of protons and neutrons in its nucleus; it is commonly written as a superscript before (or, sometimes, after) the symbol of the atom, e.g., ^6Li(preferred), or Li^6.

Note: Basic concepts and some units of measurement pertaining to specific types of sensing and analyzing devices are covered in the appropriate sections of this chapter.

8.2 ELECTROMETRIC ANALYZERS

The operation of electrometric analyzers is based on the electrical characteristics of an *electrochemical cell* in which specific reactions occur. The electrical characteristics are measured individually or in combination and comprise current, voltage, and resistance (or its reciprocal, conductance); additionally, the variation of one or more electrical characteristics with time can provide information about chemical properties and composition. The field in which *electrometric methods of analysis* are used is known as *electroanalytic chemistry*.

The primary application of electrometric analysis instruments is in the determinations of concentrations of solutions. Concentration is now most commonly expressed in terms of *molarity*, the number of gram-molecular weights of a substance present (dissolved) in 1 liter of solution; molarity is indicated by the symbol M, preceded by a number to show solute concentration (e.g., "$2.4 \times 10^{-5}\,M$"). Other applications include determinations of the acidity or alkalinity *(pH)* of a liquid, of the magnitude of the oxidation or reduction potential, of the presence/absence of substances in liquids, and of the relative amount of a specified gas in a gas mixture referred to a reference gas mixture containing a known amount of the specified gas.

Electrode potentials are considered to be composed of the potentials produced by two half-cells, in combination. One half-cell contains the electrode of interest, the other half-cell is a standard hydrogen electrode. The potential E of the electrode of interest is then given by the *Nernst equation,* which, at a temperature of 25° C, can be expressed in the form

$$E = E_0 - \frac{0.05915}{n} \log \frac{a_{\text{red}}}{a_{\text{ox}}}$$

where E_0 is the standard-electrode potential, n the valence change (number of electrons transferred in the electrode reaction), and a_{red} and a_{ox} are the activities of the reduced and oxidized forms, respectively, of the reactants (of the electrode action).

8.2.1 Conductivity Sensors

Conductivity measurements are made primarily to determine the concentration of a solution or to determine the relative amount of a salt in an aqueous solution. The principle employed is that of *electrolytic conduction,* in which the charge carriers are provided by ionization. When a current flows through a volume of a solution, the soluble inorganic compounds in the solution will partially or completely separate into *cations* (positively charged ions) and *anions* (negatively charged ions). For example, NaCl forms Na^+ and Cl^- ions, $AgNO_3$ forms Ag^+ and NO_3^- ions, and $BaCO_3$ forms Ba^{2+} and CO_3^{2-} ions. Generally, hydrogen and metal ions are cations, and negative radicals and nonmetal ions are anions. The ionizing current originates from two electrodes, a cathode and an anode. The cations will migrate to the cathode, at which they combine with the electrons of the current source to form hydrogen or metal atoms. The anions will migrate to the anode, at which they form neutral atoms or molecules and liberate their electrons, which then flow to the current source.

When a potential is applied across two electrodes which are immersed in a solution, the current flowing through the circuit will be a function of the applied voltage and the resistance of the solution. This resistance, in turn, is a function of the nature of the solvent (water, and hence a constant factor, in the case of aqueous solutions), of the number of ions present, and of the ion mobility. Conductance (G) is the reciprocal of resistance (R) or $G = 1/R$. The (electrolytic) conductance of a solution, then, is proportional to the number of ions and to ion mobility. Conductance is expressed in *siemens (S);* it was formerly expressed in *reciprocal ohms (mho).* The parameter that characterizes solution concentration is (electrolytic) *conductivity* (γ), expressed in *S/m* (submultiples such as $\mu S/cm$ are commonly used).

The conductivity measurement is given by the measurement of the conductance of the liquid column between two electrodes. Assuming two parallel-plate electrodes, each having the same area A, separated by the distance L, with a uniform separating volume, the conductivity, $\gamma = G \cdot L/A$. When the conductivity is expressed in siemens, the electrode area in cm^2, and the separation distance in cm, conductivity will be expressed in S/cm, its most common unit. The ratio L/A is a constant for a given electrode configuration and is known as *sensor constant* (also called "cell constant" or "electrode constant"), K_S; hence, $\gamma = GK_S$.

Configurations employing two parallel plates are rarely used, and the separating volume can be nonuniform. However, the more complex relationships for such electrode configurations as parallel rods (Figure 8-1) and for concentric as well as internal or external annular electrode geometries (Figure 8-2) have been developed and sensor constants have been determined accordingly. Typical electrode materials are nickel, carbon, stainless steel, and ferrous–nickel alloys; gold plating is sometimes used. Insulating materials include polyvinylchloride, epoxies, silicone rubbers, and high-temperature, corrosion-resistant (proprietary) plastics. Since measured-fluid temperature has severe effects on the conductivity measurements, metal-film or thermistor thermometers are usually incorporated in conductivity sensors; in some cases they are specified to be installed separately in a flow-through type sensor (or close to it).

The type of excitation voltage applied to conductivity sensors is critical to its performance. If pure dc were applied, a resulting plot of current flow vs. time would show, first, a short spike due to the capacitance of the sensor and its connecting leads, and next, a short period where the current is purely dependent on conductance; this is followed by a long period during which electrolysis at the probe surface causes the current to decrease until a minimum current is reached when the sensor is polarized. For this reason, ac sensor excitation is used. When the waveshape is sinusoidal, an average of the four states described above would be obtained. The only current of interest is the short plateau following the initial spike. This points to the requirement for a square-wave excitation voltage; it should have a slow rise time so that the capacitance-caused spike is minimized; it should also have a fairly high frequency so that polarity is reversed before electrolysis becomes significant. The negative error still present due to averaging can be minimized by employing a peak-detector circuit. The effects of lead resistance can be minimized by using a four-wire connection to the associated bridge circuit, as is done for resistance thermometers (see Section 4.2.3.3). Lead-resistance effects as well as polarization are further reduced by using separate voltage and current electrodes, as in the sensor shown in Figure 8-2c.

Figure 8-3 illustrates a conductivity measuring circuit. The square-wave excitation is applied to the bridge circuit, in which a potentiometer allows manual balancing and into which the electrodes as well as thermal compensation elements are connected. The signal due to current flowing across the electrodes is amplified and rectified. The time constant of the capacitor (C_1) in conjunction with the associated resistors is such that it is charged by amplifier A_2 to the peak value seen; this avoids an output averaging with the

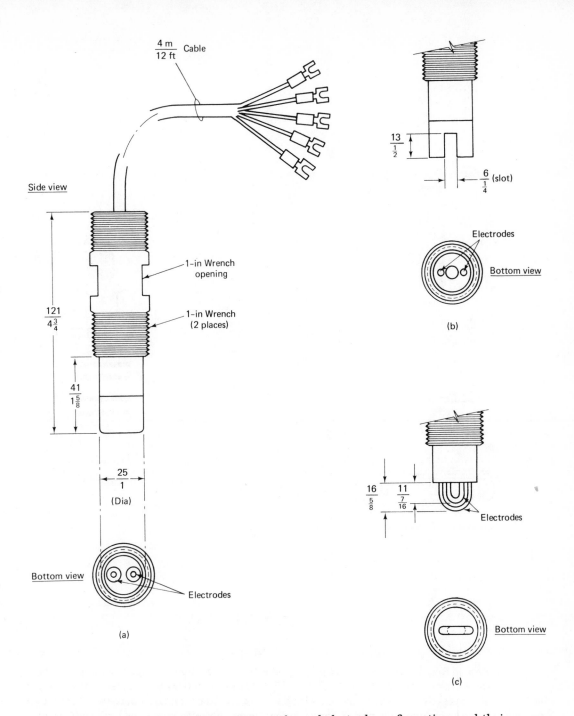

Figure 8-1. Typical conductivity probe and electrode configurations and their sensor constants, with dimensions in mm/inches: (a) $K_S = 2.0$; (b) $K_S = 1.0$; (c) $K_S = 0.1$. (Courtesy of Uniloc Div. of Rosemount, Inc.)

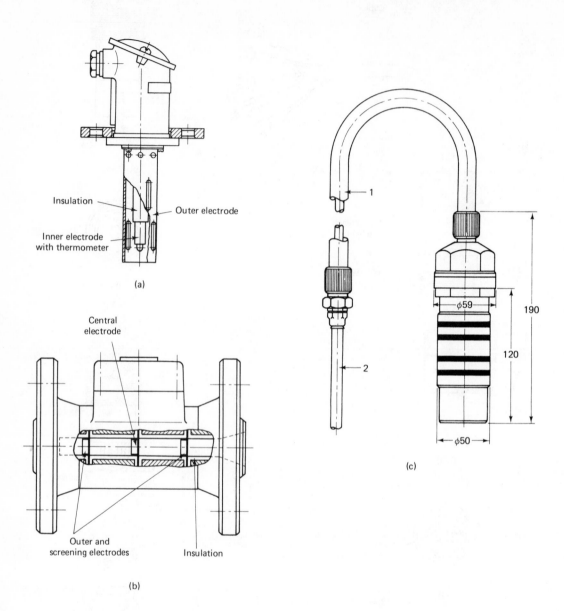

Figure 8-2. Examples of conductivity sensor configurations: (a) immersion probe with concentric electrodes ($K_S = 0.002$ to 0.06); (b) flanged flow-chamber sensor with annular electrodes ($K_S = 1.16$); (c) sensor with four-ring electrode configurations (top and bottom rings are voltage electrodes, center rings are current electrodes) for high-conductivity measurements; 1, polyamide protective sleeve over cable; 2, connecting cable. (Courtesy of Siemens A.G.)

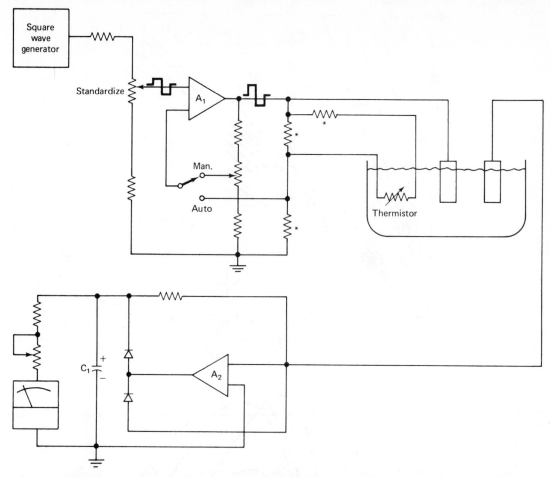

Figure 8-3. Typical conductivity measuring circuit; the effect on gain of A1 is characterized by the series-parallel resistances (*) associated with the thermistor and the combination compensates for fluid temperature variations; sensor elements are shown separately in this schematic representation. (Courtesy of Uniloc Div. of Rosemount Inc.)

lower currents seen due to electrolysis on the electrodes. The final output voltage is then displayed on a meter.

The most common applications of conductivity sensors are in concentration measurement (which can then be used for dilution control) of solutions and in measurements of the amount of total dissolved solids in natural waters. For single-component analyses of concentration the output readings are correlated with concentration by means of graphs, charts, and records of previously obtained readings. The determination of concentrations of a specific component in a mixed solution is more difficult. Generally, such a measurement can be obtained if the concentrations of the nonmeasured components remain reasonably constant, or when the measured component has a much higher conductivity than the other components. For example, most acids and bases are much more conductive than their salts since hydrogen and hydroxyl ions

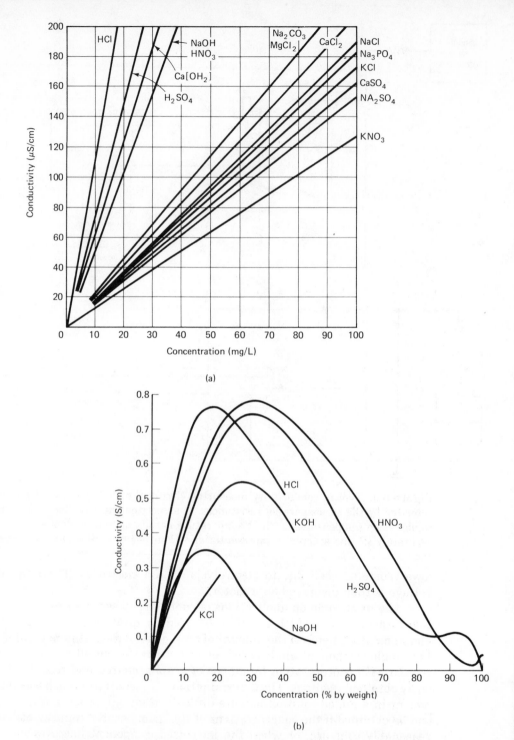

Figure 8-4. Conductivity as a function of concentration for several solutions, at 18 °C: (a) relationship is linear for relatively low concentrations; (b) relationship becomes nonlinear and slope reversal often occurs for very high concentrations. (Courtesy of Siemens A.G.)

have a very high mobility. Conductivity sensors are also used for the detection of leaks and spills (into liquids whose conductivity would be affected significantly by such events) and for salinity measurement.

Due to mass increases of ions with increasing concentrations the conductivity vs. concentration relationship becomes increasingly nonlinear, in many cases actually reaching a peak followed by a slope reversal. This characteristic is illustrated in Figure 8-4 (note that the conductivity units are $\mu S/cm$ in Figure 8-4a, whereas they are S/cm in Figure 8-4b). However, the curves will be repeatable; hence, it is still possible to determine very high concentrations even when slope reversal occurs, as long as a separate check is made to find out whether the higher or the lower concentration is being measured.

In some applications the use of electrodes for conductivity measurement is severely limited by the chemical or physical nature of the measured fluid (e.g., brine, two-phase liquids, abrasive or fibrous slurries). This problem can be overcome by using an *electrodeless (toroidal)* conductivity sensor. Such a sensor consists of two appropriately wound toroidal coils, spaced some distance apart in a single housing, and encapsulated and sealed with good physical and chemical protection from the measured fluid. One toroid, excited by ac, at audio frequencies, acts as the input coil; the second toroid acts as the output coil; the measured fluid, into which the sensor assembly is immersed, or which flows through the sensor assembly, provides the variable coupling between input and output toroids; the coupling is proportional to conductivity.

Conductivity sensors can also be used, in conjunction with elements that cause a specific chemical reaction resulting in conductivity changes, for analyses not related directly to conductivity. An example of this is a *dissolved-oxygen analyzer* using a cartridge filled with thallium shavings and two conductivity sensors. Thallium is not affected by oxygen-free water, but oxidizes in water containing dissolved oxygen. The resultant thallium oxide combines with the water to form thallium hydroxide (TlOH), which is easily soluble in water and then increases the conductivity of the water sample. In an instrument using this principle (as reported by Siemens A.G.) the sample is made to flow, first, through a cation and anion exchanger that reduces the conductivity of the sample to below 1.0 $\mu S/cm$ (to establish a low reference value), next, through a conductivity sensor, then through the thallium reactor, and finally through a second conductivity sensor. The residual conductivity, as measured by the first sensor, is subtracted from the conductivity sensed by the second sensor, and the differential value is then indicative only of the amount of TlOH created by dissolved oxygen in the sample. The quantity of dissolved oxygen can then be calculated from this value.

8.2.2 pH Sensors

The *pH* of a solution is a measure of its hydrogen ion activity and is indicative of the *acidity* or *alkinity* of the solution. pH is expressed in numbers on a scale of 0 to 14. The number 7, at the midpoint of this scale, represents a neutral solution, the pH of pure water. pH values decreasing from 7 to 0 indicate increasing acidity, whereas pH values increasing from 7 to 14 indicate increasing alkalinity. The pH number represents the negative logarithm of the hydrogen ion activity, or pH $= -\log_{10} a_{H^+}$, where a_{H^+} is the hydrogen ion activity. The activity of the H$^+$ ions (or *hydronium* ions, H$_3$O$^+$) increases with increasing acidity. As the activity of the hydrogen ion increases in a solution, the activity of the negative ions (OH$^-$, Cl$^-$, etc.) decreases accordingly. The reverse (increasing negative-ion activity, decreasing H$^+$ activity) is true for increasing alkalinity. The logarithmic relationship means that, for each pH value decreasing from 7, the activity of the hydrogen ion increases by one order of magnitude, whereas it decreases by an order of magnitude for each pH value increasing from 7 to 14.

The pH measuring circuit consists of two electrodes, immersed into the measured fluid (solution), and a voltmeter connected across the two electrodes. Of the two electrodes, one is the *pH sensing electrode,* the other is the *reference electrode.* The most commonly used pH electrode is the *glass electrode* (Figure 8-5a). The principle on which the function of this electrode is based originated in the discovery, by the German chemist Fritz Haber in 1901, of voltage

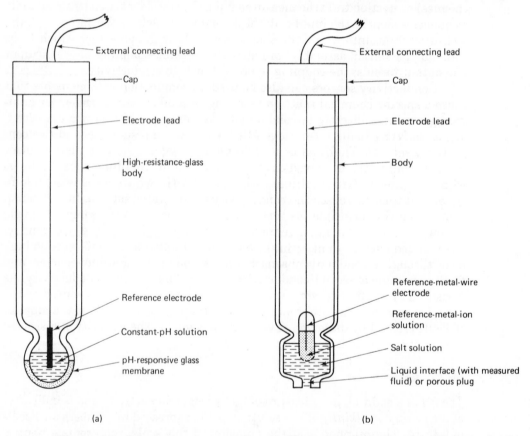

(a)

(b)

Figure 8-5. Schematic representation of pH sensing electrodes: (a) pH electrode; (b) reference electrode.

changes, seen at certain glass surfaces, that varied in a regular manner with changes in solution acidity. As shown in the illustration, the electrode assembly consists of a glass body with a cap; the electrode wire, which may be shielded, and which is connected to the insulated (typically shielded coaxial-cable) external connecting lead, extends through the center of the electrode body and terminates in an internal reference electrode. The bulb at the bottom of the electrode is filled with a solution characterized by constant pH and reference ion activity. The reference electrode is immersed in this solution, which wets the inside surface of a membrane of specially formulated glass. The outside surface of this pH-sensitive membrane is wetted by the solution to be measured.

There are three interfaces in and on this electrode at which electrical potentials are developed. The potential at the reference electrode/constant-pH solution interface remains constant. The potential at the constant-pH solution/ glass membrane interface also remains constant. The potential at the glass membrane/measured solution inteface, however, is proportional to pH. The nominal voltage produced is 60 mV per pH unit.

Figure 8-5b illustrates the generalized elements of a reference electrode. A wire electrode is immersed in a solution which is in contact with a salt solution (bridging solution) that comes in contact with the measured fluid (measured solution). Again, there are three interfaces at which electrical potentials are developed: the reference-metal-wire/reference-metal-ion solution interface, the reference-ion solution/salt solution interface, and the salt solution/measured solution interface. All three of these potentials remain constant. A frequently used reference electrode is the *silver–silver chloride* electrode. The reference electrode is a silver wire, coated with solid AgCl. The salt solution is KCl. Another reference electrode, also used quite commonly, is the *calomel* electrode. Calomel is a common name for mercurous chloride (Hg_2Cl_2). In this type of reference electrode a metal wire (platinum) is in contact with solid mercury, which, in turn is in contact with solid Hg_2Cl_2, and the calomel, in turn, is in chemical contact with a (typically saturated) solution of potassium chloride (KCl), which then acts as the bridging solution. The junction between the bridging and the measured solution is either in the form of a thin capillary opening (liquid junction) or in the form of a porous plug. Other types of reference electrodes have also been developed.

The associated voltmeter must have an input impedance that is much higher than the impedance of the electrodes, which can be up to 500 MΩ. Input stages employing a field-effect transistor (FET) can meet this requirement and are now often used in pH meters. The voltage provided by the electrodes is affected by measured-fluid temperature such that the thermal sensitivity shift of the measuring system is about 0.197 mV/pH/°C. When the measured-fluid temperature is known and constant, temperature compensation can be achieved by manual adjustment of the meter. When the measured-fluid temperature is expected to fluctuate, a temperature sensor is either immersed separately into the fluid and connected to compensating circuitry, or incorporated in one of the electrodes and similarly connected to compensate the electrode potentials for temperature effects.

Combination electrodes are often used for pH sensing. In such an electrode the pH sensing electrode and the reference electrode are simply combined in a single body, without either of the electrodes losing any of its required characteristics.

The nominal output of a pH electrode is 59.1 mV/pH, at 25 °C. The actual output of any one electrode can vary from this value. Hence, a sensitivity (slope) adjustment is provided (separate from that used to adjust for sensitivity shift due to measured-fluid temperature) on most pH meters. This is known as the "standardize" adjustment. It is intended to be used in conjunction with use of a standard solution, of accurately known pH, into which the electrodes (or combination electrode) are immersed; the "standardize" knob is then rotated until the meter reading corresponds to the pH of the standard solution.

8.2.3 ORP (Redox) Sensors

The *oxidation–reduction potential* of a solution, often referred to as "redox," is measured by the same devices as used for pH sensing, except that the pH sensing electrode is replaced by a platinum electrode (sometimes gold, or gold or silver on a platinum base). Oxidation–reduction potential *(ORP)* is related to the logarithm of the ratio of the activities of the oxidized and reduced states of the ions. The same type of reference electrode as prescribed for pH measurement is also used in conjunction with the platinum electrode for ORP measurements. The two electrodes are immersed adjacently; alternatively, both electrodes are packaged into a single combination electrode. The electrode potentials are read out directly in millivolts. A positive ORP indicates that the solution contains a significant oxidizing agent. A negative ORP indicates that the solution contains a strong reducing agent. A solution that is neither reducing nor oxidizing will have zero ORP. Various electrode constructions are used, including those employing a (usually platinum) wire protruding from, and fused into, an electrode body with a glass tip, or section of platinum foil, or platinum deposited, on a substrate. Some measurement systems allow for the measurement of pH as well as ORP, by providing a mV as well as a pH scale, and by either switching between a pH and an ORP electrode or by providing for interchange of these two electrodes.

8.2.4 Specific-Ion Sensors

In addition to the ORP-specific platinum electrode and the hydrogen-ion-specific pH electrode, electrodes have been developed that are specific (i.e., respond to the activity of, specifically) to a considerable number of other ions (see Table 8-3). Such *specific-ion,* or *ion-selective,* electrodes can be cation-specific (respond to positively charged ions) or anion-specific (respond to negatively charged ions), and can respond to monovalent or divalent ions. Specific-ion electrodes are also always used in conjunction with a reference electrode which completes the electrical circuit at the voltmeter input. The electrode potential developed over the nominal ion-activity measuring range may be symmetrically or asymmetrically bidirectional, or it may be between a set of positive voltage limits

Table 8-3 Ions for Which Specific-Ion Electrodes Are Commonly Available

Ammonia, NH_3	Cupric, Cu^{2+}	Potassium, K^+
(ammonium, NH_4^+)	Cyanide, CN^-	Silver, Ag^+
Arsenic, As^{5+}	Fluoride, F^-	Sodium, Na^+
Bromide, Br^-	Iodide, I^-	Sulfate, SO_4^{2-}
Cadmium, Cd^{2+}	Lead, Pb^{2+}	Sulfide, S^{2-}
Calcium, Ca^{2+}	Mercuric, Hg^{2+}	Sulfur dioxide
Carbonate, CO_3^{2-}	Nitrate, NO_3^-	(sulfite, SO_3^{2-})
Chloride, Cl^-	Nitrogen oxide	Thiocyanate, SCN^-
Chlorine, Cl_2	(nitrite, NO_2^-)	Zinc, Zn^{2+}
(hypochlorite, ClO_3^-	Perchlorate, ClO_4^-	
Chromium, Cr^{6+}	Phosphoric, P^{5+}	

or a set of negative voltage limits. Calibration curves are customarily plotted on semilog paper, with electrode potential linearly scaled and ion activity logarithmically scaled. Generally, the potential developed per order of magnitude (per decade) of ion activity change is 59.2 mV for monovalent ions, and it is 29.6 mV for divalent ions. With increased ion activity, the potential developed by the electrode becomes increasingly positive when cations are sensed, and it becomes increasingly negative when anions are sensed. In dilute solutions, *concentration* is usually proportional to *ion activity* and an output reading in terms of concentration can then be provided quite easily. Otherwise, concentration can be obtained by using appropriate electrode methods.

The external appearance of a specific-ion electrode is generally identical to that of a pH electrode. It is the nature of the sensing element that gives an ion-selective electrode its characteristics. The type of membrane and element used depend on the ion to be sensed. Glass membranes are used in some cases, liquid ion-exchange membranes are used for many types of ions, and solid-state membranes and sensing elements, comprised of insoluble, chemically stable ionic conductors, are available for many other ions.

Reference electrodes can be of the single-junction type, usually Ag/AgCl with a capillary-like liquid junction or porous-ceramic junction, or they can be of the double-junction type, having an inner chamber filled with a standard solution, a porous ceramic plug between inner and outer chambers, and an outer chamber filled with the bridging solution (typically KCl). Some electrode designs are intended not to need refilling; this can be accomplished, for example, by using a gel instead of a liquid for one or both of the solutions.

The *interferences* (types of ions that, if present, or if present in significant amounts, would obscure a reading of the activity of the ion of interest) must be considered for each specific-ion electrode. They are stated in applicable manufacturers' literature. In many cases the effects of interferences can be minimized by appropriate sample preparation. Also, the temperature of the measured fluid must be known and readings corrected (or meter operation adjusted) accordingly. Specific-ion ("pIon") meters are standardized by immersing the electrode in a solution of known activity of the ion of interest.

Sample-preparation methods specified for the use of each type of ion-selective electrode have been developed, are stated in applicable literature, and must be followed. Additionally, an *ionic strength adjustor* may have to be added to the sample to reduce the effects of levels of other ionic species, in the sample, on electrode potential; also, a *pH adjustor* may have to be added to avoid damage to the electrode from highly acidic or alkaline samples.

8.2.5   Coulometric Instruments

In *coulometric* instruments the quantity of electricity required to carry out a chemical reaction is measured. This quantity is based on *Faraday's law,* by which the reaction of one gram-equivalent weight of a substance will be effected by the passage of a quantity of electricity of 96 496 coulombs; this assumes that the reaction is 100% current efficient. The latter assumption as well as the requirement that only one overall reaction occurs are fundamental to coulometry.

Two principal methods are used in coulometry. The *constant-current* method requires a closely controlled constant-current source as a power supply, which is connected across two *generator electrodes*. The latter are placed in the cell assembly, which also contains the working electrode and the reference electrode, and a stirrer, which is normally driven by magnetic coupling to a permanent-magnet stirrer located outside the cell. The sample solution is placed within the cell. The current from the constant-current source is set to a value that permits the electrolysis to be completed within some reasonable period of time (3 min or less). A timer is started when the power is turned on to the generating electrodes that effect the electrolysis of the sample. The timer is stopped when the electrolysis is completed, as indicated by the potential from the working (and reference) electrode. The number of coulombs required for the electrolysis is then computed from knowledge of the current and of the elapsed time. An excess of a redox buffer substance is usually added to the sample to keep the potential developed from getting high enough to cause an unwanted reaction; the buffer will also act as an intermediate in the reaction. The area of the generating electrodes must be large enough to establish a current density low enough to keep electrode polarization within limits re-

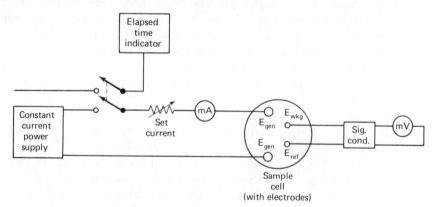

Figure 8-6. Schematic of constant-current coulometer.

quired for 100% current efficiency. A simplified instrument schematic is shown in Figure 8-6.

The *controlled-potential* method requires continuous adjustment of the power supply current to keep the working-electrode potential constant as compared to the reference electrode. The current is monitored and the integral of the current over a selected time period is displayed together with the current itself and the control potential. A typical controlled-potential coulometer uses a multiple platinum-gauze cathode (to provide a large electrode area), a platinum-wire anode, and a calomel reference electrode. Current integration is performed electronically. A typical block diagram is shown in Figure 8-7.

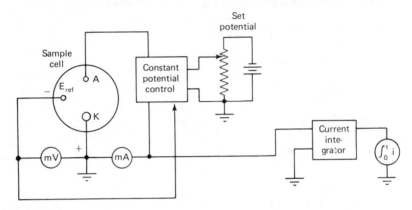

Figure 8-7. Schematic block diagram of controlled-potential coulometer.

8.2.6 Polarographs

An effect known as *concentration polarization* occurs in most electrochemical cells. A region in the solution in contact with the electrodes acts as a depletion layer where the ions of the solution are discharging at the electrode, and as an excess layer when the electrode is ionizing. The current at the electrode is then not only dependent on ion activity and electrode potential; it will include a component due to the rate of diffusion of ions from the main portion of the solution into that layer *(diffusion current)*. For many electrometric methods the concentration polarization and diffusion current are minimized by making electrode surfaces relatively large. In a polarograph the concentration polarization is maximized by using an electrode of extremely small surface area *(microelectrode)* so that the current reading is due to the diffusion effect to the greatest extent possible.

The classical polarographic microelectrode is the *dropping mercury electrode,* used as the cathode in the polarographic cell in conjunction with a mercury-pool electrode, covering the bottom of the cell, that is used as the anode. The dropping mercury electrode is, essentially, a glass capillary at the bottom of, and fed by, a mercury reservoir. The drop of mercury that grows at the bottom of the capillary and finally separates from it and falls into the mercury pool acts as the cathode surface. It has the advantage of being very small in surface area as well as being replaced constantly so that unwanted deposits have no time to form on its surface and create an unwanted polarization effect.

The operation of the polarograph, in its simplest form, involves applying a voltage, which varies in amplitude as a function of time in a predetermined manner, across the electrodes and measuring the current flowing through the circuit (see Figure 8-8). The current will typically increase with increasing potential but will reach a plateau due to the diffusion current of a particular ion. When more than one ion is present in a solution, successive plateaus at different voltages and currents will be observed.

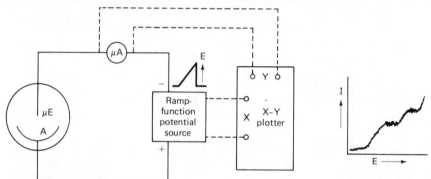

Figure 8-8. Polarograph—schematic block diagram (with example of a polarogram.)

In many applications the mercury-pool anode is replaced by a calomel reference electrode whose cell is connected to the measuring cell by a salt bridge, giving the two-cell/agar salt-bridge tube assembly the shape of an "H" ("H-cell"). The microelectrode may also be other than of the dropping mercury type (e.g., gold, platinum, carbon, or carbide). When the current–voltage curve is differentiated over a potential scan, a polarogram is obtained that shows peaks *(derivative polarography)* where the normal *polarogram* would show plateaus. Since the peaks obtained by derivative polarography are usually more pronounced than the plateaus, this method is quite attractive. Some polarographs employ a microelectrode and a counterelectrode (e.g., mercury pool) as well as a reference electrode and can then use the signal from the reference electrode to control the applied scan voltage very precisely.

8.2.7 Electrometric Gas Analyzers

Electrometric devices used to determine the amount of a specific gas in a gas mixture, or of a gas dissolved in liquid, use a variety of operating principles. In some cases the gas is admitted directly into a coulometric cell (e.g., chlorine fed into a cell filled with HCl). In other cases one of the electrodes is catalytically active and reacts with the gas to be measured. For determinations of gas dissolved in liquid (e.g., dissolved oxygen) a coulometric or polarographic

Chemical Properties and Composition

cell is equipped with a *semipermeable membrane* through which the gas diffuses into the cell.

An additional electrometric method is employed in one specific device, the *zirconium-dioxide* (zirconia) *oxygen analyzer*. This oxygen sensor consists of a tube of zirconium dioxide (in some designs stabilized with an other element such as calcium), closed at one end. Electrodes of porous platinum are coated onto the inside as well as the outside of the tube. The tube is heated electrically to a high temperature and the temperature is monitored by a platinum resistance thermometer which also provides a signal to a proportional temperature controller. The measured gas is applied to the outside of the tube and a reference gas mixture (containing a known amount of oxygen) is applied to the inside of the tube; alternatively, the measured gas is applied inside the tube and the reference gas outside the tube, as in the sensor shown in Figure 8-9. At high temperatures (400 to 900 °C) the zirconia tube becomes an electrolytic conductor due to the mobility of the oxygen ions. The tube surface seeing the higher oxygen partial pressure acts as the anode, whereas the surface seeing the lower oxygen partial pressure acts as the cathode. At high temperatures, then, the oxygen molecules at the anode absorb electrons while the reverse process takes place at the cathode. The voltage produced by the sensor is (under open-circuit conditions) given by the Nernst equation:

$$E = KT \log p_{ref}/p_{meas}$$

where K = a constant

T = absolute temperature

p_{ref} = partial pressure of oxygen in the reference gas

p_{meas} = partial pressure of oxygen in the measured gas

The reference gas can be a mixture containing a very closely controlled per-

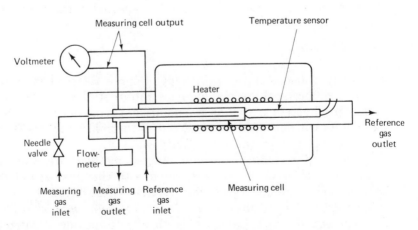

Figure 8-9. Heated-zirconia oxygen analyzer. (Courtesy of Siemens A.G.)

centage of oxygen. However, adequate measurements can be obtained using ambient air as reference, since air contains approximately 210 000 ppm O_2. In some simpler designs the inside of the tube is vented to the ambient atmosphere and the measured gas is applied to the outside of the tube. The cell potential is fed to an amplifier having a very high input impedance and the output of the amplifier is displayed on a meter calibrated in percent or parts per million (ppm) oxygen.

8.3 RESISTIVE GAS SENSORS

A number of resistive devices have been developed, and others are in various stages of development, that undergo resistance changes proportional to the concentration of a specific gas in a gas mixture. These devices are semiconductive and typically have a thin-film sensing element of a metal oxide, with or without additives.

The *titanium-oxide* (titania) *sensor* (titania resistor) is used as an oxygen analyzer. The titania film changes its resistance when oxygen molecules diffuse into the material. Since the sensor will also act as a thermistor its temperature is controlled within close limits.

Other thin-film metal–oxide (and some nonmetal–oxide, or combinations of both) sensors have been developed for different gases. Most of these incorporate an electric heating element, with or without proportional control based on a signal from an additionally incorporated temperature sensor. A platinum-activated tungsten–oxide sensor was developed to measure hydrogen concentration in air (in the 0 to 5% H_2 range). A tin–oxide sensor has been reported as usable for measuring concentrations of nitrogen oxides (NO_x) in air. A zinc–oxide sensor was reported in development for use as a detector in a gas chromatograph (see Section 8.7). The simplicity and ease of operation of such gas sensors makes them sufficiently attractive that further developments, a better understanding of the underlying physicochemical processes, and availability of mass-produced sensors can be expected in the near future.

8.4 THERMAL ANALYZERS

This section discusses the principles of three classical methods of thermal analysis (differential thermal analysis, differential scanning calorimetry, and thermogravimetry) as well as two additional types of sensors employing thermal effects but not usually considered as thermal analyzers (heat-of-combustion sensors and thermal conductivity cells).

Most of the classical thermal analysis methods are aimed at displaying heat effects, on a substance, associated with chemical and physical changes that the substance undergoes when heated. These effects may be *endothermal* (characterized by the absorption of heat) or *exothermal* (characterized by the development of heat). Causes of such effects include vaporization, boiling, sublimation, crystalline structure transformations, fusion, and such chemical reactions as oxidation, reduction, dehydration, decomposition, and direct combination. The purity of a substance can often be determined by measuring its boiling point or freezing point, usually with reference to the boiling or freezing point of the "standard" of that substance. Some of the changes that substances undergo with heating (at a known rate with reference to time) can also result in changes of sample mass. Finally, some thermally caused changes are detected by controlled cooling instead of heating.

8.4.1 DTA, DSC, and TGA

In the *differential thermal analyzer (DTA)* the temperature of a furnace is increased (or decreased) linearly with time, using a temperature sensor such as a thermocouple as input to a temperature programmer/controller in such a manner that a preselected heating rate (e.g., 20 °C per minute) or cooling rate is maintained exactly. The furnace contains a cell assembly with two cavities, one for the sample material, the other for a reference material against which the thermal behavior of the sample is to be compared. The sample temperature and the reference-material temperature are measured by a differentially connected pair of temperature sensors, typically a differential thermocouple. When the thermal behavior of both materials is identical, the output of the differential thermocouple will be zero. When the sample exhibits an endothermic or exothermic event not experienced by the reference material, the differential thermocouple will provide an output whose magnitude is indicative of the heat generated or absorbed, and whose polarity indicates whether the event was endothermic or exothermic. A schematic representation of a DTA is shown in Figure 8-10. The (amplified) outputs of the differential

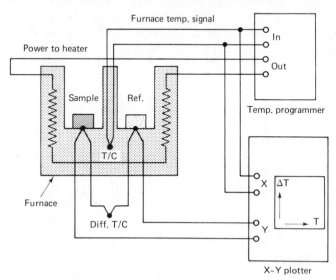

Figure 8-10. Differential thermal analyzer—simplified schematic diagram.

thermocouple and of the heater-temperature monitoring sensor are usually displayed, the former vs. the latter, on an X-Y plotter. DTA equipment is capable of heating as well as cooling at a controlled linear rate.

The *differential scanning calorimeter (DSC)* is similar to the DTA except that temperature differences between sample and reference are determined in a close-loop mode in the DSC, whereas they are detected in an open-loop mode in a DTA. In the DSC the sample and reference materials are heated by individual heaters; both heaters are initially programmed and controlled to heat (or cool) the materials at the identical rate. Temperature sensors are provided to measure both sample and reference temperatures. When the sample temperature differs from that of the reference material, due to an endothermic or exothermic event, the heat seen by the sample is rebalanced until its temperature matches that of the reference. The change in heater current required to effect this rebalance is then a measure of the heat developed or absorbed by the sample.

A *thermogravimetric analyzer (TGA)* measures the weight changes that a sample undergoes, due to thermal effects, while being heated or cooled at a known rate. The mass of the sample, which is inserted in a furnace, is measured continuously by a sensitive balance that provides an output signal indicative of sample mass. The output of this *thermobalance* is then recorded vs. a signal representative of sample temperature.

8.4.2 Thermal Conductivity Cells

The *thermal conductivity cell* (thermal conductivity detector) is used for the analysis of gases on the basis of the thermal conductivity of a sample gas with reference to the thermal conductivity of a reference gas. The device (see Figure 8-11) consists of four identical helical filaments (typically gold-sheated or Teflon-covered tungsten wire) connected as four arms of a Wheatstone bridge in the manner shown. Each filament is positioned at the center of a small cavity.

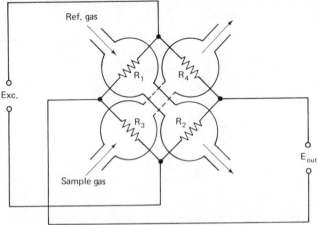

Figure 8-11. Thermal conductivity cell—schematic diagram.

The two sample-gas cavities are connected by a passage, but they are isolated from the reference-gas cavities and their interconnecting passage. The excitation power furnished to the bridge is large enough to cause heating of the four filaments. The temperature of the filaments and, hence, their resistance, is a function of heat loss into the gas. The bridge is so adjusted that it is balanced, and the bridge output voltage is zero, when the thermal conductivities of both gases are the same. When the composition of the sample gas changes, its thermal conductivity changes, and the resistance of filaments R_3 and R_4 changes accordingly, whereas the resistance of filaments R_1 and R_2 remains constant (provided that other factors, especially temperature, pressure, and flow rate of both gases, are the same).

The thermal conductivity cell has its primary application as the detector in a gas chromatograph (see Section 8.7), in which the carrier gas acts as the reference gas and the sample gas is the effluent from the column.

8.4.3 Heat-of-Combustion Sensors

Heat-of-combustion sensors exist in a variety of designs. Their principal application is in the determination of combustible-gas concentration in a gas mixture. One type employs a catalyst, of special composition, which causes oxidation of carbon monoxide to carbon dioxide. The oxidation raises the temperature of the catalyst. This temperature rise is measured with reference to the temperature of the gas mixture at the inlet to the sensor, and is proportional to the concentration of the combustible gas in the mixture. Another type of sensor uses a platinum winding coated with ceramic; the ceramic surface is treated with a catalyst. The sensor also contains a reference platinum winding of the same resistance and also coated with ceramic but without a catalyst on its surface, and not in contact with the measured gas. The two windings are connected as two arms of a Wheatstone bridge. Excitation power is high enough to cause heating of the windings. When combustible gas comes in contact with the catalyst on the sensing winding, combustion occurs and raises the temperature and, hence, the resistance of that winding. The resulting bridge unbalance voltage is proportional to the concentration of combustible gas in the gas mixture. Platinum, itself, acts as a catalyst with certain combustible gases. This principle is used in some sensors containing two heated platinum filaments, one in contact with the measured gas mixture, the other shielded from the gas mixture and used as reference. Combustion at the heated filament raises its temperature, hence its resistance, and the output of the bridge circuit into which both filaments are connected is indicative of combustible-gas concentration. All such sensors contain a flame arrestor of some type to prevent spreading of the combustion. The output of the sensor is usually displayed on a meter which is calibrated in terms of percent of the specific combustible gas measured. Many such meters are additionally calibrated in "percent lower explosive limit" *(%LEL),* based on the lower explosive limit established for the combustible gas intended to be measured by the instrument. The LEL is typically a few percent of the gas in a gas mixture.

8.5 IONIZATION ANALYZERS

The ionization principle is employed in several different types of analyzers (often referred to as "detectors" since one of their main applications is as the detector in gas chromatographs). These devices are used almost exclusively for the analysis of organic compounds in gaseous or vapor form. Only a few inorganic compounds can be analyzed by some types of ionization analyzers.

The *flame ionization detector (FID)* consists of a small chamber in which a hydrogen-fed flame burns in air or oxygen. The sample gas is introduced into the chamber by letting it mix with the hydrogen that feeds the flame. Hydrogen is used because it produces very few ions, hence provides a good signal-to-noise ratio. The ionic fragments and free electrons produced by the combustion of oxidizable carbon atoms produce an ionization current between two electrodes in close proximity to the flame. The (very small) current from the electrodes is then detected and amplified by an electrometer–amplifier, typically a solid-state amplifier with a junction FET front end. The ionization current is proportional to the flow rate of the sample and to the number of carbon atoms in the compound. In most designs the burner itself acts as one electrode; the other electrode is above the flame.

Nuclear radiation from a radioactive-isotope source is used to cause ionization in some other types of detectors. One design incorporates a source of alpha particles within a cylindrical housing into which a center electrode is partially inserted, while a portion of the housing's wall acts as the other electrode. A polarizing voltage across the electrode provides for the required migration of ions, formed by collision of alpha particles with constituents of the sample gas, and the resulting ionization current. The *helium ionization detector* receives the sample gas mixed with helium carrier gas. An H^3 (tritium) foil is used as particle source as well as the anode, and a high polarizing potential is applied between it and the cathode. The field gradient and radiation due to H^3 decay raise the helium to a metastable state and the energy stored in this medium ionizes the molecules in the sample flowing through the chamber. Compounds that contain an electronegative group and thus have an affinity for free electrons can be analyzed by an *electron-capture detector*. A typical design uses nitrogen as carrier gas and a source of beta particles (e.g., H^3, Ni^{63}), which also acts as one of the two electrodes across which a polarizing voltage is applied. The beta particles ionize the nitrogen molecules and establish a field of low-energy electrons that can then be captured by the electron-capturing components of the compound being analyzed. The removal of an electron from the medium between the electrodes causes a reduction of the baseline ionization current, and this current change then characterizes the compound. A design version of an electron-capture detector *(ECD)* has been reported using charged parallel electrodes instead of a radioisotope source to provide the required electron field density.

In a *photoionization analyzer* a source of photons having relatively high energy is used to ionize the molecules of the compound being analyzed. Since photon energy increases with decreasing wavelength, a source of ultraviolet light is most suitable. The molecules are ionized by absorption of ultraviolet light whose proton energy is greater than the ionization potential of the molecules. The resulting ions are then made to cause a current flow between two electrodes of opposite polarity.

Ionization analyzers are frequently used as *total hydrocarbon* analyzers, providing a readout directly in terms of parts per million of total hydrocarbons in a gas mixture. When specific compound concentrations are to be analyzed, appropriate calibration charts can be furnished with the instrument to convert the meter readings to parts per million of the compound in a gas mixture. When compounds are in liquid form, they can be vaporized for the analysis. When they are solids, they can be pyrolyzed and the resulting vapor can then be analyzed (see Section 8.7 for pyrolysis).

8.6 PHOTOMETRIC ANALYZERS

The general category of photometric analyzers encompasses a considerable variety of instruments. Many of these are described in other sections of this book. Opacity monitors, turbidimeters, colorimeters, fluorimeters, nephelometers, and refractometers are discussed in Section 5.4. Spectrophotometers are described in Section 8.8.1. Section 8.8 covers those instruments that are intended primarily for the determination of the spectral distribution of electromagnetic radiation. Analyzers that respond primarily to light intensity at one or two preselected or known wavelengths, and those that measure polarization of light, are discussed below.

8.6.1 Flame Photometers

Flame (emission) photometry is a form of emission spectrophotometry (see Section 8.8) wherein atoms and molecules are raised from a ground state to an excited (electronic) state by thermal collisions with flame constituents and then emit characteristic electromagnetic radiations while they return to their ground state.

The sample to be analyzed is first converted into a vapor by means of an "atomizer" ("nebulizer"), which converts the sample (if liquid) into a fine vaporlike mist. The sample is then fed into the capillary of the burner (see Figure 8-12), where it is burned in a fuel–oxidant mixture. Typical burner mixtures are hydrogen–oxygen, acetylene–air, acetylene–oxygen, and acetylene–nitrous oxide.

The light emissions from the sample, in the flame, are passed through a narrow-band-pass filter and then collimated onto a photodetector. The filter is selected for the wavelength of maximum emission of the substance whose relative abundance or concentration is to be determined. The amplified output of the photodetector can then be displayed on a meter or a strip-chart recorder (or digital printer). The use of the simple flame photometer is limited to such substances as those containing metal ions that provide a sufficiently bright emission, at a wavelength in the visible or near-visible portion of the spectrum,

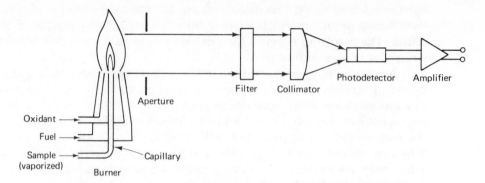

Figure 8-12. Flame photometer—basic schematic arrangement.

for a reasonably high signal-to-noise ratio. Much wider applications exist for the related *flame emission spectrometer,* in which the single band-pass filter is replaced by a scanning monochromator (see Section 8.8.6).

Related to the flame photometer as well as the emission spectrophotometer is the *spark-emission UV photometer,* which is used for the detection of halides, especially of the presence and abundance of halogen compounds in the air. The air is sampled and the sample is fed to a chamber in which an electrical spark is generated. The emission from the spark is enhanced in the ultraviolet region by the halogens and the brightness in that portion of the spectrum is indicative of halogen concentration. The light emission from the spark chamber is passed through a UV filter and then to a photodetector.

The instruments described above are in a category that has recently become known as *nondispersive photometric analyzers.* They differ from spectrophotometers and IR spectroradiometers in that they lack the scanning monochromator which disperses the polychromatic light into a set of monochromatic beams, each of which is then analyzed for intensity, usually sequentially over one scan, by a photodetector. Nondispersive analyzers employ, instead, a narrow-band-pass filter selected for the wavelength of maximum emission (or of maximum absorption) of a specific substance whose presence/absence or relative abundance or concentration in a mixture is to be determined.

8.6.2 Nondispersive Infrared Analyzers

The meaning of "nondispersive" was explained at the end of Section 8.6.1. A *nondispersive infrared analyzer (NDIR analyzer)* is an absorption spectrometer in which the scanning monochromator is replaced by one (sometimes two) narrow-band-pass filters and which operates in the near or middle infrared region of the spectrum. The operation in the IR region dictates the use of an IR source (instead of a visible or UV source), an IR detector, and good IR characteristics of all internal optical elements.

NDIR analyzers exist in many different optical configurations. A typical layout is shown in Figure 8-13. IR emission from a source is collimated into

Chemical Properties and Composition

two beams. A chopper disk alternatingly enables one beam and disables the other; it also provides synchronization signals. One beam passes through a cell containing (or exposed to) the sample being analyzed; the other beam passes through a cell containing a reference gas. The two beams exiting their respective cells are collected and collimated onto an IR detector through a filter selected to pass radiation at a wavelength corresponding to the wavelength of maximum absorption in the IR portion of the spectrum. The photodetector output then represents alternatingly a background level, established by the reference beam, and a measuring level, established by the sample beam. The difference between those two outputs is then indicative of the concentration, in the sample, of the gas of interest. When two gases in the sample are to be analyzed and their wavelengths of maximum absorption are far enough apart, two filter/photodetector sets can be employed for the concentration analyses of both gases. One design even employs three such sets for the simultaneous analyses of three different gases. When the concentration of certain gases in the ambient air is to be analyzed, the sample cell can be omitted and the optical path exposed to the ambient air instead.

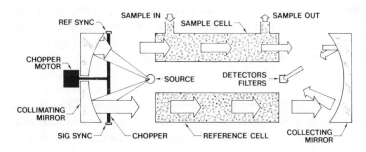

Figure 8-13. Typical schematic layout of an NDIR analyzer. (Courtesy of Infrared Industries, Inc.)

Besides optical configurations of the dual-beam type, as in the example described above, some configurations can also be of the single-beam type. An example of this is a layout in which the polychromatic beam from a source passes through the sample and is then separated into two beams by a beamsplitter. The measuring beam reaches its detector through a filter selected for narrow band-pass at the wavelength of maximum absorption of the gas of interest, whereas the reference beam reaches its photodetector through a filter passing only some wavelength chosen as reference and unaffected by the absorption characteristics of the gas mixture.

Although the IR region of the electromagnetic spectrum has been found most suitable for absorption analysis, especially of gases, some analyzers operate in the visible portion of the spectrum. About 250 different gases have usable absorption lines in the IR region. A significant proportion of NDIR analyzers, however, are used primarily for the analyses and detection of carbon monoxide, carbon dioxide, and methane in air. Among available nondispersive (non-IR) absorption analyzers are visible-light analyzers used for the detection of NO_2, and UV analyzers used for the detection of H_2S and SO_2 and of phenols (in aqueous solutions).

8.6.3 Chemiluminescence Analyzers

Certain compounds (molecules) can be detected by mixing them with a reagent with which the molecules react to form excited molecules which decay spontaneously with photon emission. This emission is then passed through an optical filter (or filters) and sensed by a photodetector. Among the reactions that have been used for gas analyses are the chemiluminescent reaction of ozone (O_3) with nitric oxide (NO); either gas can be detected by admixture of a controlled amount of the other; additionally, NO_2 can be detected by converting it to NO. Another reaction resulting in chemiluminescence is that of ozone with ethylene; this is used for O_3 analysis.

8.6.4 Polarimeters

Some substances can be analyzed by measuring the rotation of the plane of polarization of plane-polarized light when it passes through the sample. In its basic layout (see Figure 8-14) a polarimeter contains a light source whose light is linearly polarized by a device such as a Nicol prism. The polarized light is then passed through the sample and then through an analyzer (e.g., another Nicol prism) to a photodetector. The sample substance must be optically active to a sufficient extent that the optical rotation of the substance can be used to provide a qualitative or quantitative analysis of the substance. Substances that can be analyzed by polarimetry include dextrose and sucrose.

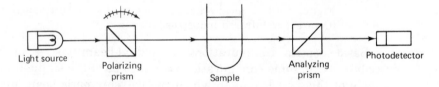

Figure 8-14. Polarimeter—basic schematic arrangement.

Various versions of electronic polarimeters (photopolarimeters) have been developed; a typical method of operation involves obtaining a null balance by rotating the polarizing prism until it matches the optical rotation produced by the sample and reading the polarizer angle when a null condition is achieved. A polarimeter becomes a *spectropolarimeter* by the addition of a scanning or adjustable monochromator between light source and polarizer. In a remote-sensing version of a spectropolarimeter, relatively coarse determinations of polarization of incident light at several different wavelengths are made by using two filter wheels, one containing wavelength filters, the other containing polarizing filters, with the wheels so positioned that a filter of one wheel is always used in conjunction with a filter of the other wheel.

Chemical Properties and Composition

8.7 CHROMATOGRAPHIC ANALYZERS

8.7.1 Gas Chromatographs

Gas chromatographs are used for the qualitative and quantitative analyses of gaseous or liquid mixtures. Their operation is based on sequential separation of compounds in a tube containing an adsorbent.

A basic schematic of a *gas chromatograph (GC)* is shown in Figure 8-15.

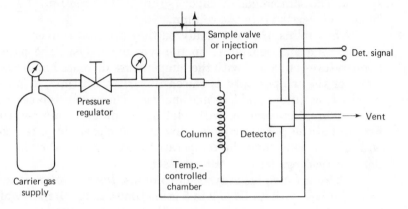

Figure 8-15. Gas chromatograph—basic schematic.

The sample is injected into a stream of carrier gas, which carries it through a *column* (separation column), a long, thin tube, typically in the form of a multiturn coil, which contains a specific adsorption material (the *packing*). Substances with a high affinity relative to the packing will travel through the column at a slower rate than substances with a low affinity. The compounds will then exit from the column in an identifiable sequence, due to the *elution* process in the column. The elution products, still carried by the carrier gas, then pass through a detector, which provides an output signal indicative of the abundance of each compound. After detection the effluent is either vented or collected.

The *carrier gas*, usually hydrogen, nitrogen, or helium, is either stored in a pressure bottle or (as is sometimes the case with hydrogen) generated in situ. A pressure regulator adjusts the pressure (and flow rate) of the carrier gas through the system. In some designs the flow rate is monitored by a gas flowmeter.

The sample valve or injection port, the column, and the detector are all mounted within a *temperature chamber*. A proportional temperature controller maintains the electrically heated chamber as well as its components, at a selectable temperature. For some analyses it is required that the temperature be raised at a specified linear rate *(programmed-temperature chromatography)*. Instrument designs capable of providing such a function are equipped with a programmer in the heater control electronics.

In process chromatographs a closely controlled quantity of the sample is introduced into the GC by means of a *sample valve*. Sample valve design and operation is critical to obtaining good analyses; the process is sampled by the valve many times during a day and the number of molecules in the sample must be repeatable. Liquid samples are vaporized upon entering the GC, either by a separate electrically heated vaporizer or (when the temperature chamber is sufficiently hot) in the sample valve or port itself. In laboratory GCs the sample is usually introduced by a *microsyringe* through a self-sealing rubber *septum*. The sample gas or vapor is thus introduced into the carrier gas as a "plug" and carried into the column.

When solids are to be analyzed they are first converted into a vapor in a *pyrolizer* oven. Depending on the type of analysis, the pyrolizer is either temperature-controlled with the temperature increased in discrete and known steps, or the temperature is raised linearly with time, at a selectable rate, which can be quite rapid for some analyses. The pyrolysis is compound-selective since different substances will volatilize at different temperatures. The temperature of the pyrolizer oven is monitored closely by a temperature sensor with fast response and the temperature readings are correlated with the GC detector readings for data interpretation.

There are two basic types of columns. *Packed columns* are coiled or U-shaped tubes, with an ID of 2 to 5 (sometimes up to 10) mm, which are packed with a solid material *(solid support)* that is then coated with a selected solvent referred to as the *stationary phase* (as opposed to the *mobile phase* constituted by the carrier gas, carrying the sample). Such columns are used in *gas–liquid chromatography* since the stationary phase is a liquid phase. *Capillary columns* are long, thin (typically 0.1 to 0.5 mm ID) tubes whose inside surface is coated with, usually, a liquid phase, sometimes liquid on a very fine mesh solid support, sometimes a solid absorbent *(gas–solid chromatography)*. Packed columns with an ID down to 0.5 mm are used sometimes. Capillary columns are usually coiled. The tubing material can be glass, metal (stainless steel, copper, aluminum), which may have an internal Teflon coating, or plastic (Teflon, nylon, polyethylene). A large variety of solid supports are used in packings, including textured glass beads, plastic powders, silica gel, activated charcoal, and activated alumina. An even larger variety of stationary phases are available; they are usually identified by trade names proprietary to a particular manufacturer; examples are Chromosorb 101, Porapak Q, Apiezon L, Carbowax 20M, OV-210, and DEXSIL 300GC. The stationary phase must be carefully selected for a given analytical problem, with emphasis on its separating ability and thermal stability.

Detectors used in GCs are described in other sections of this chapter. Among the commonly used detectors are the flame ionization detector (FID) and the electron-capture detector (see Section 8.5), and the thermal conductivity detector (TCD) described in Section 8.4.2. Some GCs use two detectors in tandem, others may use a separate detector, which sees only the carrier gas, as reference detector. Use of a TCD requires that the carrier gas is supplied to its two reference filaments; in some designs the carrier gas first travels through a reference column before it reaches the TCD.

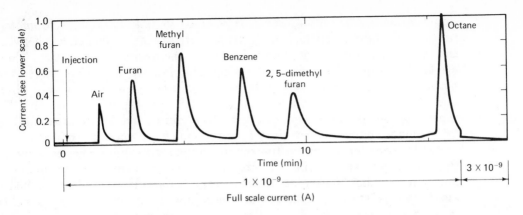

Figure 8-16. Example of a chromatogram (ionization detector output as fraction of full-scale output current).

The detector output is amplified and then usually recorded on a strip-chart recorder for data interpretation. A typical chromatogram (for a test mixture) is shown in Figure 8-16. Data interpretation involves determination of peak height and, more important, peak area. The latter can be determined coarsely by multiplying peak width at one-half peak height by one-half the peak height. More accurate results are obtainable by integration of the peak area, an operation that is greatly facilitated by use of a computer. Some GCs are equipped with microprocessors that perform the required peak analysis operations.

Very thorough analyses are made possible by combining a GC with a mass spectrometer (see Section 8.10); this combination is referred to as *GCMS*.

8.7.2 Liquid Chromatographs

Liquid chromatographs (LC) differ from gas chromatographs primarily in that no carrier gas is used. Instead, a dilute solution of the sample is prepared and is then passed through a column packed with solid particles which are either used as such or act as solid support for a liquid phase. As the sample solution elutes through the column, the components in the solution will separate, due to variations in travel time through the column. The effluent from the column is then passed through a detector and is then vented or collected. The detector provides information about each component in sequence of elution.

Detectors used in LCs are quite different from the gas detectors used in GCs. The two most widely used LC detectors are the UV photometric detector and the refractive index (RI) detector (see Sections 5.2.3.2 and 5.4). One type of RI detector is the differential refractometer, which responds to the difference in RI between the sample and a reference liquid.

When the column is packed only with solids, that reversibly adsorb the solutes, the analysis method is called *liquid/solid chromatography*. The solids are similar to materials used as solid support in GCs. When the solids in the column are coated with a liquid stationary phase, immiscible in the mobile liquid phase, the analysis method is referred to as *liquid/liquid chromatography.* The relative distribution or partition of the sample components between the mobile and stationary phases determine the degree of separation. There are two additional methods in liquid chromatography. In *ion-exchange chromatography,* ion-exchange separations are made between a polar mobile phase and a stationary ion-exchange resin with acidic or alkaline counterions. The separation depends on the ionic nature of the solutes and their relative affinity for the ion-exchange surface. In *gel permeation chromatography* molecules are sorted by size, depending on the size of the pores in the porous packing gel that the molecules can migrate into; hence, the path through the column is longer for smaller molecules than for larger molecules. This last method is also known as "steric exclusion chromatography." Liquid chromatographs exist in laboratory as well as on-line designs. In many current designs the sample solution is pressurized to a high pressure before entering the column, to speed up the analysis process. When a liquid chromatograph is combined with a mass spectrometer (LCMS) the sample is carried into the mass spectrometer in vaporized form.

8.8 SPECTRORADIOMETRIC ANALYZERS

This category of instruments is used to determine chemical composition from the spectral distribution of electromagnetic energy. The electromagnetic radiation that is analyzed can be in the spectral regions of cosmic rays, gamma rays, and X-rays (see Figure 6-1), extreme (vacuum) ultraviolet, ultraviolet, visible light, or infrared (see Figure 5-1), or microwaves. The electromagnetic radiation whose spectral characteristics are analyzed can be due to emission from a hot sample *(emission spectrometry)* or to fluorescence, phosphorescence, or luminescence from a sample. Emission spectrometry is also used in astrophysics, where the hot "sample" is a nebula, galaxy, star, planet, moon, or comet. In *absorption spectrometry* a portion of the spectrum is scanned to determine at what wavelengths what quantity of radiation from a source is absorbed. The emission or absorption of electromagnetic radiation at specific wavelengths is due primarily to changes in electronic energy levels of atoms and electronic states of molecules and in changes (transitions) of molecular vibrational and rotational states.

An emission spectrum will contain a number of peaks at certain wavelengths, whereas an absorption spectrum will show a number of valleys at certain wavelengths. The wavelengths at which such peaks or valleys occur permit identification of an atom or molecule. The peak or valley amplitudes are related to the abundance or concentration (in a mixture) of the atom or molecule. The peaks and valleys (valleys, in absorption spectra, become peaks if the spectrum is shown in terms of absorbance instead of transmission) are generally very narrow and are called *spectral lines.* A group of closely adjacent lines is called a *spectral band.* Spectra of essentially all known atoms and molecules have been determined and are available, for correlation with experimentally determined spectra, in graphical or tabular form.

It is customary to express spectral distribution (location of spectral lines) in terms of photon energy when the wavelengths in the spectrum are shorter than that of ultraviolet. When the wavelengths are between those of ultraviolet and far infrared the distribution is expressed either in wavelength (nanometers or micrometers) or in wavenumber (the reciprocal of wavelength, expressed in cm^{-1}). In the microwave region the spectral distribution is usually expressed in terms of frequency.

As the *spectral resolution* of spectroradiometers improved it became possible to discern lines. With further improvements it was discovered that some of the lines were really groups of thinner lines (*fine* spectra) and with still further improvements it was shown that even some fine lines consisted of several extremely narrow lines (*hyperfine* spectra). The definition of spectral resolution is: the smallest difference in wavelength (or in photon energy for the case of X-rays and gamma rays) for which separation of two adjacent lines is still possible. Spectral resolution can be stated in terms of $\Delta\lambda/\lambda$, where λ is wavelength, or in terms of wavenumber, or in terms of *resolving power*, $\lambda/\Delta\lambda$; the resolving power of spectrometers is generally between 5000, for simple instruments, and over 200 000, for spectrometers employing diffraction gratings. A resolving power of 200 000 means that two lines, separated by 0.0025 nm, can be resolved at 500 nm.

Analytical methods, including sample preparation, for spectrometry will not be described here. Several good texts are listed in the bibliography portion of this chapter. However, it can be noted briefly that absorption spectrometry involves the interaction of one or more beams of monochromatic radiation with the sample; emission spectroscopy involves heating the sample electrically, or by use of a flame, or by incorporating the sample material into an electrode which is then heated by causing a dc or ac arc, or spark, to be generated from this electrode; heating of gaseous samples can be attained in a discharge tube; fluorescence is short-lived light emission (10^{-8} to 10^{-3} s in duration) from a sample in response to incident electromagnetic radiation (typically UV; X-ray fluorescence is treated separately, in this chapter); phosphorescence is long-lived light emission (longer, typically much longer, than 1 ms); and chemiluminescence is light emission, caused by a chemical reaction, that persists still longer.

8.8.1   Spectrophotometers

Spectrophotometers are primarily those instruments in which the spectral distribution of radiant energy is measured in the spectral regions, including the UV, visible, and near to middle IR (see Section 5.1.1 and Figure 5-1). Instruments that are similar in their operating principle to spectrophotometers are used in the extreme ultraviolet (XUV) and far-infrared (FIR) regions. The spectral regions are delineated as follows:

	Wavelengths (nm)	Wavenumbers (cm⁻¹)
XUV (extreme ultraviolet, "vacuum ultraviolet")	10–200	1 000 000–50 000
UV (ultraviolet)	200–380	50 000–26 315
VIS (visible light)	380–780	26 315–12 820
NIR (near infrared)	780–3000	12 820–3333
MIR (middle infrared)	3000–15 000 (3–15 μm)	3333–666
FIR (far infrared)	$15 \times 10^3 - 8 \times 10^5$ (15–800 μm)	666–12.5

The MIR region is customarily included in the FIR region; however, in spectrophotometry it is useful to separate these two regions because 15 μm is approximately the upper limit of photon (quantum) detectors; thermal detectors have to be used for IR detection above this limit.

The elements comprising light sensing systems, which include spectrophotometers, are briefly described in Section 5.2.3.2. Some of these elements, which are of particular importance in spectrophotometers, are described in more detail below. Photodetectors are covered thoroughly in Section 5.2.2.

The three most commonly used types of spectrophotometers are illustrated schematically in Figure 8-17, in their most elementary form. The most essential element is the *monochromator,* whose optical input is polychromatic light and whose optical output is monochromatic light of known wavelength. Concentration and geometric delineation of the light beams are accomplished by *collimators* (typically lenses or concave mirrors) and by optical *slits* (entrance and exit slits for the monochromator). Radiation (light) at the wavelength of interest is sensed by a *photodetector,* which produces an electrical output signal proportional, in amplitude, to the light intensity at that wavelength.

In the basic *absorption spectrophotometer* (Figure 8-17a), light, from a source, is converted into monochromatic light, whose wavelength is adjustable and always known, which passes through the sample. Absorption will occur in the sample and the corresponding light changes are sensed by the photodetector. The absorption spectrum is then established by a plot of light intensity vs. wavelength. The spectral characteristics of the light source, photodetector, and all internal optical elements must be known and considered in the final readings.

The basic *emission spectrophotometer* differs from the basic absorption spectrophotometer primarily in the absence of a light source and the location of the sample. Polychromatic light from the (heated) sample is directed at the monochromator, which sweeps over the specified spectral region and then provides monochromatic light, at known wavelengths and intensities indicative of the emission spectrum, to the photodetector (see Figure 8-17b).

In the *fluorescence spectrophotometer* monochromatic light wavelengths are selected from the polychromatic emissions of a light source (which emits in a spectral region, including UV). The monochromatic light from the *exci-*

tation monochromator is directed at the sample, in which fluorescence will occur at certain excitation wavelengths. The fluorescent light, which is polychromatic, is then analyzed for spectral content by the *emission monochromator* in conjunction with the photodetector. This is illustrated schematically in Figure 8-17c.

It should be noted that the three schematics of Figure 8-17 are intended primarily to show the similarities and the differences between the three types of instruments and show only the most basic elements. An additional set of elements is common to virtually all spectrophotometers: a reference channel whose beam either does not pass through the sample or does pass through it but is then detected by a photodetector through a filter that passes only a sample-indifferent band of wavelengths.

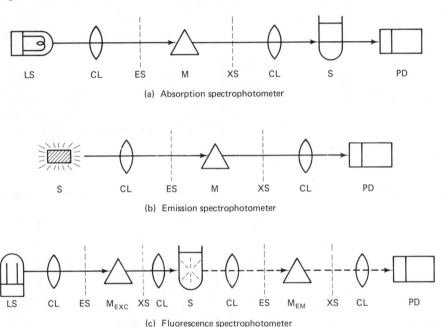

(a) Absorption spectrophotometer

(b) Emission spectrophotometer

(c) Fluorescence spectrophotometer

Figure 8-17. Basic elements of spectrophotometers: LS, light source; CL, collimator; ES, entrance slit; M, monochromator; XS, exit slit; S, sample; PD, photodetector; EXC, excitation; EM, emission. (a) Absorption spectrophotometer; (b) emission spectrophotometer; (c) fluorescence spectrophotometer.

8.8.1.1 Monochromators. The most essential part of a spectrophotometer is its light-*dispersing* device, the *monochromator,* which permits light intensity at selected wavelengths, or in narrow bands of wavelengths, to be examined. The monochromator receives polychromatic light through an entrance slit, modifies this radiation geometrically and optically, and then leads selected radiation through an exit slit so that it can be sensed by a photodetector.

Optical *filters* are used in the simplest spectrophotometers. It should be noted, however, that filters may be more suitable than other types of mono-

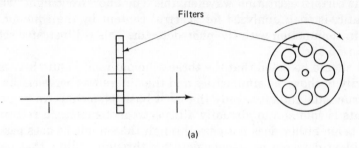

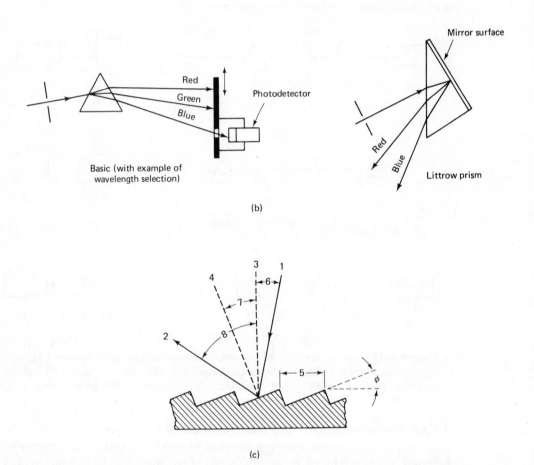

Figure 8-18. Monochromator types: (a) filter wheel; (b) prism; (c) diffraction grating: 1, incident beam; 2, diffracted beam; 3, normal to grating; 4, normal to groove face; 5, groove spacing (d); 6, angle of incidence; 7, blaze angle (ϕ); 8, angle of reflection.

chromators in XUV and FIR spectroradiometers. A number of different band-pass filters may be arranged in a *filter wheel* (Figure 8-18a), which places a specified filter in the optical path by rotating to a specified position. The band-pass characteristics of spectrophotometer filters can be established by a composite glass absorption filter or by an interference filter. *Composite glass absorption filters* consist of one or more high-pass filters and one or more low-pass filters, with some overlap in their respective cutoff regions. The passband then lies in that overlap region. The *band-pass* characteristic of a filter is usually given by the range of wavelengths at one-half the peak transmittance (*FWHM* = full width at half magnitude). Other essential filter characteristics are the transmittance at the nominal wavelength *(peak transmittance)*, typically stated in percent of the transmittance that would exist without the filter (or with a clear glass plate) and the wavelength at which the peak is observed *(nominal wavelength)*. For most composite glass absorption filters the FWHM is around 25 nm and the peak transmittance is less than 20%. Single high-pass or low-pass sharp-cutoff filters are sometimes used in the optical path of other types of filters or other types of monochromators, as blocking filters.

Interference filters employ the principles of optical interference to reject radiation at wavelengths outside a pass band by selective reflection. This reflection occurs within a thin film (½ wavelength thick) of transparent metal and dielectric layers between two glass plates. Such filters have a FWHM of around 10 nm and a peak transmittance of around 50%. *Multilayer interference filters,* essentially several reflecting layers separated by glass plates, can have a FWHM of about 3 nm and a peak transmittance around 65%. A *filter wedge* is a continuously variable interference filter, with a wedgelike layer of dielectric between semitransparent metallic layers covered by glass plates. The filter wedge is moved, if rectangular, over the exit slit to select the desired nominal wavelengths; if circular, it is rotated over the exit slit to accomplish the wavelength selection.

The *prism* is probably the best known type of monochromator (Figure 8-18b). The basic prism was used in some of the earliest instruments; wavelengths can be selected by moving the exit slit or by rotating the prism. Light dispersion is caused by the different angles of refraction for different wavelengths. There are several different prism designs that are used to varying extents in spectrophotometers. The *Littrow* prism (prism in a Littrow mount) has either a mirror placed behind it or has its rear surface mirrored (e.g., by deposition of an aluminum film) so that refraction occurs twice since the once-refracted waves are refracted again after reflection from the mirror. The *Pellin–Broca* prism, of irregular-trapezoid shape, produces a spectrum that is always at 90° to the incident beam. Two half-prisms can be cemented together back to back, or can be mounted facing each other at a specific angle with the optical path.

The *grating (diffraction grating)* is now the most frequently used dispersion device in monochromators. It consists of a flat plate or disk into which a large number of equidistant parallel grooves have been formed in its highly polished surface. Between 500 and 2500 grooves per millimeter are ruled (*blazed*) on a grating. The characteristics of a grating are illustrated in Figure 8-18c. The incident light beam is diffracted by the groove. The diffraction causes a spreading of light from the groove over a range of angles. At some of these angles, light at a specific wavelength is much more intense than the light at other angles due to constructive interference (reinforcement). Actually, several orders of spectra are produced by diffraction from the groove. For a given angle of incidence, the first-order diffraction spectrum will contain a set of wavelengths increasing with increasing angle of diffraction; the second order will contain a set of wavelengths one-half as long as those in the first-order spectrum; and the third-order spectrum will contain a set of wavelengths each of which, at the same angle of diffraction, will be one-third as long as its first-order counterpart, and so on.

The characteristics most frequently specified for grating monochromators are the number of grooves per millimeter, the focal length, the overall range of wavelengths, the resolution obtainable in the first-order spectrum, and, for the grating itself, the *blaze wavelength,* the wavelength (first order) for which the angle of diffraction and the angle of reflection are the same, and assuming that the angle of incidence (see Figure 8-18c) is the same as the angle of diffraction. The blaze wavelength is then dependent on the groove spacing and the sine of the blaze angle:

$$n\lambda_\phi = 2d \sin \phi$$

where n = order number
$\quad \lambda_\phi$ = blaze wavelength
$\quad d$ = groove spacing
$\quad \phi$ = blaze angle

The operation of a grating in a monochromator is illustrated in Figure 8-19. The grating is rotated by a drive and the band of wavelengths of interest is scanned by sweeping the diffracted light over a very narrow exit slit so that the photodetector senses (nominally) one wavelength at a time. What wavelength it senses is given by the grating characteristics, which are known, and the angular displacement of the grating, which is either measured (e.g., by an angular-displacement transducer) or whose rate with respect to time is so accurately established that it can be correlated with time. Diffraction gratings can provide resolution better than 0.01 nm and are generally usable for wavelengths between 100 nm and 50 μm, with some special UV designs extending the range down to about 30 nm and (with the grating used in a grazing-incidence mode) as low as 1 nm. Developments are continuing to improve grating performance.

Various optical mounts are used in grating monochromators. Figure 8-20 illustrates two frequently used arrangements; modifications of both of these mounts exist.

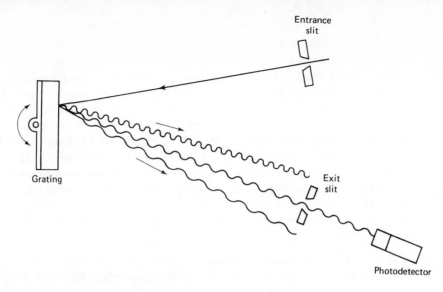

Figure 8-19. Basic grating monochromator operation.

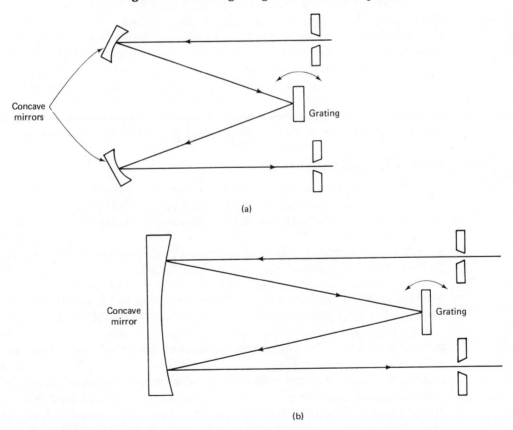

(a)

(b)

Figure 8-20. Typical grating monochromator mounts: (a) Czerny-Turner mount; (b) Ebert-Fastie mount.

8.8.1.2 Other spectrophotometer elements. The various *photodetectors* used in spectrophotometers are all of the types described in Section 5.2. They are selected primarily for spectral response and detectivity (sensitivity); in some designs the time constant is also of importance. *Optical elements,* besides the monochromator section with its entrance and exit slits, include windows, lenses, flat and parabolic mirrors, and beamsplitters. It is important that all optical elements have a high transmittance. Mirrors are coated on their front surface, typically by aluminizing; a coating may be applied over the aluminized surface to improve reflection or provide UV enhancement. Beamsplitters are usually dichroic mirrors of semitransparent material which have one surface reflection-coated; they are mounted at 45° to the incident beam and will transmit certain wavelengths while reflecting other wavelengths at an angle normal to the beam.

8.8.1.3 Spectrophotometer systems. *Single-beam* instruments, which have a single optical path from the source to the detector, are typically used for single-component analyses and are less common than *double-beam* instruments incorporating a reference channel and which may be equipped with two monochromators. The reference channel may have an optical path through a reference cell, or it may be at a sample-indifferent wavelength. In such double-beam spectrophotometers the *ratio* of the sample-dependent reading to the reference reading is often recorded. Strip-chart recorders are still very popular as display devices; however, digital data processing is used increasingly, with displays presented in tabular form or on a CRT, or both. *Mapping* spectrophotometers use detector arrays or multielement charge-coupled silicon devices to provide an image as well as the spectral characteristics of a source.

8.8.2 Infrared Spectroradiometers

Infrared spectroscopy concerns itself with analyses at wavelengths ranging from the near infrared (0.78 to 3 μm), through the middle infrared (3 to 15 μm), and into the far infrared (15 to 800 μm). Instruments for the near-IR region are essentially identical to the spectrophotometers discussed in Section 8.8.1. This similarity extends to instruments that operate well into the middle IR since quantum (photon) detectors, such as HgCdTe (when cooled), are usable to nearly the long-wavelengths limit of this region. However, monochromator gratings may not cover a spectral range extending to 15 μm. Hence, two or more grating/filter sets, designed for ease of interchangeability, are employed.

Far-IR spectroradiometers are still relatively similar to spectrophotometers up to about 30 μm. A combination of a grating and filters, mostly multilayer interference filters, is used as monochromator; however, several grating/filter sets, designed to be interchangeable, must be used if a wide range of wavelengths, extending to about 30 μm, is to be scanned. The detector is almost invariably of the thermal type (i.e., thermopile, bolometer, or pyroelectric); the Golay detector is still used in some instruments. Extrinsic silicon detectors (gold- or bismuth-doped) have been developed that are usable up to 30 μm if they are maintained at a temperature of 2 to 4 K. Successful operation of such detectors at long wavelengths requires not only cooling of the detector but also of the filters and, to a somewhat lesser extent, of the optics. As the wavelength to be analyzed increases above 30 μm, the photon energy decreases to such low levels that transmission losses (even those of good filters), associated with narrow-band-pass characteristics, can be tolerated less and less. The filters used will still tend to be multilayer interference filters, but their bandpass will get broader. Above about 50 μm gratings lose their usability and spectral selection is performed by a set of filters. These can be mounted in a filter wheel and used in conjunction with a thermal detector; however, better performance seems to be attainable when several detectors, each provided with its own filter, or set of filters, are used.

8.8.3   Interferometer Spectrometers

The use of interference techniques has been applied successfully to spectrometers, and it has been found particularly useful in high-resolution IR spectrometers for wavelengths to about 50 μm. The *Fabry–Perot interferometer* has been used in spectroscopic applications, including in determinations of hyperfine spectra. It operates on the principle of multiple reflection. It employs two glass plates, spaced some distance apart, each having a thin coating (silver or aluminum) on the surfaces facing each other. The two reflecting surfaces must be exactly parallel to each other. The incoming wave is multiply reflected between the two plates and ultimately transmitted. The spacing between the two plates may be varied (if this is done without affecting parallelism), for example, by spacers, whose length can be between 1 and 200 mm.

The *Michelson interferometer* is now employed in a number of IR spectrometers. An example of a Michelson interferometer is illustrated schematically in Figure 8-21. Such instruments are used in the process industries and in quality-control and research laboratories, in a variety of applications, as well as in atmospheric, planetary, and space research. As shown in the illustration, the beam of energy to be analyzed is divided by a beamsplitter between a fixed mirror and a moving mirror. The beam splitter is made of IR-transparent material (e.g., KBr or CsI), with a semireflecting coating, below which is attached another slice of the same IR-transparent material so as to act as compensator, to equalize the optical paths in the two branches. The compensator is constructed integrally with the beamsplitter per se. Each mirror reflects its portion of the beam back to the beamsplitter, where the reflected beams combine and the combination product is then sensed by the detector. When the two reflected beams are exactly equal in length, they will constructively interfere at the beam splitter and the detector will sense the reinforced "light" (radiation). When the Michelson mirror moves ¼ wavelength from this position, the two reflected beams will interfere destructively, because they are 180° out of phase, and the radiation sensed by the detector will be minimal. As the mirror moves another ¼ wavelength, the interference will again be constructive. Hence, the detector will see a brightness peak every ½ wavelength as the mirror moves. The output of the detector, when the incoming

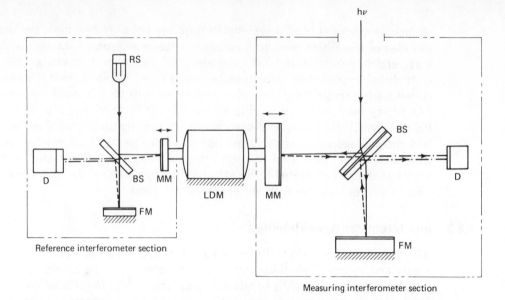

Figure 8-21. Michelson interferometer spectrometer: $h\nu$, incoming radiation to be analyzed; BS, beam splitter; MM, moving mirror (Michelson mirror); FM, fixed mirror; D, detector; RS, reference (light) source; LDM, linear-drive motor (Michelson motor).

radiation is monochromatic at a certain wavelength, will be at a frequency equal to twice the velocity of the moving mirror divided by the wavelength. The variation of signal with mirror displacement follows a cosine relationship. When the incoming radiation is polychromatic, the output signal will be the sum of all the cosine waves, the Fourier transform of the spectrum. Hence, the term *Fourier transform spectroscopy* has been applied to the technique employed by this type of spectrometer. An inverse transformation of the interferogram is used to reconstruct the spectrum; this is usually accomplished by means of a digital computer and an analog conversion device.

It is important that the mirror displacement is known very accurately at all times the instrument is operating. The motion is usually generated by electronics that make the motion a precise function of time; the interferogram can then have time as the motion-related coordinate. A reference interferometer (Figure 8-21) is used to produce a signal which is fed to the mirror-drive electronics to time-lock the mirror motion. The output of the reference-interferometer detector is additionally monitored to provide status information.

A related device is the *Hadamard-transform spectrometer*, which is based on dispersive instead of interferometric optics and operates on the principle of multislit optical encoding at the spectrometer exit focal plane.

8.8.4 Beta-, Gamma-, and X-Ray Spectrometers

In *beta-ray spectrometry* the energy levels or momentum levels of electrons are analyzed, using one of several types of magnetic-field analyzers or electrostatic analyzers *(ESA)* in conjunction with an electron detector, usually of the continuous or multiple dynode type (see Sections 6.2 and 8.11). *Gamma-ray* and *X-ray spectrometers* (Figure 8-22) analyze the number of events occurring in a detector (and proportional to intensity of incident electromagnetic radiation) over a range of photon energies (which correlate with wavelength and frequency; see Figure 6-1). Hence, they are spectroradiometers for the spectral region between about 10 and 10^{-4} nm; expressed in photon energy, as is customary in this field of spectrometry, this spectral region extends from 0.1 to 50 keV, for X-rays, and then from 50 keV to nearly 10 MeV, for gamma rays.

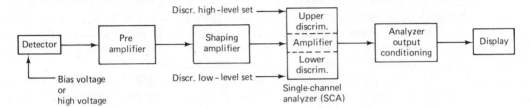

Figure 8-22. Basic block diagram of gamma ray or X-ray spectrometer with SCA.

Detectors used in gamma-ray and X-ray spectrometers are of the types described in Section 6.2. Proportional counters are useful for ultrasoft to soft X-ray detection, and some semiconductor detectors, notable Si(Li) detectors, which usually have a very thin beryllium window, are suitable for detection of soft to hard X-rays. Scintillation counters, typically those using a NaI(Tl) scintillator crystal, are usable over a wide range covering X-rays and gamma rays. Semiconductor gamma-ray detectors comprise primarily the cryogenically cooled Ge(Li) and intrinsic (high-purity, HP) germanium detectors.

The device comparable to a monochromator in spectroradiometers for longer wavelengths is the *pulse-height discriminator*. The amplitude of the output pulse from the detector is proportional to the energy of the radiation incident on the detector. By passing the pulse through an amplifier that passes only pulses having amplitudes between two voltage levels, the number of pulses in a narrow range of energies can be counted. The two voltage levels are established by two *discriminators* (gates), one acting as the upper-level discriminator, the other as the lower-level discriminator. The difference between the lower and upper level of energies (that are equivalent to the lower and upper levels of the pulse amplitude) is called the *window;* the window is comparable to the band-pass of a monochromator, and it is expressed in eV or keV.

Two basic types of pulse-height discriminators are used in gamma- and X-ray spectrometers. The *single-channel analyzer (SCA)* (see Figure 8-24) contains a single set of upper and lower discriminators. When the voltage settings of the two discriminators (and, hence, the window) are fixed, only pulses whose energy fits into that window will be passed. However, when the voltage settings of the two discriminators are increased continuously (preferably with the ramps being a precise function of time), but with the voltage difference between them (the window) kept the same, the SCA will scan a given spectral region (of energies) from its lower to its upper limit as the window slides upward. As a result, a spectrum display (Figure 8-25a) can be obtained. Such a spectrum will show peaks, whose location on the energy scale enables identification of the radiation-emitting isotope, whereas the net area under each *photopeak* is proportional to the emission rate of the isotope (having its peak at a given energy level). It can also be noted from Figure 8-24 that the peaks do not start at "zero" but protrude above a background *(Compton continuum)* due to photons losing only part of their energy to the detector. The ordinate (Y-axis) of the graph is usually logarithmic and is graduated in number of pulses *(counts),* per unit time (or obtained over a known time period), per window (i.e., in the window, as it scans increasing photon energies). In calculations of absolute emission rates by area integration, the Compton continuum can be subtracted or corrected for by comparisons to standard curves.

The *multichannel analyzer (MCA)* can be compared to an interferometric spectroradiometer in that it analyses all parts of the spectrum essentially at the same time. The MCA (Figure 8-23) contains a large number of individual

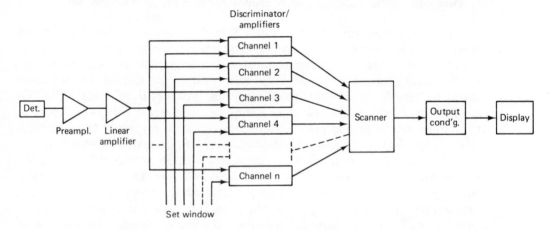

Figure 8-23. Basic block diagram of gamma-ray or X-ray spectrometer with multichannel analyzer (MCA).

discriminator sets *(channels)*. Each channel has a window in a different (and usually adjacent) location on the abscissa (denoting energy) of the resulting display. The number of counts (per time unit) for each channel (where each channel is equivalent to a very narrow band of energies) is read out sequentially by a high-speed scanner. Modern spectrometers often use digital techniques, particularly when they incorporate an MCA; the appearance of a typical spectrum, as it may appear on a CRT, is illustrated in Figure 8-24b. In MCAs the window is often specified in terms of (the location of) its center and of its width.

Various forms of output conditioning can be made available, again facilitated by use of digital techniques. These may include *scaling* (a *scaler* produces an output pulse for each specified number of input pulses), background

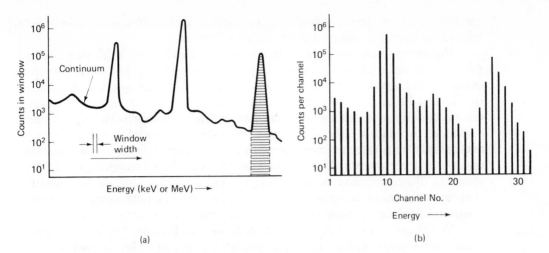

(a)

(b)

Figure 8-24. Typical spectrum displays (X-rays, keV; gamma rays, MeV): (a) from SCA, strip-chart, analog; (b) from MCA, digital, bar-chart.

removal, smoothing, and differentiation; however, a *logarithmic amplifier* is almost invariably included so that the ordinate of the display can be graduated in powers of ten of counts per channel.

Among the increasing applications of these spectrometers are uses in planetology and astrophysics, for general analytical work on materials, and in *neutron activation analysis*. The latter is used primarily for the analyses of trace impurities in nonradioactive materials. These are irradiated with thermal or fast neutrons and the resulting decay products, beta and gamma rays, are then analyzed by spectrometers.

8.8.5 X-Ray Fluorescence Spectrometers

X-ray fluorescence (XRF) spectrometry is used increasingly for the analysis of constituent elements in materials including air-pollution products (on filter paper), blood, mineral ore, clay, and ceramic glazes. The spectrometer always includes a source, X-ray optics, a pulse-height analyzer and/or monochromator, and a detector.

The source is usually an X-ray lamp, which may incorporate two selectable targets (e.g., molybdenum and tungsten), with provisions for accurate adjustment of voltage and current. Alternatively, radioactive-isotope sources (e.g., ^{55}Fe, ^{109}Cd) can be used; these sources provide low-energy X-rays or gamma rays to the sample; they may be annular in shape so that they provide a larger radiation-emitting surface to the sample. The source excites X-ray fluorescence in many elements; the mechanism involves expulsion of an electron from the atom's inner shell and emission of secondary X-rays upon the return of the electron to its normal state. The energy (or frequency or wavelength) of the secondary X-rays characterizes each element (each atom) in the sample; however, this method is best applied to the detection of elements having an atomic number of 9 (fluorine) or higher.

For many analyses it is sufficient to use an SCA or MCA (see Section 8.8.4) to obtain a usable spectrum display. In other cases, however, it is necessary to use a monochromator to obtain sufficiently fine spectral resolution (an SCA or MCA is then often used additionally). A flat or curved diffraction crystal usually provides the monochromatization, together with entrance and exit slits. In nondispersive XRF spectrometers the crystal is stationary and acts mainly as a selectable-wavelength filter. Scanning crystals are used in dispersive instruments. More than one crystal, often interchanged by mechanical "flipping," may be required. Typical crystal materials (selected for their spectral characteristics) include lithium fluoride, potassium iodide, ammonium dihydrogen phosphate (ADP), and other phosphates and tartrates.

The detector is one of the types described in Section 6.2, with semiconductor detectors, notably Si(Li) now predominating and Ge(Li) used alternatively in some instruments.

8.8.6 Atomic Absorption and Flame Emission Spectrometers

This category of spectrometers employs either a spectrophotometer or a monochromatic photometer for analysis (i.e., radiation intensity at certain wavelengths).

In *flame emission spectrometers,* the elements used are the same as in the flame photometer (see Section 8.6.1) except that a monochromator is added ahead of the photodetector so that the spectrum can be analyzed for a number of different elements and molecules. The sample is vaporized and burned in the flame, and the monochromator in conjunction with the photodetector permits identification of constituents and their abundance by examination of peak wavelength and peak area.

In *atomic absorption spectrometers,* light from a hollow-cathode lamp, whose cathode contains the element of interest, is passed through a flame in which the vaporized sample burns. The relative abundance of the element of interest in the sample will be indicated by the degree of absorption, in the flame, of a specific spectral line. The absorption line is selected by appropriate adjustment of the monochromator (if it is continuously variable) or by inserting a narrow-band-pass filter. Among the many applications of such instruments is the detection of mercury in the atmosphere and in food products, in amounts of 1 ng or less; this is accomplished by a double-beam atomic absorption spectrometer; the reference beam does not pass through the sample (through the flame) and absorption at a characteristic mercury line is determined by a ratio method. There are, of course, numerous other applications of atomic absorption spectrometers.

In the less frequently used *atomic fluorescence spectrometers* a light source irradiates the flame from an angle normal to the spectrometer optical axis and energy, first absorbed, then reemitted as fluorescence, is analyzed by the monochromator/detector system.

8.8.7 Submillimeter and Microwave Spectrometers

Besides the more commonly used magnetic resonance spectrometers (see Section 8.9) which often operate in the microwave region, recent developments in spectrometry include passive and active (radar) spectrometers used for spectroradiometric analyses of emission and absorption lines. The frequency range (see Figure 8-26) of *microwaves* extends from about 1 to 300 GHz (equivalent to wavelengths between 30 cm and 1 mm); the region between about 10 and 1 mm is sometimes called *millimeter waves*. In this region, radio-frequency (*RF*) techniques and instrumentation are generally used. In the region between 1 and 0.1 mm (1000 and 100 μm), which is now often referred to as *submillimeter waves*, there is an overlap between the applicability of far-IR-optical and RF techniques. In these regions, spectrometry is used increasingly to obtain *emission spectra* from primarily stellar and interstellar sources and *absorption spectra* through gases that use as illumination source either radiation of known spectral characteristics, such as solar radiation (in *passive microwave spectrometry*), or pulsed electromagnetic energy emanating from the spectrometer instrument (*active microwave spectrometry, radar spectrometry*).

The incident electromagnetic energy, in microwave spectrometry, is usually gathered by an antenna (*collector*), and fed, through a *waveguide*, to a *receiver*. Here it is applied to a mixer, where the incoming signal is heterodyned against a local oscillator. The output of the mixer is then a band of frequencies of a few hundred MHz, frequencies much easier to work with than the hundreds of GHz of the originally received signal. The separation of the heterodyned signal is then accomplished either by a set of parallel filters, each having a narrow and adjacent passband, or by digital techniques requiring use of Fourier transforms for data reduction.

The mixer is probably the most critical element in the receiver. It must be selected and operated so as to minimize conversion loss and any noise introduced by it into the heterodyne (output) signal. Schottky barrier diodes are commonly used as mixers; they are sometimes cooled to reduce noise (the noise is reduced by about 50% when cooled from room temperature to 20 K). Other devices, used as mixers, are still in development and they generally require operation at liquid-helium temperatures; they include Josephson devices, other superconducting devices, and an indium–antimonide bolometer ("hot electron bolometer").

8.8.8 Raman Spectrometers

When molecules of a gaseous, liquid, or solid compound are illuminated by a light source, they will scatter this light; most of the scattering products will be at the same wavelength (frequency) as the incident light; however, a small fraction of the scattering products will have undergone a wavelength change (frequency change) in the scattering process (*Raman effect*, named after its discoverer, C. V. Raman, in India, in 1928). The Raman-scattered light has no phase relationship with the incident light. The Raman spectrum, for any one molecule, will consist of several lines that are shifted in frequency by varying amounts from the incident-light frequency. This pattern is symmetric about the exciting line; however, the lines representing frequencies lower than the exciting line (*Stokes lines*) are always more intense than the corresponding lines on the high-frequency side (*anti-Stokes lines*). Since Raman spectra are based on frequency differences from the exciting frequency, they are usually shown with the abscissa graduated in wavenumber differences ($\Delta\ cm^{-1}$), with zero indicating the excitation frequency; and, since only the Stokes lines are displayed, zero is usually at the right end of the abscissa. Raman lines also show polarization to various degrees, depending on the origin of the line as well as on the optical geometry of the instrument. The excitation frequency must be chosen so that no absorption occurs in the compound analyzed. Raman spectrometers are very useful in analyses of molecular structure and behavior and for quantitative analyses of major components in complex mixtures.

The major elements of a laser spectrometer are a monochromatic light source, a scatter-collection mirror placed normal to the incident beam so as to collect the scattering products from the sample illuminated by the beam, collection optics, a scanning monochromator to enable analysis of the various frequencies (wavelengths) of the Raman-scattered light, and a photodetector.

Since a high-intensity light source is required to obtain measurable Raman scattering, a laser is used for this purpose in all modern instruments (replacing the formerly used mercury-arc lamp combined with elaborate filters). The laser wavelengths are usually in the visible-light range, and the instrument optics are of the types used in visible-light spectrophotometers. The laser is chosen for its wavelength, available beam intensity, and nature of the analysis. Commonly used lasers are He–Ne (632.8 nm), argon (488.0 and 514.5 nm), and krypton (568.2 nm) (see Table 8-4). The laser beam is focused at the sample, using appropriate collimating optics that may include a multipass mirror behind the sample. The direction of observation is normal to the laser beam and suitable collection optics are used to focus the scattering products toward the monochromator entrance slit. The monochromator may

Table 8-4　Typical Laser Wavelengths

Laser Type	Wavelength (nm)
Nd:glass (fourth harmonic)	266.0
He–Cd	325.0
Nitrogen	337.1
He–Cd	441.6
Argon ion	488.0
Argon ion	514.5
Nd:YAG (second harmonic)	532.0
He–Ne	632.8
Ruby	694.3
GaAs	905.0
Nd:YAG, Nd:glass	1064.0

be a double-grating or triple-grating type. Multiple monochromators help reduce stray light originating from the high-intensity excitation and the very intense Rayleigh scattering products at the excitation wavelength. A photomultiplier or other photon detector is used to detect the light from the monochromator exit slit.

8.9 MAGNETIC RESONANCE SPECTROMETERS

This category of instruments provides spectra originating from radio-frequency-induced transitions in the presence of a magnetic field.

8.9.1 Nuclear Magnetic Resonance (NMR) Spectrometers

Many atomic nuclei (about one-half of those known) will exhibit nuclear magnetic resonance when they are exposed to a static field; they will then absorb energy from a radio-frequency field at certain characteristic frequencies. The RF field is applied at right angles to a strong, uniform magnetic field. The resonance occurs when the frequency of the rotating component of the RF field equals the precession frequency of a nucleus that possesses spin or angular momentum in addition to charge and mass. A spinning charge creates a magnetic field. The precession is caused by changes in spin-axis alignment in the presence of the magnetic field. At the point where the nucleus absorbs RF energy it will undergo a transition to a higher energy level.

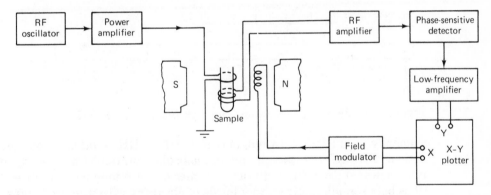

Figure 8-25. Basic block diagram of NMR spectrometer.

There are two modes in which an NMR spectrometer can operate. In the *frequency-sweep method* the magnetic field is kept constant and the output of an oscillator/power-amplifer, coupled into the sample by a coil, is swept over a range of frequencies. A pickup coil is also placed around the sample (orthogonal to the transmitter coil); it is connected to an RF amplifier. When a change in the received and phase-detected signal amplitude indicates an absorption peak, the RF transmitter frequency is recorded. In the *field-sweep method* the RF transmitter frequency is held constant and the magnetic field is modulated, by means of sweep coils around the pole pieces. Resonance is usually detected from a dispersion peak. Figure 8-25 shows a basic block diagram of an NMR spectrometer that can operate in the field-sweep mode.

The RF equipment must be capable of detecting the resonance-indicating signal within very close frequency tolerances; it must also be capable of very precise frequency control, and provide very accurate knowledge about the frequency of the RF field. The magnetic field must also be held and known within very close limits. The magnetic field is typically in the order of 1 to 3 T (10 to 30 kG); however, fields up to 15 T have been obtained using a superconducting magnet. The magnet can be a permanent magnet, or it can be an electromagnet; in the latter case, considerable heat is generated by the magnet coils and the electromagnet is usually water-cooled.

8.9.2 Electron Spin Resonance Spectrometers

Spectrometers whose operation is based on *electron spin resonance (ESR)*, also known as *electron paramagnetic resonance (EPR)*, are similar to NMR spectrometers; the main difference is that they operate in the microwave region. Figure 8-26 shows the approximate regions in which observations are based

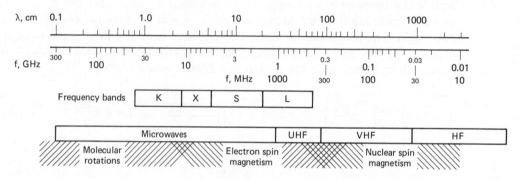

Figure 8-26. Frequency spectrum from high frequencies (HF) through microwaves.

primarily on nuclear spin magnetism (VHF to UHF), on electron spin magnetism (UHF to microwave), and on molecular rotations (microwave and millimeter-wave). In ESR, radiation (at microwave frequencies) induces transitions between magnetic energy levels of electrons with unpaired spins, in the presence of a static magnetic field. The equipment and its operation is similar to those of NMR spectrometers, except that all RF elements are microwave (X-band or S-band) elements.

8.10 MASS SPECTROMETERS

Mass spectrometers are used to analyze the mass/charge ratio of ions; the ions can be the parent ion or ionic fragments of a molecule. Most mass spectrometers ("neutral mass spectrometers") provide an ionization chamber (ionizing region) in which incoming molecules are ionized. Some types of mass spectrometers ("ion mass spectrometers") respond only to incoming ions and do not contain an ionization chamber. The peaks appearing in a mass spectrum show the number of ions having the same mass-to-charge (m/e) ratio. Normally, only positive ions are analyzed. From the mass spectrum, which shows abundance vs. mass unit (in *amu*). many types of information can be extracted, such as organic-compound structure and constituents of complex mixtures, and the molecular weight can be determined with a high degree of accuracy.

The basic elements of a mass spectrometer are the sample introduction system, the ion source, the mass analyzer, and the detector with its associated signal conditioning and display units. An electron multiplier (continuous dynode or multiple dynode; Section 6.3.6) is now most frequently used as detector. A block diagram is shown in Figure 8-27.

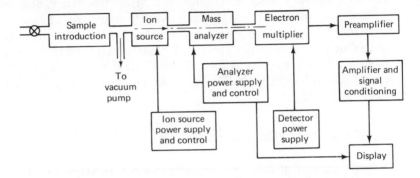

Figure 8-27. Typical mass-spectrometer block diagram.

The *sample introduction system* must be capable of accepting a sample which is at room pressure and introducing it into the ion source, which is in a vacuum. Various methods have been devised to accomplish this, including break-off devices, porous disks or membranes, probe inlet systems (mainly for solids), and pyrolysis inlet systems for solids. The sample, in gaseous form, is then usually stored in a reservoir, from which it enters the ion source through a molecular leak. Vacuum isolation is provided through valve systems.

An electron-impact *ion source* is used in many types of mass spectrometers. A heated filament (e.g., of thoriated iridium) emits electrons that are accelerated from this cathode by grids carrying a positive potential with respect to the cathode. The impact, or passage in close proximity, of the electrons ionizes the molecules of the sample material. A lens–electrode system then focuses the ions into a beam sufficiently narrow to enter the mass analyzer through its entrance aperture. Other ion sources use a high-density electrostatic field (field ionization, *FI*, or field desorption, *FD*), a high-intensity RF spark, chemical ionization (*CI*), atmospheric pressure ionization (*API*), vaporization from a surface heated to high temperatures (about 2000 °C), or a laser beam.

Mass analyzers exist in a variety of generic types and designs, all of which are covered in detail in available reference books, reports, papers, and manufacturers' technical literature. *Magnetic analyzers* accept a beam of accelerated ions and forces them to travel along a curved trajectory, permitting ions of different mass-to-charge ratio to be sorted out on the basis that each different ion will have a different trajectory through the analyzer tube in the magnetic field. In the *Dempster* analyzer system the path is a half-circle (180°). In the *Nier* system the path is curved through a 60° sector. In a *double-focusing* mass spectrometer, the ions first pass through a curved electrostatic analyzer section, which permits their selection according to energy (see Section 8.11), then through a straight section, and finally through a magnetic analyzer sector which is usually curved. In an *RF mass spectrometer*, ions are sorted by passing them through sets of grids; alternate grids are at a steady potential, whereas the other set of (alternate) grids is supplied from a radio-frequency (RF) source; the RF frequency is variable, and, at a given frequency, only ions of a given mass/charge ratio will pass through the grid structure. The operation of a *time-of-flight (TOF)* mass spectrometer is based on the difference in velocities acquired by ions of different mass if they are given the same kinetic energy; the mass can be determined by measuring the travel time (in microseconds) of the ions through a drift path. The *quadrupole* mass analyzer is described briefly in Section 8.11.

8.11   SURFACE ANALYSIS INSTRUMENTS

A large number of different instruments and instrumental methods have become available for the micro-analyses of surfaces of many types of materials. Some of those are used primarily to analyze the properties and composition of the topmost surface layer, which may be monomolecular (one *monolayer* thick); others are used to penetrate the surface down to 50 or more monlayers; one of the purposes of such analyses is subsurface *profiling*. The dimensions involved in surface analysis are microscopically small and are typically expressed in nm (or angstroms, 10 Å = 1 nm).

The basic operating principle of surface analysis instruments is the following (see Figure 8-28): the sample whose surface is to be analyzed is bombarded by a beam from a source of electrons, ions or (primarily UV or X-ray) photons; the interaction of this beam produces electrons or ions (or sometimes, photons or neutrals) which are focused into the entrance aperture of an analyzer. For most instruments this is an energy analyzer; in some instruments it is a mass analyzer, or an energy analyzer followed by a mass analyzer. A detector is mounted to the output side of the analyzer. The detector is typically an electron multiplier (see Section 6.3.6) of the multiple-dynode or continuous-dynode (e.g., channel electron multiplier, *CEM*, or microchannel plate, *MCP*) type.

Of the many instruments and instrumental methods, only a few of the more frequently used ones will be described very briefly. However, the field of surface analysis has been the birthplace of a large number of acronyms, and

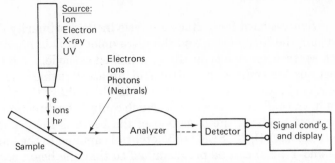

Figure 8-28. Basic elements of surface analysis instruments.

an understanding of these is essential to technical communications. The meanings of most of the acronyms used in surface analysis are listed below, in alphabetical order; in most of these, where the acronym pertains to "spectroscopy" as a method, the word "spectrometer" can be substituted to denote the instrument used; however, it should be noted that many instruments are usable for more than one instrumental method; hence, it is better to associate the acronym with a method rather than a specific instrument design.

AES	auger electron spectroscopy
APS	appearance potential spectroscopy
CELS	characteristic electron loss spectroscopy
CIS	characteristic isochromat spectroscopy
EID	electron-induced desorption
EIID	electron-impact ion desorption
ELS	electron loss spectroscopy
EMP	electron microprobe
ESCA	electron spectroscopy for chemical analysis (same as XPS)
ESD	electron-stimulated desorption (see EID and EIID)
FEM	field-emission microscope
HEED	high-energy electron diffraction
ILEED	inelastic low-energy electron diffraction
INS	ion neutralization spectroscopy
ISS	ion scattering spectroscopy
LEED	low-energy electron diffraction
LEIS	low-energy ion-scattering spectroscopy
PIX	proton-induced X-ray analysis
PLEED	polarized low-energy electron diffraction
PSD	photon-stimulated desorption
RHEED	reflected high-energy electron diffraction
SAM	scanning auger microscopy
SEM	scanning electron microscopy
SIMS	secondary ion mass spectroscopy
SLEEP	scanning low-energy electron probe
UPS	ultraviolet photoelectron spectroscopy
XPS	X-ray photoelectron spectroscopy

Sources used for surface analysis include primarily the electron gun, the ion gun, the X-ray tube, and the ultraviolet (UV) lamp. An *electron gun* (electron source) consists typically of a heated cathode, from the surface of which electrons are emitted, a control grid, an accelerating grid which increases the velocity of the electrons, focusing grids which shape the electrons into a narrow beam, and deflecting electrodes which control the direction of the exiting beam. For most methods the direction of the beam is held constant. For scanning methods (e.g., SAM, SEM) the potentials applied to the two pairs of electrodes (*X*- and *Y*-axis) can be programmed so that the beam scans over the sample surface, usually forming a raster. In an *ion gun* (ion source) an electron source is used to bombard atoms of a gas (e.g., He, Ne, Ar) that is introduced, at vacuum pressures (10^{-3} to 10^{-5} torr), into the ion gun from an external gas supply. For the usual negative-ion source, the ionization chamber is kept at a negative accelerating potential, and an extractive electrode, at a less negative potential, draws ions from the source through a small aperture. Lens electrodes are then used to form the required narrow beam of ions that is directed at the sample. Positive-ion beams can be obtained from alkali metal or sputter sources.

An *X-ray tube* is, generally, a vacuum tube in which thermionic-emission electrons are accelerated toward a target by a high potential applied between cathode and anode. X-rays are produced when the electrons collide with the metallic target. Anode shaping (e.g., use of an annular anode) or diffraction from a curved crystal can be used to maximize the flow of X-ray photons to the sample. *UV lamps* typically produce their photons by means of a gas discharge in a lamp having a quartz envelope. Photons from either source are sometimes monochromatized with diffraction gratings (see Sections 8.8.1.1 and 8.8.4).

Analyzer sections of surface analysis instruments are electron or ion energy analyzers, in most instruments, and mass analyzers, in some instruments. Magnetic energy analyzers are no longer in frequent use and the energy analyzer found in most modern instruments is the *electrostatic analyzer (ESA)*. Whereas some energy analyzers are nondispersive, most are dispersive and act as energy "monochromators" (see Sections 8.8.1). One commonly used type of ESA is the *hemispherical analyzer* (Figure 8-29a). The electron beam from the sample enters the analyzer through a lens-electrode system (which may also act so as to apply a retarding field to the electron stream). The analyzer consists of two hemispherically curved parallel plates across which a potential is applied. The higher-energy electrons will follow a trajectory through the analyzer with a larger radius than the lower-energy electrons. By selecting the appropriate electrode potential, the trajectory of electrons having a specified kinetic energy will be exactly that trajectory that causes the electron stream to pass through the exit slit and onto the detector. The detector, usually an electron multiplier, produces an output current proportional to the number of electrons detected per unit time; good electron multipliers, with appropriately designed circuitry, can produce a measurable output pulse for each electron detected.

The energy of an electron passing through the analyzer and through the

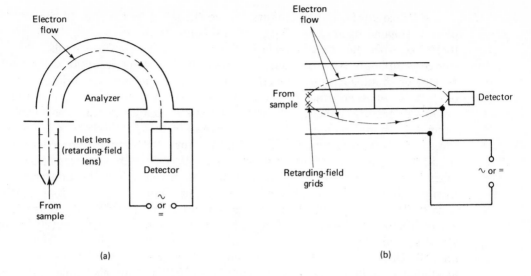

Figure 8-29. Energy analyzers: (a) hemispherical analyzer; (b) cylindrical mirror analyzer (CMA).

exit slit can be determined from knowledge of the analyzer geometry and the applied potential. For a hemispherical analyzer the kinetic energy of the electron, KE (in electron volts), is proportional to the potential applied across the electrodes (V) and the mean radius of the two plates (r), and inversely proportional to twice the separation (d) between the plates, or $KE = Vr/2d$. When the energy of ions, rather than of electrons, is to be determined, the result must be divided by the charge of the ion, q, and the relationship is then $KE/q = Vr/2d$.

Another popular ESA design is the *cylindrical mirror analyzer (CMA)*. As shown in Figure 8-29b, electrons enter the analyzer through a set of retarding-field grids. The analyzer consists of an inner cylinder, which has two annular apertures (electrically conductive) and an outer cylinder. The potential is applied across the two cylinders. The annular apertures form the entrance and exit slits. With a given potential applied, only electrons having the corresponding energy to pass through the slits will have a trajectory that reaches the detector. The usual manner of producing an energy spectrum is to apply a scanning potential across the analyzer electrodes. Another method involves applying a scanning potential to the retarding field grids and keeping the analyzer electrode potential difference at a fixed value.

Mass analyzers are of the types used in mass spectrometers (see Section 8.10). Analyzers used in such applications as SIMS are now usually of the quadrupole type; the ions pass through the line of symmetry between four parallel cylindrical rods; an alternating potential superimposed on a steady potential between pairs of rods, 180° apart, filters out all ions except those of a specific mass, as determined by the applied potentials. This type of analyzer is also known as *mass filter*.

Surface analysis instruments can be classified by the type of source employed. Depending on the energy of the beam from the source, its angle of incidence with the sample surface, the nature of the surface itself, and the source-sample-analyzer geometry, various interactions occur at the sample surface or in subsurface layers that cause either the same or different types of particles to be emitted. Analysis of the particles from the sample can then provide information about the nature, structure, composition, and so on, of the sample. It should be noted that all elements of these instruments are maintained in a vacuum, typically around 10^{-10} torr, with much higher vacuums required in some cases. Use of an *electron source* permits analyses based primarily on electrons being emitted from the surface, and the analyses can involve counting the number of electrons, or their energy, or their spatial distribution, or two or all three of these parameters. In LEED, electrons which are diffracted by the surface from a beam of low-energy electrons (20 to 200 eV) are analyzed; a higher-energy beam is employed in the less frequently applied HEED method. Reflection from the surface, when the source beam is at glancing incidence, is used in RHEED. In ILEED, only electrons that have lost energy by inelastic collisions are analyzed.

One of the most widely used methods employing an electron beam is auger electron spectroscopy (AES). The high-energy electron beam ionizes substrate atoms, which then relax by a radiationless transition. An outer electron drops into the ionized level and transfers the absorbed energy to another electron (*auger electron*) which then leaves the sample and is analyzed for its energy. The electron beam used in AES must have an energy of 2 to 3 keV. A scanning electron beam is employed for rastering in the scanning auger microscope (SAM). Particles emitted from a surface in response to an electron beam may also be desorbed ions (EIID) or neutrals (EID), or photons.

Ion sources are used primarily in ISS and SIMS. In ISS, the energies of ions scattered through a fixed scattering angle are analyzed. In secondary ion mass spectroscopy (SIMS), the ion beam is used to sputter atoms or molecules

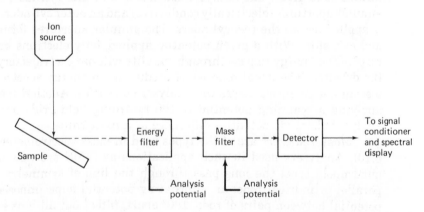

Figure 8-30. Secondary-ion mass spectrometer (SIMS) (energy-resolved) block diagram.

from the sample surface. The mass of these sputtering products (secondary ions) is then analyzed. In *energy-resolved SIMS* (see block diagram, Figure 8-30) the energy of the secondary ions is additionally analyzed.

Photon sources considered here are two types: UV and X-ray. Both are used in interaction with surfaces that produce electrons whose energy is then analyzed. Depending on the source used, the instrumental method is either UV or X-ray photoelectron spectroscopy (UPS or XPS). The term "electron spectroscopy for chemical analysis" (ESCA) is used synonymously with XPS.

Bibliography

General

1. **Siggia, S.,** *Continuous Analysis of Chemical Process Systems.* New York: John Wiley & Sons, Inc., 1959.
2. **Choppin, G. R.,** *Experimental Nuclear Chemistry.* Englewood Cliffs, NJ: Prentice-Hall, Inc., 1961.
3. **Lederer, C. M., Hollander, J. M., and Perlman, I.,** *Table of Isotopes,* 6th ed. New York: John Wiley & Sons, Inc., 1968.
4. **De Soete, D., Gybels, R., and Hoste, J.,** *Neutron Activation Analysis.* New York: Wiley-Interscience, 1972.
5. **Springer, G. S., and Patterson, D. T.** (Eds.), *Engine Emission Pollution Formation and Measurement.* New York: Plenum Press, 1973.
6. **Verdin, A.,** *Gas Analysis Instrumentation.* New York: John Wiley & Sons, Inc., 1973.
7. **Willard, H. H., Merritt, L. L., Jr., and Dean, J. A.,** *Instrumental Methods of Analysis* (5th ed.). New York: D. Van Nostrand Co., 1974.
8. **Lintz, J., and Simonett, D.,** *Remote Sensing of Environment.* Reading, MA: Addison-Wesley Publishing Co., 1976.
9. *Handbook of Chemistry and Physics* (55th ed.). Cleveland, OH: CRC Press, 1976.

Electrometric Analysis

1. **Latimer, W. M.,** *Oxidation Potentials* (2nd ed.). Englewood Cliffs, NJ: Prentice-Hall, Inc., 1952.
2. **Lingane, J. J.,** *Electroanalytical Chemistry* (2nd ed.). New York: Wiley-Interscience, 1958.
3. **Ives, D. J. G., and Janz, G. J.,** *Reference Electrodes.* New York: Academic Press, Inc., 1961.
4. **Charlot, G., Badoz-Lambling, J., and Tremillon, B.,** *Electrochemical Reactions.* New York: American Elsevier Publishing Co., 1962.
5. **Rechnitz, G. A.,** *Controlled Potential Analysis.* London: Pergamon Press, 1963.
6. **Bates, R. G.,** *Determination of pH—Theory and Practice.* New York: John Wiley & Sons, Inc., 1964.

7. **Heyrovsky, J., and Kuta, J.,** *Principles of Polarography.* New York: Academic Press, Inc., 1965.

8. **Meites, L.,** *Polarographic Techniques* (2nd ed.). New York: Wiley-Interscience, 1966.

9. **Milner, G. W. C., and Phillips, G.,** *Coulometry in Analytical Chemistry.* London: Pergamon Press, 1968.

10. **Adams, R. N.,** *Electrochemistry of Solid Electrodes.* New York: Marcel Dekker, Inc., 1969.

11. **Browning, D. R.** (Ed.), *Electrometric Methods.* Maidenhead, England: McGraw-Hill Book Co. (UK) Ltd., 1969.

12. **Durst, R. A.** (Ed.), "Ion Selective Electrodes," *NBS Special Publication 314.* Washington, DC: U.S. Government Printing Office, 1969.

13. **Smith, D. E., and Zimmerli, F. H.,** *Electrochemical Methods of Process Analysis.* Research Triangle Park, NC: Instrument Society of America, 1972.

Thermal Analysis

1. **Duval, C.,** *Inorganic Thermogravimetric Analysis* (2nd ed.). New York: American Elsevier Publishing Co., 1963.

2. **Wendlandt, W. W.,** *Thermal Methods of Analysis.* New York: Wiley-Interscience, 1964.

3. **Garn, P. D.,** *Thermoanalytical Methods of Investigation.* New York: Academic Press, Inc., 1965.

4. **Mackenzie, R. C.** (Ed.), *Differential Thermal Analysis.* London: Academic Press Inc. (London) Ltd., 1970.

Chromatography

1. **Purnell, H.,** *Gas Chromatographs.* New York: Wiley-Interscience, 1968.

2. **Jones, R. A.,** *An Introduction to Gas-Liquid Chromatography.* New York: Academic Press, Inc., 1970.

3. **Littlewood, A. B.,** *Gas Chromatography: Principles, Techniques and Applications* (2nd ed.). New York: Academic Press, Inc., 1970.

4. **Scott, R. P. W.,** *Contemporary Liquid Chromatography.* New York: Wiley-Interscience, 1976.

Photometry, UV-Vis.-IR Spectrometry, and Spectrometry (General)

1. **Djerassi, C.,** *Optical Rotatory Dispersion.* New York, McGraw-Hill Book Company, 1960.

2. **Clark, G. L.** (Ed.), *The Encyclopedia of Spectroscopy.* New York: Van Nostrand Reinhold Company, 1960.

3. **Ahrens, L. H., and Taylor, S. R.,** *Spectrochemical Analysis* (2nd ed.). Reading, MA: Addison-Wesley Publishing Co., 1961.

4. **Baumann, R. P.,** *Absorption Spectroscopy.* New York: John Wiley & Sons, Inc., 1962.

5. **Freeman, S. K.** (Ed.), *Interpretive Spectroscopy.* New York: Van Nostrand Reinhold Company, 1965.

6. **Hercules, D. M.** (Ed.), *Fluorescense and Phosphorescence Analysis.* New York: Wiley-Interscience, 1966.

7. **Guilbault, G. G.** (Ed.), *Fluorescence.* New York: Marcel Dekker, Inc., 1967.

8. **Harrick, N. J.,** *Internal Reflection Spectroscopy.* New York: John Wiley & Sons, Inc. 1967.

9. **Silverstein, R. M., and Bassler, G. C.,** *Spectrometric Identification of Organic Compounds* (2nd ed.). New York: John Wiley & Sons, Inc., 1967.

10. **Zander, M.,** *Phosphorimetry.* New York: Academic Press, Inc., 1968.

11. **Calder, A. B.,** *Photometric Methods of Analysis.* New York: American Elsevier Publishing Company, 1969.

12. **Alpert, N. L., Keiser, W. E., and Szymanski, H. A.,** *IR: Theory and Practice of Infrared Spectroscopy.* New York: Plenum Press, 1970.

13. **Pouchert, C. J.,** *The Aldrich Library of Infrared Spectra.* Milwaukee, WI: Aldrich Chemical Co., Inc., 1970.

14. **Hirayama, K.,** *Handbook of Ultraviolet and Visible Absorption of Organic Compounds.* New York: Plenum Publishing Corp., 1971.

15. **Bell, R. J.,** *Introductory Fourier Transform Spectroscopy.* New York: Academic Press, Inc., 1972.

16. **Avram, M., and Mateescu, Gh. D.,** *Infrared Spectroscopy.* New York: John Wiley & Sons, Inc., 1972.

17. **Cook, B. W., and Jones, K.,** *A Programmed Introduction to Infrared Spectroscopy.* New York: Heyden & Sons, Inc., 1972.

18. **Grove, E.** (Ed.), *Analytical Emission Spectroscopy.* New York: Marcel Dekker, Inc., 1971 (Part I), 1972 (Part II).

19. **Winefordner, J. D., Schulman, S. G., and O'Haver, T. C.,** *Luminscence Spectrometry in Analytical Chemistry.* New York: Wiley-Interscience, 1972.

20. **Meggers, W. F., Corliss, C. H., and Scribner, B. F.,** "Tables of Spectral-Line Intensities," *NBA Monograph 145.* Washington, DC: U.S. Government Printing Office, 1975.

21. **Pearse, R. W. B., and Gaydon, A. G.,** *The Identification of Molecular Spectra.* New York: Halstead Press, 1976.

22. **Mattson, J. S., Mark, H. B., Jr., and MacDonald, H. C., Jr.** (Eds.), *Infrared, Correlation, and Fourier Transform Spectroscopy.* New York: Marcel Dekker, Inc., 1977.

Microwave Spectrometry

1. **Ingram, D. J. E.,** *Radio and Microwave Spectroscopy.* New York: Halstead Press, 1976.

2. **Varma, R., and Hrubesh, L. W.,** *Chemical Analysis by Microwave Spectroscopy.* New York: John Wiley & Sons, 1979.

Flame Emission and Atomic Absorption Spectroscopy

1. Dean, J. A., *Flame Photometry*. New York: McGraw-Hill Book Company, 1960.
2. Mavrodineanu, R., and Boiteux, H., *Flame Spectrometry*. New York: John Wiley & Sons, Inc., 1965.
3. Elwell, W. T., and Gidley, J. A. F., *Atomic Absorption Spectrophotometry* (2nd ed.). Elmsford, NY: Pergamon Press, Inc., 1966.
4. Reynolds, R. J., Aldous, K., and Thompson, K. C., *Atomic Absorption Spectroscopy*. New York: Barnes & Noble, Inc., 1970.
5. Dean, J. A., and Raines, T. C. (Eds.), *Flame Emission and Atomic Absorption Spectrometry*. New York: Marcel Dekker, Inc., 1969 (Vol. 1), 1971 (Vol. 2), 1974 (Vol. 3).
6. Kirkbright, G. F., and Sargent, M., *Atomic Absorption and Fluorescence Spectroscopy*. New York: Academic Press, 1975.

X-Ray Spectrometry

1. Birks, L. S., *X-Ray Spectrochemical Analysis*. New York: Wiley-Interscience, 1959.
2. Bertin, E. P., *Principles and Practice of X-Ray Spectrometric Analysis*. New York: Plenum Press, 1970.
3. Herglotz, H. K., and Birks, L. S. (Eds.), *X-Ray Spectrometry; Practical Spectroscopy Series,* Vol. 2. New York: Marcel Dekker, Inc., 1978.

Raman Spectrometry

1. Gilson, T. R., and Hendra, P. J., *Laser Raman Spectroscopy*. London: Wiley-Interscience, 1970.
2. Tobin, M. C., *Laser Raman Spectroscopy*. New York: Wiley-Interscience, 1971.
3. Colthup, N. B., Daly, L. H., and Wiberley, S. E., *Introduction to Infrared and Raman Spectroscopy* (2nd ed.). New York: Academic Press, Inc., 1975.
4. Long, D. A., *Raman Spectroscopy*. New York: McGraw-Hill Book Company, 1977.

Magnetic Resonance Spectrometry

1. Alger, R. S., *Electron Paramagnetic Resonance, Techniques and Applications*. New York: Wiley-Interscience, 1968.
2. Jackman, L. M., and Sternhall, S., *Applications of Nuclear Magnetic Resonance Spectroscopy in Organic Chemistry*. Elmsford, NY: Pergamon Press, Inc., 1969.
3. Abraham, R. J., *Analysis of High Resolution NMR Spectra*. New York: American Elsevier Publishing Co., 1971.
4. Farrar, T. C., and Becker, E. D., *Pulse and Fourier Transform NMR*. New York: Academic Press, Inc., 1971.

5. **Kevan, L., and Kispert, L. D.,** *Electron Spin Double Resonance Spectroscopy.* New York: Wiley-Interscience, 1976.

Mass Spectrometry

1. **Beynon, J. H.,** *Mass Spectrometry and Its Applications to Organic Chemistry.* New York: American Elsevier Publishing Co., 1960.
2. **Biemann, K.,** *Mass Spectrometry: Applications to Organic Chemistry.* New York: McGraw-Hill Book Company, 1962.

Surface Analysis

1. **Shirley, D. A.,** *Electron Spectroscopy.* Amsterdam: North-Holland Publishing Co., 1972.
2. **Bottoms, W. R.** (Ed.), *Scanning Electron Microscopy.* New York: American Elsevier Publishing Co., 1975.
3. **Czanderna, A. W.** (Ed.), *Methods of Surface Analysis.* New York: American Elsevier Publishing Co., 1975.
4. **Barr, T. L., and Davis, L. E.** (Ed.), *Applied Surface Analysis (STP 699).* Philadelphia: American Society for Testing and Materials, 1980.

Index